Transcendental Functions

Satisfying

Nonhomogeneous Linear Differential Equations

A. W. BABISTER
The University of Glasgow

Transcendental Functions
Satisfying Nonhomogeneous Linear Differential Equations

THE MACMILLAN COMPANY · New York
COLLIER-MACMILLAN LIMITED · London

First Printing

Library of Congress catalog card number: 66–24890

THE MACMILLAN COMPANY, New York
COLLIER-MACMILLAN CANADA, LTD., Toronto, Ontario

PRINTED IN THE UNITED STATES OF AMERICA

Preface

Nonhomogeneous differential equations are generally treated very cursorily in books on differential equations, the method of obtaining a solution being given without any indication of the properties of such a solution. The aim of this book is to provide a comprehensive treatment of the properties of these solutions and, in particular, to study certain nonhomogeneous equations that are related to well-known transcendental equations.

The first two chapters are devoted to a general discussion of the subject. Nonhomogeneous equations related to the Bessel equation and to the various forms of the hypergeometric equation (including the Heun equation and the Lamé equation) are discussed in Chapters 3–9. At the end of each of these chapters, the solutions of related differential equations are given. Chapters 10 and 11 conclude the treatment with a study of nonhomogeneous linear partial differential equations.

Nonhomogeneous differential equations occur in applied mathematics in any problem dealing with forced motions of a linear system. More generally, equations of this type occur in mathematical physics (in field analysis) where "source points" are present. It is shown, in Chapter 11, that the solutions of equations such as Poisson's and Lorenz's can often be expressed in terms of the nonhomogeneous transcendental functions defined in Chapters 3–9.

Examples are given at the end of each chapter to clarify the discussion for students and to show the applications of the theory to physical problems.

The treatment given here is based on that set out by Bateman, Forsyth, Ince, Poole, and Webster in their major works on differential equations. Any writer in this field must also express his indebtedness to Erdélyi and his fellow workers for their encyclopedic volumes on higher transcendental functions. These indeed may be said to form the main stock of the treatment of the subject on to which the author wishes to graft the present branch.

A. W. B.

Contents

1 NONHOMOGENEOUS LINEAR DIFFERENTIAL EQUATIONS AND THEIR SOLUTIONS 1

1.1 Introduction, 1. **1.2** The Nature of the Solution, 1. **1.3** First-Order Linear Equations, 3. **1.4** Reduction of Order, 4. **1.5** Variation of Parameters, 5. **1.6** Cauchy's Method, 8. **1.7** Solution by Differentiation, 9. **1.8** The Exact Nonhomogeneous Equation, 11. **1.9** Solution by Integrating Factor, 12. **1.10** Solution of a Homogeneous Equation in Power Series, 14. **1.11** Singular Points, 14. **1.12** Solution of a Nonhomogeneous Equation in Power Series, 16. **1.13** Singular Point at Infinity, 21. **1.14** Solution in Terms of Integrals, 24. PROBLEMS, 28.

2 EQUATIONS WITH CONSTANT COEFFICIENTS 33

2.1 Introduction, 33. **2.2** The Operator D and Operational Methods, 33. **2.3** Solution in Terms of Integrals, 37. **2.4** Solution with Particular Initial Conditions; the Laplace Transform, 38. **2.5** Some Simple Laplace Transforms, 40. **2.6** General Theorems Relating to Laplace Transforms, 41. **2.7** Equations Reducible to Linear Equations with Constant Coefficients; the Operator δ, 43. **2.8** Operational Methods for Linear Differential Equations with Variable Coefficients, 46. **2.9** Systems of Simultaneous Linear Equations with Constant Coefficients, 47. PROBLEMS, 48.

3 STRUVE AND LOMMEL FUNCTIONS 53

3.1 Introduction, 53. **3.2** Some Properties of Bessel Functions, 54. **3.3** Struve Function $H_\nu(z)$, 58. **3.4** Recurrence Formulas for $H_\nu(z)$, 59. **3.5** Differential Equation Satisfied by $H_\nu(z)$, 61. **3.6** Power Series for $H_\nu(z)$, 62. **3.7** Mellin-Barnes Integrals for $H_\nu(z)$, 63. **3.8** Particular Values of $H_\nu(z)$, 64. **3.9** The Positive Zeros of $H_\nu(z)$, Where ν Is Real, 64. **3.10** Asymptotic Expansion of $H_\nu(z)$, 65. **3.11** Indefinite Integrals Connected with $H_\nu(z)$, 66. **3.12** Definite Integrals Connected with $H_\nu(z)$, 67. **3.13** Infinite Integrals Connected with $H_\nu(z)$, 68. **3.14** Modified Struve Function $L_\nu(z)$, 72. **3.15** Integrals Connected with $L_\nu(z)$, 75. **3.16** Lommel Functions, 76. **3.17** Mellin-Barnes Integrals for the Lommel Functions, 78. **3.18** Recurrence Formulas for the Lommel Functions, 80. **3.19** Particular Values of $S_{\mu,\nu}(z)$, 81.

3.20 Integrals Connected with the Lommel Functions, 83. **3.21** Related Differential Equations, 86. PROBLEMS, 87.

4 NONHOMOGENEOUS CONFLUENT HYPERGEOMETRIC FUNCTIONS 92
4.1 Introduction, 92. **4.2** Some Properties of Confluent Hypergeometric Functions, 93. **4.3** Generalized Modified Struve Function $\Omega(a, c; z)$, 96. **4.4** An Alternative Integral Relation for $\Omega(a, c; z)$, 98. **4.5** Generalized Modified Struve Function $\overline{\Omega}(a, c; z)$, 100. **4.6** Relations Between Contiguous Functions, 100. **4.7** Differential Equations Satisfied by $\Omega(a, c; z)$ and $\overline{\Omega}(a, c; z)$, 103. **4.8** Particular Values of $\Omega(a, c; z)$ and $\overline{\Omega}(a, c; z)$, 104. **4.9** Transformation Formulas for $\Omega(a, c; z)$ and $\overline{\Omega}(a, c; z)$, 108. **4.10** Power Series for $\Omega(a, c; z)$, 108. **4.11** Degenerate Cases of $\Omega(a, c; z)$, 110. **4.12** Other Particular Cases of $\Omega(a, c; z)$, 113. **4.13** Mellin-Barnes Integral for $\Omega(a, c; z)$, 114. **4.14** The Zeros of $\Omega(a, c; z)$, Where a and c Are Real, 116. **4.15** Asymptotic Expansion of $\Omega(a, c; z)$, 117. **4.16** Indefinite Integrals Connected with $\Omega(a, c; z)$ and $\overline{\Omega}(a, c; z)$, 118. **4.17** Infinite Integrals Connected with $\Omega(a, c; z)$, 120. **4.18** The Nonhomogeneous Confluent Hypergeometric Functions $\theta_\sigma(a, c; z)$ and $\Theta_\sigma(a, c; z)$, 121. **4.19** Mellin-Barnes Integrals for $\theta_\sigma(a, c; z)$ and $\Theta_\sigma(a, c; z)$, 125. **4.20** Recurrence Formulas and Relations Between Contiguous Functions, 127. **4.21** Particular Values of $\Theta_\sigma(a, c; z)$, 129. **4.22** Integrals Connected with $\theta_\sigma(a, c; z)$ and $\Theta_\sigma(a, c; z)$, 130. **4.23** The Nonhomogeneous Confluent Hypergeometric Function $\Lambda_{\rho,\sigma}(a, c; z)$, 132. **4.24** Recurrence Formulas and Relations Between Contiguous Functions, 135. **4.25** Related Differential Equations, 136. PROBLEMS, 139.

5 NONHOMOGENEOUS WHITTAKER AND PARABOLIC FUNCTIONS 143
5.1 Introduction, 143. **5.2** Whittaker's Form of the Confluent Hypergeometric Equation, 144. **5.3** Generalized Modified Struve Function $A_{\kappa,\mu}(z)$, 145. **5.4** The Nonhomogeneous Whittaker Function $N_{\kappa,\mu}^{(\nu)}(z)$, 147. **5.5** The Nonhomogeneous Whittaker Functions R and S, 148. **5.6** The Equations for the Functions of the Paraboloid of Revolution, 149. **5.7** The Equation for the Parabolic Cylinder Functions, 149. **5.8** The Parabolic Cylinder Functions $D_\nu(z)$, $E_\nu^{(0)}(z)$, and $E_\nu^{(1)}(z)$, 150. **5.9** The Nonhomogeneous Parabolic Cylinder Functions $F_\nu^{(0)}(z)$ and $F_\nu^{(1)}(z)$, 151. **5.10** Recurrence Relations for $F_\nu^{(0)}(z)$ and $F_\nu^{(1)}(z)$, 152. **5.11** Degenerate Cases of $F_\nu^{(0)}(z)$ and $F_\nu^{(1)}(z)$, 154. **5.12** The Zeros of $F_\nu^{(0)}(z)$ and $F_\nu^{(1)}(z)$, Where ν Is Real, 155. **5.13** Asymptotic Expansion of $F_\nu^{(0)}(z)$ and $F_\nu^{(1)}(z)$, 155. **5.14** The Nonhomogeneous Parabolic Cylinder Function $G_\nu^{(\sigma)}(z)$, 156. **5.15** Recurrence Relations for $G_\nu^{(\sigma)}(z)$, 158. **5.16** Related Differential Equations, 159. PROBLEMS, 161.

6 NONHOMOGENEOUS HYPERGEOMETRIC FUNCTIONS 163
6.1 Introduction, 163. **6.2** Some Properties of the Hypergeometric

Function, 164. **6.3** Nonhomogeneous Hypergeometric Function $B(a, b; c; z)$, 167. **6.4** An Alternative Integral Relation for $B(a, b; c; z)$, 170. **6.5** Differential Equation Satisfied by $B(a, b; c; z)$, 172. **6.6** Relations for Contiguous Functions, 173. **6.7** Particular Values of $B(a, b; c; z)$, 179. **6.8** Power Series for $B(a, b; c; z)$, 184. **6.9** Degenerate Cases of $B(a, b; c; z)$, 187. **6.10** Other Particular Cases of $B(a, b; c; z)$, 191. **6.11** Mellin-Barnes Integral for $B(a, b; c; z)$, 194. **6.12** The Zeros of $B(a, b; c; z)$, Where, a, b, and c Are Real, 195. **6.13** Asymptotic Expansion of $B(a, b; c; z)$, 196. **6.14** Indefinite Integrals Connected with $B(a, b; c; z)$, 198. **6.15** Definite Integrals Connected with $B(a, b; c; z)$, 200. **6.16** The Nonhomogeneous Functions $f_\sigma(a, b; c; z)$ and $F_\sigma(a, b; c; z)$, 201. **6.17** Mellin-Barnes Integral and Analytic Continuation for $f_\sigma(a, b; c; z)$, 205. **6.18** Recurrence Formulas and Relations for Contiguous Functions, 207. **6.19** Integrals Connected with $f_\sigma(a, b; c; z)$ and $F_\sigma(a, b; c; z)$, 209. **6.20** The Nonhomogeneous Hypergeometric Function $C_{\rho,\sigma}^{(\tau)}(a, b; c; z)$, 210. **6.21** Recurrence Formulas and Relations Between Contiguous Functions, 212. **6.22** Related Differential Equations, 215. PROBLEMS, 221.

7 NONHOMOGENEOUS RIEMANN AND LEGENDRE FUNCTIONS 225

7.1 Introduction, 225. **7.2** Riemann's Equation and Riemann's P Function, 226. **7.3** The Nonhomogeneous Riemann Equation and the Differential Operator p, 228. **7.4** Riemann's Equation and Legendre's Equation, 231. **7.5** Some Properties of Legendre Functions, 235. **7.6** The Nonhomogeneous Legendre Function $R_\nu^\mu(z)$, 238. **7.7** Expression for $R_\nu^\mu(-z)$ in Terms of $R_\nu^\mu(z)$, 241. **7.8** Differential Equation Satisfied by $R_\nu^\mu(z)$, 242. **7.9** Relations Between Contiguous Functions, 245. **7.10** Power Series for $R_\nu^\mu(z)$, 247. **7.11** Nonhomogeneous Legendre Function $R_\nu^\mu(x)$, 248. **7.12** Particular Cases of $R_\nu^\mu(z)$ and $R_\nu^\mu(x)$, 248. **7.13** The Zeros of $R_\nu^\mu(z)$ and $R_\nu^\mu(x)$, Where μ and ν Are Real, 250. **7.14** Indefinite Integrals Connected with $R_\nu^\mu(z)$, 250. **7.15** Infinite Integrals Connected with $R_\nu^\mu(z)$, 251. **7.16** The Nonhomogeneous Legendre Functions $s_{\nu,\sigma}^\mu(z)$ and $S_{\nu,\sigma}^\mu(z)$, 252. **7.17** Recurrence Formulas and Relations Between Contiguous Functions, 254. **7.18** Nonhomogeneous Legendre Functions, $s_{\nu,\sigma}^\mu(x)$, 256. **7.19** Integrals Connected with $s_{\nu,\sigma}^\mu(z)$ and $S_{\nu,\sigma}^\mu(z)$, 256. **7.20** The Nonhomogeneous Legendre Function $t_{\nu,\sigma}^{\mu;\tau}(z)$, 257. **7.21** Recurrence Formulas and Relations Between Contiguous Functions, 258. **7.22** Nonhomogeneous Legendre Function $t_{\nu,\sigma}^{\mu;\tau}(x)$, 260. **7.23** Related Differential Equations, 260. PROBLEMS, 262.

8 NONHOMOGENEOUS GENERALIZED HYPERGEOMETRIC FUNCTIONS 265

8.1 Introduction, 265. **8.2** Some Properties of Generalized Hypergeometric Functions, 266. **8.3** Nonhomogeneous Generalized Hypergeometric Functions ${}_pB_q[\alpha_r; \beta_t; z]$, 267. **8.4** Relations for Contiguous

Functions, 269. **8.5** Differential Equation Satisfied by ${}_pB_q[\alpha_r; \beta_t; z]$, 270. **8.6** Degenerate Cases of ${}_pB_q[\alpha_r; \beta_t; z]$, 272. **8.7** The Zeros of ${}_pB_q[\alpha_r; \beta_t; z]$, Where All α_r, β_t Are Real, 273. **8.8** Definite Integrals Connected with ${}_pB_q[\alpha_r; \beta_t; z]$, 273. **8.9** Infinite Integrals Connected with ${}_pB_q[\alpha_r; \beta_t; z]$, 276. **8.10** The Nonhomogeneous Generalized Hypergeometric Functions ${}_pf_{q,\sigma}[\alpha_r; \beta_t; z]$ and ${}_pF_{q,\sigma}[\alpha_r; \beta_t; z]$, 277. **8.11** Recurrence Formulas and Relations for Contiguous Functions, 279. **8.12** Integrals Connected with ${}_pf_{q,\sigma}[\alpha_r; \beta_t; z]$, 280. PROBLEMS, 281.

9 NONHOMOGENEOUS HEUN, LAMÉ, AND MATHIEU FUNCTIONS 283
9.1 Introduction, 283. **9.2** Some Properties of Heun Functions, 284. **9.3** The Nonhomogeneous Heun Functions $f_\sigma(a, b; \alpha, \beta, \gamma, \delta; z)$ and $F_\sigma(a, b; \alpha, \beta, \gamma, \delta; z)$, 287. **9.4** Recurrence Formulas and Differential Relations, 291. **9.5** Integrals Connected with $f_\sigma(a, b; \alpha, \beta, \gamma, \delta; z)$ and $F_\sigma(a, b; \alpha, \beta, \gamma, \delta; z)$, 294. **9.6** The Nonhomogeneous Lamé Equations, 295. **9.7** Nonhomogeneous Lamé Polynomials, 297. **9.8** The Nonhomogeneous Mathieu Equations, 301. **9.9** Solution of the Algebraic Mathieu Equation, 302. **9.10** The Nonhomogeneous Mathieu Functions, 303. **9.11** The Nonhomogeneous Mathieu Functions $N_{p,m}(\theta; s)$ and $N_{p,m+\frac{1}{2}}(\theta; s)$, 305. **9.12** Degenerate Case of the Nonhomogeneous Mathieu Equation, 308. **9.13** Related Differential Equations, 309. PROBLEMS, 315.

10 NONHOMOGENEOUS LINEAR PARTIAL DIFFERENTIAL EQUATIONS 317
10.1 Introduction, 317. **10.2** The General Nonhomogeneous Linear Partial Differential Equation, 317. **10.3** Equations with Constant Coefficients, 319. **10.4** Equations Which Are Homogeneous with Respect to the Derivatives, 326. **10.5** Equations Reducible to Linear Equations with Constant Coefficients, 327. **10.6** Separation of Variables, 330. **10.7** Integral Transforms, 335. **10.8** Green's Functions, 337. PROBLEMS, 342.

11 NONHOMOGENEOUS PARTIAL DIFFERENTIAL EQUATIONS OF MATHEMATICAL PHYSICS 348
11.1 Introduction, 348. **11.2** The Laplacian Operator Δ, 350. **11.3** Solutions of Laplace's Equation, 353. **11.4** Green's Function for Laplace's Equation, 359. **11.5** Solutions of Poisson's Equation, 361. **11.6** Solutions of Poisson's Equation Using Green's Functions, 368. **11.7** Solutions of the Wave Equation, 370. **11.8** Green's Function for Helmholtz's Equation, 373. **11.9** Other Solutions of the Wave Equation, 375. **11.10** Solutions of Lorenz's Equation, 379. **11.11** Solutions of Lorenz's Equation Using Green's Functions, 382. **11.12** Other Solutions of Lorenz's Equation, 383. **11.13** Solutions of the Diffusion Equation, 387. **11.14** Green's Function for the Diffusion Equation, 390. **11.15** Solutions of the Nonhomogeneous Diffusion

Equation, 393. **11.16** Solutions of the Nonhomogeneous Diffusion Equation Using Green's Functions, 397. PROBLEMS, 398.

BIBLIOGRAPHY AND REFERENCES 406

INDEX 409

Transcendental Functions
Satisfying
Nonhomogeneous Linear Differential Equations

CHAPTER 1

Nonhomogeneous Linear Differential Equations and Their Solutions

1.1 Introduction

The general nonhomogeneous (or inhomogeneous) ordinary linear differential equation of order n can be written in the form

$$p_0(x)D^n y + p_1(x)D^{n-1}y + \cdots + p_n(x)y = f(x), \tag{1.1}$$

where $D \equiv d/dx$. For conciseness, this equation will sometimes be written

$$\phi(D)y = f. \tag{1.2}$$

Such an equation can occur when we consider the static deflection of a loaded beam or the forced motion of a mechanical system; in the latter case, $f(x)$ is said to be the *forcing function.*

The associated homogeneous equation is

$$p_0(x)D^n y + p_1(x)D^{n-1}y + \cdots + p_n(x)y = 0. \tag{1.3}$$

In a mechanical system, this equation would correspond to the free motion of the system.

In this chapter we shall derive some properties of (1.1); we shall see that the solution of (1.1) is closely linked to that of (1.3). We shall consider in detail general methods of solving (1.1).

It will be seen that the coefficients $p_0, p_1, \ldots, p_n$ are functions of x. In Chapter 2 we shall consider the important particular case in which all the coefficients are constants.

1.2 The Nature of the Solution

Let $F(x)$ be any particular solution of (1.1); then

$$p_0 D^n F + p_1 D^{n-1} F + \cdots + p_n F = f. \tag{1.4}$$

In (1.1), let $y = Y + F$, and subtract (1.4). We find that

$$p_0 D^n Y + p_1 D^{n-1} Y + \cdots + p_n Y = 0. \tag{1.5}$$

Thus Y satisfies the homogeneous equation (1.3). As shown in textbooks on differential equations—e.g., Poole [1936], Piaggio [1937], Coddington and Levinson [1955], Ince [1926], and Murphy [1960]—the complete solution of a homogeneous linear differential equation of order n, such as (1.5), contains n arbitrary constants and can be written

$$Y(x) = C_1 y_1 + C_2 y_2 + \cdots + C_n y_n, \tag{1.6}$$

where $C_1, C_2, \ldots, C_n$ are arbitrary constants (which in any physical system would be determined by the initial conditions of the system) and $y_1, y_2, \ldots, y_n$ are n independent solutions of (1.3).

The general solution (or *complete primitive*) of (1.1) can then be written

$$y(x) = Y(x) + F(x). \tag{1.7}$$

We see that the general solution of a nonhomogeneous linear differential equation consists of two parts: (a) the *particular integral* $F(x)$, which can be any solution of the original equation, and (b) the *complementary function* $Y(x)$, which is the solution of the associated homogeneous equation. The methods of solving the latter equation, and the properties of the solutions, are fully explained in the standard textbooks on differential equations mentioned above.

The problem to be dealt with in the rest of this chapter, and, indeed, in the rest of this book, is the method of obtaining the particular integral of (1.1) and the properties of such a solution. We note that for a complete solution of a nonhomogeneous linear differential equation we require to know only *one* particular integral, together with the complementary function.

For simple equations the particular integral can be found by inspection. Thus it is easily verified that the equation

$$Dy + 2xy = x^3 \tag{1.8}$$

has as a particular integral

$$y = \tfrac{1}{2}(x^2 - 1).$$

The associated first-order homogeneous equation

$$Dy + 2xy = 0$$

has the solution $y = Ce^{-x^2}$, where C is a constant. Thus the complete primitive of (1.8) is

$$y = \tfrac{1}{2}(x^2 - 1) + Ce^{-x^2},$$

containing one arbitrary constant.

For more complicated equations it is often not easy to spot a particular integral, and more general methods are needed.

It should be noted that if a particular integral $F_1(x)$ is known for the equation $\phi(D)y = f_1$, and another particular integral $F_2(x)$ is known for the equation $\phi(D)y = f_2$, then, since the equations are linear, $K_1F_1 + K_2F_2$ is a particular integral of

$$\phi(D)y = K_1 f_1 + K_2 f_2,$$

where K_1 and K_2 are constants.

1.3 First-Order Linear Equations

We consider first the general nonhomogeneous linear equation of first order,

$$p_0(x)Dy + p_1(x)y = f(x). \tag{1.9}$$

We can divide throughout by $p_0(x)$. Then (1.9) becomes

$$Dy + p(x)y = g(x), \tag{1.10}$$

where $p = p_1/p_0$ and $g = f/p_0$. Equation (1.10) has an integrating factor z given by

$$z = \exp\left[\int p(x)\, dx\right] = \exp \phi(x). \tag{1.11}$$

Multiplying (1.10) by z, we obtain

$$zDy + zpy = zg:$$

that is, using (1.11),

$$zDy + yDz = ge^{\phi}.$$

On integrating we find

$$yz = \int ge^{\phi}\, dx + C,$$

where C is a constant.

Thus, from (1.11), the complete solution of (1.10), or (1.9), is

$$\begin{aligned} y &= Ce^{-\phi} + e^{-\phi}\int ge^{\phi}\, dx \\ &= Ce^{-\phi} + e^{-\phi}\int \frac{f}{p_0} e^{\phi}\, dx, \end{aligned} \tag{1.12}$$

where

$$\phi = \int p\, dx = \int \frac{p_1}{p_0}\, dx. \tag{1.13}$$

We see that the general solution of a linear equation of first order contains one constant of integration C and is linear in this constant.

EXTENSIONS OF THE LINEAR EQUATION

If $y = F(v)$, (1.10) becomes

$$F'(v)Dv + p(x)F(v) = f(x). \tag{1.14}$$

Conversely, a differential equation of the form (1.14) can be reduced to a linear equation by the substitution $y = F(v)$. In particular, the Bernoulli equation

$$Dv = P(x)v + Q(x)v^k \tag{1.15}$$

can be reduced to the form (1.14), for, on multiplying throughout by $(1 - k)v^{-k}$, we have

$$(1 - k)v^{-k}Dv - (1 - k)P(x)v^{1-k} = (1 - k)Q(x). \tag{1.16}$$

On putting $y = v^{1-k}$, we see that (1.16) reduces to a linear equation in y. Thus, from (1.12), the solution of (1.16) is

$$v^{1-k} = Ce^{-\phi} + (1 - k)e^{-\phi} \int Q(x)e^{\phi}\, dx, \tag{1.17}$$

where

$$\phi = -(1 - k) \int P(x)\, dx.$$

1.4 Reduction of Order

If the coefficient of y is zero in (1.1), i.e., if $p_n = 0$, we can immediately reduce the order of the equation by one on writing

$$Z = Dy.$$

More generally, if one particular integral of the associated homogeneous equation is known, the order of the given nonhomogeneous equation can be reduced by unity.

Let y_1 be a solution of (1.3); then

$$p_0D^ny_1 + p_1D^{n-1}y_1 + \cdots + p_ny_1 = 0. \tag{1.18}$$

In (1.1), put $y = zy_1$. Then

$$\begin{aligned}
Dy &= Dz \cdot y_1 + zDy_1, \\
D^2y &= D^2z \cdot y_1 + 2Dz \cdot Dy_1 + zD^2y_1, \\
&\vdots \\
D^ny &= D^nz \cdot y_1 + nD^{n-1}z \cdot Dy_1 + \frac{n(n-1)}{2!} D^{n-2}z \cdot D^2y_1 + \cdots + zD^ny_1.
\end{aligned}$$

On substituting in (1.1), we obtain

$$p_0 y_1 D^n z + (p_1 y_1 + n p_0 D y_1) D^{n-1} z + \cdots + z\phi(D) y_1 = f. \quad (1.19)$$

But, from (1.18), $\phi(D)y_1 = 0$, and thus the coefficient of z in (1.19) is zero. We can now write $Z = Dz$. Equation (1.19) becomes a nonhomogeneous linear equation of order $n - 1$ in Z.

As pointed out by Murphy [1960], in using this method the special solution y_1 of the homogeneous equation should be taken in the simplest possible form, with arbitrary constants fixed at some suitable values.

By repeated application of this process we find that, if m particular integrals of the associated homogeneous equation are known, the order of the original nonhomogeneous differential equation can be reduced by m. In particular, when $n - 1$ particular integrals of the associated homogeneous equation are known, (1.1) can be reduced to a linear equation of first order, which can then be solved by the method given in §1.3.

1.5 Variation of Parameters

The next method we consider is that of the *variation of parameters* (sometimes called the *method of Lagrange*). This method is a very elegant one, giving the solution of a nonhomogeneous linear differential equation of order n in terms of n integrals.

In §1.2, the complete solution of the homogeneous linear differential equation (1.3) was written in the form

$$Y(x) = C_1 y_1 + C_2 y_2 + \cdots + C_n y_n, \quad (1.20)$$

in which $C_1, C_2, \ldots, C_n$ were arbitrary constants. We now look for a solution of the nonhomogeneous equation in the form

$$y(x) = A_1 y_1 + A_2 y_2 + \cdots + A_n y_n, \quad (1.21)$$

where $A_1, A_2, \ldots, A_n$ are undetermined functions of x, and $y_1, y_2, \ldots, y_n$ are n independent solutions of (1.3). We note that the form of (1.21) is the same as that of (1.20), but the constants C are replaced by functions of x; hence the name *variation of parameters*.

On differentiating (1.21) with respect to x, we obtain

$$\frac{dy}{dx} = A_1 \frac{dy_1}{dx} + A_2 \frac{dy_2}{dx} + \cdots + A_n \frac{dy_n}{dx} + y_1 \frac{dA_1}{dx} + y_2 \frac{dA_2}{dx} + \cdots + y_n \frac{dA_n}{dx}. \quad (1.22)$$

The n functions A can be chosen to satisfy n conditions. One condition has already been specified: that they are such that the value of y given by (1.21) satisfies the differential equation (1.1). We can now set forth the following

$n-1$ other relations that these functions must satisfy:

$$\begin{aligned} y_1 DA_1 + y_2 DA_2 + \cdots + y_n DA_n &= 0\,, \\ Dy_1 \cdot DA_1 + Dy_2 \cdot DA_2 + \cdots + Dy_n \cdot DA_n &= 0\,, \\ &\vdots \\ D^{n-2}y_1 \cdot DA_1 + D^{n-2}y_2 \cdot DA_2 + \cdots + D^{n-2}y_n \cdot DA_n &= 0\,, \end{aligned} \qquad (1.23)$$

where $D \equiv d/dx$.

Using (1.23), we see that (1.22) simplifies to

$$Dy = A_1 Dy_1 + A_2 Dy_2 + \cdots + A_n Dy_n\,,$$

and similarly we find that

$$\begin{aligned} D^2 y &= A_1 D^2 y_1 + A_2 D^2 y_2 + \cdots + A_n D^2 y_n\,, \\ &\vdots \\ D^{n-1} y &= A_1 D^{n-1} y_1 + A_2 D^{n-1} y_2 + \cdots + A_n D^{n-1} y_n\,. \end{aligned}$$

On differentiating the last equation we obtain

$$\begin{aligned} D^n y = {} & A_1 D^n y_1 + A_2 D^n y_2 + \cdots + A_n D^n y_n \\ & + DA_1 \cdot D^{n-1} y_1 + DA_2 \cdot D^{n-1} y_2 + \cdots + DA_n \cdot D^{n-1} y_n\,. \end{aligned}$$

On substituting these expressions for y and its derivatives in (1.1), and remembering that $y_1, y_2, \ldots, y_n$ are solutions of the associated homogeneous differential equation (1.3), we find that

$$p_0(DA_1 \cdot D^{n-1}y_1 + DA_2 \cdot D^{n-1}y_2 + \cdots + DA_n \cdot D^{n-1}y_n) = f\,. \qquad (1.24)$$

Equations (1.23) and (1.24) are a set of n linear algebraic equations from which we can find the values of DA_1, DA_2, ..., DA_n uniquely in terms of $y_1, y_2, \ldots, y_n$ and their derivatives. $A_1, A_2, \ldots, A_n$ can then be obtained by quadrature. The details of the derivation are given below.

THE WRONSKIAN DETERMINANT

It is convenient to introduce the *Wronskian determinant* W given by

$$W = \begin{vmatrix} y_1 & y_2 & \cdots & y_n \\ Dy_1 & Dy_2 & \cdots & Dy_n \\ \vdots & & & \\ D^{n-1}y_1 & D^{n-1}y_2 & \cdots & D^{n-1}y_n \end{vmatrix}. \qquad (1.25)$$

As $y_1, y_2, \ldots, y_n$ are independent of one another, W will not be zero.

Let W_r be the cofactor of the element $D^{n-1}y_r$ in the last row of the determinant. Then, on solving (1.23) and (1.24) for DA_r, we find

$$p_0 W DA_r = f W_r \qquad (r = 1 \text{ to } n).$$

Thus

$$A_r = C_r + \int \frac{fW_r}{p_0 W}\, dx,$$

where C_r is an arbitrary constant.

From (1.21), the value of y is given by

$$y = \sum_{r=1}^{n} y_r \left\{ C_r + \int \frac{fW_r}{p_0 W}\, dx \right\}, \tag{1.26}$$

the particular integral being

$$y_1 \int \frac{fW_1}{p_0 W}\, dx + y_2 \int \frac{fW_2}{p_0 W}\, dx + \cdots + y_n \int \frac{fW_n}{p_0 W}\, dx. \tag{1.27}$$

In particular, if (1.1) is of second order, the particular integral is

$$-y_1 \int \frac{y_2 f}{W p_0}\, dx + y_2 \int \frac{y_1 f}{W p_0}\, dx,$$

where W is the Wronskian of y_1 and y_2.

The solution (1.26) can be expressed in the equivalent form

$$y = \int^x g(x, t) \frac{f(t)}{p_0(t)}\, dt, \tag{1.28}$$

where

$$g(x, t) = \frac{\sum_{r=1}^{n} y_r(x) W_r(t)}{W(t)},$$

the lower limit of the integral in (1.28) being arbitrary.

The value of W can be determined as follows (Forsyth [1929]). On substituting the values $y = y_1, y_2, \ldots, y_n$ in (1.3) and eliminating the coefficients $p_2, p_3, \ldots, p_n$ from these n equations, we find

$$p_1 W = -p_0 \begin{vmatrix} y_1 & y_2 & \cdots & y_n \\ Dy_1 & Dy_2 & \cdots & Dy_n \\ \vdots & & & \\ D^{n-2}y_1 & D^{n-2}y_2 & \cdots & D^{n-2}y_n \\ D^n y_1 & D^n y_2 & \cdots & D^n y_n \end{vmatrix} = -p_0 DW.$$

On integrating, we obtain

$$W = C \exp\left[-\int p_1 p_0^{-1}\, dx \right], \tag{1.29}$$

where C is a constant.

The method of variation of parameters gives a very concise expression for the solution of a nonhomogeneous linear differential equation, but, in practice, this method is often of less value than that of the reduction of order, since it requires a complete knowledge of the complementary function. The solution in the form of (1.26) or (1.28) is useful in establishing integral relations between the solutions of the nonhomogeneous equation and those of the associated homogeneous equation.

1.6 Cauchy's Method

We shall now give an alternative derivation of a solution of the nonhomogeneous equation (1.1) in the form of (1.28). This method is known as *Cauchy's method.* We shall follow the presentation of this method given by Bateman [1932].

We start from the complete solution of the homogeneous equation (1.3) in the form

$$Y = C_1 y_1 + C_2 y_2 + \cdots + C_n y_n, \tag{1.30}$$

in which $C_1, C_2, \ldots, C_n$ are n arbitrary constants. We now choose these constants so that Y satisfies the n initial conditions

$$Y(t) = DY(t) = \cdots = D^{n-2}Y(t) = 0,$$

and (1.31)

$$p_0(t)D^{n-1}Y(t) = f(t),$$

where t is the initial value of x and $D^s Y(t)$ denotes the value of $d^s Y/dx^s$ at $x = t$. We denote this solution by the symbol $Y(x, t)$, since the constants C depend upon the value of t.

Now consider the integral

$$y(x) = \int_0^x Y(x, t)\, dt. \tag{1.32}$$

Assuming that differentiation under the integral sign is valid with the given functions, we find that

$$Dy = \int_0^x DY(x, t)\, dt + Y(t);$$

that is, from (1.31),

$$Dy = \int_0^x DY(x, t)\, dt.$$

Similarly, we find

$$D^r y = \int_0^x D^r Y(x, t)\, dt \qquad (r = 1 \text{ to } n-1),$$

and

$$D^n y = \int_0^x D^n Y(x, t)\, dt + \frac{f}{p_0}.$$

Thus

$$\begin{aligned}\phi(D)y &\equiv p_0 D^n y + p_1 D^{n-1} y + \cdots + p_n y \\ &= \int_0^x \phi(D) Y(x, t)\, dt + f = f,\end{aligned}$$

since $Y(x, t)$ is a solution of the associated homogeneous equation (1.3).

Thus the integral given by (1.32) is a solution of the given nonhomogeneous equation. This particular integral has the properties

$$\begin{aligned} y(0) = Dy(0) = \cdots = D^{n-1}y(0) = 0, \\ D^n y(0) = \frac{f(0)}{p_0(0)}. \end{aligned} \tag{1.33}$$

On solving (1.31) for C_r we find

$$p_0(t)W(t)C_r = f(t)W_r(t) \qquad (r = 1 \text{ to } n), \tag{1.34}$$

where $W(t)$ and $W_r(t)$ denote the values of the Wronskian determinant W and its minor W_r (as defined in §1.5) at $x = t$. From (1.30), (1.32), and (1.34), the particular solution of the nonhomogeneous equation satisfying (1.33) is given by

$$y = \int_0^x g(x, t) \frac{f(t)}{p_0(t)}\, dt, \tag{1.35}$$

where

$$g(x, t) = \frac{\sum_{r=1}^n y_r(x) W_r(t)}{W(t)}.$$

The general solution of (1.1), with arbitrary lower limit, is given by (1.28). We see that Cauchy's method gives us the solution in the same form as that of the variation of parameters.

1.7 Solution by Differentiation

Another method of solving a nonhomogeneous linear equation is to convert it into a homogeneous equation by differentiation.

Thus, on differentiating (1.2), we obtain

$$D[\phi(D)y] = Df, \tag{1.36}$$

and, from (1.2) and (1.36), we obtain the homogeneous linear equation

$$fD[\phi(D)y] - Df \cdot \phi(D)y = 0\,;$$

that is,

$$\begin{aligned} f[p_0D^{n+1}y + (Dp_0 + p_1)D^ny + (Dp_1 + p_2)D^{n-1}y + \cdots + Dp_ny] \\ - Df \cdot [p_0D^ny + p_1D^{n-1}y + \cdots + p_ny] = 0. \end{aligned} \tag{1.37}$$

We see that every solution of a nonhomogeneous linear differential equation of order n satisfies a homogeneous equation of order $n + 1$. Conversely, it is readily seen that a solution of (1.37) will satisfy an equation of the form

$$\phi(D)y = Cf, \tag{1.38}$$

where C is a constant. Now, if $y_1, y_2, \ldots, y_n$ are n independent solutions of (1.3), they will also satisfy the equation

$$D[\phi(D)y] = 0$$

and hence also (1.37).

The complete solution of the homogeneous equation (1.37) can thus be put in the form

$$y(x) = C_1y_1 + C_2y_2 + \cdots + C_ny_n + C_{n+1}f_1(x), \tag{1.39}$$

where C_{n+1} is an arbitrary constant. As stated above, this solution will satisfy (1.38). We finally choose C_{n+1}, so that $C_{n+1}f_1(x)$ is a particular integral of (1.1).

More generally, we can differentiate (1.1) successively (a) until $f(x)$ vanishes, or (b) until it is possible to eliminate $f(x)$ and its derivatives. In either case we obtain a homogeneous equation of order $m + n$. The solution of this equation will contain $m + n$ arbitrary constants, and will be of the form

$$y(x) = C_1y_1 + C_2y_2 + \cdots + C_ny_n + F(x),$$

where

$$F(x) = C_{n+1}f_1(x) + C_{n+2}f_2(x) + \cdots + C_{n+m}f_m(x).$$

We now substitute $F(x)$ into the original nonhomogeneous equation and determine the constants C_{n+k}, so that (1.1) is satisfied. $F(x)$ will then be a particular integral of (1.1).

In general, the homogeneous equation of order $m + n$ will be difficult to solve. This method gives a very useful way of relating a solution of a nonhomogeneous equation to that of a homogeneous equation of higher order.

1.8 The Exact Nonhomogeneous Equation

In this method we endeavor to find a solution of the nonhomogeneous equation (1.1) by integration.

Equation (1.1) is said to be exact when $\phi(D)y$ is the exact differential of some function $\psi(D)y$, which must therefore be of the form

$$\psi(D)y \equiv q_0(x)D^{n-1}y + q_1(x)D^{n-2}y + \cdots + q_{n-1}(x)y. \qquad (1.40)$$

Differentiating (1.40) and comparing the result with (1.1), we obtain the n equations

$$\begin{aligned} p_0 &= q_0, \\ p_1 &= Dq_0 + q_1, \\ p_2 &= Dq_1 + q_2, \\ &\vdots \\ p_{n-1} &= Dq_{n-2} + q_{n-1}, \\ p_n &= Dq_{n-1}. \end{aligned} \qquad (1.41)$$

On eliminating all the q_s from (1.41) by successive differentiation, we see that, if (1.1) is an exact equation, the functions p_s must satisfy the relation

$$D^n p_0 - D^{n-1}p_1 + D^{n-2}p_2 - \cdots + (-1)^n p_n = 0. \qquad (1.42)$$

When this equation is satisfied, the first integral of (1.1) is

$$q_0(x)D^{n-1}y + q_1(x)D^{n-2}y + \cdots + q_{n-1}(x)y = \int f(x)\,dx + C_1, \qquad (1.43)$$

where, from (1.41),

$$\begin{aligned} q_0 &= p_0, \\ q_1 &= p_1 - Dp_0, \\ q_2 &= p_2 - Dp_1 + D^2p_0, \\ &\vdots \\ q_{n-1} &= p_{n-1} - Dp_{n-2} + D^2p_{n-3} - \cdots + (-1)^{n-1}D^{n-1}p_0, \end{aligned}$$

and C_1 is an arbitrary constant.

If the functions q_s satisfy the corresponding condition, that is,

$$D^{n-1}q_0 - D^{n-2}q_1 + D^{n-3}q_2 - \cdots + (-1)^{n-1}q_{n-1} = 0,$$

(1.43) can be integrated again; and the process of integration can be continued as long as the condition for each equation to be exact is satisfied.

1.9 Solution by Integrating Factor

It may well happen that (1.1) is not exact as it stands. If the equation is exact when multiplied throughout by some function $z(x)$, then, from (1.42),

$$D^n(zp_0) - D^{n-1}(zp_1) + D^{n-2}(zp_2) - \cdots + (-1)^n zp_n = 0; \qquad (1.44)$$

that is,

$$p_0 D^n z + (nDp_0 - p_1)D^{n-1}z + \left[\frac{n(n-1)}{2!} D^2 p_0 - (n-1)Dp_1 + p_2\right]D^{n-2}z$$

$$+ \cdots + [D^n p_0 - D^{n-1}p_1 + D^{n-2}p_2 - \cdots + (-1)^n p_n]z = 0. \qquad (1.45)$$

Thus, for a second-order equation,

$$p_0 D^2 z + (2Dp_0 - p_1)Dz + (D^2 p_0 - Dp_1 + p_2)z = 0. \qquad (1.46)$$

For conciseness, we write (1.44) and (1.45) in the form

$$\bar{\phi}(D)z = 0, \qquad (1.47)$$

where

$$\bar{\phi}(D)z \equiv (-1)^n D^n(p_0 z) + (-1)^{n-1}D^{n-1}(p_1 z) + \cdots + p_n z. \qquad (1.48)$$

The differential expression $\bar{\phi}(D)$ is said to be adjoint to $\phi(D)$, and (1.47) is the *adjoint equation* corresponding to

$$\phi(D)y = 0, \qquad (1.49)$$

where

$$\phi(D) \equiv p_0 D^n + p_1 D^{n-1} + \cdots + p_n.$$

If $\phi(D)y \equiv (-1)^n \bar{\phi}(D)y$, the two differential expressions are said to be *self-adjoint*.

If z is an integrating factor of (1.1) or (1.49), then z must satisfy the homogeneous linear differential equation (1.47). We note that, if z is an integrating factor of the nonhomogeneous equation (1.1), it will also be an integrating factor of the associated homogeneous equation (1.3). Integrating factors can sometimes be found by inspection. If (1.1) is of first order, an integrating factor can always be found, as shown in §1.3. However, for equations of higher order, an integrating factor may not exist in terms of known functions.

On multiplication of (1.1) throughout by the integrating factor z, the first integral can be written

$$q_0(x)D^{n-1}y + q_1(x)D^{n-2}y + \cdots + q_{n-1}(x)y = \int zf(x)\,dx + C_1, \qquad (1.50)$$

where we find, in a manner similar to that of §1.8, that

$$
\begin{aligned}
q_0 &= p_0 z\,, \\
q_1 &= p_1 z - D(p_0 z)\,, \\
q_2 &= p_2 z - D(p_1 z) + D^2(p_0 z)\,, \\
&\vdots \\
q_{n-1} &= p_{n-1} z - D(p_{n-2} z) + D^2(p_{n-3} z) + \cdots + (-1)^{n-1} D^{n-1}(p_0 z)\,,
\end{aligned}
\tag{1.51}
$$

and C_1 is an arbitrary constant.

THE LAGRANGE IDENTITY

Ince [*123*, 1926] gives a number of properties of the adjoint equation. We shall now derive an expression relating $\phi(D)y$ and $\bar{\phi}(D)z$.

From (1.49),

$$
\begin{aligned}
z\phi(D)y &= \sum_{r=0}^{n} p_r z D^{n-r} y \\
&= \sum_{r=0}^{n} D[D^{n-r-1}y \cdot (p_r z) - D^{n-r-2} y \cdot D(p_r z) + D^{n-r-3} y \cdot D^2(p_r z) \\
&\qquad + \cdots + (-1)^{n-r-1} y D^{n-r-1}(p_r z)] + \sum_{r=0}^{n} (-1)^{n-r} y D^{n-r}(p_r z)\,.
\end{aligned}
$$

From (1.48), the second summation on the right side of the last equation is precisely $y\bar{\phi}(D)z$. Thus we obtain the *Lagrange identity*,

$$
z\phi(D)y - y\bar{\phi}(D)z = \frac{d}{dx} P(y, z)\,, \tag{1.52}
$$

where the *bilinear concomitant* $P(y, z)$ is given by

$$
P(y, z) = q_0 D^{n-1} y + q_1 D^{n-2} y + \cdots + q_{n-1} y\,, \tag{1.53}
$$

the q_s being given by (1.51).

If one integrating factor z can be found that satisfies (1.47), equation (1.1) can be reduced to an equation of order $n - 1$, given by (1.50). We see that this equation can also be written

$$
P(y, z) = \int z f(x)\, dx + C_1. \tag{1.54}
$$

If m independent solutions of (1.47) can be found, we shall have m equations of the form

$$
P(y, z_r) = \int z_r f(x)\, dx + C_r\,,
$$

each of order $n - 1$. On eliminating the $m - 1$ highest derivatives of y between these m equations, we arrive at a linear differential equation in y of order $n - m$, the coefficients of which involve the arbitrary constants

$C_1, C_2, \ldots, C_m$. In particular, if all the n independent solutions of (1.47) are known, (1.1) can be integrated completely.

1.10 Solution of a Homogeneous Equation in Power Series

Methods of solving a homogeneous linear differential equation, such as (1.3), in terms of power series are given in the textbooks on differential equations mentioned in §1.2. The method most commonly used is that due to Frobenius, in which a solution of the form

$$y = (x - x_0)^c\{a_0 + a_1(x - x_0) + a_2(x - x_0)^2 + \cdots\} \tag{1.55}$$

is assumed, where the a_s are constants. This series, and the corresponding ones for the derivatives of y, are then substituted in the differential equation (which must then be identically satisfied). On equating to zero the coefficient of the term of the lowest degree in $x - x_0$, we obtain a polynomial in c of the form

$$P(c) = 0; \tag{1.56}$$

this is called the *indicial equation* (see also §1.12). The degree of the indicial equation will be equal to (or less than) the order of the original differential equation. For every value of c satisfying (1.56), the coefficients of the higher powers of $x - x_0$ in the identity can now be equated to zero, enabling various relations to be established between $a_0, a_1, a_2, \ldots$. Equation (1.55) will then be a solution of the homogeneous equation for values of c satisfying (1.56) and for all values of x for which this series is convergent.

If (1.56) has n distinct roots, and no two of them differ by an integer, then (as shown by Ince [*359*, 1926]), there are n linearly distinct solutions of the type (1.55). If two or more of the roots of (1.56) are equal, or differ by an integer, there may be some solutions of (1.3) which are not of the form (1.55).

1.11 Singular Points

Before proceeding further, we have to distinguish between a *singular point* and an *ordinary point*. At an ordinary (or nonsingular) point, $x = x_0$, there exists a unique solution of the differential equation (1.1) such that $y(x)$ and its first $n - 1$ derivatives can assume a set of arbitrarily assigned values when $x = x_0$, and such that y can be expressed as a power series which converges in some interval $a \leqslant x_0 \leqslant b$. It is shown by Ince [*73*, 1926] that if, in the nonhomogeneous linear differential equation

$$p_0(x)D^ny + p_1(x)D^{n-1}y + \cdots + p_n(x)y = f(x), \tag{1.57}$$

$p_0(x), p_1(x), \ldots, p_n(x)$ and $f(x)$ are continuous functions of x in the interval

$a \leqslant x \leqslant b$, and $p_0(x)$ does not vanish at any point in that interval, the differential equation (1.57) has a unique solution y which, together with its first $n-1$ derivatives is (1) continuous in (a, b) and (2) satisfies arbitrarily assigned initial conditions at a point x_0 in this interval. When complex values of x are considered, $p_0(x), p_1(x), \ldots, p_n(x)$ and $f(x)$ are analytic at an ordinary point, with $p_0(x) \neq 0$. At an ordinary point, the roots of the indicial equation are $c = 0, 1, \ldots, n-1$, which lead to n independent integrals of the associated homogeneous equation.

Points which are not ordinary are called *singular*. For (1.57), if $p_0(x), p_1(x), \ldots, p_n(x)$ and $f(x)$ are continuous functions in the interval $a \leqslant x \leqslant b$, the only singular points which can occur within that interval are the zeros of $p_0(x)$. We note that the singularities of the solutions of (1.57) can be seen by inspection of the coefficients.

Suppose that the point $x = x_0$ be a singular point; it may be either a *regular* or an *irregular* singularity. For simplicity, we take $x_0 = 0$; it can always be made zero by an appropriate transformation. As above, we substitute a series of the form (1.55) in the associated homogeneous linear differential equation

$$p_0(x)D^n y + p_1(x)D^{n-1}y + \cdots + p_n(x)y = 0, \tag{1.58}$$

and equate to zero the term of lowest degree in x. If the coefficient of this term is a polynomial $P(c)$ of degree n, the singularity is said to be *regular*. If this coefficient is independent of c, or if the degree of $P(c)$ is less than n, the singularity is said to be *irregular*.

Fuchs [1866] showed that a necessary and sufficient condition that the point $x = x_0$ should be a regular singular point of (1.58) is that

$$\frac{p_r}{p_0} = (x - x_0)^{-r}R(x) \qquad (r = 1 \text{ to } n) \tag{1.59}$$

where $R(x)$ is analytic in the neighborhood of x_0 (see Ince [*365*, 1926]). This condition may be expressed in an alternative manner by

$$\frac{p_r}{p_0} = 0([x - x_0]^{-r}) \qquad (r = 1 \text{ to } n). \tag{1.60}$$

If this equation is not satisfied by all the $p_r(x)$, the point $x = x_0$ is an irregular point.

Thus the origin will be a regular singular point of the equation

$$D^2y + P(x)Dy + Q(x)y = 0$$

if $P(x)$ has a pole of order one or less at $x = 0$ and $Q(x)$ a pole of order two or less at $x = 0$. Alternatively, we see that the equation

$$x^2D^2y + xp(x)Dy + q(x)y = 0$$

will have all its integrals regular at the origin if p and q are analytic there.

Singularities of the nonhomogeneous differential equation (1.57) also occur at points at which $f(x)$ is not analytic.

REAL AND APPARENT SINGULARITIES

It must be pointed out that singularities of the differential equation do not always give rise to solutions that have singularities. Thus it may happen that every integral is analytic at the point $x = x_0$; in this case, the singularity is said to be *apparent*. In all other cases the singularity is said to be real. As shown by Ince [*407*, 1926], at an apparent singularity the roots of the indicial equation are unequal positive integers (one root may be zero). No logarithmic terms must occur in the general solution at an apparent singularity.

1.12 Solution of a Nonhomogeneous Equation in Power Series

The solution of a nonhomogeneous linear differential equation, such as (1.1), in terms of a power series can be carried out in a manner very similar to that for the homogeneous equation. For simplicity we shall confine our attention to an equation of second order, given by

$$D^2y + P(x)Dy + Q(x)y = R(x). \tag{1.61}$$

SOLUTION NEAR AN ORDINARY POINT

If the origin is an ordinary point of the equation, we can write

$$P(x) = P_0 + P_1x + P_2x^2 + \cdots,$$
$$Q(x) = Q_0 + Q_1x + Q_2x^2 + \cdots,$$

and

$$R(x) = x^M(R_0 + R_1x + R_2x^2 + \cdots),$$

where $M \geqslant 0$ and $R_0 \neq 0$.

The complementary function of (1.61) can be found as in §1.10. We write

$$y = x^c(a_0 + a_1x + a_2x^2 + \cdots), \tag{1.62}$$

where $a_0 \neq 0$. On substituting for y in the associated homogeneous equation

$$D^2y + P(x)Dy + Q(x)y = 0, \tag{1.63}$$

and equating to zero the coefficient of the term of lowest degree in x (i.e., in this case, the coefficient of x^{c-2}), we obtain the indicial equation

$$c(c - 1) = 0,$$

i.e., $c = 0$ or 1, and the corresponding power series can be obtained.

For the particular integral, we assume for y the same form of series as in

(1.62), but with $c = M + 2$. On substituting for y in (1.61), and equating the coefficients of the term of lowest degree (i.e., in this case, the coefficient of x^M) on both sides of the equation, we obtain

$$(M + 2)(M + 1)a_0 = R_0,$$

from which a_0 can be found.

The other coefficients in the power series for the particular integral can be found in like manner, by equating the coefficients of the terms of higher degree on both sides of (1.61) and solving the resulting equations successively to determine $a_1, a_2, \ldots$.

This power-series solution will be valid for all values of x for which the series is convergent. This method is particularly simple to apply if the function $R(x)$ is merely a power of x (i.e., if $R_1 = R_2 = \cdots = 0$). If $R(x)$ contains many terms, it may be easier to solve the separate equations

$$D^2y + P(x)Dy + Q(x)y = x^{M_1}$$

and then to add these particular solutions to determine a particular integral, as explained in §1.2.

SOLUTION NEAR A REGULAR SINGULAR POINT

If the origin is a regular singular point of (1.63) then, in the neighborhood of the origin, we can write (1.61) in the form

$$x^2D^2y + xp(x)Dy + q(x)y = r(x), \tag{1.64}$$

where

$$\begin{aligned} p(x) &= p_0 + p_1x + p_2x^2 + \cdots, \\ q(x) &= q_0 + q_1x + q_2x^2 + \cdots, \end{aligned} \tag{1.65}$$

and

$$r(x) = x^m(r_0 + r_1x + r_2x^2 + \cdots),$$

where $r_0 \neq 0$.

To find the complementary function we write y in the form given by (1.62) and substitute in the associated homogeneous equation

$$x^2D^2y + xp(x)Dy + q(x)y = 0. \tag{1.66}$$

The indicial equation is then

$$c(c - 1) + p_0c + q_0 = 0. \tag{1.67}$$

Let the roots of this equation be c_1 and c_2. As shown in textbooks on differential equations, if $c_1 = c_2 \pm n$, where n is any integer, the complementary function will, in general, contain logarithmic terms (see also Ince [*404*, 1926]).

For the particular integral, we assume for y the same form as in (1.62), but with $c = m$. On substituting for y in (1.64) and equating the coefficients of the terms of lowest degree (i.e., in this case, the coefficients of x^m) on both sides of the equation, we obtain

$$\{m(m-1) + p_0 m + q_0\}a_0 = r_0;$$

that is, using (1.67),

$$(m - c_1)(m - c_2)a_0 = r_0. \tag{1.68}$$

Similarly, equating coefficients of x^{m+n}, we obtain

$$(m + n - c_1)(m + n - c_2)a_n + g(a_0, a_1, \cdots, a_{n-1}) = r_n, \tag{1.69}$$

where g is a linear function of $a_0, a_1, \ldots, a_{n-1}$.

From (1.68) and (1.69) we see that a_n becomes infinite or indeterminate if m equals $c_1 - n$ or $c_2 - n$, where n is zero or a positive integer. If m does not equal $c_1 - n$ or $c_2 - n$, where n is zero or a positive integer, all the coefficients in the power series (1.62) (with $c = m$) can be determined.

SOLUTIONS CONTAINING LOGARITHMIC TERMS

We shall now consider the cases in which m equals $c_1 - n$ or $c_2 - n$, where n is zero or a positive integer. The form of the solutions in these cases is found most easily by considering the third-order homogeneous equation which can be derived from the second-order nonhomogeneous equation (1.64), as shown in §1.7.

Differentiating (1.64) with respect to x, we obtain

$$x^2D^3y + x(p+2)D^2y + (p + q + xDp)Dy + Dq \cdot y = Dr. \tag{1.70}$$

From (1.64) and (1.70),

$$x^3D^3y + x^2(p+2)D^2y + x(p+q+xDp)Dy + xDq \cdot y - x\frac{Dr}{r}(x^2D^2y + xpDy + qy) = 0. \tag{1.71}$$

Now, from (1.65),

$$Dr = x^{m-1}[mr_0 + (m+1)r_1x + (m+2)r_2x^2 + \cdots],$$

and thus, in the neighborhood of the origin, we can write

$$\frac{xDr}{r} = m(1 + \bar{r}_1x + \bar{r}_2x^2 + \cdots), \tag{1.72}$$

where the coefficients $\bar{r}_1, \bar{r}_2, \ldots$ are functions of the r_s.

We now write y in the form (1.62) and substitute power series for p, q, and xDr/r in (1.71). Equating to zero the coefficient of the lowest power of x (i.e., the coefficient of x^c), we obtain the indicial equation in the form

$$c(c-1)(c-2)+(p_0+2)c(c-1)+(p_0+q_0)c$$
$$-m[c(c-1)+p_0c+q_0]=0,$$

that is,

$$(c-m)[c(c-1)+p_0c+q_0]=0;$$

that is, using (1.67),

$$(c-m)(c-c_1)(c-c_2)=0. \tag{1.73}$$

The solution of (1.64) for the special cases in which m equals c_1, c_2, c_1-n, or c_2-n (where n is a positive integer) can be obtained immediately by considering the corresponding particular solution of the third-order homogeneous equation (1.71), as shown in §1.7. Using the Frobenius method, it follows that, if $m=c_1-n$ (where n is a positive integer, or zero, and c_1 does not equal c_2 or differ from it by an integer), a particular solution is

$$A_1[y_1\log x+F_1(x)],$$

where y_1 is the series solution of the associated homogeneous equation (1.66) corresponding to $c=c_1$, $F_1(x)$ is a series of the form (1.62) with $c=m$, and A_1 is a constant to be determined. Similarly, if $m=c_2-n$ (where n is a positive integer, or zero, and c_2 does not equal c_1 or differ from it by an integer), a particular solution is

$$A_2[y_2\log x+F_2(x)],$$

where y_2 is the series solution of the associated homogeneous equation (1.66) corresponding to $c=c_2$, $F_2(x)$ is a series of the form (1.62) with $c=m$, and A_2 is a constant to be determined.

If c_1 and c_2 are equal or differ from one another by an integer, and if $m=c_1-n$ or c_2-n, where n is a positive integer or zero, a particular solution of (1.64) is

$$A_3[y_1(\log x)^2+F_3(x)\log x+F_4(x)],$$

where y_1 is the series solution of the associated homogeneous equation (1.66) corresponding to $c=c_1$ ($\geqslant c_2$), $F_3(x)$ and $F_4(x)$ are series of the form (1.62) with $c=m$, and A_3 is a constant to be determined.

In particular cases, the logarithmic terms may be absent; this is considered in detail by Ince [*404*, 1926].

SOLUTION NEAR AN IRREGULAR SINGULAR POINT

The form of the solution of a second-order nonhomogeneous equation near an irregular singular point is most easily found by considering the third-order homogeneous equation found in a similar manner to that given above. As above, we suppose that the singular point is at the origin.

Let us write the nonhomogeneous equation in the form (1.64), where, in this case,

$$\begin{aligned} p(x) &= \frac{a_0}{x^{\lambda}} + \frac{a_1}{x^{\lambda-1}} + \cdots, \\ q(x) &= \frac{b_0}{x^{\mu}} + \frac{b_1}{x^{\mu-1}} + \cdots, \end{aligned} \tag{1.74}$$

and at least one of λ and μ is a positive integer.

The indicial equation corresponding to (1.71) will be in one of three forms:

(a) If $\lambda > \mu$,

$$c^2 - c(\lambda + m) = 0.$$

(b) If $\lambda = \mu$,

$$a_0[c^2 - c(\lambda + m)] + b_0(c - \lambda - m) = 0.$$

(c) If $\lambda < \mu$,

$$c - \mu - m = 0.$$

We see that (1.71), and hence (1.64), has (at most) two regular integrals if $\lambda \geqslant \mu$, and one regular integral if $\mu > \lambda$. The associated homogeneous equation (1.66) has (at most) one regular integral (corresponding to $c = 0$) if $\lambda > \mu$, one regular integral (corresponding to $c = -b_0/a_0$) if $\lambda = \mu$, and two regular integrals if $\mu > \lambda$. We thus see that, at an irregular singular point (taken to be the origin), the nonhomogeneous equation (1.64) may have as a particular solution a regular integral of the form (1.62), given by

$$c = \lambda + m \qquad \text{if } \lambda \geqslant \mu,$$

or

$$c = \mu + m \qquad \text{if } \mu > \lambda,$$

when the coefficients $p(x)$ and $q(x)$ appearing in (1.64) are written in the form (1.74). The resulting series may terminate; in that case, the particular solution is regular at the origin. In general, however, the series does not terminate. As shown by Ince [*422*, 1926], the series will then be divergent; in that case, no particular solution exists which is regular at the origin.

1.13 Singular Point at Infinity

To determine the nature of the differential equation at the point at infinity, we take a new variable $z = 1/x$, write $\bar{D} = d/dz$, and apply the above criteria to the transformed equation.

For simplicity, we shall consider only the second-order equation

$$D^2y + P(x)Dy + Q(x)y = R(x). \tag{1.75}$$

Now

$$Dy = \frac{dz}{dx}\bar{D}y = -z^2\bar{D}y$$

and

$$D^2y = \frac{dz}{dx}\bar{D}\left[\frac{dz}{dx}\bar{D}y\right] = \left(\frac{dz}{dx}\right)^2\bar{D}^2y + \frac{d^2z}{dx^2}\bar{D}y$$
$$= z^4\bar{D}^2y + 2z^3\bar{D}y.$$

Thus the transformed equation is

$$\bar{D}^2y + \left[\frac{2}{z} - \frac{P(z^{-1})}{z^2}\right]\bar{D}y + \frac{Q(z^{-1})}{z^4}y = \frac{R(z^{-1})}{z^4}. \tag{1.76}$$

The point $z = 0$ will be an ordinary point of the equation if

$$\frac{2}{z} - \frac{P(z^{-1})}{z^2} = 0(1),$$

$$\frac{Q(z^{-1})}{z^4} = 0(1),$$

and

$$\frac{R(z^{-1})}{z^4} = 0(1)$$

as $z \to 0$, that is,

$$P(x) = \frac{2}{x} + 0\left(\frac{1}{x^2}\right),$$

$$Q(x) = 0\left(\frac{1}{x^4}\right), \tag{1.77}$$

and

$$R(x) = 0\left(\frac{1}{x^4}\right)$$

as $x \to \infty$.

The point $z = 0$ will be a regular singularity if

$$\frac{2}{z} - \frac{P(z^{-1})}{z^2} = 0\left(\frac{1}{z}\right),$$

$$\frac{Q(z^{-1})}{z^4} = 0\left(\frac{1}{z^2}\right)$$

as $z \to 0$, that is,

$$P(x) = 0\left(\frac{1}{x}\right),$$

and (1.78)

$$Q(x) = 0\left(\frac{1}{x^2}\right)$$

as $x \to \infty$.

If the point at infinity is either an ordinary point or a singular point, we can derive a solution of (1.76) as a power series in z. We write (1.76) in the form

$$z^2\bar{D}^2 y + [2z - P]\bar{D}y + \frac{Q}{z^2} = \frac{R}{z^2}. \tag{1.79}$$

Then if, for large values of x,

$$P(x) = \frac{P_0}{x} + 0\left(\frac{1}{x^2}\right) = P_0 z + 0(z^2),$$

$$Q(x) = \frac{Q_0}{x^2} + 0\left(\frac{1}{x^3}\right) = Q_0 z^2 + 0(z^3),$$

and

$$R(x) = \frac{R_0}{x^{\nu+2}} + 0\left(\frac{1}{x^{\nu+3}}\right) = R_0 z^{\nu+2} + 0(z^{\nu+3}),$$

we can find the complementary function and the particular integral in a precisely similar manner to that given in §1.12.

Thus we assume a solution for y in the form

$$y = z^c(a_0 + a_1 z + a_2 z^2 + \cdots)$$

$$= \frac{1}{x^c}\left(a_0 + \frac{a_1}{x} + \frac{a_2}{x^2} + \cdots\right) \quad . \tag{1.80}$$

The indicial equation (sometimes called the *descending* indicial equation) is now

$$c(c-1)+(2-P_0)c+Q_0=0$$

and, for the particular integral, we put $c = v$ in (1.80). The series (1.80) will converge for sufficiently large values of $|x|$.

IRREGULAR SINGULAR POINT AT INFINITY

If neither conditions (1.77) nor (1.78) hold true, the point at infinity is an irregular singular point. This would be the case, for example, with a linear equation with constant coefficients. Such an irregular singular point is a common occurrence in the equations of higher transcendental functions (e.g., Bessel's equation, Weber's equation, and the confluent hypergeometric equation). As shown by Ince [*169*, 1926], the solution for the complementary function of (1.75) can be expressed in the form

$$y = e^{\phi(x)}\, u(x),$$

where ϕ (the determining factor) is a polynomial in x, and u is an infinite series in $1/x$ which, though divergent, is asymptotic.

The particular solution of (1.75) can be found as in §1.12. If, for large values of x,

$$P(x) = \frac{A_0}{x^{\lambda+1}} + 0\left(\frac{1}{x^{\lambda+2}}\right) = A_0 z^{\lambda+1} + 0(z^{\lambda+2}),$$

$$Q(x) = \frac{B_0}{x^{\mu+2}} + 0\left(\frac{1}{x^{\mu+3}}\right) = B_0 z^{\mu+2} + 0(z^{\mu+3}),$$

and

$$R(x) = \frac{R_0}{x^{v+2}} + 0\left(\frac{1}{x^{v+3}}\right) = R_0 z^{v+2} + 0(z^{v+3}),$$

where at least one of λ and μ is a negative integer, we find as in §1.12 that the nonhomogeneous equation (1.75) has as a particular solution a regular integral of the form (1.80), given by

$$c = v - \lambda \qquad \text{if } \mu \geqslant \lambda,$$

or

$$c = v - \mu \qquad \text{if } \lambda > \mu.$$

We see that the series solution for the particular integral is, in general, easier to obtain than that for the complementary function since, in this case, the determining factor ϕ is not needed.

As in §1.12, the resulting series may terminate; in that case, the particular solution is regular at the point at infinity. In general, the series does not terminate, and is divergent; in this case the series is said to be the *asymptotic expansion* of the particular integral y provided that, as $x \to \infty$,

$$y = \frac{1}{x^c}\left(a_0 + \frac{a_1}{x} + \cdots + \frac{a_n}{x^n}\right) + O\left(\frac{1}{x^{c+n+\varepsilon}}\right) \qquad (\varepsilon > 0), \tag{1.81}$$

for any fixed value of n (Whittaker and Watson [*151*, 1935] and Erdélyi [1956]). It is to be noted that such a series will represent a particular integral of the nonhomogeneous equation, but not necessarily the same particular integral as that given by the series in *ascending* powers of x.

1.14 Solution in Terms of Integrals

We shall now consider the solution of the nonhomogeneous equation in terms of an integral; with real variables, it will be a definite integral, but the method is more useful with complex variables, in which case the integral will be a contour integral. The method given here is adapted from that given by Ince [*186*, 1926].

As in the case of a homogeneous linear equation (Ince [*186*, 1926]), we look for a solution of

$$\phi(D)y = f(x) \tag{1.82}$$

in the form

$$y(x) = \int K(x, t)v(t)\,dt, \tag{1.83}$$

in which the function $K(x, t)$ satisfies a partial differential equation of the form

$$\phi(D)[K] = M(T)[K], \tag{1.84}$$

where $M(T)$ is a linear differential operator involving only t and $\partial/\partial t$.

Then, from (1.83) and (1.84),

$$\begin{aligned}\phi(D)[y(x)] &= \int \phi(D)[K(x, t)]v(t)\,dt \\ &= \int M(T)[K(x, t)]v(t)\,dt.\end{aligned} \tag{1.85}$$

Now if $\overline{M}(T)$ is the operator which is adjoint to $M(T)$ (see §1.9), the Lagrange identity (1.52) can be written

$$v(t)M(T)[K(x, t)] - K(x, t)\overline{M}(T)[v(t)] = \frac{\partial}{\partial t} P(K, v), \tag{1.86}$$

where $P(K, v)$ is the bilinear concomitant. On integrating (1.86) with respect to t and using (1.85), we see that

$$\phi(D)[y(x)] = \int K(x, t)\overline{M}(T)[v(t)]\, dt + P(K, v).$$

The integral (1.83) will satisfy the nonhomogeneous equation (1.82) (a) if $v(t)$ is a solution of the equation

$$\overline{M}(T)v(t) = 0 \tag{1.87}$$

and (b) if the contour of integration (or, for a definite integral, the limit) is such that

$$[P(K, v)]_C = f(x). \tag{1.88}$$

As shown by Ince [*186*, 1926], the integral (1.83) will satisfy the *associated* homogeneous equation if (1.87) is satisfied and if $[P(K, v)]_C = 0$.

We see that, if the function $v(t)$ is known for the associated homogeneous equation (as is the case with standard equations such as the hypergeometric equation, Legendre's equation, and Bessel's equation), all we have to find to solve the nonhomogeneous equation is the appropriate contour C such that (1.88) is satisfied. In practice, $K(x, t)$, the *nucleus* of the definite integral, is generally taken to be some fairly simple function, such as exp xt, exp ixt, or $(x - t)^p$. Examples of the application of this method are given in Chapters 3 to 5. As shown in those chapters, if the contours of the integrals are appropriately chosen, and the integrands expressed as power series, it may be possible to derive asymptotic representations of the particular integral $y(x)$ by this method.

MELLIN-BARNES INTEGRALS

Another method of solution in terms of integrals is that due to Barnes [1908a]. In this method we look for a solution of the nonhomogeneous equation in the form

$$y(x) = \int x^s w(s) F(s)\, ds, \tag{1.89}$$

where

$$w(s) = \frac{\prod_{j=1}^{m} \Gamma(b_j - s) \prod_{j=1}^{n} \Gamma(1 - a_j + s)}{\prod_{j=m+1}^{q} \Gamma(1 - b_j + s) \prod_{j=n+1}^{r} \Gamma(a_j - s)}$$

and the integral is taken around a suitable contour. The form of $F(s)$ will depend upon $f(x)$, the right-hand member of the nonhomogeneous equation. We see that $w(s)$ has poles at the points $s = b_j + p$ and at the points $s = a_j - 1 - p$, where p is zero or a positive integer. By finding the residue at these poles (and by a suitable choice of contour), we can determine y as a power series in either ascending or descending powers of x. $F(s)$ is chosen so that this expansion is in agreement with that found for y by some other method.

The integrand (1.89) is very similar to that used in defining Mejer's G function (Erdélyi [*207*, 1953a]). This method is most suitable when the solution of the associated homogeneous equation is itself a G function (as is the case for the hypergeometric equation). Examples of the application of this method are given in Chapters 3 to 6.

GREEN'S FUNCTIONS

The last integral solution we shall consider is particularly suitable if the solution of the differential equation has certain assigned boundary conditions. We follow here the analysis given by Ince [*254*, 1926].

Consider the associated homogeneous system defined by

$$\phi(D)y \equiv p_0(x)D^n y + p_1(x)D^{n-1}y + \cdots + p_n(x)y = 0 \tag{1.90}$$

together with the boundary conditions

$$U_i(D)y = 0 \qquad (i = 1, 2, \ldots, n), \tag{1.91}$$

where U_i involves no derivatives of y of higher order than $n-1$.

These two sets of equations are supposed to be *incompatible*; that is, they have no solution, not identically zero, which together with its first $n-1$ derivatives is continuous throughout the interval (a, b). However, as shown by Ince, there exists a Green's function $G(x, \xi)$ which (a) is continuous and possesses continuous derivatives of orders up to and including $n-2$ for $a \leqslant x \leqslant b$; (b) is such that its derivative of order $n-1$ is discontinuous at a point ξ within (a, b), the discontinuity being equal to $-1/p_0(\xi)$; and (c) formally satisfies (1.90) and (1.91) at all points of (a, b) except ξ.

Thus, if y_1 and y_2 are linearly distinct solutions of the equation

$$p_0(x)\frac{d^2y}{dx^2} + p_1(x)\frac{dy}{dx} + p_2(x)y = 0,$$

the function

$$F(x, \xi) = A_1 y_1(x) + A_2 y_2(x) + \theta\,\frac{y_1(x)y_2(\xi) - y_2(x)y_1(\xi)}{2p_0(\xi)\{y_1(\xi)y_2'(\xi) - y_2(\xi)y_1'(\xi)\}}$$

is such a Green's function, where $\theta = -1$ for $a \leqslant x \leqslant \xi$ and $\theta = 1$ for $\xi \leqslant x \leqslant b$, and A_1 and A_2 are constants that can be chosen to satisfy the assigned boundary conditions. As shown by Ince, if the given system is self-adjoint, the Green's function $G(x, \xi)$ is symmetrical in x and ξ.

Consider now the nonhomogeneous system defined by

$$\phi(D)y = f(x), \tag{1.92}$$

together with the boundary conditions given by (1.91). Then the solution of

(1.92) will be shown to be

$$y = -\int_a^b G(x, \xi) f(\xi)\, d\xi. \tag{1.93}$$

On differentiating (1.93) with respect to x, we find

$$D^r y = -\int_a^b \frac{\partial^r}{\partial x^r} G(x, \xi) f(\xi)\, d\xi \qquad (r = 1 \text{ to } n-1)$$

and

$$D^n y = -\frac{\partial}{\partial x}\int_a^x \frac{\partial^{n-1}}{\partial x^{n-1}} G(x, \xi) f(\xi)\, d\xi - \frac{\partial}{\partial x}\int_x^b \frac{\partial^{n-1}}{\partial x^{n-1}} G(x, \xi) f(\xi)\, d\xi$$

$$= -\int_a^b \frac{\partial^n}{\partial x^n} G(x, \xi) f(\xi)\, d\xi - \lim_{\varepsilon \to 0}\left[\frac{\partial^{n-1}}{\partial x^{n-1}} G(x, \xi) f(\xi)\right]_{\xi = x - \varepsilon}^{\xi = x + \varepsilon}$$

$$= -\int_a^b \frac{\partial^n}{\partial x^n} G(x, \xi) f(\xi)\, d\xi + \frac{f(x)}{p_0(x)}.$$

On substituting in (1.92), we obtain

$$\phi(D)y = -\int_a^b \phi\left(\frac{\partial}{\partial x}\right) G(x, \xi) f(\xi)\, d\xi + f(x) = f(x),$$

since G is a solution of (1.90). Also

$$U_i(D)y = -\int_a^b U_i\left(\frac{\partial}{\partial x}\right) G(x, \xi) f(\xi)\, d\xi = 0,$$

since $U_i(\partial/\partial x)G = 0$.

Thus the solution given by (1.93) satisfies both the nonhomogeneous equation and the boundary conditions.

For the more general boundary conditions,

$$U_r(D)y = c_r \qquad (r = 1 \text{ to } n), \tag{1.94}$$

where c_r are constants, we let $G_r(x)$ be the solution of the system

$$\phi(D)y = 0,$$

$$U_i(D)y = 0 \qquad (i = 1 \text{ to } n,\ i \neq r),$$

$$U_r(D)y = 1.$$

Then it can be shown that the solution of (1.92) with the boundary conditions (1.94) is given by

$$y = -\int_a^b G(x, \xi) f(\xi)\, d\xi - \sum_{r=1}^{n} c_r G_r(x). \tag{1.95}$$

From (1.93) we see that the contribution to $y(x)$ due to the forcing function $f(\xi)d\xi$ is $-G(x, \xi)f(\xi)d\xi$. Thus the Green's function $G(x, \xi)$ equals the contribution to $y(x)$ due to a unit (negative) forcing function at the point ξ. For this reason, the Green's function is often called the *influence function.* We see that, if the system is self-adjoint (as is the case in many physical applications), the displacement y at the point x due to a unit force at ξ is the same as that at the point ξ due to a unit force at x.

Consider now the important particular case of (1.92), for which

$$f(x) = -\delta(x - \eta), \tag{1.96}$$

where η is a constant ($a \leqslant \eta \leqslant b$) and the function δ is Dirac's delta function, defined by

$$\int_{-\infty}^{\infty} g(x)\delta(x - \xi)\, dx = g(\xi),$$

where g is any continuous function. Thus

$$\int_{-\infty}^{\infty} \delta(x - \xi)\, dx = 1$$

and $\delta(x - \xi)$ vanishes if $x \neq \xi$.

From (1.93) and (1.96), we see that a particular solution of

$$\phi(D)y = -\delta(x - \eta)$$

is

$$y = \int_a^b G(x, \xi)\delta(\xi - \eta)\, d\xi = G(x, \eta),$$

since $\delta(\xi - \eta)$ vanishes if $\xi \neq \eta$. Thus, replacing η by ξ, we see that the Green's function $G(x, \xi)$ of the homogeneous linear differential equation

$$\phi(D)y = 0$$

is also a solution of the nonhomogeneous equation

$$\phi(D)y = -\delta(x - \xi).$$

As shown in Chapter 10, these properties of the Green's function can be extended for use in solving partial differential equations.

PROBLEMS

1. If Y_1 and Y_2 are two solutions of the nonhomogeneous linear equation of order n,

$$\phi(D)y = f(x),$$

then

$$Y_1 - Y_2 = \sum_{r=1}^{n} c_r y_r,$$

where the c_r are constants and the y_r ($r = 1$ to n) are n independent solutions of the associated homogeneous equation.

2. Show that the solution of the equation

$$Dy + p(x)y = g(x)$$

can be expressed in the form

$$y = e^{-\phi}\left(C - \int e^{\phi}\, du\right) + u,$$

where $u = g/p$ and $\phi = \int p\, dx$.

3. Solve the following first-order equations:

(a) $Dy = x(e^{-x^2} + ay)$, for the cases $a \neq -2$ and $a = -2$.
(b) $Dy = x^2(ax^3 + by)$.
(c) $Dy = (1 - y)\sec x - \tan x$; $y = 1$ when $x = 0$.

4. Verify that a particular integral of the first-order equation

$$xDy + (a - x)y = 1$$

(where a is a constant) is

$$y = x^{-a}e^{x}\gamma(a, x),$$

where the *incomplete gamma function* $\gamma(a, x)$ is defined by

$$\gamma(a, x) = \int_0^x e^{-t}t^{a-1}\, dt.$$

5. Verify that a particular integral of the first-order equation

$$x(1 - x)Dy + [p - (p + q)x]y = 1$$

(where p and q are constants) is

$$y = x^{-p}(1 - x)^{-q}B_x(p, q),$$

where the *incomplete beta function* $B_x(p, q)$ is defined by

$$B_x(p, q) = \int_0^x t^{p-1}(1 - t)^{q-1}\, dt.$$

Show that, on making the substitution $y = x^{-p}z$, the differential equation reduces to

$$(1 - x)Dz - qz = x^{p-1}.$$

By solving this equation as a power series in x, show that

$$B_x(p, q) = p^{-1}x^p(1-x)^q F(1, p+q; p+1; x),$$

where F is the hypergeometric function.

6. Solve the following second-order equations by reduction of order:

(a) $D^2y - x^2Dy + xy = x$, given that $y_1 = x$ is a solution of the associated homogeneous equation.

(b) $(3-x)D^2y - (9-4x)Dy + (6-3x)y = 9 - 10x + 3x^2$, given that $y_1 = e^x$ is a solution of the associated homogeneous equation.

7. Solve by variation of parameters:

(a) $(x-1)D^2y - xDy + y = (x-1)^2$, given $y_1 = x$, $y_2 = e^x$.

(b) $xD^2y - (1+x)Dy + y = 2(1+x)e^{-x}$, given $y_1 = (1+x)$, $y_2 = e^x$.

8. If $f_1(x)$, $f_2(x)$, and $f_3(x)$ are three particular integrals of

$$D^3y + p_1(x)D^2y + p_2(x)Dy + p_3(x)y = 0,$$

show that a particular integral of

$$D^3y + p_1(x)D^2y + p_2(x)Dy + p_3(x)y = r(x)$$

is given by

$$y = \int^x r(\xi)\exp\left[\int_a^\xi p_1(z)\,dz\right]\begin{vmatrix} \dfrac{df_1(\xi)}{d\xi} & \dfrac{df_2(\xi)}{d\xi} & \dfrac{df_3(\xi)}{d\xi} \\ f_1(\xi) & f_2(\xi) & f_3(\xi) \\ f_1(x) & f_2(x) & f_3(x) \end{vmatrix} = 0,$$

where a is a constant (Forsyth [1929]).

9. Show that, if the Wronskian determinant vanishes for $x = x_0$, it will be identically zero if $p_0(x_0) \neq 0$.

10. Find Cauchy's integral formula for the solution of the equation $D^ny = f(x)$, with the initial conditions $D^{r-1}y = 0$ ($r = 1$ to n) when $x = x_0$.

11. Use Cauchy's method to find particular solutions of the following equations, with the conditions $y = 0$, $Dy = 0$ at $x = 0$:

(a) $D^2y + 4xDy + 2(1+2x^2)y = 2(1+2x+2x^2)$, given $y_1 = e^{-x^2}$, $y_2 = xe^{-x^2}$.

(b) $D^2y + 4Dy + 5y = \sin x$, given $y_1 = e^{-2x}\cos x$, $y_2 = e^{-2x}\sin x$.

12. Show that, in the $(n+1)$th-order homogeneous linear equation of the form

$$q_0D^{n+1}y + q_1D^ny + \cdots + q_{n+1}y = 0,$$

which can be derived by differentiating an nth-order nonhomogeneous linear equation, the coefficients satisfy the equation

$$D^{n+1}q_0 - D^n q_1 + D^{n-1}q_2 + \cdots + (-1)^{n+1}q_{n+1} = 0,$$

where $q_0 = p_0/f$.

13. Solve by differentiation:
(a) $D^2y - 5Dy + 6y = e^x$.
(b) $D^2y + 2aDy + b^2y = \sin kx$.

14. Show that the equation

$$(x^3 + ax^2 + bx + c)D^3y + (3x^2 + ex + f)D^2y + (x + g)Dy + y = 1$$

is exact.

15. Find the integrating factor, and obtain the integral, of the equation

$$x^3D^3y + 5x^2D^2y + 4xDy + 2y = 1.$$

16. Examine the nature of the singular points of the following equations, and find the particular solution as a series in ascending and in descending powers of x:
(a) $x^2D^2y + xDy + (x^2 - \nu^2)y = x^{\mu+1}$ (Lommel's equation).
(b) $(x - x^2)D^2y + 3Dy + 2y = x^2$.

17. Show that a particular integral of the equation

$$x^2D^2y + xDy + (x^2 - \nu^2)y = \frac{(\frac{1}{2}x)^{\nu-1}}{\sqrt{\pi}\,\Gamma(\nu + \frac{1}{2})}$$

is the Struve function of order ν, given by

$$H_\nu(x) = \sum_{r=0}^{\infty}(-1)^r \frac{(\frac{1}{2}x)^{\nu+2r+1}}{\Gamma(r + \frac{3}{2})\Gamma(\nu + r + \frac{3}{2})}.$$

18. Find the conditions for $x = a$, $x = b$ to be regular singular points of the equation

$$(a - x)^2(b - x)^2D^2y + (a - x)(b - x)(A + 2x)Dy + By = 0.$$

19. Examine the nature of the singularities of the equation

$$x(1 - x)D^2y + [c - (a + b + 1)x]Dy - aby = 0$$

(hypergeometric equation).

20. Examine the nature of the singular points of the following equation:

$$Dy + y = \frac{1}{x},$$

and find a solution in descending powers of x.

Derive the solution also in the form of an integral, and hence show that the series is asymptotic.

21. State the conditions for which

$$C \int e^{(1/2)xu}(1+u)^{a-1}(1-u)^{c-a-1}\,du$$

will be a solution of

(a) the nonhomogeneous confluent hypergeometric equation

$$xD^2y + (c-x)Dy - ay = ke^{(1/2)x},$$

(b) the associated homogeneous equation.

22. The deflection of a beam of length l, which is clamped at both ends $x = 0$ and $x = l$, and which carries a concentrated load W at the point $x = \xi$, is given by

$$By = -\frac{1}{6l^3}Wx^2(l-\xi)^2[x(l+2\xi) - 3\xi l] \qquad (x < \xi),$$

$$= -\frac{1}{6l^3}W\xi^2(l-x)^2[\xi(l+2x) - 3xl] \qquad (x > \xi)$$

(Bateman [*17*, 1932]). Verify that, if $By = -WG(x, \xi)$, the function $G(x, \xi)$ has the properties of a Green's function for the differential expression d^4y/dx^4, and the prescribed boundary conditions. Hence show that if

$$By = -\int_0^l G(x, \xi)w(\xi)d\xi,$$

y is a solution of the differential equation

$$BD^4y = w(x).$$

(This solution corresponds to the case of a distributed loading $w\,dx$ per length dx.)

23. Verify that the Green's function for the differential expression

$$\phi(D) \equiv x\frac{d^2y}{dx^2} + \frac{dy}{dx},$$

for the interval $0 \leqslant x \leqslant 1$ and the boundary conditions $y(1) = 0$, $y(0)$ finite, is

$$G(x, \xi) = -\log \xi, \qquad (x \leqslant \xi),$$

$$G(x, \xi) = -\log x \qquad (x > \xi).$$

Verify that the given operator $\phi(D)$ is self-adjoint.

CHAPTER 2

Equations with Constant Coefficients

2.1 Introduction

In Chapter 1 the properties of nonhomogeneous linear differential equations were discussed, together with various methods of solution. The methods given there are general in their application. We shall now consider the important particular case of nonhomogeneous linear differential equations that have constant coefficients. Such equations can be written

$$A_0 D^n y + A_1 D^{n-1} y + \cdots + A_n y = f(x), \tag{2.1}$$

where $D \equiv d/dx$, and all the A_r are constants. For conciseness, this equation will sometimes be written

$$\psi(D) y = f. \tag{2.2}$$

Such equations occur frequently in the theory of forced vibrations of mechanical systems that undergo only small displacements from their equilibrium position. Equations of this type also occur in electric circuit theory; in this case, the function f represents a variable electromotive force.

This class of equations can be solved most readily by operational methods, as shown below. The Laplace transform method, described in §2.4, is very appropriate when a solution is required which satisfies assigned initial conditions. The application of these methods to certain types of equations with variable coefficients is discussed in §§2.7 and 2.8.

2.2 The Operator D and Operational Methods

We shall first determine the particular solution of (2.1) using Boole's symbolic calculus applied to the operator D. It is shown in textbooks on differential equations—e.g., Ince [1926], Poole [1936], Piaggio [1937], Coddington and Levinson [1955], and Murphy [1960]—that the operator D ($\equiv d/dx$) obeys most of the fundamental laws of algebra. Thus the linear operator

$$\psi(D) \equiv A_0 D^n + A_1 D^{n-1} + \cdots + A_n$$

can be factorized in the form

$$\psi(D) \equiv A_0 (D - \lambda_1)(D - \lambda_2) \cdots (D - \lambda_n), \tag{2.3}$$

where the λ_r are the roots of the equation

$$A_0\lambda^n + A_1\lambda^{n-1} + \cdots + A_n = 0. \tag{2.4}$$

This is the *characteristic equation* corresponding to the differential equation (2.1). For a linear equation with constant coefficients, such as (2.1), the factors of the form (2.3) are permutable.

As is well known, the general solution of the associated homogeneous linear equation is

$$y = C_1e^{\lambda_1 x} + C_2e^{\lambda_2 x} + \cdots + C_ne^{\lambda_n x}, \tag{2.5}$$

where $C_1, C_2, \ldots, C_n$ are arbitrary constants and (2.4) has unequal roots. The case of equal roots is dealt with in the textbooks mentioned above.

As in Chapter 1, our task is to find a particular integral of the nonhomogeneous equation (2.1). Equation (2.2) can be written in the alternative form,

$$y = [\psi(D)]^{-1}f. \tag{2.6}$$

Now the operator D can be treated as an algebraic quantity, and the expression $[\psi(D)]^{-1}$ can be resolved into partial fractions. If all the roots of (2.3) are distinct, we find that

$$[\psi(D)]^{-1} = \sum_{r=1}^{n} \frac{\alpha_r}{D - \lambda_r} \tag{2.7}$$

where

$$\alpha_r = 1/A_0 \prod_{\substack{s=1 \\ s\neq r}}^{r} (\lambda_r - \lambda_s) = 1/D\psi(\lambda_r).$$

Hence the particular integral is

$$y = \sum_{r=1}^{n} \left[1/A_0 \prod_{\substack{s=1 \\ s\neq r}}^{n} (\lambda_r - \lambda_s) \right] (D - \lambda_r)^{-1}f. \tag{2.8}$$

If $\psi(\lambda) = 0$ has a repeated root λ_p (of order q), the corresponding partial-fraction expansion will contain q terms $\beta_m(D - \lambda_p)^{-m}f$ ($m = 1$ to q), where β_m is a constant.

MEANING OF THE INVERSE OPERATOR $(D - \lambda)^{-p}$

The operator D^{-1} is the inverse of D; i.e., it represents a simple indefinite integration. Thus

$$D^{-1} \cdot D = 1.$$

For the purpose of determining the particular integral, we can disregard any arbitrary constant of integration. More generally, we shall now determine the effect of operating on f by $(D-\lambda)^{-1}$ or by $(D-\lambda)^{-p}$, where f is some simple function of x.

Case a. Let

$$f(x) = e^{ax},$$

where a is a constant. Then

$$(D-\lambda)e^{ax} = (a-\lambda)e^{ax}. \tag{2.9}$$

More generally,

$$F(D)e^{ax}V = e^{ax}F(D+a)V, \tag{2.10}$$

where F is any polynomial in D, and V is a function of x.

Operating upon both sides of (2.9) by $(D-\lambda)^{-1}$, where $\lambda \neq a$, we see that

$$(D-\lambda)^{-1}(a-\lambda)e^{ax} = (D-\lambda)^{-1}\cdot(D-\lambda)e^{ax} = e^{ax};$$

that is,

$$(D-\lambda)^{-1}e^{ax} = (a-\lambda)^{-1}e^{ax} \qquad (\lambda \neq a). \tag{2.11}$$

Similarly,

$$(D-\lambda)^{-r}e^{ax} = (a-\lambda)^{-r}e^{ax} \qquad (\lambda \neq a) \tag{2.12}$$

and

$$\prod_{r=1}^{n}(D-\lambda_r)^{-1}e^{ax} = \prod_{r=1}^{n}(a-\lambda_r)^{-1}e^{ax};$$

that is,

$$[\psi(D)]^{-1}e^{ax} = [\psi(a)]^{-1}e^{ax} \qquad (\lambda_r \neq a). \tag{2.13}$$

Thus, if $f = e^{ax}$, a particular integral of (2.1) is $e^{ax}/\psi(a)$, if $\psi(a) \neq 0$.

More generally, it can be shown that (2.10) holds when F is any rational function of D. As shown by Ince [*139*, 1926], if $f(x) = e^{ax}V(x)$, the particular integral is

$$y = [\psi(D)]^{-1}[e^{ax}V(x)] = e^{ax}[\psi(D+a)]^{-1}V(x). \tag{2.14}$$

If $\psi(a) = 0$, $(D-a)$ must be a factor of $\psi(D)$. Suppose that

$$\psi(D) = (D-a)^p\phi(D),$$

where $\phi(a) \neq 0$. Equation (2.6) then becomes, with $f = e^{ax}$,

$$y = (D-a)^{-p}[\phi(D)]^{-1}e^{ax} = (D-a)^{-p}e^{ax}[\phi(a)]^{-1}$$

and

$$D^p(ye^{-ax}) = D^p[e^{-ax}(D-a)^{-p}e^{ax}][\phi(a)]^{-1},$$

that is, using (2.10), with a replaced by $-a$,

$$D^p(ye^{-ax}) = e^{-ax}[(D-a)^p(D-a)^{-p}e^{ax}][\phi(a)]^{-1}$$
$$= e^{-ax}e^{ax}[\phi(a)]^{-1} = [\phi(a)]^{-1}.$$

Integrating both sides p times, we obtain

$$ye^{-ax} = [\phi(a)]^{-1}\frac{x^p}{p!}.$$

Thus, if $f = e^{ax}$ and a is a repeated root of $\psi(\lambda) = 0$ of order p, a particular integral of (2.1) is

$$\frac{x^p e^{ax}}{\phi(a)\cdot p!}.$$

Case b. If

$$f(x) = P\cos ax + Q\sin ax,$$

where a, P, and Q are constants, we can write

$$f(x) = \tfrac{1}{2}P(e^{iax} + e^{-iax}) - \tfrac{1}{2}iQ(e^{iax} - e^{-iax})$$

and use the above method. On simplifying and writing

$$\psi(D) = \psi_1(D^2) + D\psi_2(D^2),$$

we find that a particular integral is

$$\frac{\psi_1(-a^2)(P\cos ax + Q\sin ax) + a\psi_2(-a^2)(P\sin ax - Q\cos ax)}{[\psi_1(-a^2)]^2 + a^2[\psi_2(-a^2)]^2}.$$

Case c. If $f(x) = x^m$, where m is a positive integer,

$$(D-\lambda)x^m = mx^{m-1} - \lambda x^m,$$

$$(D-\lambda)\frac{m}{\lambda}x^{m-1} = \frac{m(m-1)}{\lambda}x^{m-2} - mx^{m-1},$$

$$(D-\lambda)\frac{m(m-1)}{\lambda^2}x^{m-2} = \frac{m(m-1)(m-2)}{\lambda^2}x^{m-3} - \frac{m(m-1)}{\lambda}x^{m-2},$$

$$\vdots$$

$$(D-\lambda)\frac{m(m-1)\cdots 2}{\lambda^{m-1}}x = \frac{m!}{\lambda^{m-1}} - \frac{m(m-1)\cdots 2}{\lambda^{m-2}}x,$$

$$(D-\lambda)\frac{m!}{\lambda^m} = -\frac{m!}{\lambda^{m-1}}.$$

Adding these equations, we obtain

$$(D-\lambda)\left[x^m + \frac{m}{\lambda}x^{m-1} + \frac{m(m-1)}{\lambda^2}x^{m-2} + \cdots + \frac{m!}{\lambda^m}\right] = -\lambda x^m.$$

Hence

$$(D-\lambda)^{-1}x^m = -\sum_{r=0}^{m} \frac{m!}{r!\lambda^{m-r+1}}x^r.$$

We see that the right side of the last equation can be expressed in the alternative form

$$-\frac{1}{\lambda}\left(1-\frac{D}{\lambda}\right)^{-1}x^m,$$

the latter expression being expanded in ascending powers of D.

Similarly,

$$(D-\lambda)^{-p}x^m = \frac{1}{(-\lambda)^p}\left(1-\frac{D}{\lambda}\right)^{-p}x^m.$$

More generally, if $f(x) = x^m V(x)$, then, on using Leibnitz's theorem, as shown by Forsyth [*63*, 1929], we find that the particular integral is

$$\begin{aligned} y &= \frac{1}{\psi(D)}x^m V \\ &= x^m\frac{1}{\psi(D)}V + mx^{m-1}\left\{\frac{d}{dD}\frac{1}{\psi(D)}\right\}V + \frac{m(m-1)}{2!}x^{m-2}\left\{\frac{d^2}{dD^2}\frac{1}{\psi(D)}\right\}V + \cdots. \end{aligned}$$

2.3 Solution in Terms of Integrals

The particular solution given by (2.8) can be expressed in terms of integrals. From (2.6) and (2.7),

$$\begin{aligned} y &= \sum_{r=1}^{n}\frac{\alpha_r}{D-\lambda_r}f \\ &= \sum_{r=1}^{n}\alpha_r(D-\lambda_r)^{-1}e^{\lambda_r x}[e^{-\lambda_r x}f], \end{aligned}$$

that is, using (2.14),

$$\begin{aligned} y &= \sum_{r=1}^{n}\alpha_r e^{\lambda_r x}D^{-1}[e^{-\lambda_r x}f] \\ &= \sum_{r=1}^{n}\alpha_r e^{\lambda_r x}\int e^{-\lambda_r x}f\,dx \\ &= \sum_{r=1}^{n}\alpha_r\int^{x} e^{\lambda_r(x-t)}f(t)\,dt, \end{aligned} \tag{2.15}$$

in which the lower limit of the integral can be arbitrarily fixed. Changing this lower limit only gives rise to terms of the form

$$C_r e^{\lambda_r x};$$

these terms are identical in form with the complementary function.

Thus, for a second-order equation,

$$y = \frac{1}{A_0(\lambda_1 - \lambda_2)}\left\{\int^x e^{\lambda_1(x-t)}f(t)dt - \int^x e^{\lambda_2(x-t)}f(t)dt\right\}. \tag{2.16}$$

If the roots λ_1 and λ_2 are complex, we can put

$$\lambda_1 = \mu + i\omega,$$

and

$$\lambda_2 = \mu - i\omega,$$

and (2.16) reduces to

$$\begin{aligned} y &= \frac{1}{A_0\omega}\int^x e^{\mu(x-t)}\sin[\omega(x-t)]f(t)dt \\ &= \frac{e^{\mu x}}{A_0\omega}\left[\sin\omega x\int^x e^{-\mu t}\cos\omega t\, f(t)dt - \cos\omega x\int^x e^{-\mu t}\sin\omega t\, f(t)dt\right]. \end{aligned} \tag{2.17}$$

The particular solution, as given by (2.15), can be seen to be an extension of that given in §1.3 for first-order equations. Equation (2.15) is only valid, of course, for linear equations with constant coefficients. Equation (2.16) is the same as that obtained by variation of parameters (see §1.5).

If $\psi(\lambda)$ has a repeated root $\lambda = \lambda_p$ (of order q), the q corresponding terms in the particular integral are given by

$$\begin{aligned} \sum_{m=1}^{q}\frac{\beta_m}{(D-\lambda_p)^m}f &= \sum_{m=1}^{q}\beta_m(D-\lambda_p)^{-m}e^{\lambda_p x}[e^{-\lambda_p x}f] \\ &= \sum_{m=1}^{q}\beta_m e^{\lambda_p x}D^{-m}[e^{-\lambda_p x}f] \\ &= \sum_{m=1}^{q}\beta_m\int^x\int^t\cdots\int^t e^{\lambda_p(x-t)}f(t)dt^m. \end{aligned} \tag{2.18}$$

2.4 Solution with Particular Initial Conditions; the Laplace Transform

The solutions of (2.1) given so far in this chapter are general solutions that take no account of any particular initial conditions. As stated above, when a solution of (2.1) is required that satisfies assigned initial conditions, the solution can be found by a simpler method, such as the Laplace transform method outlined below.

We consider the equation

$$A_0D^ny + A_1D^{n-1}y + \cdots + A_ny = f(x), \tag{2.19}$$

where $A_0, \ldots, A_n$ are constants and $f(x)$ is a known function of x. We want to find the solution that satisfies the n initial conditions

$$y = y_0, Dy = Dy_0, \ldots, D^{n-1}y = D^{n-1}y_0 \qquad (\text{when } x = 0).$$

As in §2.1, it will be convenient to write

$$\psi(D) \equiv A_0D^n + A_1D^{n-1} + \cdots + A_n. \tag{2.20}$$

On multiplying (2.19) through by e^{-px}, where p is a positive constant, and integrating with respect to x from 0 to ∞, we obtain

$$\int_0^\infty e^{-px}\psi(D)y\,dx = \int_0^\infty e^{-px}f(x)\,dx. \tag{2.21}$$

Now

$$\int_0^\infty e^{-px}D^ry\,dx = \Big[e^{-px}D^{r-1}y\Big]_0^\infty + p\int_0^\infty e^{-px}D^{r-1}y\,dx$$

$$= -D^{r-1}y_0 + p\int_0^\infty e^{-px}D^{r-1}y\,dx, \tag{2.22}$$

provided that $\lim_{x\to\infty}(e^{-px}D^{r-1}y) = 0$ and that the integrals are convergent. By repeated application of (2.22), we find

$$\int_0^\infty e^{-px}D^ry\,dx = -(D^{r-1}y_0 + pD^{r-2}y_0 + \cdots + p^{r-2}Dy_0 + p^{r-1}y_0)$$

$$+ p^r\int_0^\infty e^{-px}y\,dx \qquad (r \le n). \tag{2.23}$$

Using (2.21) and (2.23), we can replace (2.19) by the "subsidiary" equation

$$\begin{aligned}\psi(p)\int_0^\infty e^{-px}y\,dx = {} & A_0(D^{n-1}y_0 + pD^{n-2}y_0 + p^2D^{n-3}y_0 + \cdots + p^{n-1}y_0) \\ & + A_1(D^{n-2}y_0 + pD^{n-3}y_0 + \cdots + p^{n-2}y_0) + \cdots \\ & + A_{n-2}(Dy_0 + py_0) + A_{n-1}y_0 + \int_0^\infty e^{-px}f\,dx.\end{aligned} \tag{2.24}$$

We write

$$\bar{y} = \int_0^\infty e^{-px}y\,dx$$

and (2.25)

$$\bar{f} = \int_0^\infty e^{-px}f\,dx.$$

$\bar{y}$ and $\bar{f}$ are the *Laplace transforms of* y and f respectively. In (2.25), p is taken to be a real positive number large enough to make the integrals converge. Equation (2.24) can now be written

$$\bar{y} = \frac{\Omega + \bar{f}}{\psi(p)}, \tag{2.26}$$

where

$$\begin{aligned}\Omega = {} & A_0(D^{n-1}y_0 + pD^{n-2}y_0 + p^2D^{n-3}y_0 + \cdots + p^{n-2}Dy_0 + p^{n-1}y_0) \\ & + A_1(D^{n-2}y_0 + pD^{n-3}y_0 + \cdots + p^{n-3}Dy_0 + p^{n-2}y_0) + \cdots \\ & + A_{n-2}(Dy_0 + py_0) + A_{n-1}y_0 .\end{aligned} \tag{2.27}$$

We see that Ω contains only terms involving the initial conditions y_0, Dy_0, $\ldots$, $D^{n-1}y_0$, and is independent of f; $\bar{f}$ depends upon f and is independent of the initial conditions. If $y_0 = Dy_0 = \cdots = D^{n-1}y_0 = 0$, we see that $\Omega = 0$, and, on using (2.7), (2.26) reduces to

$$\bar{y} = \sum_{r=1}^{n} \alpha_r \frac{\bar{f}}{p - \lambda_r}. \tag{2.28}$$

More generally, it can be shown that

$$\bar{y} = \sum_{r=1}^{n} \sum_{s=1}^{n} \left[\frac{D^{s-1}y_0 A_{sr}}{\Delta} \frac{1}{p - \lambda_r} \right] + \sum_{r=1}^{n} \alpha_r \frac{\bar{f}}{p - \lambda_r}, \tag{2.29}$$

where A_{sr} is the cofactor of the sth row and the rth column in the determinant Δ given by

$$\Delta = \begin{vmatrix} 1 & 1 & \cdots & 1 \\ \lambda_1 & \lambda_2 & \cdots & \lambda_n \\ \lambda_1^2 & \lambda_2^2 & \cdots & \lambda_n^2 \\ \vdots & \vdots & & \vdots \\ \lambda_1^{n-1} & \lambda_2^{n-1} & \cdots & \lambda_n^{n-1} \end{vmatrix} = \prod_{\substack{r=1 \text{ to } n \\ s=1 \text{ to } n \\ r>s}} (\lambda_r - \lambda_s) \tag{2.30}$$

and $\lambda_r \neq \lambda_s$. We find, too, that

$$\alpha_r = \frac{A_{nr}}{\Delta A_0}. \tag{2.31}$$

Equation (2.29) is the transformed equation corresponding to (2.19), with the given initial conditions. The solution for y is derived by applying the inverse Laplace transformation.

2.5 Some Simple Laplace Transforms

In Table 2.1 the Laplace transforms of some simple functions are given. A more complete set of Laplace transforms is given by Carslaw and Jaeger [1947] and by Erdélyi [1954a].

TABLE 2.1

$f(x)$	$\bar{f}(p) = \int_0^\infty e^{-px} f(x)\, dx$
1	$\frac{1}{p}$
$\frac{x^{n-1}}{(n-1)!}$	$\frac{1}{p^n},\ n = 1, 2, 3, \ldots$
$\frac{x^\nu}{\Gamma(\nu+1)}$	$\frac{1}{p^{\nu+1}},\ \nu > -1$
e^{ax}	$\frac{1}{p-a},\ p > R(a)$
$\sin ax$	$\frac{a}{p^2+a^2}$
$\cos ax$	$\frac{p}{p^2+a^2}$
$\frac{1}{2a} x \sin ax$	$\frac{p}{(p^2+a^2)^2}$
$\frac{1}{2a}(\sin ax - ax \cos ax)$	$\frac{a^2}{(p^2+a^2)^2}$

Using Table 2.1 we can find $\bar{f}$ if f is of a simple form; finally, we can apply the inverse transformation to expressions of the form $g(p)/\psi(p)$ by resolving them into partial fractions, and then using Table 2.1 to determine the expression for y.

2.6 General Theorems Relating to Laplace Transforms

A number of general theorems relating to Laplace transforms are given in Carslaw and Jaeger [1947]. Thus, if $\bar{f}_1$ and $\bar{f}_2$ are the transforms of f_1 and f_2, then $K_1\bar{f}_1 + K_2\bar{f}_2$ is the transform of $K_1 f_1 + K_2 f_2$, where K_1 and K_2 are constants. It is easily verified that if $\bar{f}(p)$ is the transform of $f(x)$ and b is any constant, then $\bar{f}(p-b)$ is the transform of $e^{bx}f(x)$. Thus, from Table 2.1

we find immediately that the transform of $e^{bx}\sin ax$ is $a/[(p-b)^2+a^2]$ and that of $e^{bx}\cos ax$ is $(p-b)/[(p-b)^2+a^2]$. These expressions are useful in enabling the inverse transform to be found for any quadratic factors of $\psi(p)$.

Two other important general theorems are:

(a) If two continuous functions have the same Laplace transform, then they are identically equal.

(b) If $\bar{f}_1(p)$ and $\bar{f}_2(p)$ are the transforms of $f_1(x)$ and $f_2(x)$, then $\bar{f}_1(p)\bar{f}_2(p)$ is the transform of

$$\int_0^x f_1(t)f_2(x-t)dt$$

and this is equal to

$$\int_0^x f_1(x-t)f_2(t)dt.$$

The proofs of both of these theorems are given in Carslaw and Jaeger [1947]. The latter theorem is known as *Duhamel's theorem.*

We can use Duhamel's theorem to find the transform of

$$\int_0^x e^{\lambda(x-t)}f(t)dt.$$

We put $f_1(x)=e^{\lambda x}$ and $f_2(x)=f(x)$. Then $f_1(x-t)=e^{\lambda(x-t)}$ and $\bar{f}_1 = 1/(p-\lambda)$.

Applying Duhamel's theorem we see that the transform of

$$\int_0^x e^{\lambda(x-t)}f(t)dt$$

is $\bar{f}/(p-\lambda)$. Thus, applying the inverse transformation to (2.29), we obtain

$$y=\sum_{r=1}^{n}\sum_{s=1}^{n}\frac{D^{s-1}y_0A_{sr}}{\Delta}e^{\lambda_r x}+\sum_{r=1}^{n}\alpha_r\int_0^x e^{\lambda_r(x-t)}f(t)dt, \tag{2.32}$$

which has the same form as (2.15).

It can be verified, by differentiation, that the solution in the form (2.32) satisfies the initial conditions

$$y=y_0,\quad Dy=Dy_0,\ \ldots,\ D^{n-1}y=D^{n-1}y_0 \qquad (\text{at } x=0).$$

If $y_0=Dy_0=\cdots=D^{n-1}y_0=0$, solution (2.32) is identical with that particular integral given by (2.15). In that case, (2.32) is the same as the solution obtained by Cauchy's method (§1.6), since, for a linear equation with constant coefficients,

$$\frac{y_r(x)W_r(t)}{A_0W(t)}=\frac{y_{r0}e^{\lambda_r x}}{A_0}\frac{A_{nr}}{\Delta y_r(t)}$$
$$=\alpha_r e^{\lambda_r(x-t)} \qquad [\text{on using } (2.31)].$$

Equation (2.32) can be written in the alternative form,

$$y = \sum_{r=1}^{n} \sum_{s=1}^{n} \frac{D^{s-1} y_0 A_{sr}}{\Delta} e^{\lambda_r x} + \sum_{r=1}^{n} \alpha_r \int_0^x e^{\lambda_r t} f(x-t)\,dt. \tag{2.33}$$

Equations (2.32) and (2.33) enable the solution of a nonhomogeneous equation to be found which satisfies given initial conditions. In a physical system, we see that, once the response of the system is known in the free motion, the response due to any forcing function can be readily found.

The Laplace transform method can also be used to find solutions which have to satisfy certain conditions at $x = 0$ and certain other conditions at $x = l$; such a problem is known as a *two-point boundary problem.* The transformed equation can be found in the usual manner, with values $y_0, Dy_0, \ldots, D^{n-1}y_0$ at $x = 0$. Some of these quantities may be specified in the boundary conditions at $x = 0$; the others are to be taken as arbitrary constants whose values are to be found from the boundary conditions at $x = l$ (see Carslaw and Jaeger [*321*, 1947]).

2.7 Equations Reducible to Linear Equations with Constant Coefficients; the Operator δ

Consider the *Euler equation*

$$B_0 x^n D^n y + B_1 x^{n-1} D^{n-1} y + \cdots + B_n y = f(x), \tag{2.34}$$

in which the B_r are constants. As shown in textbooks on differential equations (see §2.2), on putting $x = e^t$, (2.34) reduces to a linear differential with constant coefficients. This is most readily seen by using the symbolic operator $\delta \equiv d/dt = x d/dx = xD$. Now

$$\delta^2 = xD(xD) = xD + x^2D^2$$

and thus $x^2D^2 = \delta(\delta - 1)$.

In general, $x^rD^r = \delta(\delta-1)\cdots(\delta - r + 1)$. Thus (2.34) becomes

$$[B_0\delta(\delta-1)\cdots(\delta-n+1) + B_1\delta(\delta-1)\cdots(\delta-n+2) + \cdots + B_{n-1}\delta + B_n]y = f(x) = F(t);$$

that is, (2.35)

$$B_0'\delta^n y + B_1'\delta^{n-1} y + \cdots + B_n' y = F(t).$$

This is a linear differential equation with constant coefficients, with t as the independent variable.

Similarly, the *Legendre linear equation*

$$\sum_{r=1}^{n} B_r (a + bx)^r D^r y = f(x), \tag{2.36}$$

where a, b, and B_r are constants, can be reduced to a linear equation with constant coefficients by the substitution $a + bx = e^t$.

Equations such as (2.34) can be solved directly by making use of the properties of the operator δ. For conciseness, we shall write (2.34), or (2.35), in the form

$$\Omega(\delta)y = f. \tag{2.37}$$

The general solution of the associated homogeneous linear equation is

$$y = C_1 e^{\mu_1 t} + C_2 e^{\mu_2 t} + \cdots + C_n e^{\mu_n t},$$

that is,

$$y = C_1 x^{\mu_1} + C_2 x^{\mu_2} + \cdots + C_n x^{\mu_n}, \tag{2.38}$$

where $C_1, C_2, \ldots, C_n$ are constants, and the equation

$$\Omega(\delta) = (\delta - \mu_1)(\delta - \mu_2)\cdots(\delta - \mu_n) = 0 \tag{2.39}$$

has unequal roots.

The particular integral of (2.37) is

$$y = [\Omega(\delta)]^{-1} f. \tag{2.40}$$

As in §2.2, the inverse operator $[\Omega(\delta)]^{-1}$ can be expressed in terms of partial fractions. If all the roots of (2.29) are distinct, we find that

$$[\Omega(\delta)]^{-1} = \sum_{r=1}^{n} \frac{\gamma_r}{\delta - \mu_r}.$$

Hence the particular integral is

$$y = \sum_{r=1}^{n} \gamma_r (\delta - \mu_r)^{-1} f. \tag{2.41}$$

If $\Omega(\delta) = 0$ has a repeated root μ_p (of order q), the corresponding partial-fraction expansion contains terms of the form $\beta_m(\delta - \mu_r)^{-m} f$ ($m = 1$ to q).

MEANING OF THE INVERSE OPERATOR $(\delta - \mu)^{-1}$

The meaning of the inverse operator $(\delta - \mu)^{-1}$ can be found in a similar way to that given above for the operator $(D - \lambda)^{-1}$. We define δ^{-1} to be such that

$$\delta^{-1} y = \int \frac{y}{x}\, dx.$$

Hence

$$\delta \cdot \delta^{-1} = 1. \tag{2.42}$$

Thus

$$\delta \log x = 1 \qquad \text{and} \qquad \delta^{-1}[1] = \log x. \tag{2.43}$$

Similarly,

$$\delta^p[(\log x)^p] = p! \qquad \text{and} \qquad \delta^{-p}[1] = \frac{(\log x)^p}{p!}. \tag{2.44}$$

Now, if $f(x) = x^m$,

$$(\delta - \mu)x^m = (m - \mu)x^m. \tag{2.45}$$

More generally,

$$F(\delta)[x^m V] = x^m F(\delta + m)V, \tag{2.46}$$

where F is any polynomial in δ and V is a function of x.

Operating on both sides of (2.45) by $(\delta - \mu)^{-1}$ we see that

$$(\delta - \mu)^{-1}(m - \mu)x^m = (\delta - \mu)^{-1}(\delta - \mu)x^m = x^m;$$

that is,

$$(\delta - \mu)^{-1}x^m = (m - \mu)^{-1}x^m \qquad (m \neq \mu). \tag{2.47}$$

Similarly,

$$\prod_{r=1}^{n}(\delta - \mu_r)^{-1}x^m = \prod_{r=1}^{n}(m - \mu_r)^{-1}x^m;$$

that is,

$$[\Omega(\delta)]^{-1}x^m = [\Omega(m)]^{-1}x^m. \tag{2.48}$$

Thus, if $f = x^m$, a particular integral of (2.37) is $x^m/\Omega(m)$, if $\Omega(m) \neq 0$. More generally, it can be shown that equation (2.46) holds when F is any rational function of δ; thus, if $f(x) = x^m V(x)$, the particular integral is

$$y = [\Omega(\delta)]^{-1}x^m V(x) = x^m[\Omega(\delta + m)]^{-1}V(x). \tag{2.49}$$

If $f = x^m$ and $\Omega(m) = 0$, it can be shown, in a manner similar to that in §2.2, that a particular integral of (2.37) is

$$\frac{(\log x)^p x^m}{\phi(m) \cdot p!},$$

where $\Omega(\delta) = (\delta - m)^p\phi(\delta)$ and $\phi(m) \neq 0$.

As in §2.3, the particular solution given by (2.41) can also be expressed in terms of integrals. From (2.41),

$$y = \sum_{r=1}^{n} \frac{\gamma_r}{\delta - \mu_r} f$$

$$= \sum_{r=1}^{n} \gamma_r (\delta - \mu_r)^{-1} x^{\mu_r} (x^{-\mu_r} f);$$

that is, using (2.46),

$$y = \sum_{r=1}^{n} \gamma_r x^{\mu_r} \delta^{-1} (x^{-\mu_r} f)$$

$$= \sum_{r=1}^{n} \gamma_r x^{\mu_r} \int x^{-1-\mu_r} f \, dx, \tag{2.50}$$

If $\Omega(\delta)$ has a repeated factor $\delta - \mu_p$ (of order q), the q corresponding terms in the particular integral are given by

$$\sum_{m=1}^{q} \frac{\varepsilon_m}{(\delta - \mu_p)^m} f = \sum_{m=1}^{q} \varepsilon_m (\delta - \mu_p)^{-m} x^{\mu_p} (x^{-\mu_p} f)$$

$$= \sum_{m=1}^{q} \varepsilon_m x^{\mu_p} \delta^{-m} (x^{-\mu_p} f)$$

$$= \sum_{m=1}^{q} \varepsilon_m x^{\mu_p} \int x^{-1} \int x^{-1} \cdots \int x^{-1} \int x^{-1-\mu_p} f \, dx^m. \tag{2.51}$$

2.8 Operational Methods for Linear Differential Equations with Variable Coefficients

Consider the second-order equation

$$D^2 y + P(x) D y + Q(x) y = R(x). \tag{2.52}$$

If the operator $D^2 + PD + Q$ can be factorized in the form

$$(D + u)(D + v),$$

where u and v may both be functions of x, (2.52) can be integrated. Thus putting

$$(D + v) y = z, \tag{2.53}$$

we have

$$Dz + uz = R,$$

a linear equation which can be solved by the method given in §1.3. When z is known, (2.53) can be solved in like manner for y.

This method of factorization will be possible only in very special cases. In other cases it may be possible, by a simple transformation, to reduce a linear differential equation with varying coefficients to either one with constant coefficients or one of the same type as Euler's equation (2.34) (see Problem 15 at the end of the chapter).

2.9 Systems of Simultaneous Linear Equations with Constant Coefficients

So far we have considered only single linear differential equations. A linear differential equation of order n can be replaced by a system of simultaneous differential equations each of lower order than n (and in particular by n first-order equations). Conversely, a system of simultaneous differential equations can be replaced by a single linear equation of higher order.

Consider the three nonhomogeneous linear equations

$$Du_1 + a_{11}u_1 + a_{12}u_2 + a_{13}u_3 = f_1(x),$$

$$Du_2 + a_{21}u_1 + a_{22}u_2 + a_{23}u_3 = f_2(x), \tag{2.54}$$

and

$$Du_3 + a_{31}u_1 + a_{32}u_2 + a_{33}u_3 = f_3(x),$$

where the a_{rs} are constants and $D \equiv d/dx$.

On eliminating u_2 and u_3 between these three equations, we obtain the following third-order linear differential equation for u_1:

$$\begin{vmatrix} D + a_{11} & a_{12} & a_{13} \\ a_{21} & D + a_{22} & a_{23} \\ a_{31} & a_{32} & D + a_{33} \end{vmatrix} u_1 = \begin{vmatrix} a_{12} & a_{13} & f_1 \\ D + a_{22} & a_{23} & f_2 \\ a_{32} & D + a_{33} & f_3 \end{vmatrix}. \tag{2.55}$$

As the f_r are functions of x, it is not permissible to interchange the columns of the determinant on the right side of (2.55). Equation (2.55) can be solved by any of the methods given in this chapter.

In particular, if the initial conditions are $u_1 = u_2 = u_3 = 0$ when $x = 0$, we can obtain the solution of (2.54) very easily by the use of the Laplace transform method. The transformed equations corresponding to (2.54) are

$$p\bar{u}_1 + a_{11}\bar{u}_1 + a_{12}\bar{u}_2 + a_{13}\bar{u}_3 = \bar{f}_1,$$

$$p\bar{u}_2 + a_{21}\bar{u}_1 + a_{22}\bar{u}_2 + a_{23}\bar{u}_3 = \bar{f}_2,$$

and

$$p\bar{u}_3 + a_{31}\bar{u}_1 + a_{32}\bar{u}_2 + a_{33}\bar{u}_3 = \bar{f}_3.$$

Let

$$\Delta(p) = \begin{vmatrix} p + a_{11} & a_{12} & a_{13} \\ a_{21} & p + a_{22} & a_{23} \\ a_{31} & a_{32} & p + a_{33} \end{vmatrix}.$$

$\Delta(p) = 0$ is said to be the *determinantal* (or *characteristic*) *equation* of the system. Let Δ_{rs} be the cofactor of the element of the rth row and sth column in this determinant. Then

$$\bar{u}_r = \frac{\Delta_{1r}}{\Delta}\bar{f}_1 + \frac{\Delta_{2r}}{\Delta}\bar{f}_2 + \frac{\Delta_{3r}}{\Delta}\bar{f}_3 \qquad (r = 1 \text{ to } 3).$$

Let

$$\frac{\Delta_{rs}}{\Delta} = \int_0^\infty e^{-px} Q_{rs}(x)dx.$$

Then, from Duhamel's theorem, the solution of (2.54) with the given initial condition is

$$u_r = \sum_{s=1}^{3} \int_0^x Q_{sr}(x - t) f_s(t) dt \qquad (r = 1 \text{ to } 3). \tag{2.56}$$

PROBLEMS

1. Show that, if $F(D)$ and $G(D)$ are polynomials in $D(\equiv d/dx)$ with constant coefficients,

$$F(D)G(D)y = G(D)F(D)y.$$

Verify that this relation does not hold if the coefficients in the polynomials are functions of x.

2. Show that, if $\psi(x)$ denotes a rational algebraical function of x,
(a) $\psi(D)e^{ax} = \psi(a)e^{ax}$.
(b) $\psi(D)(e^{ax}X) = e^{ax}\psi(D + a)X$.

3. Use operational methods to find the particular integral and the complementary function of the equation

$$D^2y + k^2y = A \sin px,$$

for (a) $p^2 \neq k^2$ and (b) $p^2 = k^2$.

[If x represents time and y a displacement, this is the equation of motion of a particle (normally free to oscillate with simple harmonic motion) when acted upon by a periodic disturbing force. The motion consists of a free oscillation superposed on an oscillation of the same period as that of the disturbing force. Note that there will be a phase difference between the two motions. If $p^2 = k^2$, the period of the disturbing force is equal to that of the free motion of the system, and resonance occurs.]

4. Find the solution of

$$D^2y + 2kDy + n^2y = C \sin mx.$$

Show that the particular integral can be expressed in the form

$$y = A \sin(mx - \varepsilon),$$

where

$$A = C[(n^2 - m^2)^2 + 4k^2m^2]^{-1/2} \quad \text{and} \quad \tan \varepsilon = 2km/(n^2 - m^2).$$

[If x represents time and y a displacement, this is the equation of motion of a particle when acted upon by a periodic disturbing force, as well as by a spring and by a frictional force proportional to the velocity. The amplitude A is a maximum when m is such that $m^2 = n^2 - 2k^2$, i.e., when the forcing frequency is close to that of the natural frequency of the system (if k is small). The phase difference ε between the external force and the response of the system is then approximately $\frac{1}{2}\pi$.]

5. Show that the complete solution of

$$\frac{d^2y}{dt^2} + p^2y = Q(t)$$

can be put in the form

$$y = A \cos pt + B \sin pt + \frac{1}{p}\int_0^t Q(\tau)\sin p(t - \tau)\, d\tau.$$

Verify this solution by differentiation.

6. Find the general solutions of the equations

$$\frac{d^2y}{dx^2} + p^2y = \sin qx$$

and

$$\frac{d^2y}{dx^2} + p^2y = \cos qx.$$

Under what conditions are the solutions of these equations periodic functions of x?

By expanding $(\sin x)^{m-2}$ (where m is a positive integer $\geqslant 2$) in terms of $\sin qx$ or $\cos qx$ (where $q = 1$ to $m - 2$), show that the equation

$$\frac{d^2y}{dx^2} + p^2y = (\sin x)^{m-2}$$

will have a periodic solution if $m - p$ is not an even positive integer (where p is taken to be positive). Find the period of this solution. [This last equation is a degenerate form of the nonhomogeneous Mathieu equation (see Chapter 9).]

7. Find the complete solution of the first-order equation

$$Dy - y = x^{a-1},$$

where a is a constant. Show that a particular integral is

$$y = e^x\gamma(a, x),$$

where $\gamma(a, x)$ is the incomplete gamma function (see Problem 4, Chapter 1). By finding the solution of the differential equation as a power series in x, show that

$$\gamma(a, x) = a^{-1}x^ae^{-x}\ {}_1F_1(1; 1 + a; x)$$

where ${}_1F_1$ is the confluent hypergeometric function.

8. Use (a) Cauchy's method and (b) operational methods to show that the solution of

$$D^2y + y = x^{a-1} \qquad (a > 1),$$

which satisfies the initial conditions $y = 0$, $Dy = 0$, is

$$y = [C(0, a) - C(x, a)]\sin x - [S(0, a) - S(x, a)]\cos x,$$

where the generalized Fresnel integrals $C(x, a)$ and $S(x, a)$ are given by

$$C(x, a) = \int_x^\infty t^{a-1}\cos t\,dt \qquad \text{and} \qquad S(x, a) = \int_x^\infty t^{a-1}\sin t\,dt.$$

9. Show that the solution of

$$D^2y + kDy = a + kD[f(x)],$$

which satisfies the initial conditions $y = 0$, $Dy = 0$, is

$$y = \frac{at}{k} - \frac{a}{k^2}(1 - e^{-kt}) - k\int_0^x f(x - t)e^{-kt}\,dt,$$

with $f(0) = 0$.

[If x represents time and y a downward displacement, this is the equation of a particle moving in a fluctuating vertical stream of air, the free stream having an upward velocity $Df(x)$ at time x, and the resistance being proportional to the relative velocity of the particle. If $Df(x) = (a + C\cos px)/k$, where C is a constant, then as $x \to \infty$, the particle performs simple harmonic motion of the same frequency as that of the disturbing force (see Bateman [*45*, 1932]).

10. Verify the following Laplace transforms:

(a) $f(x) = \sinh ax, \quad \bar{f}(p) = \dfrac{a}{p^2 - a^2} \qquad (p > |a|).$

(b) $f(x) = \cosh ax, \quad \bar{f}(p) = \dfrac{p}{p^2 - a^2} \qquad (p > |a|).$

(c) $f(x) = x^n e^{ax}, \quad \bar{f}(p) = \dfrac{n!}{(p-a)^{n+1}} \qquad (n = 0, 1, 2, \ldots).$

11. Show that the solution of $\phi(D)y = 1$ [where $\phi(D)$ is a polynomial of degree n with constant coefficients], with $y_0 = Dy_0 = \cdots = D^{n-1}y_0 = 0$, is

$$y = \frac{1}{\phi(0)} + \sum_{r=1}^{n} \frac{1}{\lambda_r \phi'(\lambda_r)} e^{\lambda_r x},$$

where $\lambda_r (r = 1$ to $n)$ are the roots of $\phi(\lambda) = 0$. Hence derive a series for y in terms of ascending powers of x and verify directly that this series satisfies the given differential equation and the initial conditions. (This is a special case of Heaviside's expansion theorem.)

12. Using Duhamel's theorem, show that if the response of any linear system (with constant coefficients) to a unit step-function disturbance is $\alpha(x)$, the response due to a forcing function $f(x)$ is

$$\int_0^x f(x-t)\alpha(t)\,dt,$$

the system being at rest at $x = 0$.

13. Obtain the particular integral of the equation

$$D^4 y = f(x)$$

which satisfies the boundary conditions $y(0) = 0$, $y(a) = 0$, $Dy(0) = 0$, and $Dy(a) = 0$.

[This is the equation for the deflection y of a loaded beam, where $f(x)$ is proportional to the density of loading, the beam coinciding with the x axis when unloaded and having its extremities at $x = 0$ and $x = a$. The given boundary conditions are for the case in which the beam is clamped at both ends.]

14. Show that, if $\psi(x)$ denotes a rational algebraical function of x,
(a) $\psi(\delta)x^m = \psi(m)x^m$.
(b) $\psi(\delta)(x^m X) = x^m\psi(\delta + m)X$.

15. Show that, on making the substitution

$$y = (1 - x)^{-q}z,$$

the equation

$$x(1 - x)Dy + [p - (p + q)x]y = 1$$

(where p and q are constants) reduces to

$$xDz + pz = (1 - x)^{q-1}.$$

Use operational methods to show that a particular integral of the first equation is

$$y = x^{-p}(1 - x)^{-q}B_x(p, q),$$

where $B_x(p, q)$ is the incomplete beta function (see Problem 5, Chapter 1).

16. From the simultaneous equations

$$a_1D^2y_1 + bD^2y_2 + c_1y_1 = \omega \cos \omega x,$$
$$a_2D^2y_2 + bD^2y_1 + c_2y_2 = 0,$$

obtain the characteristic equation of the system and show that

$$y_r = A_r \cos \omega x + B_{1r} \cos(mx + \alpha) + B_{2r} \cos(nx + \beta) \qquad (r = 1, 2)$$

where A_r, B_{sr}, m, n, α and β are constants. How many of these constants are arbitrary? Find expressions for A_1, A_2, m, and n in terms of a_1, a_2, b, c_1, c_2, and ω.

[These equations occur in electric circuit theory, in which x denotes the time and y_1 and y_2 are the primary and secondary currents between two mutually reacting circuits, the impressed e.m.f. of the primary being $\sin \omega x$.]

CHAPTER 3

Struve and Lommel Functions

3.1 Introduction

In this chapter and in the following ones, we shall consider in detail the properties of the solutions of certain nonhomogeneous linear differential equations of the second order with variable coefficients. The particular nonhomogeneous equations to be considered have as their associated homogeneous equations Bessel's equation (Chapter 3), the confluent hypergeometric equation (Chapter 4), and the hypergeometric equation (Chapter 6). The solutions of the nonhomogeneous equations will be found by using the methods of Chapter 1. In particular, we shall find it convenient to define the solution with which we are interested in terms of certain contour integrals (see §1.14).

We consider first the *Struve function* $H_\nu(z)$, defined in §3.3. As shown in §3.5, this function is a particular integral of the nonhomogeneous equation

$$\frac{d^2y}{dz^2} + \frac{1}{z}\frac{dy}{dz} + \left(1 - \frac{\nu^2}{z^2}\right)y = \frac{(\frac{1}{2}z)^{\nu-1}}{\pi^{1/2}\Gamma(\nu + \frac{1}{2})}, \tag{3.1}$$

where ν is a constant (ν is known as the *order* of the corresponding function). The Struve function occurs in the determination of the fluid pressure on a vibrating disk (McLachlan [1934]).

The associated homogeneous equation is

$$\frac{d^2y}{dz^2} + \frac{1}{z}\frac{dy}{dz} + \left(1 - \frac{\nu^2}{z^2}\right)y = 0, \tag{3.2}$$

which is Bessel's equation.

In §3.2, we summarize various properties of the solutions of (3.2), and in the succeeding sections we discuss in detail the properties of the Struve function $H_\nu(z)$. Finally, in §§3.14 to 3.20, we discuss the properties of the modified Struve function $L_\nu(z)$, which satisfies the equation

$$\frac{d^2y}{dz^2} + \frac{1}{z}\frac{dy}{dz} - \left(1 + \frac{\nu^2}{z^2}\right)y = \frac{(\frac{1}{2}z)^{\nu-1}}{\pi^{1/2}\Gamma(\nu + \frac{1}{2})}, \tag{3.3}$$

and the Lommel functions $S_{\mu,\nu}(z)$ and $s_{\mu,\nu}(z)$, which satisfy the equation

$$\frac{d^2y}{dz^2} + \frac{1}{z}\frac{dy}{dz} + \left(1 - \frac{\nu^2}{z^2}\right)y = z^{\mu-1}. \tag{3.4}$$

As shown in Chapter 11, all these functions are related to solutions of Poisson's equation in terms of cylindrical polar coordinates.

3.2 Some Properties of Bessel Functions

The theory of Bessel functions is fully set out in Watson [1944], Erdélyi [1953b] and McLachlan [1955]. We shall here briefly summarize various properties of these functions.

If ν is not an integer, two independent solutions of Bessel's equation (3.2) are

$$J_\nu(z) = \sum_{m=0}^{\infty} \frac{(-1)^m(\frac{1}{2}z)^{2m+\nu}}{m!\Gamma(m+\nu+1)}$$

and (3.5)

$$J_{-\nu}(z) = \sum_{m=0}^{\infty} \frac{(-1)^m(\frac{1}{2}z)^{2m-\nu}}{m!\Gamma(m-\nu+1)}.$$

$J_\nu(z)$ is called the *Bessel function of the first kind* (of order ν). In terms of generalized hypergeometric series,

$$J_\nu(z) = \frac{(\frac{1}{2}z)^\nu \,{}_0F_1(\nu+1; -\frac{1}{4}z^2)}{\Gamma(\nu+1)}. \tag{3.6}$$

The Wronskian of $J_\nu(z)$ and $J_{-\nu}(z)$ is

$$J_\nu(z)J'_{-\nu}(z) - J_{-\nu}(z)J'_\nu(z) = -\frac{2\sin\nu\pi}{\pi z}. \tag{3.7}$$

When $\nu = n$, an integer,

$$J_{-n}(z) = (-1)^n J_n(z),$$

and the solutions given by (3.5) are no longer independent. We see that, in this case, the Wronskian vanishes.

Another solution of (3.2) is

$$Y_\nu(z) = \frac{J_\nu(z)\cos\nu\pi - J_{-\nu}(z)}{\sin\nu\pi}. \tag{3.8}$$

$Y_\nu(z)$ is called the *Bessel function of the second kind* (of order ν). If $\nu = n$, an integer, $Y_n(z)$ is the limit of this expression as $\nu \to n$, and the solution is of the logarithmic type.

Replacing z by iz in (3.2), we obtain

$$\frac{d^2y}{dz^2} + \frac{1}{z}\frac{dy}{dz} - \left(1 + \frac{\nu^2}{z^2}\right)y = 0. \tag{3.9}$$

This has the solutions $J_\nu(iz)$ and $J_{-\nu}(iz)$, or, in terms of real functions,

$$I_\nu(z) = e^{-(1/2)\nu\pi i} J_\nu(ze^{(1/2)\pi i}) = \sum_{m=0}^{\infty} \frac{(\frac{1}{2}z)^{2m+\nu}}{m!\Gamma(m+\nu+1)}$$

and (3.10)

$$I_{-\nu}(z) = \sum_{m=0}^{\infty} \frac{(\frac{1}{2}z)^{2m-\nu}}{m!\Gamma(m-\nu+1)}.$$

$I_\nu(z)$ is the modified Bessel function of the first kind. The Wronskian of $I_\nu(z)$ and $I_{-\nu}(z)$ is

$$I_\nu(z)I'_{-\nu}(z) - I_{-\nu}(z)I'_\nu(z) = -\frac{2\sin\nu\pi}{\pi z}. \tag{3.11}$$

When $\nu = n$, an integer,

$$I_n(z) = I_{-n}(z). \tag{3.12}$$

Now

$$K_\nu(z) = \tfrac{1}{2}\pi(\sin\nu\pi)^{-1}[I_{-\nu}(z) - I_\nu(z)] \tag{3.13}$$

also satisfies (3.9) and is finite for all ν. $K_\nu(z)$ is called a *modified Bessel function of the third kind.*

Consider next the solution of (3.2) in terms of contour integrals. Let $w = z^{-\nu}y$, where y is a solution of (3.2). Then

$$z\frac{d^2w}{dz^2} + (2\nu+1)\frac{dw}{dz} + zw = 0. \tag{3.14}$$

As shown by Poole [*148*, 1936], the solutions of (3.14) can be expressed in terms of contour integrals of the form

$$\frac{1}{2\pi i}\int_C e^{izt}(1-t^2)^{\nu-(1/2)}\,dt,$$

where the contour C must satisfy the condition

$$[e^{izt}(1-t^2)^{\nu+(1/2)}]_C = 0. \tag{3.15}$$

Thus the solutions of (3.2) can be expressed in terms of the contour integrals

$$y_1 = \frac{z^\nu}{2\pi i}\int_I^{(1+)} e^{izt}(t^2-1)^{\nu-(1/2)}\,dt \tag{3.16}$$

and

$$y_2 = \frac{z^\nu}{2\pi i}\int_I^{(-1+)} e^{izt}(t^2-1)^{\nu-(1/2)}\,dt, \tag{3.17}$$

where I is the point at infinity taken in such a direction that Re (izt) is negative. The contours for these integrals are shown in Figure 3.1, for the case Re $z > 0$.

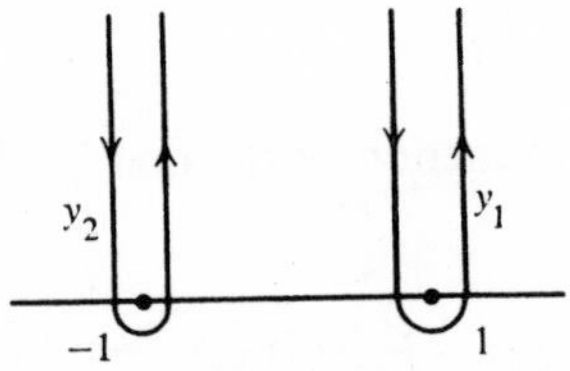

Figure 3.1 Contours for y_1 and y_2.

Thus, if $\arg z = \theta\ (-\frac{1}{2}\pi < \theta < \frac{1}{2}\pi)$, we take I as the point at infinity having argument $\frac{1}{2}\pi$, and

$$\arg(t-1) = \arg(t+1) = -\tfrac{3}{2}\pi \tag{3.18}$$

at the start of the contours.

From Watson [*166*, 1944], with the arguments defined by (3.18), if $\nu+\frac{1}{2}$ is not a positive integer,

$$J_\nu(z) = -2^{-\nu}\pi^{-(1/2)}e^{2\pi i\nu}\Gamma(\tfrac{1}{2}-\nu)y_3, \tag{3.19}$$

and

$$J_{-\nu}(z) = 2^{-\nu}\pi^{-(1/2)}e^{\pi i\nu}\Gamma(\tfrac{1}{2}-\nu)y_4, \tag{3.20}$$

where

$$\begin{aligned} y_3 &= \frac{z^\nu}{2\pi i}\int_I^{(1+,-1-)} e^{izt}(t^2-1)^{\nu-(1/2)}\,dt \\ &= y_1 - y_2 \end{aligned} \tag{3.21}$$

and

$$\begin{aligned} y_4 &= \frac{z^\nu}{2\pi i}\int_I^{(-1+,1+)} e^{izt}(t^2-1)^{\nu-(1/2)}\,dt \\ &= y_2 - e^{2\pi i\nu}y_1. \end{aligned} \tag{3.22}$$

As shown by Watson, the path of integration for y_3 may be contracted to a finite contour; no such finite contour is permissible with y_4. The simplest contours for y_3 and y_4 are shown in Figure 3.2. Thus we can write

$$y_3 = -e^{-2\pi i\nu}(2\pi i)^{-1}z^\nu$$
$$\times \left[\int_0^{(1+)} e^{izt}(t^2-1)^{\nu-(1/2)}\,dt - \int_0^{(-1+)} e^{izt}(t^2-1)^{\nu-(1/2)}\,dt\right], \tag{3.23}$$

where $\arg(t-1) = -\pi$ and $\arg(t+1) = 0$ at the start of both contours.

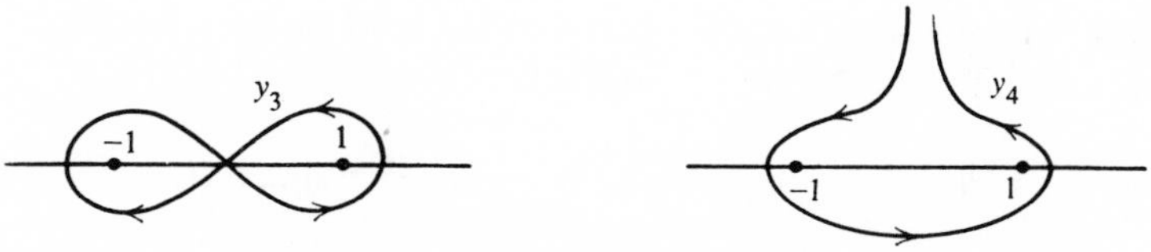

Figure 3.2 Contours for y_3 and y_4.

Equation (3.23) can be put in the simpler form

$$y_3 = i\pi^{-1}e^{-2\pi i\nu}z^\nu\int_0^{(1+)}(t^2-1)^{\nu-(1/2)}\cos zt\,dt. \tag{3.24}$$

The integral representations of the Bessel functions have been given for $\operatorname{Re} z > 0$. A representation of $J_\nu(z)$ or $J_{-\nu}(z)$ for $-\pi < \arg z < \pi$ can be found by analytic continuation of the above formulas.

For $\operatorname{Re}\nu > -\frac{1}{2}$, the contour of integration for y_3 may be replaced by portions of the real axis. We find that

$$\begin{aligned} J_\nu(z) &= \frac{2\pi^{-(1/2)}(\frac{1}{2}z)^\nu}{\Gamma(\nu+\frac{1}{2})}\int_0^1(1-t^2)^{\nu-(1/2)}\cos zt\,dt \\ &= \frac{2\pi^{-(1/2)}(\frac{1}{2}z)^\nu}{\Gamma(\nu+\frac{1}{2})}\int_0^{(1/2)\pi}\cos(z\cos\theta)\sin^{2\nu}\theta\,d\theta. \end{aligned} \tag{3.25}$$

Similarly, if $\operatorname{Re} z > 0$ and $\operatorname{Re}\nu > -\frac{1}{2}$, the contour of integration for y_4 may be replaced by portions of the real and imaginary axes. As shown by Watson [*165*, 1944], (3.20) then reduces to

$$J_{-\nu}(z) = \frac{2\pi^{-(1/2)}(\frac{1}{2}z)^\nu}{\Gamma(\nu+\frac{1}{2})}\left[\sin\nu\pi\int_0^\infty e^{-zt}(1+t^2)^{\nu-(1/2)}\,dt\right.$$
$$\left.+\int_0^1\cos(zt+\nu\pi)(1-t^2)^{\nu-(1/2)}\,dt\right]. \tag{3.26}$$

3.3 Struve Function $H_\nu(z)$

Consider the function $H_\nu(z)$ defined, for $-\pi < \arg z < \pi$, by

$$H_\nu(z) = -2^{-\nu}\pi^{-(1/2)}e^{2\pi i\nu}\Gamma(\tfrac{1}{2}-\nu)h\,, \tag{3.27}$$

where

$$h = e^{-2\pi i\nu}(2\pi)^{-1}z^\nu\left[\int_0^{(1+)} e^{izt}(t^2-1)^{\nu-(1/2)}\,dt + \int_0^{(-1+)} e^{izt}(t^2-1)^{\nu-(1/2)}\,dt\right] \tag{3.28}$$

and $\arg(t-1) = -\pi$ and $\arg(t+1) = 0$ at the start of the contours.

Equation (3.28) can be put in the simpler form

$$h = ie^{-2\pi i\nu}\pi^{-1}z^\nu \int_0^{(1+)} (t^2-1)^{\nu-(1/2)}\sin zt\,dt\,. \tag{3.29}$$

From (3.19) and (3.27), $H_\nu(z)/J_\nu(z) = h/y_3$. Using (3.24) and (3.29), we see that

$$J_\nu(z) + iH_\nu(z) = \pi^{-(1/2)}\Gamma(\tfrac{1}{2}-\nu)\frac{(\frac{1}{2}z)^\nu}{\pi i}\int_0^{(1+)} e^{izt}(t^2-\tfrac{1}{2})^{\nu-(1/2)}\,dt\,. \tag{3.30}$$

For Re $\nu > -\frac{1}{2}$, the contours of integration in (3.29) may be replaced by portions of the real axis. We find that

$$\begin{aligned} H_\nu(z) &= \frac{2\pi^{-(1/2)}(\frac{1}{2}z)^\nu}{\Gamma(\nu+\frac{1}{2})}\int_0^1 (1-t^2)^{\nu-(1/2)}\sin zt\,dt \\ &= \frac{2\pi^{-(1/2)}(\frac{1}{2}z)^\nu}{\Gamma(\nu+\frac{1}{2})}\int_0^{(1/2)\pi} \sin(z\cos\theta)\sin^{2\nu}\theta\,d\theta\,. \end{aligned} \tag{3.31}$$

As shown by Watson [*330*, 1944], an alternative integral representation for

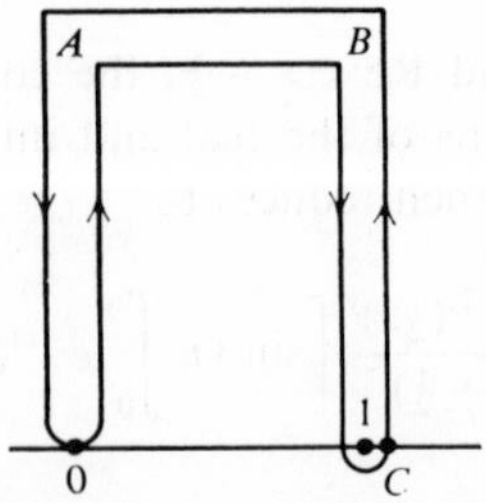

Figure 3.3 Deformed contour.

$H_\nu(z)$ can be obtained by deforming the contour of the integral in (3.30). Thus, if $\arg\ z = \theta\ (-\frac{1}{2}\pi < \theta < \frac{1}{2}\pi)$, we can deform the contour as shown in Figure 3.3, in which the four parallel lines stretch to infinity. Now, from (3.30), the contribution to the integral from AB will tend to zero as A and B tend to infinity.

Now, from Watson [*166*, 1944],

$$J_\nu(z) + iY_\nu(z) = \pi^{-(1/2)}\Gamma(\tfrac{1}{2} - \nu)\frac{(\frac{1}{2}z)^\nu}{\pi i}\int_B^{(1+)} e^{izt}(t^2 - 1)^{\nu-(1/2)}\,dt, \tag{3.32}$$

in which $\arg(t-1) = \arg(t+1) = 0$ at the point C.

From (3.30) and (3.32), we obtain, on eliminating $J_\nu(z)$,

$$H_\nu(z) = Y_\nu(z) + \pi^{-(1/2)}\Gamma(\tfrac{1}{2} - \nu)\frac{(\frac{1}{2}z)^\nu}{\pi i}\left[\int_0^A e^{izt}(t^2 - 1)^{\nu-(1/2)}\,dt + \int_A^0 e^{izt}(t^2 - 1)^{\nu-(1/2)}\,dt\right];$$

that is, putting $t = iu$ and taking $\arg(1 + u^2) = 0$ at O,

$$H_\nu(z) = Y_\nu(z) + \frac{2\pi^{-(1/2)}(\frac{1}{2}z)^\nu}{\Gamma(\nu + \frac{1}{2})}\int_0^\infty e^{-zu}(1 + u^2)^{\nu-(1/2)}\,du \qquad (Re\ z > 0). \tag{3.33}$$

More generally, if arg z lies between $-\frac{1}{2}\pi + \omega$ and $\frac{1}{2}\pi + \omega$, where $|\omega| < \frac{1}{2}\pi$,

$$H_\nu(z) = Y_\nu(z) + \frac{2\pi^{-(1/2)}(\frac{1}{2}z)^\nu}{\Gamma(\nu + \frac{1}{2})}\int_0^{\infty\exp(-i\omega)} e^{-zu}(1 + u^2)^{\nu-(1/2)}\,du. \tag{3.34}$$

We note that (3.28) and (3.34) are valid for all values of ν.

3.4 Recurrence Formulas for $H_\nu(z)$

Consider the integral

$$I(\nu, z) = \int_0^{\infty\exp(-i\omega)} e^{-zu}(1 + u^2)^{\nu-(1/2)}\,du. \tag{3.35}$$

Now

$$\frac{dI(\nu, z)}{dz} = -\int_0^{\infty\exp(-i\omega)} e^{-zu}u(1 + u^2)^{\nu-(1/2)}\,du. \tag{3.36}$$

On integrating (3.36) by parts, we obtain

$$\frac{dI(\nu, z)}{dz} = \frac{1}{2\nu + 1} - \frac{z}{2\nu + 1}I(\nu + 1, z). \tag{3.37}$$

Again, from (3.35),

$$I(\nu, z) - I(\nu - 1, z) = \int_0^{\infty \exp(-i\omega)} e^{-zu} u^2 (1 + u^2)^{\nu - (3/2)} \, du. \tag{3.38}$$

On integrating (3.38) by parts we obtain

$$\begin{aligned} I(\nu, z) - I(\nu - 1, z) &= -\frac{1}{2\nu - 1} \int_0^{\infty \exp(-i\omega)} (1 + u^2)^{\nu - (1/2)} (1 - zu) e^{-zu} \, du \\ &= -\frac{1}{2\nu - 1} \left[I(\nu, z) + z \frac{dI(\nu, z)}{dz} \right]; \end{aligned}$$

that is,

$$\frac{d}{dz} [z^{2\nu} I(\nu, z)] = (2\nu - 1) z^{2\nu - 1} I(\nu - 1, z). \tag{3.39}$$

From (3.34), (3.35), and (3.39), using the recurrence formulas for $Y_\nu(z)$ given by Watson [*66*, 1944], we find that

$$\frac{d}{dz} [z^\nu H_\nu(z)] = z^\nu H_{\nu - 1}(z),$$

that is, (3.40)

$$(\delta + \nu) H_\nu(z) = z H_{\nu - 1}(z),$$

where $\delta \equiv z(d/dz)$.

Equation (3.40) can be written in the form

$$H_{\nu - 1}(z) = z^{1 - \nu} \left(\frac{1}{z} \frac{d}{dz} \right) [z^\nu H_\nu(z)]. \tag{3.41}$$

By repeated application of this formula we find that

$$H_{\nu - m}(z) = z^{m - \nu} \left(\frac{1}{z} \frac{d}{dz} \right)^m [z^\nu H_\nu(z)], \tag{3.42}$$

where m is a positive integer.

Similarly, from (3.34), (3.35), and (3.37),

$$\frac{d}{dz} [z^{-\nu} H_\nu(z)] = \frac{2^{-\nu} \pi^{-(1/2)}}{\Gamma(\nu + \frac{3}{2})} - z^{-\nu} H_{\nu + 1}(z);$$

that is, (3.43)

$$(\delta - \nu) H_\nu(z) = \frac{2\pi^{-(1/2)} (\frac{1}{2} z)^{\nu + 1}}{\Gamma(\nu + \frac{3}{2})} - z H_{\nu + 1}(z).$$

In particular, we see that

$$\frac{d}{dz}[zH_1(z)] = zH_0(z) \tag{3.44}$$

and

$$\frac{d}{dz}H_0(z) = \frac{2}{\pi} - H_1(z). \tag{3.45}$$

From (3.40) and (3.43),

$$H_{\nu-1}(z) + H_{\nu+1}(z) = 2\nu z^{-1}H_\nu(z) + \frac{\pi^{-(1/2)}(\frac{1}{2}z)^\nu}{\Gamma(\nu + \frac{3}{2})} \tag{3.46}$$

and

$$H_{\nu-1}(z) - H_{\nu+1}(z) = 2\frac{dH_\nu(z)}{dz} - \frac{\pi^{-(1/2)}(\frac{1}{2}z)^\nu}{\Gamma(\nu + \frac{3}{2})}. \tag{3.47}$$

3.5 Differential Equation Satisfied by $H_\nu(z)$

From (3.40) and (3.43),

$$\begin{aligned}(\delta - \nu)(\delta + \nu)H_\nu(z) &= (\delta - \nu)[zH_{\nu-1}(z)] \\ &= z(\delta - \nu + 1)H_{\nu-1}(z) \\ &= \frac{4\pi^{-(1/2)}(\frac{1}{2}z)^{\nu+1}}{\Gamma(\nu + \frac{1}{2})} - z^2H_\nu(z).\end{aligned}$$

Thus $H_\nu(z)$ is a particular integral of the nonhomogeneous linear equation

$$(\delta^2 + z^2 - \nu^2)y = \frac{4\pi^{-(1/2)}(\frac{1}{2}z)^{\nu+1}}{\Gamma(\nu + \frac{1}{2})};$$

that is, (3.48)

$$\frac{d^2y}{dz^2} + \frac{1}{z}\frac{dy}{dz} + \left(1 - \frac{\nu^2}{z^2}\right)y = \frac{\pi^{-(1/2)}(\frac{1}{2}z)^{\nu-1}}{\Gamma(\nu + \frac{1}{2})}.$$

This equation is sometimes written

$$\nabla_\nu H_\nu(z) = \frac{4\pi^{-(1/2)}(\frac{1}{2}z)^{\nu+1}}{\Gamma(\nu + \frac{1}{2})},$$

where (3.49)

$$\nabla_\nu \equiv z^2\frac{d^2}{dz^2} + z\frac{d}{dz} + z^2 - \nu^2.$$

The associated homogeneous equation is Bessel's equation (3.2), which has one regular singularity at $z=0$ and an irregular singular point at infinity. The complete primitive of (3.48) is $C_1 J_\nu(z) + C_2 Y_\nu(z) + H_\nu(z)$, where C_1 and C_2 are arbitrary constants.

By differentiating (3.48) it can be shown that $H_\nu(z)$ is a solution of the homogeneous third-order equation

$$z^3 \frac{d^3 y}{dz^3} + (2-\nu) z^2 \frac{d^2 y}{dz^2} + [z^3 - \nu(1+\nu)z] \frac{dy}{dz}$$

$$+ [z^2(1-\nu) + \nu^2(\nu+1)]y = 0. \tag{3.50}$$

The other solutions of (3.50) are $J_\nu(z)$ and $Y_\nu(z)$.

3.6 Power Series for $H_\nu(z)$

The expansion of the particular integral of (3.48) as a power series in z can be found by using the Frobenius method (see §1.12). Alternatively, from (3.31), on expanding $\sin(z\cos\theta)$ as a power series in z, and integrating term by term, we obtain, for $\operatorname{Re}\nu > -\frac{1}{2}$,

$$H_\nu(z) = \frac{2\pi^{-(1/2)}(\frac{1}{2}z)^\nu}{\Gamma(\nu+\frac{1}{2})} \sum_{m=0}^{\infty} \frac{(-1)^m z^{2m+1}}{(2m+1)!} \int_0^{(1/2)\pi} \cos^{2m+1}\theta \sin^{2\nu}\theta \, d\theta$$

$$= \pi^{-(1/2)}(\tfrac{1}{2}z)^\nu \sum_{m=0}^{\infty} \frac{(-1)^m z^{2m+1}}{(2m+1)!} \frac{\Gamma(m+1)}{\Gamma(\nu+m+\frac{3}{2})},$$

that is,

$$H_\nu(z) = \sum_{m=0}^{\infty} \frac{(-1)^m (\frac{1}{2}z)^{\nu+2m+1}}{\Gamma(m+\frac{3}{2})\Gamma(\nu+m+\frac{3}{2})}. \tag{3.51}$$

It is readily shown that this series is convergent for all values of z. Using the recurrence formulas given above, the expansion (3.51) can be shown to hold for all values of ν. Thus $z^{-\nu}H_\nu(z)$ is an entire function of ν and z.

From (3.51) we see that the Struve function $H_\nu(z)$ can be expressed in terms of a generalized hypergeometric series, in the form

$$H_\nu(z) = \frac{2\pi^{-(1/2)}(\frac{1}{2}z)^{\nu+1} \, {}_1F_2(1; \frac{3}{2}+\nu, \frac{3}{2}; -\frac{1}{4}z^2)}{\Gamma(\nu+\frac{3}{2})}. \tag{3.52}$$

The interpretation of this formula when $\nu + \frac{3}{2}$ is zero or a negative integer is considered in §3.8.

3.7 Mellin-Barnes Integrals for $H_\nu(z)$

Consider the contour integral

$$I(z) = \frac{1}{2\pi i}\int_C \frac{\Gamma(1+s)\Gamma(-s)}{\Gamma(\nu+\frac{3}{2}+s)\Gamma(\frac{3}{2}+s)}(\tfrac{1}{2}z)^{\nu+2s+1}\,ds$$

$$= -\frac{1}{2\pi i}\int_C \frac{\pi}{\Gamma(\nu+\frac{3}{2}+s)\Gamma(\frac{3}{2}+s)}\frac{(\frac{1}{2}z)^{\nu+2s+1}}{\sin \pi s}\,ds, \tag{3.53}$$

where $\nu + \frac{3}{2} > 0$, taken around a contour consisting of the imaginary axis (the contour being indented to include the origin) together with the semicircle of large radius $N + \frac{1}{2}$ (where N is an integer) with center at the origin lying in the right half of the s plane. We shall evaluate this integral by a method which is precisely similar to that given by Whittaker and Watson [*287*, 1935].

On the semicircle, put $s = (N+\frac{1}{2})e^{i\theta} = \xi + i\eta$ and $z = Re^{i\psi}$. Now, for large $|s|$, with $|\arg s| < \pi$,

$$|\Gamma(s)| = (2\pi)^{1/2}\exp[-\xi + (\xi - \tfrac{1}{2})\log(N+\tfrac{1}{2}) - \eta\theta].$$

On the semicircle,

$$|\sin \pi s| = \sqrt{\sin^2 \pi\xi + \sinh^2 \pi\eta} = 0(\exp \pi|\eta|),$$

and the integrand of (3.53) is

$$0[\exp\{2\xi - (\xi+\nu+2)\log(N+\tfrac{1}{2}) + 2\eta\theta + 2\xi\log(\tfrac{1}{2}R) - 2\eta\psi - \pi|\eta|\}].$$

Thus the integrand represents a function of s which tends to zero as $N \to \infty$ if $\pi - \delta \geqslant \psi \geqslant \delta$, where δ is positive. If $\pi - \delta \geqslant \arg z \geqslant \delta$, on the semicircle the integrand is $0[N^{-\nu-2}\exp(-2N\delta)]$ and thus the contribution to $I(z)$ from this part of the contour tends to zero as $N \to \infty$, when $\pi > \arg z > 0$.

The integrand has simple poles at $s = 0, 1, 2, \ldots$. The sum of the residues at these poles is

$$\sum_{m=0}^{\infty} \frac{(-1)^m(\frac{1}{2}z)^{\nu+2m+1}}{[\Gamma(m+\frac{3}{2})\Gamma(\nu+m+\frac{3}{2})]} = H_\nu(z) \qquad \text{[from (3.51)]}.$$

Hence, equating the contour integral to $2\pi i \times$ sum of the residues within the contour, we see that, if $\pi > \arg z > 0$, and $\nu + \frac{3}{2} > 0$,

$$H_\nu(z) = \frac{1}{2\pi i}\int_{-\infty i}^{\infty i} \frac{\Gamma(1+s)\Gamma(-s)}{\Gamma(\nu+\frac{3}{2}+s)\Gamma(\frac{3}{2}+s)}(\tfrac{1}{2}z)^{\nu+2s+1}\,ds. \tag{3.54}$$

On replacing s by $s - \frac{1}{2}\mu$, we see that

$$z^{\mu} H_{\nu}(z) = \frac{2^{\mu}}{2\pi i} \int_{-\infty i + (1/2)\mu}^{\infty i + (1/2)\mu} \frac{\Gamma(1 - \frac{1}{2}\mu + s)\Gamma(\frac{1}{2}\mu - s)}{\Gamma(\nu - \frac{1}{2}\mu + \frac{3}{2} + s)\Gamma(-\frac{1}{2}\mu + \frac{3}{2} + s)} (\tfrac{1}{2}z)^{\nu + 2s + 1}\, ds. \tag{3.55}$$

3.8 Particular Values of $H_{\nu}(z)$

We see that, for small values of z,

$$H_{\nu}(z) \sim \frac{2\pi^{-(1/2)}(\frac{1}{2}z)^{\nu+1}}{\Gamma(\nu + \frac{3}{2})},$$

provided $\nu + \frac{3}{2}$ is not zero or a negative integer.

Thus:

If $\nu > -1$, $\quad H_{\nu}(0) = 0$.

If $\nu = -1$, $\quad H_{\nu}(0) = \dfrac{2}{\pi}$.

If $\nu < -1$, $\quad H_{\nu}(0)$ is infinite.

So far we have not defined $H_{\nu}(z)$ for negative values of z. Using the series (3.51), we define $H_{\nu}(z)$ for unrestricted values of arg z by the equation

$$H_{\nu}(ze^{m\pi i}) = e^{m(\nu+1)\pi i} H_{\nu}(z), \tag{3.56}$$

where m is an integer.

If $\nu + \frac{1}{2}$ is zero, or a negative integer, $\Gamma(\nu + \frac{1}{2})$ is infinite, and the right side of (3.48) vanishes identically. In that case, $H_{\nu}(z)$ can be expressed in terms of Bessel functions. From (3.33) we see that

$$H_{-n-(1/2)}(z) = Y_{-n-(1/2)}(z) = (-1)^n J_{n+(1/2)}(z) \qquad (n = 0, 1, 2, 3, \ldots). \tag{3.57}$$

Now

$$H_{-(1/2)}(z) = Y_{-(1/2)}(z) = J_{1/2}(z) = \left(\frac{2}{\pi z}\right)^{1/2} \sin z. \tag{3.58}$$

Using (3.42) we see that $H_{-n-1/2}(z)$ can be expressed in terms of elementary trigonometric functions (together with a terminating series in $1/z$).

3.9 The Positive Zeros of $H_{\nu}(z)$, Where ν Is Real

From (3.40), using Rolle's theorem, we see that between two consecutive positive zeros of $H_{\nu}(z)$ there lies at least one zero of $H_{\nu-1}(z)$. However, the converse is not true. Indeed, it can be shown that, if $\nu > \frac{1}{2}$, $H_{\nu}(z)$ is positive when z is positive. We give below the proof as given by Watson [*337*, 1944].

From (3.31), integrating by parts, if $\nu > \frac{1}{2}$,

$$\int_0^{(1/2)\pi} \sin(z\cos\theta)\sin^{2\nu}\theta\, d\theta = \Big[\cos(z\cos\theta)\sin^{2\nu-1}\theta\Big]_0^{(1/2)\pi}$$
$$-(2\nu-1)\int_0^{(1/2)\pi}\cos(z\cos\theta)\sin^{2\nu-2}\theta\cos\theta\, d\theta$$
$$= 1-(2\nu-1)\int_0^{(1/2)\pi}\cos(z\cos\theta)\sin^{2\nu-2}\theta\cos\theta\, d\theta$$
$$> 1-(2\nu-1)\int_0^{(1/2)\pi}\sin^{2\nu-2}\theta\cos\theta\, d\theta = 0.$$

Thus, from (3.31), if $\nu > \frac{1}{2}$, $H_\nu(z)$ is positive for all positive values of z.

Also, from (3.31),

$$H_{1/2}(z) = 2\pi^{-1/2}(\tfrac{1}{2}z)^{1/2}\int_0^{(1/2)\pi}\sin(z\cos\theta)\sin\theta\, d\theta$$
$$= 2\pi^{-1/2}(\tfrac{1}{2}z)^{1/2}\,[z^{-1}\cos(z\cos\theta)]_0^{(1/2)\pi}$$
$$= (2/\pi z)^{1/2}(1-\cos z). \tag{3.59}$$

Thus $H_{1/2}(z)$ has zeros at $z = 2m\pi$, where $m = 0, 1, 2, 3, \ldots$, but is positive for all other positive values of z.

From (3.43), applying Rolle's theorem, we see that between two consecutive positive zeros of $H_\nu(z)$ there lies at least one value of z for which

$$z^{-\nu}H_{\nu+1}(z) = \frac{2^{-\nu}\pi^{-(1/2)}}{\Gamma(\nu+\frac{3}{2})}.$$

In particular, putting $\nu = 0$, we see that between two consecutive positive zeros of $H_0(z)$ there lies at least one value of z for which $H_1(z) = 2/\pi$.

3.10 Asymptotic Expansion of $H_\nu(z)$

From (3.34), putting $v = zu$,

$$H_\nu(z) = Y_\nu(z) + \frac{\pi^{-(1/2)}(\frac{1}{2}z)^{\nu-1}}{\Gamma(\nu+\frac{1}{2})}\int_0^{\infty\exp i\beta} e^{-v}\left(1+\frac{v^2}{z^2}\right)^{\nu-(1/2)} dv, \tag{3.60}$$

where $\beta = \theta - \omega$ $(-\frac{1}{2}\pi < \beta < \frac{1}{2}\pi)$ and $\arg z = \theta$ $(-\pi < \theta < \pi)$. On writing the integrand as a power series in descending powers of z and integrating term by term, we obtain

$$H_\nu(z) = Y_\nu(z) + \frac{\pi^{-(1/2)}(\frac{1}{2}z)^{\nu-1}}{\Gamma(\nu+\frac{1}{2})}$$
$$\times\left[\sum_{m=0}^{p-1}\int_0^{\infty\exp i\beta} e^{-v}\frac{\Gamma(\nu+\frac{1}{2})}{\Gamma(\nu+\frac{1}{2}-m)m!}\frac{v^{2m}}{z^{2m}}\, dv + 0(z^{-2p})\right]$$
$$= Y_\nu(z) + \frac{1}{\pi}\sum_{m=0}^{p-1}\frac{\Gamma(m+\frac{1}{2})}{\Gamma(\nu+\frac{1}{2}-m)(\frac{1}{2}z)^{2m-\nu+1}} + 0(z^{\nu-2p-1}). \tag{3.61}$$

The justification for such an integration and the proof that this is an asymptotic expansion are given in Watson [*332*, 1944].

If $\nu = n - \frac{1}{2}$, where n is a positive integer, the series in (3.61) terminates after n terms. For these values of ν, $Y_\nu(z)$ can also be expressed in a finite form, in terms of trigonometric functions. Thus $H_{n-1/2}(z)$ can be expressed in terms of trigonometric functions together with a terminating series of $1/z$. $H_{1/2}(z)$ is given by (3.59). $H_{n-1/2}(z)$ can be found using the recurrence formulas given in §3.4.

We note that, if $\nu < 1$, the series in (3.61) contains only negative powers of z. Now $Y_\nu(z) \to 0$ as $z \to \infty$. Thus

$$H_\nu(z) \to 0 \quad \text{as } z \to \infty \qquad (\nu < 1). \tag{3.62}$$

If $\nu = 1$,

$$H_1(z) \sim Y_1(z) + \frac{2}{\pi} + 0\left(\frac{1}{z^2}\right).$$

Now $Y_1(z) \to 0$ as $z \to \infty$. Thus

$$H_1(z) \to \frac{2}{\pi} \quad \text{as } z \to \infty. \tag{3.63}$$

If $\nu > 1$, the series in (3.61) contains some positive powers of z, and

$$H_\nu(z) \to \infty \quad \text{as } z \to \infty \qquad (\nu > 1). \tag{3.64}$$

The asymptotic expansion of $H_\nu(z)$ when both $|\nu|$ and $|z|$ are large is given by Watson [*336*, 1944].

3.11 Indefinite Integrals Connected with $H_\nu(z)$

A number of indefinite integrals connected with $H_\nu(z)$ can be obtained directly from the recurrence formulas given in §3.4. Thus

$$\int z^\nu H_{\nu-1}(z)dz = z^\nu H_\nu(z) \tag{3.65}$$

and

$$\int z^{-\nu} H_{\nu+1}(z)dz = -z^{-\nu} H_\nu(z) + \frac{2^{-\nu}\pi^{-(1/2)}z}{\Gamma(\nu + \frac{3}{2})}. \tag{3.66}$$

More generally, writing $H_\nu(z)$ as a power series in z and integrating term by term, we find

$$\int z^\mu H_\nu(z)dz = \frac{z^{\mu+\nu+2}}{2^\nu \pi^{1/2}(\mu + \nu + 2)\Gamma(\nu + \frac{3}{2})} \times {}_2F_3\left(1, \tfrac{1}{2}[\mu + \nu + 2]; \tfrac{3}{2}, \nu + \tfrac{3}{2}, \tfrac{1}{2}[\mu + \nu + 4]; -\frac{z^2}{4}\right). \tag{3.67}$$

Other integrals can be obtained by solving the differential equation

$$\frac{d^2y}{dz^2}+\frac{1}{z}\frac{dy}{dz}+\left(1-\frac{\nu^2}{z^2}\right)y=\frac{(\frac{1}{2}z)^{\nu-1}}{\pi^{1/2}\Gamma(\nu+\frac{1}{2})} \tag{3.68}$$

by the method of variation of parameters (see §1.5). The Wronskian of $J_\nu(z)$ and $J_{-\nu}(z)$ is given by (3.7). We find that

$$H_\nu(z)=\frac{2^{-\nu}\pi^{1/2}}{\Gamma(\nu+\frac{1}{2})\sin\nu\pi}\left[J_\nu(z)\int z^\nu J_{-\nu}(z)dz-J_{-\nu}(z)\int z^\nu J_\nu(z)dz\right]. \tag{3.69}$$

Now $x=J_\nu(z)$ is a solution of the differential equation

$$\frac{d^2x}{dz^2}+\frac{1}{z}\frac{dx}{dz}+\left(1-\frac{\nu^2}{z^2}\right)x=0. \tag{3.70}$$

On multiplying (3.68) by xz and (3.70) by yz and subtracting, we obtain

$$z\left(x\frac{d^2y}{dz^2}-y\frac{d^2x}{dz^2}\right)+\left(x\frac{dy}{dz}-y\frac{dx}{dz}\right)=\frac{2^{1-\nu}xz^\nu}{\pi^{1/2}\Gamma(\nu+\frac{1}{2})},$$

that is,

$$\frac{d}{dz}\left[z\left(x\frac{dy}{dz}-y\frac{dx}{dz}\right)\right]=\frac{2^{1-\nu}xz^\nu}{\pi^{1/2}\Gamma(\nu+\frac{1}{2})}. \tag{3.71}$$

On integrating (3.71), and putting $x=J_\nu(z)$, we see that

$$\begin{aligned}\int z^\nu J_\nu(z)dz&=2^{\nu-1}\pi^{1/2}\Gamma(\nu+\tfrac{1}{2})z[J_\nu(z)H'_\nu(z)-H_\nu(z)J'_\nu(z)]\\&=2^{\nu-1}\pi^{1/2}\Gamma(\nu+\tfrac{1}{2})z[J_\nu(z)H_{\nu-1}(z)-H_\nu(z)J_{\nu-1}(z)],\end{aligned} \tag{3.72}$$

on using the recurrence formulas for $J_\nu(z)$ and $H_\nu(z)$.

Similarly, putting $x=J_{-\nu}(z)$, we find that

$$\begin{aligned}\int z^\nu J_{-\nu}(z)dz&=2^{\nu-1}\pi^{1/2}\Gamma(\nu+\tfrac{1}{2})z[J_{-\nu}(z)H'_\nu(z)-H_\nu(z)J'_{-\nu}(z)]\\&=2^{\nu-1}\pi^{1/2}\Gamma(\nu+\tfrac{1}{2})z[J_{-\nu}(z)H_{\nu-1}(z)+H_\nu(z)J_{1-\nu}(z)].\end{aligned} \tag{3.73}$$

3.12 Definite Integrals Connected with $H_\nu(z)$

The formula

$$H_{\mu+\nu}(z)=\frac{z^\mu}{2^{\mu-1}\Gamma(\mu)}\int_0^{(1/2)\pi}H_\nu(z\sin\theta)\sin^{\nu+1}\theta\cos^{2\mu-1}\theta\,d\theta, \tag{3.74}$$

which is valid for Re $\mu > 0$ and Re $\nu > -\frac{3}{2}$, may be proved by expanding $H_\nu(z \sin\theta)$ as a power series in z and integrating term by term. This corresponds to Sonine's first integral for Bessel functions. We see from (3.74) that any Struve function can be expressed in terms of an integral involving a Struve function of lower order. In particular, putting $\mu = -\nu + \frac{1}{2}$, and using (3.59), we see that

$$\int_0^{(1/2)\pi} H_\nu(z \sin\theta)(\sin\theta)^{\nu+1}(\cos\theta)^{-2\nu}\,d\theta = 2^{-\nu}\pi^{-(1/2)}\Gamma(\tfrac{1}{2}-\nu)z^{\nu-1}(1-\cos z)$$

$$(-\tfrac{3}{2} < \text{Re}\,\nu < \tfrac{1}{2}). \quad (3.75)$$

As shown by Watson [374, 1944], the formula

$$H_{\nu-(1/2)}(z) = \left(\frac{2z}{\pi}\right)^{1/2} \int_0^{(1/2)\pi} J_\nu(z\sin\theta)\sin^{1-\nu}\theta\,d\theta \quad (3.76)$$

is obtained by expanding $J_\nu(z \sin\theta)$ as a series in z and integrating term by term.

More generally we find, in a similar manner,

$$\int_0^{(1/2)\pi} H_\nu(z\sin\theta)\sin^\lambda\theta\cos^{2\mu-1}\theta\,d\theta = \frac{z^{\nu+1}\Gamma(\mu)\Gamma\left(\dfrac{\lambda+\nu}{2}+1\right)}{2^{\nu+1}\pi^{1/2}\Gamma(\nu+\frac{3}{2})\Gamma\left(\dfrac{\lambda+\nu}{2}+\mu+1\right)}$$

$$\times\, {}_2F_3\left(1, \frac{\lambda+\nu}{2}+1; \tfrac{3}{2}, \nu+\tfrac{3}{2}, \frac{\lambda+\nu}{2}+\mu+1; -\frac{z^2}{4}\right),$$

$$[\text{Re}\,\mu > 0, \text{Re}(\lambda+\nu) > -2]. \quad (3.77)$$

3.13 Infinite Integrals Connected with $H_\nu(z)$

The formula

$$\int_0^\infty e^{-az}H_\nu(bz)z^\mu\,dz = \frac{b^{\nu+1}\Gamma(\mu+\nu+2)}{2^\nu a^{\mu+\nu+2}\pi^{1/2}\Gamma(\nu+\frac{3}{2})}$$

$$\times\, {}_3F_2\left(1, \frac{\mu+\nu}{2}+1, \frac{\mu+\nu+3}{2}; \frac{3}{2}, \nu+\frac{3}{2}; -\frac{b^2}{a^2}\right),$$

$$[\text{Re}(a \pm ib) > 0, \text{Re}(\mu+\nu) > -2] \quad (3.78)$$

can be proved by expanding $H_\nu(bz)$ as a power series and integrating term by term.

Some special cases of (3.78) are of interest. If $\mu = 0$,

$$\int_0^\infty e^{-az}H_\nu(bz)dz = \frac{b^{\nu+1}\Gamma(\nu+2)}{2^\nu a^{\nu+2}\pi^{1/2}\Gamma(\nu+\frac{3}{2})}$$

$$\times\, {}_3F_2\left(1, \frac{\nu}{2}+1, \frac{\nu+3}{2}; \frac{3}{2}, \nu+\frac{3}{2}; -\frac{b^2}{a^2}\right),$$

$$[\mathrm{Re}(a \pm ib) > 0, \mathrm{Re}\,\nu > -2]; \quad (3.79)$$

if $\mu = -\nu$,

$$\int_0^\infty e^{-az}H_\nu(bz)z^{-\nu}\,dz = \frac{b^{\nu+1}}{2^\nu a^2\pi^{1/2}\Gamma(\nu+\frac{3}{2})}F\left(1, 1; \nu+\frac{3}{2}; -\frac{b^2}{a^2}\right)$$

$$= \frac{b^{\nu+1}}{2^\nu(a^2+b^2)\pi^{1/2}\Gamma(\nu+\frac{3}{2})}$$

$$\times F\left(1, \nu+\frac{1}{2}; \nu+\frac{3}{2}; \frac{b^2}{a^2+b^2}\right),$$

$$[\mathrm{Re}(a \pm ib) > 0]; \quad (3.80)$$

if $\mu = 1-\nu$,

$$\int_0^\infty e^{-az}H_\nu(bz)z^{1-\nu}\,dz = \frac{b^{\nu+1}}{2^{\nu-1}a^3\pi^{1/2}\Gamma(\nu+\frac{3}{2})}F\left(1, 2; \nu+\frac{3}{2}; -\frac{b^2}{a^2}\right)$$

$$= \frac{b^{\nu+1}}{2^{\nu-1}a(a^2+b^2)\pi^{1/2}\Gamma(\nu+\frac{3}{2})}$$

$$\times F\left(1, \nu-\frac{1}{2}; \nu+\frac{3}{2}; \frac{b^2}{a^2+b^2}\right),$$

$$[\mathrm{Re}(a \pm ib) > 0]; \quad (3.81)$$

if $\mu = \nu$,

$$\int_0^\infty e^{-az}H_\nu(bz)z^\nu\,dz = \frac{(2b)^{\nu+1}\Gamma(\nu+1)}{\pi a^{2\nu+2}}F\left(1, \nu+1; \frac{3}{2}; -\frac{b^2}{a^2}\right)$$

$$= \frac{(2b)^{\nu+1}\Gamma(\nu+1)}{\pi a^{2\nu}(a^2+b^2)}F\left(1, \frac{1}{2}-\nu; \frac{3}{2}; \frac{b^2}{a^2+b^2}\right),$$

$$[\mathrm{Re}(a \pm ib) > 0, \mathrm{Re}\,\nu > -1]; \quad (3.82)$$

and if $\mu = \nu+1$,

$$\int_0^\infty e^{-az}H_\nu(bz)z^{\nu+1}\,dz = 2\frac{(2b)^{\nu+1}\Gamma(\nu+2)}{\pi a^{2\nu+3}}F\left(1, \nu+2; \frac{3}{2}; -\frac{b^2}{a^2}\right)$$

$$= 2\frac{(2b)^{\nu+1}\Gamma(\nu+2)}{\pi a^{2\nu+1}(a^2+b^2)}F\left(1, -\frac{1}{2}-\nu; \frac{3}{2}; \frac{b^2}{a^2+b^2}\right),$$

$$[\operatorname{Re}(a \pm ib) > 0, \operatorname{Re}\nu > -2]. \quad (3.83)$$

The hypergeometric functions on the right sides of (3.80) to (3.83) can be expressed in terms of the incomplete beta function $B_x(p, q)$, since [see Problem 5, Chapter 1]

$$F(1, p+q; p+1; x) = px^{-p}(1-x)^{-q}B_x(p, q), \quad (3.84)$$

where

$$B_x(p, q) = \int_0^x t^{p-1}(1-t)^{q-1}\,dt. \quad (3.85)$$

The hypergeometric function in (3.84) can be evaluated in terms of elementary functions for certain values of the parameters p and q. Thus, on expanding both sides as power series in x, we see that

$$F(1, p+1; p+1; -x) = (1+x)^{-1}, \quad (3.86)$$

$$F(1, 1; 2; -x) = x^{-1}\log(1+x), \quad (3.87)$$

$$F(1, \tfrac{1}{2}; \tfrac{3}{2}; x^2) = \tfrac{1}{2}x^{-1}\log\frac{1+x}{1-x}$$

$$= x^{-1}\log\frac{1+x}{(1-x^2)^{1/2}}, \quad (3.88)$$

$$F(1, \tfrac{1}{2}; \tfrac{3}{2}; -x^2) = x^{-1}\tan^{-1}x. \quad (3.89)$$

From (3.80) and (3.88), with $\nu = 0$,

$$\int_0^\infty e^{-az}H_0(bz)\,dz = \frac{2}{\pi(a^2+b^2)^{1/2}}\log\left[\frac{b+(a^2+b^2)^{1/2}}{a}\right]. \quad (3.90)$$

From (3.80) and (3.86), with $\nu = -\frac{1}{2}$,

$$\int_0^\infty e^{-az}H_{-1/2}(bz)z^{1/2}\,dz = (2\pi b)^{1/2}(a^2+b^2)^{-1}. \quad (3.91)$$

From (3.80) and (3.87), with $\nu = \frac{1}{2}$,

$$\int_0^\infty e^{-az}H_{1/2}(bz)z^{-1/2}\,dz = (2\pi b)^{-1/2}\log\frac{a^2+b^2}{a^2}. \quad (3.92)$$

From (3.82) and (3.89), with $\nu = -\frac{1}{2}$,

$$\int_0^\infty e^{-az} H_{-(1/2)}(bz) z^{-(1/2)}\, dz = (\tfrac{1}{2}\pi b)^{-(1/2)} \tan^{-1}\left(\frac{b}{a}\right). \tag{3.93}$$

By using (3.90) to (3.93) together with the recurrence formulas for $H_\nu(z)$ given in §3.4, the integrals in (3.78) can be evaluated in terms of elementary functions for certain other values of μ and ν (see Erdélyi [*206*, 1954a]).

From Smith [1938], we find that

$$\lim_{z\to 0+} z^{-a_3}\, {}_3F_2\left(a_3, 1 - c_1 + a_3, 1 - c_2 + a_3; 1 - a_1 + a_3, 1 - a_2 + a_3; -\frac{1}{z}\right)$$

$$= \frac{\Gamma(1 - c_1)\Gamma(1 - c_2)\Gamma(1 - a_1 + a_3)\Gamma(1 - a_2 + a_3)}{\Gamma(1 - a_1)\Gamma(1 - a_2)\Gamma(1 - c_1 + a_3)\Gamma(1 - c_2 + a_3)}, \tag{3.94}$$

if no two of the a_i or c_i are equal or differ by an integer, and $\mathrm{Re}(1 - c_1) > 0$, $\mathrm{Re}(1 - c_2) > 0$.

On letting $a \to 0$ in (3.78), and using (3.94), we find

$$\int_0^\infty z^\mu H_\nu(bz)\, dz = \frac{\pi^{1/2}\Gamma(\mu + \nu + 2)\Gamma\left(-\dfrac{\mu + \nu}{2}\right)}{2^{\nu+1} b^{\mu+1} \Gamma\left(\dfrac{1 - \mu - \nu}{2}\right)\Gamma\left(\dfrac{1 - \mu + \nu}{2}\right)\Gamma\left(\dfrac{\mu + \nu + 3}{2}\right)}$$

$$= \frac{2^\mu \Gamma\left(\dfrac{\mu + \nu}{2} + 1\right)\Gamma\left(-\dfrac{\mu + \nu}{2}\right)}{b^{\mu+1}\Gamma\left(\dfrac{1 - \mu - \nu}{2}\right)\Gamma\left(\dfrac{1 - \mu + \nu}{2}\right)}$$

$$= \frac{2^\mu \Gamma\left(\dfrac{\mu + \nu + 1}{2}\right)}{b^{\mu+1}\Gamma\left(\dfrac{1 - \mu + \nu}{2}\right)} \tan \frac{\mu + \nu + 1}{2}\pi,$$

$$[b > 0, 0 > \mathrm{Re}(\mu + \nu) > -2, \tfrac{1}{2} > \mathrm{Re}\,\mu]. \tag{3.95}$$

Equation (3.95) is the Mellin inversion of (3.54).

This result can be written in the alternative forms

$$\int_0^\infty z^{\mu-\nu-1} H_\nu(bz)\, dz = \frac{2^{\mu-\nu-1}\Gamma(\frac{1}{2}\mu)\tan(\frac{1}{2}\mu\pi)}{b^{\mu-\nu}\Gamma(\nu - \frac{1}{2}\mu + 1)}$$

$$= \frac{2^{\mu-\nu-1}\pi \sec(\frac{1}{2}\mu\pi)}{b^{\mu-\nu}\Gamma(\nu - \frac{1}{2}\mu + 1)\Gamma(1 - \frac{1}{2}\mu)},$$

$$[b > 0, -1 < \mathrm{Re}\,\mu < 1, \mathrm{Re}(\nu + \tfrac{3}{2}) > \mathrm{Re}\,\mu]. \tag{3.96}$$

In particular, if $\mu = 0$, and $\mathrm{Re}(\nu + 1) > 0$,

$$\int_0^\infty z^{-\nu-1} H_\nu(bz)\, dz = \frac{\pi b^\nu}{2^{\nu+1}\Gamma(\nu+1)}. \tag{3.97}$$

The formula

$$\int_0^\infty e^{-a^2z^2} H_\nu(bz) z^{\mu-1}\, dz = \frac{b^{\nu+1}\Gamma\left(\dfrac{\mu+\nu+1}{2}\right)}{2^{\nu+1}\pi^{1/2}a^{\mu+\nu+1}\Gamma(\nu+\frac{3}{2})} \times {}_2F_2\left(1, \frac{\mu+\nu+1}{2}, \frac{3}{2}, \nu+\frac{3}{2}; -\frac{b^2}{4a^2}\right)$$

$$[|\arg a| < \tfrac{1}{4}\pi, \mathrm{Re}(\mu+\nu) > -1] \tag{3.98}$$

can be proved by expanding $H_\nu(bz)$ as a power series and integrating term by term. In particular, if $\mu = \nu + 2$,

$$\begin{aligned}\int_0^\infty e^{-a^2z^2} H_\nu(bz) z^{\nu+1}\, dz &= \frac{b^{\nu+1}}{2^{\nu+1}\pi^{1/2}a^{2\nu+3}}\, {}_1F_1\left(1; \frac{3}{2}; -\frac{b^2}{4a^2}\right)\\ &= \frac{b^{\nu+1}}{2^{\nu+1}\pi^{1/2}a^{2\nu+3}} \exp\left(-\frac{b^2}{4a^2}\right) {}_1F_1\left(\frac{1}{2}; \frac{3}{2}; \frac{b^2}{4a^2}\right)\\ &= \frac{b^\nu}{2^\nu\pi^{1/2}a^{2\nu+2}} \exp\left(-\frac{b^2}{4a^2}\right) \operatorname{erfi}\left(\frac{b}{2a}\right),\end{aligned} \tag{3.99}$$

where erfi x is given by

$$\operatorname{erfi} x = \int_0^x e^{t^2}\, dt.$$

Other infinite integrals involving the product of two Struve functions, or the product of a Struve function and a Bessel function, are given by Watson [*398*, 1944] and Erdélyi [*72*, 1954b].

3.14 Modified Struve Function $L_\nu(z)$

The modified Struve function $L_\nu(z)$ is defined by the equation

$$L_\nu(z) = -ie^{-(1/2)\nu\pi i} H_\nu(ze^{(1/2)\pi i}). \tag{3.100}$$

The properties of this function can be obtained immediately from those given above for $H_\nu(z)$.

Thus, from (3.31), if Re $\nu > -\frac{1}{2}$,

$$L_\nu(z) = \frac{2\pi^{-1/2}(\frac{1}{2}z)^\nu}{\Gamma(\nu+\frac{1}{2})}\int_0^1 (1-t^2)^{\nu-(1/2)}\sinh zt\, dt$$

$$= \frac{2\pi^{-1/2}(\frac{1}{2}z)^\nu}{\Gamma(\nu+\frac{1}{2})}\int_0^{(1/2)\pi} \sinh(z\cos\theta)\sin^{2\nu}\theta\, d\theta. \qquad (3.101)$$

More generally, from (3.30), using (3.10) and (3.100), we see that

$$I_\nu(z) - L_\nu(z) = \frac{\pi^{-(1/2)}\Gamma(\frac{1}{2}-\nu)(\frac{1}{2}z)^\nu}{\pi i}\int_0^{(1+)} e^{-zt}(t^2-1)^{\nu-(1/2)}\, dt$$

$$= -\frac{\pi^{-(1/2)}\Gamma(\frac{1}{2}-\nu)(\frac{1}{2}z)^\nu}{\pi i}\int_0^{(-1+)} e^{zt}(t^2-1)^{\nu-(1/2)}\, dt, \qquad (3.102)$$

in which $\arg(t-1) = -\pi$ and $\arg(t+1) = 0$ at the start of the contours.

These two contours can be deformed into lines parallel to the imaginary axis in a similar way to that shown in Figure 3.3. Now, from Watson [*167*, 1944], if $z > 0$,

$$K_\nu(z) = \tfrac{1}{2}i\pi e^{(1/2)\nu\pi i}H_\nu^{(1)}(ze^{(1/2)\pi i})$$

$$= \tfrac{1}{2}\pi^{-(1/2)}e^{\nu\pi i}\Gamma(\tfrac{1}{2}-\nu)(\tfrac{1}{2}z)^\nu \int_{\infty i}^{(1+)} e^{-zt}(t^2-1)^{\nu-(1/2)}\, dt, \qquad (3.103)$$

in which $\arg(t-1) = -\frac{3}{2}\pi$ and $\arg(t+1) = \frac{1}{2}\pi$ at the start of the contour. Again, if $z > 0$ and Re $\nu < \frac{1}{2}$,

$$K_\nu(z) = -\tfrac{1}{2}i\pi e^{-(1/2)\nu\pi i}H_\nu^{(2)}(ze^{-(1/2)\pi i})$$

$$= -\tfrac{1}{2}\pi^{-(1/2)}e^{-\nu\pi i}\Gamma(\tfrac{1}{2}-\nu)(\tfrac{1}{2}z)^\nu \int_{\infty i}^{(-1-)} e^{zt}(t^2-1)^{\nu-(1/2)}\, dt, \qquad (3.104)$$

in which $\arg(t-1) = \frac{1}{2}\pi$ and $\arg(t+1) = \frac{1}{2}\pi$ at the start of the contour. From (3.102) to (3.104), remembering that

$$K_\nu(z) = \tfrac{1}{2}\pi[\sin\nu\pi]^{-1}\,[I_{-\nu}(z) - I_\nu(z)],$$

we find that

$$L_\nu(z) = I_{-\nu}(z) - \frac{2\pi^{-(1/2)}(\frac{1}{2}z)^\nu}{\Gamma(\nu+\frac{1}{2})}\int_0^\infty (1+u^2)^{\nu-(1/2)}\sin(zu)\, du$$

$$(z > 0, \text{Re } \nu < \tfrac{1}{2}). \qquad (3.105)$$

Using (3.105), we can obtain recurrence formulas for $L_\nu(z)$. We find that

$$\frac{d}{dz}[z^\nu L_\nu(z)] = z^\nu L_{\nu-1}(z),$$

that is, (3.106)

$$(\delta + \nu)L_\nu(z) = zL_{\nu-1}(z),$$

where $\delta \equiv z d/dz$.

$$\frac{d}{dz}[z^{-\nu}L_\nu(z)] = \frac{2^{-\nu}\pi^{-(1/2)}}{\Gamma(\nu+\frac{3}{2})} + z^{-\nu}L_{\nu+1}(z);$$

that is, (3.107)

$$(\delta - \nu)L_\nu(z) = \frac{2\pi^{-(1/2)}(\frac{1}{2}z)^{\nu+1}}{\Gamma(\nu+\frac{3}{2})} + zL_{\nu+1}(z),$$

$$L_{\nu-1}(z) - L_{\nu+1}(z) = 2\nu z^{-1}L_\nu(z) + \frac{\pi^{-(1/2)}(\frac{1}{2}z)^\nu}{\Gamma(\nu+\frac{3}{2})}, \tag{3.108}$$

$$L_{\nu-1}(z) + L_{\nu+1}(z) = 2\frac{dL_\nu(z)}{dz} - \frac{\pi^{-(1/2)}(\frac{1}{2}z)^\nu}{\Gamma(\nu+\frac{3}{2})}. \tag{3.109}$$

From (3.106) and (3.107),

$$\begin{aligned}(\delta - \nu)(\delta + \nu)L_\nu(z) &= (\delta - \nu)[zL_{\nu-1}(z)] \\ &= z(\delta - \nu + 1)L_{\nu-1}(z) \\ &= \frac{4\pi^{-(1/2)}(\frac{1}{2}z)^{\nu+1}}{\Gamma(\nu+\frac{1}{2})} + z^2L_\nu(z).\end{aligned}$$

Thus $L_\nu(z)$ is a particular integral of the nonhomogeneous linear equation

$$(\delta^2 - z^2 - \nu^2)y = \frac{4\pi^{-(1/2)}(\frac{1}{2}z)^{\nu+1}}{\Gamma(\nu+\frac{1}{2})},$$

that is, (3.110)

$$\frac{d^2y}{dz^2} + \frac{1}{z}\frac{dy}{dz} - \left(1 + \frac{\nu^2}{z^2}\right)y = \frac{\pi^{-(1/2)}(\frac{1}{2}z)^{\nu-1}}{\Gamma(\nu+\frac{1}{2})}.$$

The associated homogeneous equation (3.9) has the solutions $I_\nu(z)$ and $I_{-\nu}(z)$.

From (3.51) and (3.100), we see that the power series for $L_\nu(z)$ is

$$L_\nu(z) = \sum_{m=0}^{\infty} \frac{(\frac{1}{2}z)^{\nu+2m+1}}{[\Gamma(m+\frac{3}{2})\Gamma(\nu+m+\frac{3}{2})]}. \tag{3.111}$$

This series is convergent for all values of z. We see that if z is positive and $\nu + \frac{3}{2} > 0$, all the terms in (3.111) have the same sign; thus $L_\nu(z)$ is positive for all positive z if $\nu > -\frac{3}{2}$. Now $z^{-\nu-1}L_\nu(z)$ is an even function of z, and is thus positive for all real z if $\nu > -\frac{3}{2}$.

From (3.111) we see that the modified Struve function $L_\nu(z)$ can be expressed in terms of a generalized hypergeometric series, in the form

$$L_\nu(z) = \frac{2\pi^{-(1/2)}(\frac{1}{2}z)^{\nu+1}\ {}_1F_2(1; \frac{3}{2}+\nu, \frac{3}{2}; \frac{1}{4}z^2)}{\Gamma(\nu+\frac{3}{2})}. \tag{3.112}$$

If $\nu + \frac{1}{2}$ is zero or a negative integer, the right side of (3.110) vanishes identically. From (3.105) we see that

$$L_{-n-(1/2)}(z) = I_{n+(1/2)}(z) \qquad (n = 0, 1, 2, 3, \cdots). \tag{3.113}$$

Now

$$L_{-(1/2)}(z) = I_{1/2}(z) = \left(\frac{2}{\pi z}\right)^{1/2} \sinh z. \tag{3.114}$$

By repeated differentiation of (3.114) we find that $L_{-n-(1/2)}(z)$ can be expressed in terms of hyperbolic functions (together with a terminating series in $1/z$).

3.15 Integrals Connected with $L_\nu(z)$

As in §3.11, a number of indefinite integrals connected with $L_\nu(z)$ can be obtained from the recurrence formulas given in §3.14. Other integrals can be obtained by solving the differential equation (3.110) by the method of variation of parameters. The Wronskian of $I_\nu(z)$ and $I_{-\nu}(z)$ is given by (3.11). We find that

$$L_\nu(z) = \frac{2^{-\nu}\pi^{1/2}}{\Gamma(\nu+\frac{1}{2})\sin\nu\pi}\left[I_\nu(z)\int z^\nu I_{-\nu}(z)dz - I_{-\nu}(z)\int z_\nu I_\nu(z)dz\right]. \tag{3.115}$$

In a similar manner to that given in §3.11, we can show that

$$\begin{aligned}\int z^\nu I_\nu(z)\,dz &= 2^{\nu-1}\pi^{1/2}\Gamma(\nu+\tfrac{1}{2})z[I_\nu(z)L_\nu'(z) - L_\nu(z)I_\nu'(z)] \\ &= 2^{\nu-1}\pi^{1/2}\Gamma(\nu+\tfrac{1}{2})z[I_\nu(z)L_{\nu-1}(z) - L_\nu(z)I_{\nu-1}(z)]\end{aligned} \tag{3.116}$$

and

$$\begin{aligned}\int z^{\nu} I_{-\nu}(z)\,dz &= 2^{\nu-1}\pi^{1/2}\Gamma(\nu+\tfrac{1}{2})z[I_{-\nu}(z)L_{\nu}'(z) - L_{\nu}(z)I_{-\nu}'(z)] \\ &= 2^{\nu-1}\pi^{1/2}\Gamma(\nu+\tfrac{1}{2})z[I_{-\nu}(z)L_{\nu-1}(z) - L_{\nu}(z)I_{1-\nu}(z)].\end{aligned} \qquad (3.117)$$

Subtracting the last two results, and using (3.13), we obtain

$$\int z^{\nu} K_{\nu}(z)\,dz = 2^{\nu-1}\pi^{1/2}\Gamma(\nu+\tfrac{1}{2})z[K_{\nu}L_{\nu-1}(z) + L_{\nu}(z)K_{\nu-1}(z)]. \qquad (3.118)$$

Similarly, from (3.78), using (3.100), we obtain

$$\begin{aligned}\int_0^{\infty} e^{-az} L_{\nu}(bz) z^{\mu}\,dz &= \frac{b^{\nu+1}\Gamma(\mu+\nu+2)}{2^{\nu}a^{\mu+\nu+2}\pi^{1/2}\Gamma(\nu+\frac{3}{2})} \\ &\quad\times {}_3F_2\left(1, \frac{\mu+\nu}{2}+1, \frac{\mu+\nu+3}{2}; \frac{3}{2}, \nu+\frac{3}{2}; \frac{b^2}{a^2}\right), \\ &\qquad [\operatorname{Re} a > |\operatorname{Re} b|, \operatorname{Re}(\mu+\nu) > -2]. \end{aligned} \qquad (3.119)$$

Putting $\mu = -\nu$, we see that

$$\begin{aligned}\int_0^{\infty} e^{-az} L_{\nu}(bz) z^{-\nu}\,dz &= \frac{b^{\nu+1}}{2^{\nu}a^{2}\pi^{1/2}\Gamma(\nu+\frac{3}{2})} F\left(1, 1; \nu+\frac{3}{2}; \frac{b^2}{a^2}\right) \\ &= \frac{b^{\nu+1}(a^2-b^2)^{\nu-(1/2)}}{2^{\nu}a^{2\nu+1}\pi^{1/2}\Gamma(\nu+\frac{3}{2})} F\left(\nu+\frac{1}{2}, \nu+\frac{1}{2}; \nu+\frac{3}{2}; \frac{b^2}{a^2}\right), \\ &\qquad (\operatorname{Re} a > |\operatorname{Re} b|). \end{aligned} \qquad (3.120)$$

Thus, if $\nu = 0$,

$$\int_0^{\infty} e^{-az} L_0(bz)dz = \frac{2}{\pi}(a^2-b^2)^{-(1/2)} \sin^{-1}\left(\frac{b}{a}\right) \qquad (\operatorname{Re} a > |\operatorname{Re} b|), \qquad (3.121)$$

since $F(\frac{1}{2}, \frac{1}{2}; \frac{3}{2}; x^2) = x^{-1}\sin^{-1}x$.

Other special cases of (3.119) are given by Erdélyi [*207*, 1954a].

3.16 Lommel Functions

We consider next the solutions of the nonhomogeneous Bessel equation

$$\frac{d^2y}{dz^2} + \frac{1}{z}\frac{dy}{dz} + \left(1 - \frac{\nu^2}{z^2}\right)y = z^{\mu-1}, \qquad (3.122)$$

where μ and ν are constants. As stated above, the associated homogeneous equation has one regular singular point at $z = 0$ and an irregular singular point at infinity.

Using the method of Frobenius (§1.12), we see that a particular integral of (3.122) is

$$s_{\mu,\nu}(z) = z^{\mu+1} \sum_{m=0}^{\infty} \frac{(-1)^m z^{2m}}{[(\mu+1)^2 - \nu^2][(\mu+3)^2 - \nu^2] \cdots [(\mu+2m+1)^2 - \nu^2]}$$

$$= \tfrac{1}{4} z^{\mu+1} \sum_{m=0}^{\infty} \frac{(-1)^m (\tfrac{1}{2}z)^{2m} \Gamma(\tfrac{1}{2}\mu - \tfrac{1}{2}\nu + \tfrac{1}{2}) \Gamma(\tfrac{1}{2}\mu + \tfrac{1}{2}\nu + \tfrac{1}{2})}{\Gamma(\tfrac{1}{2}\mu - \tfrac{1}{2}\nu + m + \tfrac{3}{2}) \Gamma(\tfrac{1}{2}\mu + \tfrac{1}{2}\nu + m + \tfrac{3}{2})}$$

$$= \frac{z^{\mu+1}}{(\mu - \nu + 1)(\mu + \nu + 1)} \, {}_1F_2\left(1; \frac{1}{2}\mu - \frac{1}{2}\nu + \frac{3}{2}, \frac{1}{2}\mu + \frac{1}{2}\nu + \frac{3}{2}; -\frac{z^2}{4}\right). \tag{3.123}$$

This series is convergent for all values of z.

The complete primitive of (3.122) is then

$$y = C_1 J_\nu(z) + C_2 Y_\nu(z) + s_{\mu,\nu}(z), \tag{3.124}$$

where C_1 and C_2 are arbitrary constants.

The series solution in the form (3.123) is not valid if $\mu \pm \nu$ is an odd negative integer (since, in that case, all the coefficients in the series after a certain value of m become infinite). As shown in §1.12, for these values of μ, the particular solution of (3.123) will, in general, contain logarithmic terms.

Another particular integral of (3.123) is $S_{\mu,\nu}(z)$, defined by the equation

$$S_{\mu,\nu}(z) = s_{\mu,\nu}(z) + \frac{2^{\mu-1}\Gamma(\tfrac{1}{2}\mu - \tfrac{1}{2}\nu + \tfrac{1}{2})\Gamma(\tfrac{1}{2}\mu + \tfrac{1}{2}\nu + \tfrac{1}{2})}{\sin \nu\pi}$$
$$\times \left[\cos \frac{\mu - \nu}{2}\pi \cdot J_{-\nu}(z) - \cos \frac{\mu + \nu}{2}\pi \cdot J_\nu(z)\right]$$
$$= s_{\mu,\nu}(z) + 2^{\mu-1}\Gamma(\tfrac{1}{2}\mu - \tfrac{1}{2}\nu + \tfrac{1}{2})\Gamma(\tfrac{1}{2}\mu + \tfrac{1}{2}\nu + \tfrac{1}{2})$$
$$\times \left[\sin \frac{\mu - \nu}{2}\pi \cdot J_\nu(z) - \cos \frac{\mu - \nu}{2}\pi \cdot Y_\nu(z)\right]. \tag{3.125}$$

From (3.123) and (3.125), we see that

$$s_{\mu,-\nu}(z) = s_{\mu,\nu}(z)$$

and (3.126)

$$S_{\mu,-\nu}(z) = S_{\mu,\nu}(z).$$

Comparing (3.52) and (3.123), we see that

$$s_{\nu,\nu}(z) = 2^{\nu-1}\pi^{1/2}\Gamma(\nu+\tfrac{1}{2})H_\nu(z), \tag{3.127}$$

and, from (3.125) and (3.127),

$$S_{\nu,\nu}(z) = 2^{\nu-1}\pi^{1/2}\Gamma(\nu+\tfrac{1}{2})[H_\nu(z) - Y_\nu(z)]. \tag{3.128}$$

Consider now the solution of (3.122) expressed as a series of descending powers of z (see §1.13). Such a particular integral is

$$\begin{aligned} y &= z^{\mu-1}\left[1 - \frac{(\mu-1)^2-\nu^2}{z^2} + \frac{\{(\mu-1)^2-\nu^2\}\{(\mu-3)^2-\nu^2\}}{z^4} - \cdots\right] \\ &= z^{\mu-1}\sum_{m=0}^{\infty}(-1)^m\frac{\Gamma(\frac{1}{2}-\frac{1}{2}\mu+\frac{1}{2}\nu+m)\Gamma(\frac{1}{2}-\frac{1}{2}\mu-\frac{1}{2}\nu+m)}{\Gamma(\frac{1}{2}-\frac{1}{2}\mu+\frac{1}{2}\nu)\Gamma(\frac{1}{2}-\frac{1}{2}\mu-\frac{1}{2}\nu)}\left(\frac{2}{z}\right)^{2m}. \end{aligned} \tag{3.129}$$

If $\mu \pm \nu$ is an odd positive integer, i.e., if $\mu \pm \nu = 2m+1$, the series terminates after $m+1$ terms. The series can then be written as a series of ascending powers of z, starting with $z^{\mu-2m-1}$. On equating coefficients of powers of z we find that

$$S_{\mu,\nu}(z) = z^{\mu-1}\left[1 - \frac{(\mu-1)^2-\nu^2}{z^2} + \frac{\{(\mu-1)^2-\nu^2\}\{(\mu-3)^2-\nu^2\}}{z^4} - \cdots\right], \tag{3.130}$$

if $\mu \pm \nu$ is an odd positive integer.

In particular, we see that

$$S_{\nu+1,\nu}(z) = z^\nu. \tag{3.131}$$

If $\mu \pm \nu$ is not an odd integer, the series (3.129) does not terminate and is divergent; as shown in §3.17, the series is an asymptotic expansion of $S_{\mu,\nu}(z)$ when $|z|$ is large and $|\arg z| < \pi$.

3.17 Mellin-Barnes Integrals for the Lommel Functions

In a precisely similar manner to that of §3.7, it can be shown that, if $\pi > \arg z > 0$ and $\mu + 1 \pm \nu > 0$,

$$s_{\mu,\nu}(z) = \frac{1}{4}\Gamma\left(\frac{\mu}{2}+\frac{\nu}{2}+\frac{1}{2}\right)\Gamma\left(\frac{\mu}{2}-\frac{\nu}{2}+\frac{1}{2}\right)z^{\mu+1}I_1 \tag{3.132}$$

where

$$I_1 = \frac{1}{2\pi i}\int_{-\infty i}^{\infty i} \frac{\Gamma(1+s)\Gamma(-s)}{\Gamma\left(\frac{\mu}{2}+\frac{\nu}{2}+\frac{3}{2}+s\right)\Gamma\left(\frac{\mu}{2}-\frac{\nu}{2}+\frac{3}{2}+s\right)}(\tfrac{1}{2}z)^{2s}\,ds$$

$$= -\frac{1}{2\pi i}\int_{-\infty i}^{\infty i} \frac{\pi}{\Gamma\left(\frac{\mu}{2}+\frac{\nu}{2}+\frac{3}{2}+s\right)\Gamma\left(\frac{\mu}{2}-\frac{\nu}{2}+\frac{3}{2}+s\right)}\frac{(\frac{1}{2}z)^{2s}}{\sin \pi s}\,ds, \quad (3.133)$$

the contour being indented to pass to the left of the origin.

Consider next the contour integral

$$I = \frac{z^{\mu-1}}{2\pi i}\int_C \frac{\Gamma(\frac{1}{2}-\frac{1}{2}\mu+\frac{1}{2}\nu-s)\Gamma(\frac{1}{2}-\frac{1}{2}\mu-\frac{1}{2}\nu-s)}{\Gamma(\frac{1}{2}-\frac{1}{2}\mu+\frac{1}{2}\nu)\Gamma(\frac{1}{2}-\frac{1}{2}\mu-\frac{1}{2}\nu)}\frac{\pi(\frac{1}{2}z)^{2s}}{\sin \pi s}\,ds, \quad (3.134)$$

where $|\arg z| < \pi$, taken round a contour consisting of the line $s = -p + \frac{1}{2}$ together with a semicircle lying to the right of this line of large radius $N + \frac{1}{2}$ with center at the point $(-p - \frac{1}{2})$, where N and p are integers, p being chosen so that $(p - \frac{1}{2}\mu \pm \frac{1}{2}\nu)$ is positive.

As in §3.7, it can be shown that the contribution to the integral arising from the semicircle tends to zero as $N \to \infty$. Now the integrand has poles at the points

$$-(p-1), \quad -(p-2), \cdots, -2, -1, 0, 1, 2, \cdots$$

$$\tfrac{1}{2}-\tfrac{1}{2}\mu \pm \tfrac{1}{2}\nu, \quad \tfrac{3}{2}-\tfrac{1}{2}\mu \pm \tfrac{1}{2}\nu, \quad \tfrac{5}{2}-\tfrac{1}{2}\mu \pm \tfrac{1}{2}\nu, \cdots.$$

As shown by Watson [352, 1944], on evaluating the residues at these poles we find that

$$I = z^{\mu-1}\sum_{m=0}^{p-1}\frac{(-1)^m\Gamma(\frac{1}{2}-\frac{1}{2}\mu+\frac{1}{2}\nu+m)\Gamma(\frac{1}{2}-\frac{1}{2}\mu-\frac{1}{2}\nu+m)}{\Gamma(\frac{1}{2}-\frac{1}{2}\mu+\frac{1}{2}\nu)\Gamma(\frac{1}{2}-\frac{1}{2}\mu-\frac{1}{2}\nu)}\left(\frac{2}{z}\right)^{2m}$$

$$- s_{\mu,\nu}(z) - \frac{2^{\mu-1}\Gamma(\frac{1}{2}+\frac{1}{2}\mu-\frac{1}{2}\nu)\Gamma(\frac{1}{2}+\frac{1}{2}\mu+\frac{1}{2}\nu)}{\sin \nu\pi}$$

$$\times\left[\cos\frac{\mu-\nu}{2}\pi\cdot J_{-\nu}(z) - \cos\frac{\mu+\nu}{2}\pi\cdot J_\nu(z)\right]$$

$$= z^{\mu-1}\sum_{m=0}^{p-1}\frac{(-1)^m\Gamma(\frac{1}{2}-\frac{1}{2}\mu+\frac{1}{2}\nu+m)\Gamma(\frac{1}{2}-\frac{1}{2}\mu-\frac{1}{2}\nu+m)}{\Gamma(\frac{1}{2}-\frac{1}{2}\mu+\frac{1}{2}\nu)\Gamma(\frac{1}{2}-\frac{1}{2}\mu-\frac{1}{2}\nu)}\left(\frac{2}{z}\right)^{2m} - S_{\mu,\nu}(z).$$

Thus

$$S_{\mu,\nu}(z) = z^{\mu-1}\sum_{m=0}^{p-1}\frac{(-1)^m\Gamma(\frac{1}{2}-\frac{1}{2}\mu+\frac{1}{2}\nu+m)\Gamma(\frac{1}{2}-\frac{1}{2}\mu-\frac{1}{2}\nu+m)}{\Gamma(\frac{1}{2}-\frac{1}{2}\mu+\frac{1}{2}\nu)\Gamma(\frac{1}{2}-\frac{1}{2}\mu-\frac{1}{2}\nu)}\left(\frac{2}{z}\right)^{2m} + I_2,$$

(3.135)

where

$$I_2 = \frac{z^{\mu-1}}{2\pi i}\int_{-\infty i-p+(1/2)}^{\infty i-p+(1/2)} \frac{\Gamma(\frac{1}{2}-\frac{1}{2}\mu+\frac{1}{2}\nu-s)\Gamma(\frac{1}{2}-\frac{1}{2}\mu-\frac{1}{2}\nu-s)}{\Gamma(\frac{1}{2}-\frac{1}{2}\mu+\frac{1}{2}\nu)\Gamma(\frac{1}{2}-\frac{1}{2}\mu-\frac{1}{2}\nu)}\frac{\pi(\frac{1}{2}z)^{2s}}{\sin \pi s}\,ds. \tag{3.136}$$

Again, consider the integral (3.134) taken around a contour C' consisting of the line $s = -p + \frac{1}{2}$ together with a semicircle lying to the left of this line of large radius $N + \frac{1}{2}$ with center at the point $(-p - \frac{1}{2})$, where N and p are integers, p being chosen so that $(p - \frac{1}{2}\mu \pm \frac{1}{2}\nu)$ is positive.

The only poles within this contour are the poles of csc $s\pi$. The integral is convergent when $|\arg z| < \pi$, and we see that it is $0(z^{\mu-2p})$. Thus

$$I_2 = 0(z^{\mu-2p}) \tag{3.137}$$

and we see that the series (3.130) or (3.135) is the asymptotic expansion for $S_{\mu,\nu}(z)$ when $|z|$ is large and $|\arg z| < \pi$. Equation (3.135) can be written in the alternative form

$$S_{\mu,\nu}(z) \sim z^{\mu-1}\,{}_3F_0\left(1, \frac{1-\mu+\nu}{2}, \frac{1-\mu-\nu}{2}; -\frac{4}{z^2}\right). \tag{3.138}$$

Alternatively, we see that if $|\arg z| < \pi$ and $1 - \mu \pm \nu > 0$, then

$$\begin{aligned} S_{\mu,\nu}(z) &= \frac{z^{\mu-1}}{2\pi i}\int_{-\infty i}^{\infty i} \frac{\Gamma(\frac{1}{2}-\frac{1}{2}\mu+\frac{1}{2}\nu-s)\Gamma(\frac{1}{2}-\frac{1}{2}\mu-\frac{1}{2}\nu-s)}{\Gamma(\frac{1}{2}-\frac{1}{2}\mu+\frac{1}{2}\nu)\Gamma(\frac{1}{2}-\frac{1}{2}\mu-\frac{1}{2}\nu)}\frac{\pi(\frac{1}{2}z)^{2s}}{\sin \pi s}\,ds \\ &= \frac{z^{\mu-1}}{2\pi i}\int_{-\infty i}^{\infty i} \frac{\Gamma(s)\Gamma(1-s)\Gamma(\frac{1}{2}-\frac{1}{2}\mu+\frac{1}{2}\nu-s)\Gamma(\frac{1}{2}-\frac{1}{2}\mu-\frac{1}{2}\nu-s)}{\Gamma(\frac{1}{2}-\frac{1}{2}\mu+\frac{1}{2}\nu)\Gamma(\frac{1}{2}-\frac{1}{2}\mu-\frac{1}{2}\nu)}(\tfrac{1}{2}z)^{2s}\,ds \end{aligned} \tag{3.139}$$

the contour being indented slightly to pass to the left of the origin. On replacing s by $s + \frac{1}{2} - \frac{1}{2}\mu$, we see that

$$\begin{aligned} S_{\mu,\nu}(z) &= \frac{2^{\mu-1}}{2\pi i}\int_{-\infty i+(1/2)\mu-(1/2)}^{\infty i+(1/2)\mu-(1/2)} \frac{\Gamma(\frac{1}{2}-\frac{1}{2}\mu+s)\Gamma(\frac{1}{2}+\frac{1}{2}\mu-s)\Gamma(\frac{1}{2}\nu-s)\Gamma(-\frac{1}{2}\nu-s)}{\Gamma(\frac{1}{2}-\frac{1}{2}\mu+\frac{1}{2}\nu)\Gamma(\frac{1}{2}-\frac{1}{2}\mu-\frac{1}{2}\nu)} \\ &\qquad \times (\tfrac{1}{2}z)^{2s}\,ds. \end{aligned} \tag{3.140}$$

3.18 Recurrence Formulas for the Lommel Functions

From the series (3.123) we see that

$$s_{\mu+2,\nu}(z) = z^{\mu+1} - [(\mu+1)^2 - \nu^2]s_{\mu,\nu}(z). \tag{3.141}$$

On differentiating (3.123) we find that

$$\frac{d}{dz}[z^\nu s_{\mu,\nu}(z)] = (\mu + \nu - 1)z^\nu s_{\mu-1,\nu-1}(z);$$

that is, (3.142)

$$(\delta + \nu)s_{\mu,\nu}(z) = (\mu + \nu - 1)zs_{\mu-1,\nu-1}(z),$$

where $\delta \equiv zd/dz$. Similarly, we find that

$$\frac{d}{dz}[z^{-\nu} s_{\mu,\nu}(z)] = (\mu - \nu - 1)z^{-\nu} s_{\mu-1,\nu+1}(z);$$

that is, (3.143)

$$(\delta - \nu)s_{\mu,\nu}(z) = (\mu - \nu - 1)zs_{\mu-1,\nu+1}(z).$$

Subtracting and adding (3.142) and (3.143) we see that

$$\frac{2\nu}{z} s_{\mu,\nu}(z) = (\mu + \nu - 1)s_{\mu-1,\nu-1}(z) - (\mu - \nu - 1)s_{\mu-1,\nu+1}(z) \quad (3.144)$$

and

$$2\frac{d}{dz} s_{\mu,\nu}(z) = (\mu + \nu - 1)s_{\mu-1,\nu-1}(z) + (\mu - \nu - 1)s_{\mu-1,\nu+1}(z). \quad (3.145)$$

From (3.125), on using the recurrence relations for $J_\nu(z)$ and $Y_\nu(z)$, we find that the relations (3.141) to (3.145) hold if the function s is replaced throughout by S.

3.19 Particular Values of $S_{\mu,\nu}(z)$

Consider now the value of $S_{\mu,\nu}(z)$ when $\mu \pm \nu$ is an odd negative integer; as shown in §3.16, the series solution for $s_{\mu,\nu}(z)$ is then no longer valid. We shall now show that $S_{\mu,\nu}(z)$ has a finite limit when $\mu \pm \nu$ is an odd negative integer. We follow the method given by Watson [*349*, 1944].

We shall determine first the value of $S_{\nu-1,\nu}(z)$, $\nu \neq 0$. From (3.141), replacing s by S, we see that

$$S_{\nu-1,\nu}(z) = \lim_{\mu\to\nu-1} \frac{z^{\mu+1} - S_{\mu+2,\nu}(z)}{(\mu+1)^2 - \nu^2}. \quad (3.146)$$

Now, from (3.141), both numerator and denominator vanish when $\mu = \nu - 1$. From L'Hospital's rule,

$$S_{\nu-1,\nu}(z) = \frac{1}{2\nu}\left[z^\nu \log z - \frac{\partial S_{\mu+2,\nu}(z)}{\partial \mu}\right]_{\mu=\nu-1}. \quad (3.147)$$

From (3.125), together with the power series for $s_{\mu+2,\nu}(z)$, it can be shown (see Watson [*349*, 1944]) that (3.147) reduces to

$$\begin{aligned}
S_{\nu-1,\nu}(z) &\\
&= \tfrac{1}{4}\Gamma(\nu)z^{\nu}\sum_{m=0}^{\infty}\frac{(-1)^m(\frac{1}{2}z)^{2m}}{m!\Gamma(\nu+m+1)}\\
&\quad\times\{2\log\tfrac{1}{2}z-\psi(\nu+m+1)-\psi(m+1)\}-2^{\nu-2}\pi\Gamma(\nu)Y_\nu(z)\\
&= \tfrac{1}{2}\Gamma(\nu)J_\nu(z)\log z-2^{\nu-2}\pi\Gamma(\nu)Y_\nu(z)\\
&\quad-\tfrac{1}{4}z^{\nu}\Gamma(\nu)\sum_{m=0}^{\infty}\frac{(-1)^m(\frac{1}{2}z)^{2m}}{m!\Gamma(\nu+m+1)}[2\log 2+\psi(\nu+m+1)+\psi(m+1)]\,,
\end{aligned}\tag{3.148}$$

where ψ is the logarithmic derivative of the gamma function.

Now, by analogy with (3.126), we define

$$\begin{aligned}
S_{-\nu-1,\nu}(z) = S_{-\nu-1,-\nu}(z)&\\
&= \tfrac{1}{2}\Gamma(-\nu)J_{-\nu}(z)\log z-2^{-\nu-2}\pi\Gamma(-\nu)Y_{-\nu}(z)\\
&\quad-\tfrac{1}{4}\Gamma(-\nu)z^{-\nu}\sum_{m=0}^{\infty}\frac{(-1)^m(\frac{1}{2}z)^{2m}}{m!\Gamma(-\nu+m+1)}\\
&\quad\times[2\log 2+\psi(-\nu+m+1)+\psi(m+1)]\,.
\end{aligned}\tag{3.149}$$

$S_{\nu-2p-1,\nu}(z)$ and $S_{-\nu-2p-1,\nu}(z)$, where p is a positive integer, can be found from (3.148) and (3.149) by repeated use of the recurrence formula (3.141) with s replaced by S. We note that, if ν is a positive integer, (3.149) is nugatory; however, the required solution can be found by using (3.148). Similarly, if ν is a negative integer, (3.148) is nugatory, the required solution being found from (3.149).

We consider finally the case $\nu=0$. From (3.146),

$$S_{-1,0}(z)=\frac{1}{2}\left[\frac{\partial^2}{\partial\mu^2}\{z^{\mu+1}-S_{\mu+2,0}(z)\}\right]_{\mu=-1}\,. \tag{3.150}$$

As shown by Watson [*349*, 1944], (3.150) reduces to

$$\begin{aligned}
S_{-1,0}(z) &= \frac{1}{2}\sum_{m=0}^{\infty}\frac{(-1)^m(\frac{1}{2}z)^{2m}}{(m!)^2}[\{\log(\tfrac{1}{2}z)-\psi(m+1)\}^2-\tfrac{1}{2}\psi'(m+1)+\tfrac{1}{4}\pi^2]\\
&= \tfrac{1}{2}J_0(z)(\log z)^2-\log z\left[J_0(z)\log 2+\sum_{m=0}^{\infty}\frac{(-1)^m(\frac{1}{2}z)^{2m}}{(m!)^2}\psi(m+1)\right]\\
&\quad+\frac{1}{2}\sum_{m=0}^{\infty}\frac{(-1)^m(\frac{1}{2}z)^{2m}}{(m!)^2}[\{\log 2+\psi(m+1)\}^2-\tfrac{1}{2}\psi'(m+1)+\tfrac{1}{4}\pi^2]\,.
\end{aligned}\tag{3.151}$$

As above, $S_{-2p-1,0}(z)$, where p is a positive integer, can be found from (3.151) by repeated use of the recurrence formula.

3.20 Integrals Connected with the Lommel Functions

As in §3.11, a number of indefinite integrals connected with $s_{\mu,\nu}(z)$ and $S_{\mu,\nu}(z)$ can be obtained from the recurrence formulas given in §3.18. Other integrals can be obtained by solving the differential equation (3.122) by the method of variation of parameters. We find that

$$s_{\mu,\nu}(z) = \frac{\pi}{2\sin\nu\pi}\left[J_\nu(z)\int z^\mu J_{-\nu}(z)\,dz - J_{-\nu}(z)\int z^\mu J_\nu(z)\,dz\right]$$
$$= \tfrac{1}{2}\pi\left[Y_\nu(z)\int z^\mu J_\nu(z)\,dz - J_\nu(z)\int z^\mu Y_\nu(z)\,dz\right]. \tag{3.152}$$

In a similar manner to that of §3.11, we can show that

$$\int z^\mu J_\nu(z)\,dz = z[J_\nu(z)s'_{\mu,\nu}(z) - s_{\mu,\nu}(z)J'_\nu(z)]$$
$$= (\mu+\nu-1)zJ_\nu(z)s_{\mu-1,\nu-1}(z) - zJ_{\nu-1}(z)s_{\mu,\nu}(z) \tag{3.153}$$

and

$$\int z^\mu J_{-\nu}(z)\,dz = z[J_{-\nu}(z)s'_{\mu,\nu}(z) - s_{\mu,\nu}(z)J'_{-\nu}(z)]$$
$$= (\mu+\nu-1)zJ_{-\nu}(z)s_{\mu-1,\nu-1}(z) + zJ_{1-\nu}(z)s_{\mu,\nu}(z). \tag{3.154}$$

In (3.153) and (3.154) we can substitute S for s on the right side, the integrals on the left side being indefinite. Other integrals of this kind are given by McLachlan [1936].

The formula

$$s_{\mu+\sigma,\nu+\sigma}(z) = \frac{2\Gamma(\frac{1}{2}\mu+\frac{1}{2}\nu+\sigma+\frac{1}{2})}{\Gamma(\frac{1}{2}\mu+\frac{1}{2}\nu+\frac{1}{2})\Gamma(\sigma)}\, z^\sigma \int_0^{(1/2)\pi} s_{\mu,\nu}(z\sin\theta)\sin^{\nu+1}\theta\cos^{2\sigma-1}\theta\,d\theta$$
$$[\operatorname{Re}\sigma > 0, \operatorname{Re}(\mu\pm\nu) > -1] \tag{3.155}$$

may be proved by expanding $s_{\mu,\nu}(z\sin\theta)$ as a power series in z and integrating term by term. When $\mu = \nu$, (3.155) reduces to (3.74).

Similarly

$$s_{\mu+\sigma,\nu-\sigma}(z) = \frac{2\Gamma(\frac{1}{2}\mu+\frac{1}{2}\nu+\sigma+\frac{1}{2})}{\Gamma(\frac{1}{2}\mu-\frac{1}{2}\nu+\frac{1}{2})\Gamma(\sigma)}\, z^\sigma \int_0^{(1/2)\pi} s_{\mu,\nu}(z\sin\theta)\sin^{1-\nu}\theta\cos^{2\sigma-1}\theta\,d\theta$$
$$[\operatorname{Re}\sigma > 0, \operatorname{Re}(\mu\pm\nu) > -1]. \tag{3.156}$$

Again, as shown by Watson [374, 1944], if $\operatorname{Re}(\nu + \mu + 1) > 0$,

$$s_{\mu,\nu}(z) = 2^{\mu}(\tfrac{1}{2}z)^{(1/2)(1+\nu+\mu)}\Gamma(\tfrac{1}{2} + \tfrac{1}{2}\mu - \tfrac{1}{2}\nu) \times \int_0^{(1/2)\pi} J_{(1/2)(1+\mu-\nu)}(z \sin\theta)(\sin\theta)^{(1/2)(1+\nu-\mu)}(\cos\theta)^{\nu+\mu}\, d\theta\,. \tag{3.157}$$

Consider next the integral

$$\int_0^{\pi} \sin(z \sin\theta) \sin \nu\theta\, d\theta\,.$$

On expanding the integral as a power series in z, and using the formula (Watson [309, 1944])

$$\int_0^{\pi} \sin^m\theta \sin\nu\theta\, d\theta = \frac{\pi \sin(\frac{1}{2}\nu\pi)\Gamma(m+1)}{2^m\Gamma(\frac{1}{2}m + \frac{1}{2}\nu + 1)\Gamma(\frac{1}{2}m - \frac{1}{2}\nu + 1)},$$

where m is a positive integer, we see that

$$\int_0^{\pi} \sin(z\sin\theta)\sin\nu\theta\, d\theta = \sum_{m=0}^{\infty}(-1)^m \frac{\pi \sin(\frac{1}{2}\nu\pi)(\frac{1}{2}z)^{2m+1}}{\Gamma(m + \frac{1}{2}\nu + \frac{3}{2})\Gamma(m - \frac{1}{2}\nu + \frac{3}{2})} = \sin\nu\pi\, s_{0,\nu}(z)\,. \tag{3.158}$$

Similarly, we find

$$\int_0^{\pi} \cos(z\sin\theta)\sin\nu\theta\, d\theta = -\nu(1 - \cos\nu\pi)s_{-1,\nu}(z)\,. \tag{3.159}$$

On using the formula (Watson [309, 1944])

$$\int_0^{\pi} \sin^m\theta \cos\nu\theta\, d\theta = \frac{\pi \cos(\frac{1}{2}\nu\pi)\Gamma(m+1)}{2^m\Gamma(\frac{1}{2}m + \frac{1}{2}\nu + 1)\Gamma(\frac{1}{2}m - \frac{1}{2}\nu + 1)},$$

we can show that

$$\int_0^{\pi} \sin(z\sin\theta)\cos\nu\theta\, d\theta = (1 + \cos\nu\pi)s_{0,\nu}(z) \tag{3.160}$$

and

$$\int_0^{\pi} \cos(z\sin\theta)\cos\nu\theta\, d\theta = -\nu\sin\nu\pi\, s_{-1,\nu}(z)\,. \tag{3.161}$$

It is also shown by Watson [312, 1944] that, if $\operatorname{Re} z > 0$,

$$\int_0^{\infty} e^{-\nu t - z\sinh t}\, dt = s_{0,\nu}(z) - \nu s_{-1,\nu}(z) - \frac{\pi}{\sin\nu\pi} J_\nu(z) \tag{3.162}$$

and

$$\int_0^\infty e^{\nu t - z\sinh t}\, dt = s_{0,-\nu}(z) + \nu s_{-1,-\nu}(z) + \frac{\pi}{\sin \nu\pi} J_{-\nu}(z)$$

$$= s_{0,\nu}(z) + \nu s_{-1,\nu}(z) + \frac{\pi}{\sin \nu\pi} J_{-\nu}(z), \qquad (3.163)$$

since $s_{\mu,\nu}(z)$ is an even function of ν. Adding (3.162) and (3.163), and using (3.125), we obtain, if $\operatorname{Re} z > 0$,

$$S_{0,\nu}(z) = \int_0^\infty e^{-z\sinh t} \cosh \nu t\, dt = \frac{z}{\nu} \int_0^\infty e^{-z\sinh t} \sinh \nu t \cosh t\, dt, \qquad (3.164)$$

on integrating by parts.

Using the recurrence formulae in §3.18, we see that, if $\operatorname{Re} z > 0$,

$$S_{1,\nu}(z) = \tfrac{1}{2} z \{S_{0,\nu+1}(z) + S_{0,\nu-1}\}$$

$$= \tfrac{1}{2} z \int_0^\infty e^{-z\sinh t} [\cosh(\nu+1)t + \cosh(\nu-1)t]\, dt$$

$$= z \int_0^\infty e^{-z\sinh t} \cosh \nu t \cosh t\, dt. \qquad (3.165)$$

The formula

$$\int_0^\infty e^{-az} z^\lambda s_{\mu,\nu}(bz)\, dz = \frac{b^{\mu+1}\Gamma(\lambda+\mu+2)}{a^{\lambda+\mu+2}(\mu+\nu+1)(\mu-\nu+1)}$$

$$\times\, {}_3F_2\left(1, \frac{\lambda+\mu}{2}+1, \frac{\lambda+\mu+3}{2}; \frac{\mu+\nu+3}{2}, \frac{\mu-\nu+3}{2}; -\frac{b^2}{a^2}\right)$$

$$[\operatorname{Re} a > 0, \operatorname{Re}(\lambda+\mu) > -2, \operatorname{Re}(\mu \pm \nu) > -1] \qquad (3.166)$$

can be proved by expanding $s_{\mu,\nu}(bz)$ as a power series and integrating term by term.

On letting $a \to 0$, and using (3.94), we find

$$\int_0^\infty z^\lambda s_{\mu,\nu}(bz)\, dz$$

$$= \frac{\pi^{1/2}\Gamma(\lambda+\mu+2)\Gamma\left(-\frac{\lambda+\mu}{2}\right)\Gamma\left(\frac{\mu+\nu+3}{2}\right)\Gamma\left(\frac{\mu-\nu+3}{2}\right)}{b^{\lambda+1}(\mu+\nu+1)(\mu-\nu+1)\Gamma\left(\frac{1-\lambda+\nu}{2}\right)\Gamma\left(\frac{1-\lambda-\nu}{2}\right)\Gamma\left(\frac{\lambda+\mu+3}{2}\right)}$$

$$= \frac{2^{\lambda+\mu-1}\Gamma\left(\frac{\lambda+\mu+2}{2}\right)\Gamma\left(-\frac{\lambda+\mu}{2}\right)\Gamma\left(\frac{\mu+\nu+1}{2}\right)\Gamma\left(\frac{\mu-\nu+1}{2}\right)}{b^{\lambda+1}\Gamma\left(\frac{1-\lambda+\nu}{2}\right)\Gamma\left(\frac{1-\lambda-\nu}{2}\right)}$$

$$[b > 0, 0 > \operatorname{Re}(\lambda+\mu) > -2, > \tfrac{1}{2}\operatorname{Re}\lambda, \operatorname{Re}(\mu \pm \nu) > -1]. \qquad (3.167)$$

3.21 Related Differential Equations

We shall now briefly consider a certain class of second-order differential equations, the solutions of which can be expressed in terms of Lommel functions.

In the equation

$$\frac{d^2y}{dz^2}+\frac{1}{z}\frac{dy}{dz}+\left(1-\frac{\nu^2}{z^2}\right)y=z^{\mu-1}, \tag{3.168}$$

put

$$x=\zeta^\alpha y \qquad \text{and} \qquad z=\beta\zeta^\gamma, \tag{3.169}$$

where α, β, and γ are constants.

Equation (3.168) is then transformed into

$$\zeta^2\frac{d^2x}{d\zeta^2}+(1-2\alpha)\zeta\frac{dx}{d\zeta}+(\beta^2\gamma^2\zeta^{2\gamma}+\alpha^2-\nu^2\gamma^2)x=\beta^{\mu+1}\gamma^2\zeta^{\alpha+\gamma\mu+\gamma}. \tag{3.170}$$

A particular integral of (3.170) is $x=\zeta^\alpha s_{\mu,\nu}(\beta\zeta^\gamma)$. The complementary function is

$$\zeta^\alpha[C_1J_\nu(\beta\zeta^\gamma)+C_2J_{-\nu}(\beta\zeta^\gamma)].$$

Some special cases of this transformation are of interest. In (3.170) put $\gamma=1$. Then (3.170) becomes

$$\frac{d^2x}{d\zeta^2}+\frac{1-2\alpha}{\zeta}\frac{dx}{d\zeta}+\left(\beta^2+\frac{\alpha^2-\nu^2}{\zeta^2}\right)x=\beta^{\mu+1}\zeta^{\alpha+\mu-1} \tag{3.171}$$

with a particular integral $x=\zeta^\alpha s_{\mu,\nu}(\beta\zeta)$.

In (3.171) put $\alpha=0$. Then (3.171) becomes

$$\frac{d^2x}{d\zeta^2}+\frac{1}{\zeta}\frac{dx}{d\zeta}+\left(\beta^2-\frac{\nu^2}{\zeta^2}\right)x=\beta^{\mu+1}\zeta^{\mu-1} \tag{3.172}$$

with a particular integral $x=s_{\mu,\nu}(\beta\zeta)$.

In (3.171) put $\alpha=\frac{1}{2}$, $\nu=p+\frac{1}{2}$. Then (3.171) becomes

$$\frac{d^2x}{d\zeta^2}+\left[\beta^2-\frac{p(p+1)}{\zeta^2}\right]x=\beta^{\mu+1}\zeta^{\mu-(1/2)} \tag{3.173}$$

with a particular integral $x=\zeta^{1/2}s_{\mu,p+(1/2)}(\beta\zeta)$.

In (3.171) put $\alpha=\nu=p+\frac{1}{2}$. Then (3.171) becomes

$$\frac{d^2x}{d\zeta^2}-\frac{2p}{\zeta}\frac{dx}{d\zeta}+\beta^2x=\beta^{\mu+1}\zeta^{p+\mu-(1/2)} \tag{3.174}$$

with a particular integral $x=\zeta^{p+(1/2)}s_{\mu,p+(1/2)}(\beta\zeta)$.

In (3.170) put $\alpha = \frac{1}{2}$. Then (3.170) becomes

$$\zeta^2 \frac{d^2x}{d\zeta^2} + (\beta^2\gamma^2\zeta^{2\gamma} + \tfrac{1}{4} - \nu^2\gamma^2)x = \beta^{\mu+1}\gamma^2\zeta^{\gamma\mu+\gamma+(1/2)} \tag{3.175}$$

with a particular integral $x = \zeta^{1/2}s_{\mu,\nu}(\beta\zeta^\gamma)$.

In (3.170) put $\alpha = 0$. Then (3.170) becomes

$$\frac{d^2x}{d\zeta^2} + \frac{1}{\zeta}\frac{dx}{d\zeta} + \gamma^2\left(\beta^2\zeta^{2\gamma-2} - \frac{\nu^2}{\zeta^2}\right)x = \beta^{\mu+1}\gamma^2\zeta^{\gamma\mu+\gamma-2} \tag{3.176}$$

with a particular integral $x = s_{\mu,\nu}(\beta\zeta^\gamma)$.

In (3.170) put $\alpha = \nu\gamma$. Then (3.170) becomes

$$\zeta\frac{d^2x}{d\zeta^2} + (1 - 2\nu\gamma)\frac{dx}{d\zeta} + \beta^2\gamma^2\zeta^{2\gamma-1}x = \beta^{\mu+1}\gamma^2\zeta^{\gamma\nu+\gamma\mu+\gamma-1} \tag{3.177}$$

with a particular integral $x = \zeta^{\nu\gamma}s_{\mu,\nu}(\beta\zeta^\gamma)$.

In (3.177) put $\gamma = \frac{1}{2}$. Then (3.177) becomes

$$\zeta\frac{d^2x}{d\zeta^2} + (1 - \nu)\frac{dx}{d\zeta} + \frac{1}{4}\beta^2 x = \frac{1}{4}\beta^{\mu+1}\zeta^{(1/2)\nu+(1/2)\mu-(1/2)} \tag{3.178}$$

with a particular integral $x = \zeta^{(1/2)\nu}s_{\mu,\nu}(\beta\zeta^{1/2})$.

In (3.177) put $\nu\gamma = \frac{1}{2}$. Then (3.177) becomes

$$\frac{d^2x}{d\zeta^2} + \beta^2\gamma^2\zeta^{2\gamma-2}x = \beta^{\mu+1}\gamma^2\zeta^{\gamma\mu+\gamma-(3/2)} \tag{3.179}$$

with a particular integral $x = \zeta^{1/2}s_{\mu,1/2\gamma}(\beta\zeta^\gamma)$.

PROBLEMS

1. Show that

$$\int_{-(1/2)\pi}^{(1/2)\pi} e^{iz\cos\theta}\cos\theta\, d\theta = 2 - \pi\{H_1(z) - iJ_1(z)\}.$$

2. Use the relation

$$\sin(z\cos\theta) = 2\sum_{m=0}^{\infty}(-1)^m J_{2m+1}(z)\cos(2m+1)\theta$$

to prove that

$$H_0(z) = \frac{4}{\pi}\sum_{m=0}^{\infty}\frac{J_{2m+1}(z)}{2m+1}.$$

3. Show that

$$\int z^3 H_0(z)\,dz = z^3 H_1(z) - 2z^2 H_2(z).$$

4. Deduce the power series for $H_\nu(z)$ directly from the differential equation

$$\frac{d^2y}{dz^2} + \frac{1}{z}\frac{dy}{dz} + \left(1 - \frac{\nu^2}{z^2}\right)y = \frac{\pi^{-(1/2)}(\frac{1}{2}z)^{\nu-1}}{\Gamma(\nu + \frac{1}{2})}.$$

5. Determine the power series for $H_0(z)$ and $H_1(z)$, and show, by differentiating term by term, that

$$\frac{d}{dz}[zH_1(z)] = zH_0(z)$$

and

$$\frac{d}{dz}H_0(z) = \frac{2}{\pi} - H_1(z).$$

[The functions $H_0(z)$ and $H_1(z)$ occur in the analysis of fluid pressures on vibrating disks and in the theory of loud-speaker diaphragms (McLachlan, [1934]).]

6. Show that

$$H_\nu(z) = \frac{(\frac{1}{2}z)^{\nu+1}}{\Gamma(\frac{3}{2})\Gamma(\nu + \frac{3}{2})}(1 + \theta)$$

where

$$|\theta| < \frac{2}{3}\exp\left\{\frac{\frac{1}{4}|z|^2}{|\nu_0 + \frac{3}{2}|} - 1\right\}$$

and $|\nu_0 + \frac{3}{2}|$ is the smallest of the numbers $|\nu + \frac{3}{2}|$, $|\nu + \frac{5}{2}|$, $|\nu + \frac{7}{2}|, \ldots$. (Watson [1944]).

7. Show that

$$H_{3/2}(z) = \sqrt{\frac{z}{2\pi}}\left(1 + \frac{2}{z^2}\right) - \sqrt{\frac{2}{\pi z}}\left(\sin z + \frac{\cos z}{z}\right).$$

8. The function $E_\nu(z)$ is defined by the equation

$$E_\nu(z) = \frac{1}{\pi}\int_0^\pi \sin(\nu\theta - z\sin\theta)\,d\theta.$$

Show that

$$E_\nu(z) = \sin\tfrac{1}{2}\nu\pi \sum_{m=0}^{\infty} \frac{(-1)^m(\frac{1}{2}z)^{2m}}{\Gamma(m - \frac{1}{2}\nu + 1)\Gamma(m + \frac{1}{2}\nu + 1)}$$

$$- \cos\tfrac{1}{2}\nu\pi \sum_{m=0}^{\infty} \frac{(-1)^m(\frac{1}{2}z)^{2m+1}}{\Gamma(m - \frac{1}{2}\nu + \frac{3}{2})\Gamma(m + \frac{1}{2}\nu + \frac{3}{2})}.$$

Hence show that, when ν is a positive integer (or zero), $E_\nu(z)$ differs from $-H_\nu(z)$ by a polynomial in z; and, when ν is a negative integer, the two functions differ by a polynomial in $1/z$ (Watson [1944].)

9. Prove that, if $\mathrm{Re}(a \pm ib) > 0$,

$$\int_0^\infty e^{-az}H_1(bz)dz = \frac{2}{\pi a} - \frac{2a}{\pi b(a^2+b^2)^{1/2}}\log\left[\frac{b+(a^2+b^2)^{1/2}}{a}\right]$$

and

$$\int_0^\infty e^{-az}H_2(bz)dz$$

$$= \frac{2}{\pi}\left\{-\frac{2}{b} + \frac{b}{3a^2} + \frac{2a^2+b^2}{b^2(a^2+b^2)^{1/2}}\log\left[\frac{b+(a^2+b^2)^{1/2}}{a}\right]\right\}.$$

10. Prove that, if $\mathrm{Re}(a \pm ib) > 0$,

$$\int_0^\infty e^{-az}H_1(bz)z^{-1}\,dz = \frac{2}{\pi}\left\{-1 + \frac{(a^2+b^2)^{1/2}}{b}\log\left[\frac{b+(a^2+b^2)^{1/2}}{a}\right]\right\}.$$

11. Prove that, if $\mathrm{Re}(a \pm ib) > 0$,

$$\int_0^\infty e^{-az}H_{3/2}(bz)z^{3/2}\,dz = \frac{(2/\pi)^{1/2}b^{5/2}(3a^2+b^2)}{a^3(a^2+b^2)^2}.$$

12. Show that, if $\mathrm{Re}\,\nu > \frac{1}{2}$,

$$H_\nu(z) = \frac{(2\nu-1)(\frac{1}{2}z)^{\nu-1}}{\Gamma(\nu+1)\Gamma(\frac{1}{2})}\int_0^{(1/2)\pi}\sin^{2\nu-2}\theta\cos\theta\{1-\cos(z\cos\theta)\}d\theta.$$

Hence prove that, when $\mathrm{Re}(\mu+\nu) > 0$,

$$\int_0^\infty \frac{H_\mu(t)H_\nu(t)}{t^{\mu+\nu}}dt = \frac{\Gamma(\mu+\nu)\Gamma(\frac{1}{2})}{2^{\mu+\nu}\Gamma(\mu+\nu+\frac{1}{2})\Gamma(\mu+\frac{1}{2})\Gamma(\nu+\frac{1}{2})}$$

(Watson [1944]).

13. Show that

$$I_0(z) - L_0(z) = \frac{1}{\pi}\int_{-(1/2)\pi}^{(1/2)\pi} e^{-z\cos\theta}\,d\theta.$$

14. Deduce the power series for $L_\nu(z)$ directly from the differential equation

$$\frac{d^2y}{dz^2} + \frac{1}{z}\frac{dy}{dz} - \left(1+\frac{\nu^2}{z^2}\right)y = \frac{\pi^{-(1/2)}(\frac{1}{2}z)^{\nu-1}}{\Gamma(\nu+\frac{1}{2})}.$$

15. Prove that, if $\operatorname{Re} a > |\operatorname{Re} b|$,

$$\int_0^\infty e^{-az} L_1(bz)\, dz = \frac{2}{\pi a}\left\{-1 + \frac{a^2}{b}(a^2 - b^2)^{-(1/2)} \sin^{-1}\left(\frac{b}{a}\right)\right\}.$$

16. Verify that $y = z^\nu$ is a particular solution of the differential equation satisfied by $S_{\nu+1,\nu}(z)$.

17. Neumann's polynomial $O_n(z)$ is defined by

$$O_n(z) = \frac{1}{4}\sum_{m=0}^{(1/2)n} \frac{n \cdot \Gamma(\frac{1}{2}n + m)}{\Gamma(\frac{1}{2}n - m + 1)(\frac{1}{2}z)^{2m+1}} \qquad (n \text{ even})$$

and

$$O_n(z) = \frac{1}{4}\sum_{m=0}^{(1/2)(n-1)} \frac{n \cdot \Gamma(\frac{1}{2}n + m + \frac{1}{2})}{\Gamma(\frac{1}{2}n - m + \frac{1}{2})(\frac{1}{2}z)^{2m+2}} \qquad (n \text{ odd}).$$

Show that

$$O_{2m}(z) = \left(\frac{1}{z}\right) S_{1,2m}(z),$$

and

$$O_{2m+1}(z) = \frac{(2m+1)}{z} S_{0,2m+1}(z)$$

(Watson [1944]).

18. Derive recurrence formulas for $S_{\mu,\nu}(z)$ from the expansion in terms of descending powers of z.

19. Show that the function $E_\nu(z)$, defined in Problem 8, can be expressed in terms of Lommel functions in the form

$$E_\nu(z) = -2\pi^{-1}\{\cos^2\tfrac{1}{2}\nu\pi \cdot s_{0,\nu}(z) + \nu \sin^2\tfrac{1}{2}\nu\pi \cdot s_{-1,\nu}(z)\}.$$

20. Show that

$$(k^2 - h^2)\int J_\nu(kz) \cdot xz\, dz = z\left[J_\nu(kz)\frac{dx}{dz} - x\frac{d}{dz}J_\nu(kz)\right] - k\left(\frac{h}{k}\right)^{\mu+1}\int (kz)^\mu J_\nu(kz)\, dz.$$

Hence prove that

$$(\nu^2 - \mu^2)\int \frac{H_\nu(hz)J_\mu(hz)}{z}\, dz = hz[J_\mu(hz)H_\nu'(hz) - H_\nu(hz)J_\mu'(hz)] - hz[2^{\nu-1}\pi^{1/2}\Gamma(\nu + \tfrac{1}{2})]^{-1} \times [(\mu + \nu - 1)J_\mu(hz)S_{\nu-1,\mu-1}(hz) - J_{\nu-1}(hz)S_{\nu,\mu}(hz)]$$

(McLachlan [1936]).

21. The function $\mathbf{J}_\nu(z)$ is defined by the equation

$$\mathbf{J}_\nu(z) = \frac{1}{\pi}\int_0^\pi \cos(\nu\theta - z\sin\theta)\cdot d\theta.$$

Show that

$$\mathbf{J}_\nu(z) = \frac{1}{\pi}\sin\nu\pi[s_{0,\nu}(z) - \nu s_{-1,\nu}(z)].$$

22. Use the results of Problems 19 and 21 to show that

$$\int_0^\infty e^{-z\sinh t}\cosh\nu t\,dt = \tfrac{1}{2}\pi\tan\tfrac{1}{2}\nu\pi\{\mathbf{J}_\nu(z) - J_\nu(z)\} - \tfrac{1}{2}\pi\{E_\nu(z) + Y_\nu(z)\}$$

and

$$\int_0^\infty e^{-z\sinh t}\sinh\nu t\,dt = \tfrac{1}{2}\pi\cot\tfrac{1}{2}\nu\pi\{J_\nu(z) - \mathbf{J}_\nu(z)\} - \tfrac{1}{2}\pi\{E_\nu(z) + Y_\nu(z)\}$$

(Watson [1944]).

23. Use the substitution $u = y^{1-k}$ to show that the solution of the nonlinear differential equation

$$y\frac{d^2y}{dz^2} = k\left(\frac{dy}{dz}\right)^2 - \frac{y}{z}\frac{dy}{dz} - \left(1 - \frac{\nu^2}{z^2}\right)\frac{y^2}{1-k} + \frac{z^{\mu-1}y^{k+1}}{1-k}$$

is

$$y = [C_1 J_\nu(z) + C_2 Y_\nu(z) + S_{\mu,\nu}(z)]^{1/(1-k)},$$

where C_1 and C_2 are arbitrary constants.

CHAPTER 4

Nonhomogeneous Confluent Hypergeometric Functions

4.1 Introduction

In this chapter we consider the properties of the solutions of certain nonhomogeneous linear differential equations which have as their associated homogeneous equation the confluent hypergeometric equation

$$z \frac{d^2y}{dz^2} + (c - z) \frac{dy}{dz} - ay = 0, \tag{4.1}$$

where a and c are constants.

We consider first two *generalized modified Struve functions* $\Omega(a, c; z)$ and $\overline{\Omega}(a, c; z)$, defined in §§4.3 and 4.5 (see also Babister [1959]). As shown in §4.3, $\Omega(a, c; z)$ bears the same relation to the modified Struve function $L_\nu(z)$ as the confluent hypergeometric function $\Phi(a, c; z)$ does to the modified Bessel function $I_\nu(z)$. As shown in §4.7, these functions are particular integrals of the nonhomogeneous equations

$$z \frac{d^2y}{dz^2} + (c - z) \frac{dy}{dz} - ay = \frac{2^{1-c}\Gamma(c)}{\Gamma(a)\Gamma(c-a)} e^{(1/2)z} \tag{4.2}$$

and

$$z \frac{d^2y}{dz^2} + (c - z) \frac{dy}{dz} - ay = \frac{2^{c-1}\Gamma(2-c)}{\Gamma(a-c+1)\Gamma(1-a)} e^{(1/2)z} z^{1-c}. \tag{4.3}$$

In §4.2 we summarize various properties of the solutions of (4.1), and in the following sections we discuss in detail the properties of $\Omega(a, c; z)$ and $\overline{\Omega}(a, c; z)$. As in Chapter 3, we find it convenient to define these functions in terms of certain contour integrals (see §1.14).

In §§4.18 to 4.24 we discuss the properties of the nonhomogeneous confluent hypergeometric functions $\theta_\sigma(a, c; z)$ and $\Theta_\sigma(a, c; z)$, which satisfy the equation

$$z \frac{d^2y}{dz^2} + (c - z) \frac{dy}{dz} - ay = z^{\sigma-1}, \tag{4.4}$$

and those of $\Lambda_{\rho,\sigma}(a, c; z)$, which satisfies the equation

$$z\frac{d^2y}{dz^2} + (c - z)\frac{dy}{dz} - ay = e^{\rho z}z^{\sigma-1}. \tag{4.5}$$

In §4.24 and in Chapter 5 we consider the solutions of some differential equations (such as the nonhomogeneous Whittaker confluent hypergeometric equation and the equations for the parabolic cylinder functions) which are related to (4.5).

4.2 Some Properties of Confluent Hypergeometric Functions

The theory of confluent hypergeometric functions is fully set out in Buchholz [1953a] and Erdélyi [1953a]. We shall here briefly summarize various properties of these functions.

If c is not an integer, two independent solutions of (3.1) are

$$\Phi(a, c; z) = \frac{\Gamma(c)}{\Gamma(a)}\sum_{n=0}^{\infty}\frac{\Gamma(a+n)z^n}{\Gamma(c+n)n!} \tag{4.6}$$

and

$$\overline{\Phi}(a, c; z) = z^{1-c}\Phi(a - c + 1, 2 - c; z). \tag{4.7}$$

When $c = 2a$, as shown by Erdélyi [*265*, 1953a], these solutions can be expressed in terms of modified Bessel functions (see §3.2). Thus

$$\Phi(a, 2a; z) = \Gamma(a + \tfrac{1}{2})(\tfrac{1}{4}z)^{(1/2)-a}e^{(1/2)z}I_{a-(1/2)}(\tfrac{1}{2}z) \tag{4.8}$$

and

$$\overline{\Phi}(a, 2a; z) = \Gamma(\tfrac{3}{2} - a)(4z)^{(1/2)-a}e^{(1/2)z}I_{(1/2)-a}(\tfrac{1}{2}z). \tag{4.9}$$

Two other solutions of (4.1) are

$$\Psi(a, c; z) = \frac{\Gamma(1-c)}{\Gamma(a-c+1)}\Phi(a, c; z) + \frac{\Gamma(c-1)}{\Gamma(a)}\overline{\Phi}(a, c; z) \tag{4.10}$$

and

$$\overline{\Psi}(a, c; z) = e^z\,\Psi(c - a, c; -z). \tag{4.11}$$

In terms of generalized hypergeometric series we see that

$$\Phi(a, c; z) = {}_1F_1(a, c; z). \tag{4.12}$$

The Wronskian of Φ and $\overline{\Phi}$ is

$$\Phi(a, c; z)\overline{\Phi}'(a, c; z) - \overline{\Phi}(a, c; z)\Phi'(a, c; z) = -(c - 1)z^{-c}e^z. \tag{4.13}$$

When $c = 1$, from (4.6) and (4.7),

$$\Phi(a, 1; z) = \overline{\Phi}(a, 1; z) \tag{4.14}$$

and the solutions are no longer independent. We see that in this case the Wronskian vanishes.

When $c - 1$ is a negative integer, $\Phi(a, c; z)$ is infinite. Similarly, when $c - 1$ is a positive integer, $\overline{\Phi}(a, c; z)$ is infinite. Thus, when c is an integer, one solution is given by Φ or $\overline{\Phi}$, and the second solution will contain logarithmic terms. Now $\Psi(a, c; z)$ and $\overline{\Psi}(a, c; z)$ form a fundamental set of solutions of (4.1) under all circumstances.

Consider next the solution of (4.1) in terms of contour integrals. As shown by Poole [*143*, 1936], these contour integrals can be of the form

$$\frac{1}{2\pi i}\int_C e^{zt} t^{a-1}(1-t)^{c-a-1}\,dt,$$

where the contour C must satisfy the condition

$$[e^{zt} t^a (1-t)^{c-a}]_C = 0. \tag{4.15}$$

Thus the solutions of (4.1) can be expressed in terms of the contour integrals

$$y_1 = \frac{1}{2\pi i}\int_I^{(1+)} e^{zt} t^{a-1}(t-1)^{c-a-1}\,dt \tag{4.16}$$

and

$$y_2 = \frac{1}{2\pi i}\int_I^{(0+)} e^{zt} t^{a-1}(t-1)^{c-a-1}\,dt, \tag{4.17}$$

where I is the point at infinity taken in such a direction that zt is real and negative. The contours for these integrals are shown in Figure 4.1.

Thus, if $\arg z = \theta$ $(-\pi < \theta < \pi)$, we take I as the point at infinity having argument $\pi - \theta$ and

$$\arg t = \arg(t-1) = -\pi - \theta$$

at the start of the contour.

From Erdélyi [1953a] and Poole [1936],

$$\Phi(a, c; z) = i(2\pi)^{-1} e^{i\pi a}\Gamma(1-a)\Gamma(c)\Gamma(1+a-c)y_3, \tag{4.18}$$

$$\overline{\Phi}(a, c; z) = \Gamma(2-c)y_4, \tag{4.19}$$

$$\Psi(a, c; z) = -e^{i\pi(c-a)}\Gamma(1-a)y_2, \tag{4.20}$$

$$\overline{\Psi}(a, c; z) = e^{i\pi(a+c)}\Gamma(1+a-c)y_1 \qquad (\operatorname{Im} z > 0), \tag{4.21}$$

$$\overline{\Psi}(a, c; z) = e^{i\pi(a-c)}\Gamma(1+a-c)y_5 \qquad (\operatorname{Im} z < 0), \tag{4.22}$$

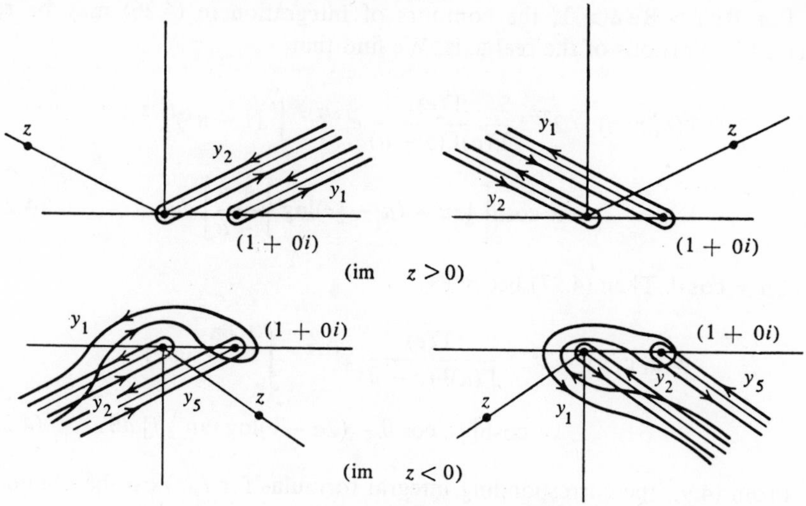

Figure 4.1 Contours for y_1, y_2, and y_5.

where

$$y_3 = \frac{1}{2\pi i}\int_I^{(1+,0+,1-,0-)} e^{zt}t^{a-1}(t-1)^{c-a-1}\,dt$$

$$= y_1[1 - e^{2\pi ia}] - y_2[1 - e^{2\pi i(c-a)}], \tag{4.23}$$

$$y_4 = \frac{1}{2\pi i}\int_I^{(0+,1+)} e^{zt}t^{a-1}(t-1)^{c-a-1}\,dt$$

$$= y_2 + y_1 e^{2\pi ia}, \tag{4.24}$$

$$y_5 = y_1 e^{2\pi ia} + y_2[1 - e^{2\pi i(c-a)}]. \tag{4.25}$$

The contour for y_5 is shown in Figure 4.1.

As shown by Erdélyi [1953a], the path of integration for y_3 may be contracted to a finite contour (1+, 0+, 1−, 0−). Finally, putting $t = \frac{1}{2}(u + 1)$, we find that (4.23) can be reduced to

$$y_3 = i\frac{2^{-c}}{\pi}\,e^{-i\pi(a+c)}e^{(1/2)z}\Bigg[(1 - e^{2i\pi a})\int_0^{(1+)} e^{(1/2)zu}(1+u)^{a-1}(1-u)^{c-a-1}\,du$$

$$- \{1 - e^{2i\pi(c-a)}\}\int_0^{(-1+)} e^{(1/2)zu}(1+u)^{a-1}(1-u)^{c-a-1}\,du\Bigg], \tag{4.26}$$

where the arguments of $1 + u$ and $1 - u$ are both taken as zero at the start of the contours.

For $\operatorname{Re} c > \operatorname{Re} a > 0$, the contours of integration in (4.26) may be replaced by portions of the real axis. We find that

$$\Phi(a, c; z) = 2^{2-c} \frac{\Gamma(c)}{\Gamma(a)\Gamma(c-a)} e^{(1/2)z} \int_0^1 (1-u^2)^{(1/2)c-1}$$

$$\times \cosh\left[\tfrac{1}{2}zu + (a - \tfrac{1}{2}c)\log\frac{1+u}{1-u}\right] du. \tag{4.27}$$

Put $u = \cos\theta$. Then (4.27) becomes

$$\Phi(a, c; z) = 2^{2-c} \frac{\Gamma(c)}{\Gamma(a)\Gamma(c-a)} e^{(1/2)z} \int_0^{(1/2)\pi} (\sin\theta)^{c-1}$$

$$\times \cosh[\tfrac{1}{2}z\cos\theta - (2a-c)\log\tan\tfrac{1}{2}\theta]\, d\theta. \tag{4.28}$$

From (4.9), the corresponding integral formulas for $I_\nu(z)$ can be obtained immediately by putting $c = 2a$ in (4.27) and (4.28).

Similarly, if $\operatorname{Re} z > 0$ and $\operatorname{Re} a > 0$, the contour of integration in (4.17) may be replaced by the negative part of the real axis. On replacing t by $-t$ we find that (4.20) reduces to

$$\Psi(a, c; z) = \frac{1}{\Gamma(a)} \int_0^\infty e^{-zt} t^{a-1} (1+t)^{c-a-1}\, dt. \tag{4.29}$$

4.3 Generalized Modified Struve Function $\Omega(a, c; z)$

Consider the function $\Omega(a, c; z)$ defined by

$$\Omega(a, c; z) = i(2\pi)^{-1} e^{i\pi a} \Gamma(1-a)\Gamma(c)\Gamma(1+a-c)\omega, \tag{4.30}$$

where

$$\omega = i\frac{2^{-c}}{\pi} e^{-i\pi(a+c)} e^{(1/2)z} \left[(1 - e^{2i\pi a}) \int_0^{(1+)} e^{(1/2)zu} (1+u)^{a-1} (1-u)^{c-a-1}\, du \right.$$

$$\left. + \{1 - e^{2i\pi(c-a)}\} \int_0^{(-1+)} e^{(1/2)zu} (1+u)^{a-1} (1-u)^{c-a-1}\, du \right]. \tag{4.31}$$

From (4.18) and (4.30),

$$\frac{\Omega(a, c; z)}{\Phi(a, c; z)} = \frac{\omega}{y_3}.$$

In (4.31) the arguments of $1+u$ and $1-u$ are both to be taken as zero at the start of the contours.

For $\operatorname{Re} c > \operatorname{Re} a > 0$, the contours of integration in (4.31) may be replaced by portions of the real axis. We find that

$$\Omega(a, c; z) = 2^{2-c} \frac{\Gamma(c)}{\Gamma(a)\Gamma(c-a)} e^{(1/2)z} \int_0^1 (1-u^2)^{(1/2)c-1} \times \sinh\left[\tfrac{1}{2}zu + (a - \tfrac{1}{2}c)\log\frac{1+u}{1-u}\right] du. \tag{4.32}$$

Put $u = \cos\theta$. Then (4.32) becomes

$$\Omega(a, c; z) = 2^{2-c} \frac{\Gamma(c)}{\Gamma(a)\Gamma(c-a)} e^{(1/2)z} \int_0^{(1/2)\pi} (\sin\theta)^{c-1} \times \sinh[\tfrac{1}{2}z\cos\theta + (2a-c)\log\tan\tfrac{1}{2}\theta]\, d\theta. \tag{4.33}$$

When $c = 2a$, from Erdélyi [*38*, 1953b],

$$\Omega(a, 2a; z) = \Gamma(a + \tfrac{1}{2})(\tfrac{1}{4}z)^{(1/2)-a} e^{(1/2)z} L_{a-(1/2)}(\tfrac{1}{2}z), \tag{4.34}$$

where $L_{a-(1/2)}(\frac{1}{2}z)$ is the modified Struve function (see §3.14).

In a precisely similar manner, it can be shown that

$$\Phi(a, c; z) + \Omega(a, c; z) = 2^{2-c} \frac{\Gamma(c)}{\Gamma(a)\Gamma(c-a)} e^{(1/2)z} \times \int_0^1 e^{(1/2)zu}(1+u)^{a-1}(1-u)^{c-a-1}\, du \quad (\operatorname{Re} c > \operatorname{Re} a) \tag{4.35}$$

and

$$\Phi(a, c; z) - \Omega(a, c; z) = 2^{2-c} \frac{\Gamma(c)}{\Gamma(a)\Gamma(c-a)} e^{(1/2)z} \times \int_0^1 e^{-(1/2)zu}(1+u)^{c-a-1}(1-u)^{a-1}\, du \quad (\operatorname{Re} a > 0). \tag{4.36}$$

From (4.31), putting $t = \frac{1}{2}(u+1)$, we see that

$$\omega = \frac{1}{2\pi i}\left[(1 - e^{2\pi i a}) \int_{1/2}^{(1+)} e^{zt} t^{a-1}(t-1)^{c-a-1}\, dt + \{1 - e^{2\pi i(c-a)}\} \int_{1/2}^{(0+)} e^{zt} t^{a-1}(t-1)^{c-a-1}\, dt\right], \tag{4.37}$$

where $\arg t = -2\pi$ and $\arg(t-1) = -\pi$ at the start of the contours.

Using (4.16), (4.17), and (4.25) we see, by deforming the contours, that the formula (4.37) can be put in the form

$$\omega = \frac{1}{2\pi i}\left[(1 - e^{2\pi i a})\left\{\int_{1/2}^{I} X\,dt + 2\pi i y_1 - e^{2\pi i(c-a)}\int_{1/2}^{I} X\,dt\right\}\right.$$

$$\left. + \left\{1 - e^{2\pi i(c-a)}\right\}\left\{\int_{1/2}^{I} X\,dt + 2\pi i y_2 - e^{2\pi i a}\int_{1/2}^{I} X\,dt\right\}\right], \qquad \operatorname{Im} z > 0, \tag{4.38}$$

$$\omega = \frac{1}{2\pi i}\left[(1 - e^{2\pi i a})\left\{\int_{1/2}^{I} X\,dt + 2\pi i e^{-2\pi i a} y_5 - e^{2\pi i(c-a)}\int_{1/2}^{I} X\,dt\right\}\right.$$

$$\left. + \left\{1 - e^{2\pi i(c-a)}\right\}\left\{\int_{1/2}^{I} X\,dt + 2\pi i e^{-2\pi i a} y_2 - e^{2\pi i a}\int_{1/2}^{I} X\,dt\right\}\right],$$

$$\operatorname{Im} z < 0, \tag{4.39}$$

where $X = e^{zt}t^{a-1}(t-1)^{c-a-1}$, and the contours for y_1, y_2, and y_5 are given above. The integrals $\int_{1/2}^{I} X\,dt$ can be taken along a line through $t = \frac{1}{2}$ having argument $\pi - \theta$, where $\arg z = \theta\ (-\pi < \theta < \pi)$.

Putting $t = \frac{1}{2} + v$, we find that

$$\int_{1/2}^{I} X\,dt = e^{-2\pi i c} e^{(1/2)z} \int_0^{\infty \exp(i\pi - i\theta)} e^{zv}(v + \tfrac{1}{2})^{a-1}(v - \tfrac{1}{2})^{c-a-1}\,dv, \tag{4.40}$$

where the arguments of $v + \frac{1}{2}$ and $v - \frac{1}{2}$ are to be taken as 0 and π at the origin.

From (4.30), using (4.20) to (4.22), we find that

$$\Omega(a, c; z) = \frac{\Gamma(c)}{\Gamma(a)} e^{i\pi(a-c)\varepsilon} e^{z}\Psi(c - a, c; -z) - \frac{\Gamma(c)}{\Gamma(c-a)} e^{i\pi a\varepsilon}\Psi(a, c; z)$$

$$- \frac{2e^{i\pi(a-c)}\Gamma(c)}{\Gamma(a)\Gamma(c-a)} e^{(1/2)z} \int_0^{\infty \exp(i\pi - i\theta)} e^{zv}(v + \tfrac{1}{2})^{a-1}(v - \tfrac{1}{2})^{c-a-1}\,dv, \tag{4.41}$$

where $\varepsilon = \operatorname{sgn}(\operatorname{Im} z) = 1,\ -1$, according as $\operatorname{Im} z > 0,\ < 0$. As shown in §4.15, the asymptotic expansion of $\Omega(a, c; z)$ for large z can be obtained from (4.41).

4.4 An Alternative Integral Relation for $\Omega(a, c; z)$

When z is real and positive, and $\operatorname{Re} c < 1$, the contours for the two integrals in (4.37) can be deformed as shown in Figure 4.2, part of each contour being a semicircle of large radius. Then, for $z > 0$, $\operatorname{Re} c < 1$, the contribution from the semicircles vanishes as their radius increases to infinity, and we find that

$$\omega = \frac{1}{2\pi i}\left[(1 - e^{2\pi i a})\left\{\int_{1/2}^{(1/2)-\infty i} X\,dt + 2\pi i e^{-2\pi i a} y_4 - e^{2\pi i(c-a)}\int_{1/2}^{(1/2)+\infty i} X\,dt\right\}\right.$$

$$\left. + \left\{1 - e^{2\pi i(c-a)}\right\}\left\{\int_{1/2}^{(1/2)+\infty i} X\,dt - e^{2\pi i a}\int_{1/2}^{(1/2)-\infty i} X\,dt\right\}\right];$$

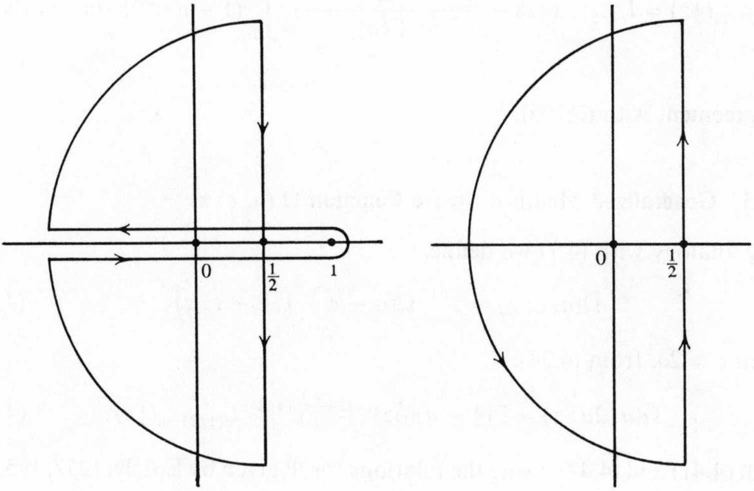

Figure 4.2.

that is,

$$\omega = (e^{-2\pi i a} - 1)y_4 + \frac{1}{2\pi i}\left[1 - 2e^{2\pi i a} + e^{2\pi i c}\right]\int_{1/2}^{(1/2)-\infty i} X\,dt$$

$$+ \frac{1}{2\pi i}\left[1 - 2e^{2\pi i(c-a)} + e^{2\pi i c}\right]\int_{1/2}^{(1/2)+\infty i} X\,dt. \tag{4.42}$$

Equation (4.42) can be simplified to give

$$\omega = (e^{-2\pi i a} - 1)y_4 - i\pi^{-1}e^{-i\pi a}e^{(1/2)z}[\operatorname{Re} Z(a, c; z)], \tag{4.43}$$

where

$$Z(a, c; z) = ie^{-i\pi[a-(1/2)c]}\{e^{2\pi i a} - 2 + e^{-2\pi i(c-a)}\}$$

$$\times \int_0^\infty e^{isz}(s - \tfrac{1}{2}i)^{a-1}(s + \tfrac{1}{2}i)^{c-a-1}\,ds. \tag{4.44}$$

From (4.19), (4.30), and (4.43), if $z > 0$ and $\operatorname{Re} c < 1$,

$$\Omega(a, c; z) = \frac{\Gamma(c)\Gamma(1 + a - c)}{\Gamma(2 - c)\Gamma(a)} \overline{\Phi}(a, c; z)$$
$$+ (2\pi^2)^{-1}\Gamma(1 - a)\Gamma(c)\Gamma(1 + a - c)e^{(1/2)z}[\operatorname{Re} Z(a, c; z)]. \quad (4.45)$$

When $c = 2a$, using (4.9) and (4.34), we obtain

$$L_{a-(1/2)}(\tfrac{1}{2}z) = I_{(1/2)-a}(\tfrac{1}{2}z) - \frac{2\pi^{-(1/2)}(\frac{1}{4}z)^{a-(1/2)}}{\Gamma(a)} \int_0^\infty (1 + u^2)^{a-1} \sin \tfrac{1}{2}zu \, du, \quad (4.46)$$

in agreement with (3.105).

4.5 Generalized Modified Struve Function $\overline{\Omega}$ $(a, c; z)$

By analogy with (4.7) we define

$$\overline{\Omega}(a, c; z) = z^{1-c}\Omega(a - c + 1, 2 - c; z). \quad (4.47)$$

When $c = 2a$, from (4.34),

$$\overline{\Omega}(a, 2a; z) = \Gamma(\tfrac{3}{2} - a)(4z)^{(1/2)-a}e^{(1/2)z}L_{(1/2)-a}(\tfrac{1}{2}z). \quad (4.48)$$

From (4.41) and (4.47), using the relations for Ψ given by Erdélyi [*257*, 1953a], we see that

$$\overline{\Omega}(a, c; z) = \frac{\Gamma(2 - c)}{\Gamma(1 - a)} e^{i\pi(a-c)\varepsilon}\Psi(a, c; z)$$
$$- \frac{\Gamma(2 - c)}{\Gamma(a - c + 1)} e^{i\pi a\varepsilon}e^z\Psi(c - a, c; -z)$$
$$+ \frac{2e^{\pi i a}\Gamma(2 - c)}{\Gamma(1 - a)\Gamma(a - c + 1)} z^{1-c}e^{(1/2)z}$$
$$\times \int_0^{\infty \exp(i\pi - i\theta)} e^{zv}(v + \tfrac{1}{2})^{a-c}(v - \tfrac{1}{2})^{-a} \, dv. \quad (4.49)$$

We note that (4.41) and (4.49) are true for all values of a and c.

$\overline{\Omega}$ is a many-valued function of z. We shall consider its principal branch in the z plane with a cut along the negative real axis.

4.6 Relations Between Contiguous Functions

The four functions $\Omega(a + 1, c; z)$, $\Omega(a - 1, c; z)$, $\Omega(a, c + 1; z)$ and $\Omega(a, c - 1; z)$ are said to be *contiguous* to $\Omega(a, c; z)$. We shall now derive linear relations between $\Omega(a, c; z)$ and these contiguous functions.

Consider the integral

$$I(a, c; z) = \int_0^{\infty \exp(i\pi - i\theta)} e^{z[v+(1/2)]}(v + \tfrac{1}{2})^{a-1}(v - \tfrac{1}{2})^{c-a-1}\, dv. \tag{4.50}$$

Now

$$I(a + 1, c; z) = I(a, c; z) + I(a, c - 1; z). \tag{4.51}$$

Integrating (4.50) by parts we obtain

$$\begin{aligned} zI(a, c; z) = e^{i\pi(c-a)}2^{2-c}e^{(1/2)z} &- (a - 1)I(a - 1, c - 1; z) \\ &- (c - a - 1)I(a, c - 1; z); \end{aligned}$$

that is,

$$(c - a)I(a, c; z) + (a - 1)I(a - 1, c; z) + zI(a, c + 1; z) = -e^{i\pi(c-a)}2^{1-c}e^{(1/2)z}. \tag{4.52}$$

From (4.50),

$$\frac{dI(a, c; z)}{dz} = I(a + 1, c + 1; z). \tag{4.53}$$

From (4.41), (4.51), and (4.52), using the recurrence formulas for Ψ given by Erdélyi [*257*, 1953a], we find that

$$(a - c + 1)\Omega(a, c; z) - a\Omega(a + 1, c; z) + (c - 1)\Omega(a, c - 1; z) = 0 \tag{4.54}$$

and

$$\Omega(a, c; z) - \Omega(a - 1, c; z) - zc^{-1}\Omega(a, c + 1; z) = \frac{2^{2-c}\Gamma(c)}{\Gamma(a)\Gamma(c - a + 1)}\, e^{(1/2)z}. \tag{4.55}$$

From (4.54) and (4.55),

$$(a + z)\Omega(a, c; z) - \frac{(c - a)z}{c}\,\Omega(a, c + 1; z) - a\Omega(a + 1, c; z) = -\frac{2^{2-c}\Gamma(c)}{\Gamma(a)\Gamma(c - a)}\, e^{(1/2)z}. \tag{4.56}$$

From (4.55) and (4.56),

$$(c - a)\Omega(a - 1, c; z) + (2a - c + z)\Omega(a, c; z) - a\Omega(a + 1, c; z) = -\frac{2^{3-c}\Gamma(c)}{\Gamma(a)\Gamma(c - a)}\, e^{(1/2)z}. \tag{4.57}$$

From (4.54) and (4.56),

$$(c-1)\Omega(a, c-1; z) - (c-1+z)\Omega(a, c; z) + \frac{(c-a)z}{c}\Omega(a, c+1; z) = \frac{2^{2-c}\Gamma(c)}{\Gamma(a)\Gamma(c-a)} e^{(1/2)z}. \quad (4.58)$$

From (4.54) and (4.57),

$$(a-1+z)\Omega(a, c; z) + (c-a)\Omega(a-1, c; z) - (c-1)\Omega(a, c-1; z) = -\frac{2^{3-c}\Gamma(c)}{\Gamma(a)\Gamma(c-a)} e^{(1/2)z}. \quad (4.59)$$

From (4.54), (4.55), and (4.57),

$$(c-1)\Omega(a-1, c-1; z) + (1-c+z)\Omega(a, c; z) - \frac{az}{c}\Omega(a+1, c+1; z) = -\frac{2^{2-c}\Gamma(c)}{\Gamma(a)\Gamma(c-a)} e^{(1/2)z}. \quad (4.60)$$

Similarly, using (4.47), we find that

$$\bar{\Omega}(a, c; z) - \bar{\Omega}(a+1, c; z) - \frac{1}{c-2}\bar{\Omega}(a, c-1; z) = -\frac{2^{c}\Gamma(2-c)}{\Gamma(a-c+2)\Gamma(1-a)} e^{(1/2)z} z^{1-c}, \quad (4.61)$$

$$(c-a)\bar{\Omega}(a, c; z) + (a-1)\bar{\Omega}(a-1, c; z) - (c-1)\bar{\Omega}(a, c+1; z) = 0, \quad (4.62)$$

$$(a+z)\bar{\Omega}(a, c; z) - (c-1)z\bar{\Omega}(a, c+1; z) + (c-a-1)\bar{\Omega}(a+1, c; z) = -\frac{2^{c+1}\Gamma(2-c)}{\Gamma(a-c+1)\Gamma(1-a)} e^{(1/2)z} z^{1-c}, \quad (4.63)$$

$$(a-1)\bar{\Omega}(a-1, c; z) - (2a-c+z)\bar{\Omega}(a, c; z) - (c-a-1)\bar{\Omega}(a+1, c; z) = \frac{2^{c+1}\Gamma(2-c)}{\Gamma(a-c+1)\Gamma(1-a)} e^{(1/2)z} z^{1-c}, \quad (4.64)$$

$$\frac{c-a-1}{c-2}\bar{\Omega}(a, c-1; z) - (c-1+z)\bar{\Omega}(a, c; z) + (c-1)z\bar{\Omega}(a, c+1; z) = \frac{2^{c}\Gamma(2-c)}{\Gamma(a-c+1)\Gamma(1-a)} e^{(1/2)z} z^{1-c}, \quad (4.65)$$

$$(a-1+z)\bar{\Omega}(a, c; z) - (a-1)\bar{\Omega}(a-1, c; z) - \frac{c-a-1}{c-2}\bar{\Omega}(a, c-1; z)$$
$$= -\frac{2^c\Gamma(2-c)}{\Gamma(a-c+1)\Gamma(1-a)} e^{(1/2)z} z^{1-c}, \quad (4.66)$$

and

$$\frac{a-1}{c-2}\bar{\Omega}(a-1, c-1; z) - (1-c+z)\bar{\Omega}(a, c; z) - (c-1)z\bar{\Omega}(a+1, c+1; z)$$
$$= \frac{2^c\Gamma(2-c)}{\Gamma(a-c+1)\Gamma(1-a)} e^{(1/2)z} z^{1-c} \quad (4.67)$$

4.7 Differential Equations Satisfied by $\Omega(a, c; z)$ and $\bar{\Omega}(a, c; z)$

From (4.41) and (4.53), using the recurrence formulas for Ψ given by Erdélyi [*257*, 1953a], we see that

$$\frac{d\Omega(a, c; z)}{dz} = \frac{a}{c}\Omega(a+1, c+1; z) \quad (4.68)$$

and

$$\frac{d^n\Omega(a, c; z)}{dz^n} = \frac{\Gamma(a+n)\Gamma(c)}{\Gamma(a)\Gamma(c+n)}\Omega(a+n, c+n; z). \quad (4.69)$$

These formulas can be used, in conjunction with Taylor's series, to express $\Omega(a, c; z)$ as a power series in z (see §4.10).

From (4.60), (4.68), and (4.69), we find that $\Omega(a, c; z)$ satisfies the nonhomogeneous linear differential equation

$$z\frac{d^2y}{dz^2} + (c-z)\frac{dy}{dz} - ay = \frac{2^{1-c}\Gamma(c)}{\Gamma(a)\Gamma(c-a)} e^{(1/2)z}. \quad (4.70)$$

The associated homogeneous equation is the confluent hypergeometric equation (4.1), which has one regular singularity at $z = 0$ and an irregular singular point at infinity. The complete primitive of (4.70) is $C_1\Phi(a, c; z) + C_2\bar{\Phi}(a, c; z) + \Omega(a, c; z)$, where C_1 and C_2 are arbitrary constants.

From (4.68) we find that

$$\frac{d}{dz}[e^{-z}\Omega(a, c; z)] = -\frac{c-a}{c} e^{-z}\Omega(a, c+1; z) \quad (4.71)$$

and

$$\frac{d^n}{dz^n}[e^{-z}\Omega(a, c; z)] = (-1)^n\frac{\Gamma(c-a+n)\Gamma(c)}{\Gamma(c-a)\Gamma(c+n)} e^{-z}\Omega(a, c+n; z). \quad (4.72)$$

Similarly, using (4.47), we find that

$$\frac{d\bar{\Omega}(a,c;z)}{dz} = -(c-1)\bar{\Omega}(a+1,c+1;z) - \frac{2^c\Gamma(2-c)}{\Gamma(a-c+1)\Gamma(1-a)}\, e^{(1/2)z}z^{-c}, \tag{4.73}$$

and

$$\frac{d^2\bar{\Omega}(a,c;z)}{dz^2} = c(c-1)\bar{\Omega}(a+2,c+2;z) + \frac{2^c\Gamma(2-c)}{\Gamma(a-c+1)\Gamma(1-a)}\, e^{(1/2)z}z^{-c-1}(2a+c-\tfrac{1}{2}z). \tag{4.74}$$

From (4.67), (4.73), and (4.74), we find that $\bar{\Omega}(a,c;z)$ satisfies the nonhomogeneous linear differential equation

$$z\frac{d^2y}{dz^2} + (c-z)\frac{dy}{dz} - ay = \frac{2^{c-1}\Gamma(2-c)}{\Gamma(a-c+1)\Gamma(1-a)}\, e^{(1/2)z}z^{1-c}. \tag{4.75}$$

By differentiating (4.70) and (4.75), it can be shown that $\Omega(a,c;z)$ and $\bar{\Omega}(a,c;z)$ are, respectively, the solutions of the homogeneous third-order equations

$$z\frac{d^3y}{dz^3} + (c+1-\tfrac{3}{2}z)\frac{d^2y}{dz^2} - (\tfrac{1}{2}c+a+1-\tfrac{1}{2}z)\frac{dy}{dz} + \tfrac{1}{2}ay = 0 \tag{4.76}$$

and

$$z\frac{d^3y}{dz^3} + (2c-\tfrac{3}{2}z)\frac{d^2y}{dz^2} - \left\{\tfrac{3}{2}c+a-\tfrac{1}{2}z+\frac{c(1-c)}{z}\right\}\frac{dy}{dz} + \left\{\frac{1}{2}+\frac{1-c}{z}\right\}ay = 0. \tag{4.77}$$

The other solutions of (4.76) and (4.77) are $\Phi(a,c;z)$ and $\bar{\Phi}(a,c;z)$.

4.8 Particular Values of $\Omega(a,c;z)$ and $\bar{\Omega}(a,c;z)$

DETERMINATION OF $\Omega(a,c;0)$

From (4.35) and (4.36), for $\operatorname{Re} c > \operatorname{Re} a > 0$,

$$\Omega(a,c;0) = \frac{\Gamma(c)}{\Gamma(a)\Gamma(c-a)}\,[B_{1/2}(c-a,a) - B_{1/2}(a,c-a)], \tag{4.78}$$

where

$$B_{1/2}(c-a,a) = 2^{1-c}\int_0^1 (1+u)^{a-1}(1-u)^{c-a-1}\,du,$$

that is,

$$B_{1/2}(c-a, a) = \int_0^{1/2} t^{c-a-1}(1-t)^{a-1}\, dt, \tag{4.79}$$

on putting $t = \frac{1}{2}(1-u)$. $B_{1/2}$ is the incomplete beta function (see Problem 5, Chapter 1).

If either a or $c-a$ are positive integers, $\Omega(a, c; 0)$ can be found from (4.78) and (4.79) in terms of elementary functions. Thus $\Omega(1, c; 0) = 2^{2-c} - 1$ $(c > 1)$.

The corresponding formula for the confluent hypergeometric function is

$$\Phi(a, c; 0) = \frac{\Gamma(c)}{\Gamma(a)\Gamma(c-a)}[B_{1/2}(c-a, a) + B_{1/2}(a, c-a)] = 1, \tag{4.80}$$

since $B_{1/2}(c-a, a) + B_{1/2}(a, c-a) = B(c-a, a)$.

From (4.79), for real values of a and c $(c > a > 0)$, the integrals are finite and positive and

$$B_{1/2}(c-a, a) > \text{ or } < B_{1/2}(a, c-a) \quad \text{as} \quad 2a > \text{ or } < c.$$

Thus, from (4.78) and (4.80), for real values of a and c,

$$1 > \Omega(a, c; 0) > 0 \qquad \text{if} \quad 2a > c > a > 0 \tag{4.81}$$

and

$$0 > \Omega(a, c; 0) > -1 \qquad \text{if} \quad c > 2a > 0. \tag{4.82}$$

Equation (4.77) only holds for $\operatorname{Re} c > \operatorname{Re} a > 0$. For values of a and c outside this range, $\Omega(a, c; 0)$ can be found by using the relations between contiguous functions given in §4.6.

Thus, from (4.55), on replacing a by $a+1$,

$$\Omega(a+1, c; 0) - \Omega(a, c; 0) = \frac{2^{2-c}\Gamma(c)}{\Gamma(a+1)\Gamma(c-a)} \qquad (c \neq 0). \tag{4.83}$$

From (4.58),

$$\Omega(a, c-1; 0) - \Omega(a, c; 0) = \frac{2^{2-c}\Gamma(c-1)}{\Gamma(a)\Gamma(c-a)} \qquad (c \neq 0, 1). \tag{4.84}$$

From (4.60),

$$\Omega(a-1, c-1; 0) - \Omega(a, c; 0) = -\frac{2^{2-c}\Gamma(c-1)}{\Gamma(a)\Gamma(c-a)} \qquad (c \neq 0, 1). \tag{4.85}$$

From (4.84) and (4.85),

$$\Omega(a+1, c+2; 0) - \Omega(a, c; 0) = -\frac{2^{-c}(2a-c)\Gamma(c)}{\Gamma(a+1)\Gamma(c-a+1)}$$

$$(c \neq 0, -1, -2). \quad (4.86)$$

Now, if $c = 2a$, from (4.78), for Re $a > 0$,

$$\Omega(a, 2a; 0) = 0. \quad (4.87)$$

Using (4.86), we see that (4.87) applies for all values of $2a$, except zero and negative integral values.

SPECIAL VALUES OF $\Omega(a, c; 0)$

We shall consider first the values of $\Omega(a, c; 0)$ when either a or $c - a$ (but not both) is zero or a negative integer. In these cases (4.70) reduces to the confluent hypergeometric equation.

When a is zero or a negative integer, from (4.26) and (4.31),

$$\omega = -y_3$$

and

$$\Omega(a, c; z) = -\Phi(a, c; z). \quad (4.88)$$

Then

$$\Omega(a, c; 0) = -1. \quad (4.89)$$

When $c - a$ is zero or negative integer, from (4.26) and (4.31),

$$\omega = y_3$$

and

$$\Omega(a, c; z) = \Phi(a, c; z). \quad (4.90)$$

Then

$$\Omega(a, c; 0) = 1. \quad (4.91)$$

Equations (4.88) to (4.91) are not valid when c is zero or a negative integer.

Considered as a function of c, we see from (4.30) that $\Omega(a, c; z)$ has poles at the poles of $\Gamma(c)$, that is, at $c = 0, -1, -2, \ldots$ (if a or $c - a$ is also zero or a negative integer, the function is indeterminate). However, $\Omega(a, c; z)/\Gamma(c)$ is an entire function of a, c, and z; this is considered further in §4.11. As shown in §4.11, when a is an integer,

$$\lim_{c \to 1-n} \frac{\Omega(a, c; 0)}{\Gamma(c)} = 0 \qquad (n = 1, 2, 3, \ldots). \quad (4.92)$$

VALUES OF $\Omega(a, c; 0)$ FOR LARGE VALUES OF THE PARAMETERS

Consider the variation of the right side of (4.36) as $\operatorname{Re} a \to \infty$ while c is a constant ($\operatorname{Re} c > 0$).
Then

$$\frac{1}{\Gamma(a)\Gamma(c-a)} = \frac{1}{\Gamma(1-c+a)\Gamma(c-a)} \frac{\Gamma(1-c+a)}{\Gamma(a)} \sim 0(a^{1-c})$$

and the integral on the right side of (4.36) is $0(a^{-1})$. Thus, from (4.36), when $\operatorname{Re} a \to \infty$ while c is a constant ($\operatorname{Re} c > 0$),

$$\lim_{\operatorname{Re} a \to \infty} |\Omega(a, c; z) - \Phi(a, c; z)| = 0, \tag{4.93}$$

and thus

$$\lim_{\operatorname{Re} a \to \infty} \Omega(a, c; 0) = 1. \tag{4.94}$$

Similarly, from (4.35), when $\operatorname{Re} a \to -\infty$ while c is a constant ($\operatorname{Re} c > 0$),

$$\lim_{\operatorname{Re} a \to -\infty} |\Omega(a, c; z) + \Phi(a, c; z)| = 0, \tag{4.95}$$

and thus

$$\lim_{\operatorname{Re} a \to -\infty} \Omega(a, c; 0) = -1. \tag{4.96}$$

From (4.78) and (4.80), for $\operatorname{Re} c > \operatorname{Re} a > 0$,

$$\Omega(a, c; 0) = \frac{B_{1/2}(c-a, a) - B_{1/2}(a, c-a)}{B_{1/2}(c-a, a) + B_{1/2}(a, c-a)}, \tag{4.97}$$

where $B_{1/2}(c-a, a)$ is given by (4.79). When $\operatorname{Re} c \to \infty$ while a is a constant ($\operatorname{Re} a > 0$),

$$|2^{c-1}B_{1/2}(c-a, a)| \to 0 \qquad \text{and} \qquad |2^{c-1}B_{1/2}(a, c-a)| \to \infty.$$

Then, from (4.97),

$$\Omega(a, c; 0) \to -1. \tag{4.98}$$

When $\operatorname{Re} c \to \infty$ while $c - a$ is a constant ($\operatorname{Re} c > \operatorname{Re} a > 0$),

$$|2^{c-1}B_{1/2}(c-a, a)| \to \infty \qquad \text{and} \qquad |2^{c-1}B_{1/2}(a, c-a)| \to 0.$$

Then, from (4.97),

$$\Omega(a, c; 0) \to 1. \tag{4.99}$$

DETERMINATION OF $\overline{\Omega}(a, c; 0)$

$\overline{\Omega}(a, c; 0)$ can be found from (4.47). We see that $\overline{\Omega}(a, c; 0)$ is zero if $c < 1$, is equal to $\Omega(a, 1; 0)$ if $c = 1$, and is infinite if $c > 1$.

Using (4.88) and (4.90), we find that, when a is a positive integer,

$$\overline{\Omega}(a, c; z) = z^{1-c}\Phi(a - c + 1, 2 - c; z), \tag{4.100}$$

if $c - 1$ is not a positive integer.

When $c - a$ is a positive integer,

$$\overline{\Omega}(a, c; z) = -z^{1-c}\Phi(a - c + 1, 2 - c; z), \tag{4.101}$$

if $c - 1$ is not a positive integer.

Considered as a function of c, $\overline{\Omega}(a, c; z)$ has poles at the poles of $\Gamma(2 - c)$, that is, at $c = 2, 3, 4, \ldots$ (if a or $c - a$ is also a positive integer, the function is indeterminate). $\overline{\Omega}(a, c; z)/\Gamma(2 - c)$ is an entire function of a, c, and z (except, possibly, for $z = 0$).

4.9 Transformation Formulas for $\Omega(a, c; z)$ and $\overline{\Omega}(a, c; z)$

From (4.30) and (4.31),

$$\Omega(a, c; z) = -e^{z}\Omega(c - a, c; -z). \tag{4.102}$$

This corresponds to Kummer's transformation formula for $\Phi(a, c; z)$. In particular,

$$\Omega(a, c; 0) = -\Omega(c - a, c; 0). \tag{4.103}$$

Similarly, using (4.47), and remembering that for $\overline{\Omega}$ there is a cut along the negative real axis (§4.5), we find that

$$\overline{\Omega}(a, c; z) = e^{-i\pi c\varepsilon}e^{z}\overline{\Omega}(c - a, c; -z), \tag{4.104}$$

where $\varepsilon = \operatorname{sgn}(\operatorname{Im} z) = 1, -1$, according as $\operatorname{Im} z > 0, < 0$.

4.10 Power Series for $\Omega(a, c; z)$

The expansion of $\Omega(a, c; z)$ as a power series in z can be found most easily by means of a Taylor-series expansion, using (4.68) and (4.69). We find that, if c is not zero or a negative integer,

$$\Omega(a, c; z) = \Omega(a, c; 0) + \frac{a}{c}\,\Omega(a + 1, c + 1; 0)\frac{z}{1!} + \frac{a(a + 1)}{c(c + 1)}\,\Omega(a + 2, c + 2; 0)\frac{z^2}{2!} + \cdots \tag{4.105}$$

Using the results of §4.8, we see that

$$\lim_{n\to\infty} \Omega(a+n, c+n; 0) = 1 \qquad (\operatorname{Re} c > \operatorname{Re} a)$$

and hence the power series (4.105) is convergent for all z ($\operatorname{Re} c > \operatorname{Re} a$). The corresponding series for $\Phi(a, c; z)$ is

$$\Phi(a, c; z) = \Phi(a, c; 0) + \frac{a}{c}\Phi(a+1, c+1; 0)\frac{z}{1!} + \frac{a(a+1)}{c(c+1)}\Phi(a+2, c+2; 0)\frac{z^2}{2!} + \cdots$$

$$= 1 + \frac{a}{c}\frac{z}{1!} + \frac{a(a+1)}{c(c+1)}\frac{z^2}{2!} + \cdots$$

$$= \sum_{n=0}^{\infty} \frac{\Gamma(a+n)\Gamma(c)}{\Gamma(a)\Gamma(c+n)}\frac{z^n}{n!}. \tag{4.106}$$

From (4.105) and (4.106),

$$\Omega(a, c; z) - \Omega(a, c; 0)\Phi(a, c; z) = \sum_{n=1}^{\infty} \frac{\Gamma(a+n)\Gamma(c)}{\Gamma(a)\Gamma(c+n)}[\Omega(a+n, c+n; 0) - \Omega(a, c; 0)]\frac{z^n}{n!};$$

that is, using (4.85),

$$\Omega(a, c; z) - \Omega(a, c; 0)\Phi(a, c; z) = \frac{2^{1-c}\Gamma(c)}{\Gamma(a+1)\Gamma(c-a)} \sum_{n=1}^{\infty} \frac{\Gamma(a+n)\Gamma(c)}{\Gamma(a)\Gamma(c+n)} F_{(n)}(1, c; a+1; \tfrac{1}{2})\frac{z^n}{n!}, \tag{4.107}$$

where $F_{(n)}$ stands for the first n terms of the hypergeometric series with the given parameters.

From (4.69), we have, using Taylor's expansion,

$$\Omega(a, c; y+z) = \sum_{n=0}^{\infty} \frac{z^n}{n!}\frac{d^n}{dy^n}\Omega(a, c; y)$$

$$= \sum_{n=0}^{\infty} \frac{\Gamma(a+n)\Gamma(c)}{\Gamma(a)\Gamma(c+n)}\Omega(a+n, c+n; y)\frac{z^n}{n!}. \tag{4.108}$$

The coefficients of the power series (4.105) can be expressed in terms of incomplete beta functions. From (4.78) and (4.105), for $\operatorname{Re} c > \operatorname{Re} a > 0$,

$$\Omega(a, c; z) = \frac{\Gamma(c)}{\Gamma(a)\Gamma(c-a)} \sum_{n=0}^{\infty} [B_{1/2}(c-a, a+n) - B_{1/2}(a+n, c-a)]\frac{z^n}{n!}. \tag{4.109}$$

From (4.105) and (4.106), using (4.35) and (4.36), we find that

$$\Phi(a, c; z) + \Omega(a, c; z) = 2\frac{\Gamma(c)}{\Gamma(a)\Gamma(c-a)}\sum_{n=0}^{\infty} B_{1/2}(c-a, a+n)\frac{z^n}{n!} \qquad (\operatorname{Re} c > \operatorname{Re} a) \quad (4.110)$$

and

$$\Phi(a, c; z) - \Omega(a, c; z) = 2\frac{\Gamma(c)}{\Gamma(a)\Gamma(c-a)}\sum_{n=0}^{\infty} B_{1/2}(a+n, c-a)\frac{z^n}{n!} \qquad (\operatorname{Re} a > 0). \quad (4.111)$$

Now for all real values of p and q, $B_{1/2}(p, q)$ is positive. Thus, for $c > a > 0$, for all positive values of z,

$$|\Phi(a, c; z)| \geqslant |\Omega(a, c; z)|. \qquad (4.112)$$

Using (4.102) and the corresponding formula for $\Phi(a, c; z)$, we see that (4.112) applies also for all negative values of z (for $c > a > 0$).

More generally, if a, c, and z are all real, we see from (4.35) that, if $c > a$, the sign of $\{\Phi(a, c; z) + \Omega(a, c; z)\}$ is the same as that of $\Gamma(c)/\Gamma(a)$. Similarly, from (4.36), if a, c, and z are all real and $a > 0$, the sign of $\{\Phi(a, c; z) - \Omega(a, c; z)\}$ is the same as that of $\Gamma(c)/\Gamma(c-a)$.

From §4.8, if $\operatorname{Re} c \to \infty$ while a is a constant ($\operatorname{Re} a > 0$), using (4.98) and (4.105), we see that

$$\Omega(a, c; z) = -\lim_{c\to\infty}\Phi(a, c; z) = -1 + 0(|c|^{-1}). \qquad (4.113)$$

Similarly, if $\operatorname{Re} c \to \infty$ while $c - a$ is a constant ($\operatorname{Re} c > \operatorname{Re} a > 0$), from (4.102) and (4.113),

$$\Omega(a, c; z) = -e^z \lim_{c\to\infty}\Omega(c-a, c; -z) = e^z[1 + 0(|c|^{-1})]. \qquad (4.114)$$

The asymptotic expansion of $\Omega(a, c; z)$ for large values of z is given in §4.15.

4.11 Degenerate Cases of $\Omega(a, c; z)$

When a is zero or a negative integer, and c is not zero or a negative integer, the power series (4.105) terminates and, as shown in §4.8,

$$\Omega(a, c; z) = -\Phi(a, c; z).$$

As shown by Erdélyi [*268*, 1953a], $\Phi(a, c; z)$ can then be expressed in terms of Laguerre polynomials. In particular,

$$\Omega(0, c; z) = -1. \qquad (4.115)$$

When $a = 1 - n$ (n being a positive integer), a particular solution of

$$z\frac{d^2y}{dz^2} + (c - z)\frac{dy}{dz} - ay = \frac{2^{1-c}\Gamma(c)}{\Gamma(c - a)}\, e^{(1/2)z}$$

is

$$\lim_{a \to 1-n} \{\Gamma(a)[\Omega(a, c; z) + \Phi(a, c; z)]\}.$$

The power series for the latter function can be found from (4.110), for $\operatorname{Re} c > \operatorname{Re} a$.

Similarly, as shown in §4.8, when $c - a$ is zero or a negative integer, and c is not zero or a negative integer,

$$\Omega(a, c; z) = \Phi(a, c; z).$$

As shown by Erdélyi [*268*, 1953a], $\Phi(a, c; z)$ can then be expressed in terms of Laguerre polynomials. In particular,

$$\Omega(a, a; z) = \Phi(a, a; z) = e^z. \tag{4.116}$$

When $c - a = 1 - n$ (n being a positive integer), a particular solution of

$$z\frac{d^2y}{dz^2} + (c - z)\frac{dy}{dz} - ay = \frac{2^{1-c}\Gamma(c)}{\Gamma(a)}\, e^{(1/2)z}$$

is

$$\lim_{c-a \to 1-n} \{\Gamma(c - a)[\Omega(a, c; z) - \Phi(a, c; z)]\}.$$

The power series for the latter function can be found from (4.111), for $\operatorname{Re} a > 0$.

As shown in §4.8, $\Omega(a, c; z)$ has poles at $c = 0 -1, -2, \ldots$. From (4.47),

$$\Omega(a, 1; z) = \bar{\Omega}(a, 1; z). \tag{4.117}$$

We shall now show that, when $c = 1 - n$ (n being a negative integer), $\lim_{c \to 1-n} \Omega(a, c; z)/\Gamma(c)$ can be expressed in terms of $\bar{\Omega}(a, 1 - n; z)$.

From (4.58), replacing c by $c + 1$, we obtain

$$c\Omega(a, c; z) - (c + z)\Omega(a, c + 1; z) + \frac{c - a + 1}{c + 1}\, z\Omega(a, c + 2; z)$$
$$= \frac{2^{1-c}\Gamma(c + 1)}{\Gamma(a)\Gamma(c - a + 1)}\, e^{(1/2)z}, \tag{4.118}$$

and, from (4.54), replacing c by $c + 2$, we obtain

$$(a - c - 1)\Omega(a, c + 2; z) - a\Omega(a + 1, c + 2; z) + (c + 1)\Omega(a, c + 1; z) = 0. \tag{4.119}$$

From (4.118) and (4.119), eliminating $\Omega(a, c+2; z)$, we obtain

$$c\Omega(a, c; z) - c\Omega(a, c+1; z) - \frac{az}{c+1}\,\Omega(a+1, c+2; z) = \frac{2^{1-c}\Gamma(c+1)}{\Gamma(a)\Gamma(c-a+1)}\,e^{(1/2)z}; \quad (4.120)$$

that is,

$$\frac{\Omega(a, c; z)}{\Gamma(c)} = c\,\frac{\Omega(a, c+1; z)}{\Gamma(c+1)} + az\,\frac{\Omega(a+1, c+2; z)}{\Gamma(c+2)} + \frac{2^{1-c}}{\Gamma(a)\Gamma(c-a+1)}\,e^{(1/2)z}. \quad (4.121)$$

Thus

$$\lim_{c\to 0}\frac{\Omega(a, c; z)}{\Gamma(c)} = az\Omega(a+1, 2; z) + \frac{2e^{(1/2)z}}{\Gamma(a)\Gamma(1-a)}; \quad (4.122)$$

that is, from (4.47),

$$\lim_{c\to 0}\frac{\Omega(a, c; z)}{\Gamma(c)} = a\overline{\Omega}(a, 0; z) + \frac{2e^{(1/2)z}}{\Gamma(a)\Gamma(1-a)}. \quad (4.123)$$

Now, from (4.58),

$$\frac{\Omega(a, c-1; z)}{\Gamma(c-1)} - (c-1+z)\frac{\Omega(a, c; z)}{\Gamma(c)} + (c-a)z\,\frac{\Omega(a, c+1; z)}{\Gamma(c+1)} = \frac{2^{2-c}}{\Gamma(a)\Gamma(c-a)}\,e^{(1/2)z}, \quad (4.124)$$

and, from (4.65), on multiplying both sides of the equation by $\Gamma(a-c+1)/\Gamma(a)\Gamma(2-c)$, we obtain

$$\frac{\Gamma(a-c+2)}{\Gamma(a)\Gamma(3-c)}\overline{\Omega}(a, c-1; z) - (c-1+z)\,\frac{\Gamma(a-c+1)}{\Gamma(a)\Gamma(2-c)}\,\overline{\Omega}(a, c; z) + (c-a)z\,\frac{\Gamma(a-c)}{\Gamma(a)\Gamma(1-c)}\,\overline{\Omega}(a, c+1; z) = \frac{2^{c}}{\Gamma(a)\Gamma(1-a)}\,e^{(1/2)z}z^{1-c}. \quad (4.125)$$

From (4.124) and (4.125), using (4.117) and (4.123), we find that

$$\lim_{c\to 1-n}\frac{\Omega(a, c; z)}{\Gamma(c)} = \frac{\Gamma(a+n)}{\Gamma(a)\Gamma(n+1)}\,\overline{\Omega}(a, 1-n; z) + \frac{e^{(1/2)z}}{\Gamma(a)\Gamma(1-a)}f_n(z) \quad (n = 0, 1, 2, \ldots), \quad (4.126)$$

where $f_0 = 0, f_1 = 2$, and

$$f_n + (n - z - 1)f_{n-1} + (a + n - 2)zf_{n-2} = \frac{2^n\Gamma(1-a)}{\Gamma(2-n-a)} - 2^{2-n}z^{n-1} \qquad (n \geqslant 2).$$

We see that $f_n(z)$ is a polynomial in z of degree $n - 1$ $(n \geqslant 1)$.

Alternatively, from (4.47),

$$\lim_{c\to 1-n} \frac{\Omega(a, c; z)}{\Gamma(c)} = \frac{\Gamma(a+n)}{\Gamma(a)} \frac{z^n}{n!} \Omega(a + n, n + 1; z) + \frac{e^{(1/2)z} f_n(z)}{\Gamma(a)\Gamma(1-a)} \qquad (n = 0, 1, 2, \ldots). \quad (4.127)$$

We note that, when a is an integer, the second term on the right side of (4.127) vanishes.

4.12 Other Particular Cases of $\Omega(a, c; z)$

In §4.11 we considered certain degenerate cases of $\Omega(a, c; z)$, and in §4.3 we saw that, if $c = 2a$, $\Omega(a, c; z)$ can be expressed in terms of Struve functions (see Chapter 3). Thus

$$\Omega(a, 2a; z) = \Gamma(a + \tfrac{1}{2})(\tfrac{1}{4}z)^{(1/2)-a} e^{(1/2)z} L_{a-(1/2)}(\tfrac{1}{2}z) \qquad (4.128)$$

and

$$\Omega(a, 2a; iz) = i\Gamma(a + \tfrac{1}{2})(\tfrac{1}{4}z)^{(1/2)-a} e^{(1/2)iz} H_{a-(1/2)}(\tfrac{1}{2}z). \qquad (4.129)$$

In certain cases, $\Omega(a, c; z)$ can be expressed in terms of incomplete gamma functions. When $a = 1$, from (4.35),

$$\Phi(1, c; z) + \Omega(1, c; z) = 2^{2-c}(c-1)e^{(1/2)z} \int_0^1 e^{(1/2)zu}(1-u)^{c-2}\, du$$

$$= 2(c-1)z^{1-c}e^z \int_0^{(1/2)z} e^{-v}v^{c-2}\, dv \qquad (\text{Re } c > 1),$$

on putting $v = \tfrac{1}{2}z(1 - u)$; i.e., in terms of the incomplete gamma function (see Problem 4, Chapter 1),

$$\Phi(1, c; z) + \Omega(1, c; z) = 2(c-1)z^{1-c}e^z\gamma(c - 1, \tfrac{1}{2}z) \qquad (\text{Re } c > 1). \quad (4.130)$$

Similarly, from (4.36),

$$\Phi(1, c; z) - \Omega(1, c; z) = 2^{2-c}(c-1)e^{(1/2)z} \int_0^1 e^{-(1/2)zu}(1+u)^{c-2}\, du$$

$$= 2(c-1)z^{1-c}e^z \int_{(1/2)z}^{z} e^{-v}v^{c-2}\, dv,$$

on putting $v = \frac{1}{2}z(1 + u)$; i.e., in terms of the incomplete gamma function,

$$\Phi(1, c; z) - \Omega(1, c; z) = 2(c-1)z^{1-c}e^{z}[\gamma(c-1, z) - \gamma(c-1, \tfrac{1}{2}z)] \qquad (\operatorname{Re} c > 1). \quad (4.131)$$

From (4.130) and (4.131), we have

$$\Omega(1, c; z) = (1-c)z^{1-c}e^{z}[\gamma(c-1, z) - 2\gamma(c-1, \tfrac{1}{2}z)] \qquad (\operatorname{Re} c > 1). \quad (4.132)$$

Using (4.115) and the recurrence formulas for Ω, we see that when a is any positive integer, $\Omega(a, c; z)$ can be expressed in terms of incomplete gamma functions.

From (4.102) and (4.132), if $\operatorname{Re} c > 1$,

$$\Omega(c-1, c; -z) = (c-1)z^{1-c}[\gamma(c-1, z) - 2\gamma(c-1, \tfrac{1}{2}z)]. \quad (4.133)$$

Using (4.116) and the recurrence formulas for Ω, we see that when $c - a$ is any positive integer, $\Omega(c-a, c; z)$ can be expressed in terms of incomplete gamma functions.

When $c = \frac{1}{2}$ or $\frac{3}{2}$, $\Omega(a, c; z)$ and $\overline{\Omega}(a, c; z)$ can be expressed in terms of nonhomogeneous parabolic cylinder functions. This is considered in detail in Chapter 5. In particular, when $a = \frac{1}{2}$ and $c = \frac{3}{2}$, we find, from (4.133),

$$\Omega(\tfrac{1}{2}, \tfrac{3}{2}; -z) = \tfrac{1}{2}z^{-1/2}[\gamma(\tfrac{1}{2}, z) - 2\gamma(\tfrac{1}{2}, \tfrac{1}{2}z)]. \quad (4.134)$$

Now the error function erf x is given by

$$\operatorname{erf} x = \int_0^x e^{-t^2}\,dt = \tfrac{1}{2}\gamma(\tfrac{1}{2}, x^2). \quad (4.135)$$

From (4.134) and (4.135),

$$\Omega(\tfrac{1}{2}, \tfrac{3}{2}; -z^2) = z^{-1}\left[\operatorname{erf}(z) - 2\operatorname{erf}\left(\frac{z}{\sqrt{2}}\right)\right]. \quad (4.136)$$

4.13 Mellin-Barnes Integral for $\Omega(a, c; z)$

Consider the integral

$$I(z) = \int_C \frac{\Gamma(-s)\Gamma(a+s)}{\Gamma(c+s)}[\Omega(a+s, c+s; 0) - 1](-z)^s\,ds. \quad (4.137)$$

The contour for C consists of the line $s = \gamma$, parallel to the imaginary axis, together with the sector of the circle (center at the origin) of large radius $N + \frac{1}{2}$ lying to the right of this line, where N is an integer. We take $0 > \gamma > -\operatorname{Re} a$, and assume that $c \neq 0, 1, 2, \ldots$. We shall now show that the part of the integral arising from the sector of the circle vanishes as $N \to \infty$.

From (4.36), with $z = 0$,

$$\Omega(a, c; 0) - 1 = -2^{2-c}\frac{\Gamma(c)}{\Gamma(a)\Gamma(c-a)}\int_0^1 (1+u)^{c-a-1}(1-u)^{a-1}\,du$$

(Re $a > 0$)

and thus

$$\Omega(a+s, c+s; 0) - 1 = -2^{2-c-s}\frac{\Gamma(c+s)}{\Gamma(a+s)\Gamma(c-a)}$$

$$\times \int_0^1 (1+u)^{c-a-1}(1-u)^{a+s-1}\,du \qquad [\operatorname{Re}(a+s) > 0]. \quad (4.138)$$

Equation (4.137) can thus be written

$$I(z) = -\frac{1}{\Gamma(c-a)}\int_C \Gamma(-s)(-z)^s J(s)\,ds, \qquad (4.139)$$

where

$$J(s) = \int_0^1 \left(\frac{1+u}{2}\right)^{c-a-1}\left(\frac{1-u}{2}\right)^{a+s-1} du\,.$$

Now

$$|J(s)| < K\int_0^1 \left(\frac{1-u}{2}\right)^{\operatorname{Re}(a+s)-1} du = K\frac{2^{1-\operatorname{Re}(a+s)}}{\operatorname{Re}(a+s)} \qquad [\operatorname{Re}(a+s)] > 0, \quad (4.140)$$

where K is a constant which does not depend upon s. Finally, consider the value of

$$\Gamma(-s)(-z)^s = -\frac{\pi(-z)^s}{\Gamma(1+s)\sin\pi s}.$$

Put

$$s = (N + \tfrac{1}{2})e^{i\theta} = \xi + i\eta$$

and

$$-z = Re^{i\psi}.$$

Now, on the sector of the circle,

$$|\sin\pi s| = \sqrt{\sin^2\pi\xi + \sinh^2\pi\eta} = 0(\exp\pi|\eta|).$$

Using the asymptotic expansion of the gamma function, we find that

$$|\Gamma(-s)(-z)^s| = 0(\exp[\xi - (\xi + \tfrac{1}{2})\log(N + \tfrac{1}{2}) + \eta\theta - \pi|\eta| + \xi\log R - \eta\psi]). \quad (4.141)$$

Thus $\Gamma(-s)(-z)^s$ represents a function of s which tends to zero as $N \to \infty$ if $|\psi| \leqslant \frac{1}{2}\pi - \delta$, where δ is any positive quantity. From (4.141), if $|\arg(-z)| \leqslant \frac{1}{2}\pi - \delta$, on the sector of the circle,

$$|\Gamma(-s)(-z)^s| = 0[\exp(-N\delta)] \qquad \text{as} \quad N \to \infty . \tag{4.142}$$

From (4.139), (4.140), and (4.142), we see that the contribution to $I(z)$ which arises from the sector of the circle tends to zero as $N \to \infty$ when $|\arg(-z)| < \frac{1}{2}\pi$.

Now, in (4.137), the integrand has simple poles at $s = 0, 1, 2, 3, \ldots$. Thus

$$\int_{\gamma-i\infty}^{\gamma+i\infty} \frac{\Gamma(-s)\Gamma(a+s)}{\Gamma(c+s)} [\Omega(a+s, c+s; 0) - 1](-z)^s \, ds$$
$$= 2\pi i \sum_{n=0}^{\infty} \frac{\Gamma(a+n)}{\Gamma(c+n)} [\Omega(a+n, c+n; 0) - 1] \frac{z^n}{n!}. \tag{4.143}$$

Now, from Erdélyi [*256*, 1953a], if $|\arg(-z)| < \frac{1}{2}\pi$ and $0 > \gamma > -\operatorname{Re} a$,

$$\int_{\gamma-i\infty}^{\gamma+i\infty} \frac{\Gamma(-s)\Gamma(a+s)}{\Gamma(c+s)} (-z)^s \, ds = 2\pi i \frac{\Gamma(a)}{\Gamma(c)} \Phi(a, c; z). \tag{4.144}$$

From (4.143) and (4.144), using (4.105) amd (4.106), we obtain the Mellin-Barnes integral for $\Omega(a, c; z)$:

$$\Omega(a, c; z) = \frac{1}{2\pi i} \frac{\Gamma(c)}{\Gamma(a)} \int_{\gamma-i\infty}^{\gamma+1\infty} \frac{\Gamma(-s)\Gamma(a+s)}{\Gamma(c+s)} \Omega(a+s, c+s; 0)(-z)^s \, ds, \tag{4.145}$$

where $|\arg(-z)| < \frac{1}{2}\pi$, $0 > \gamma > -\operatorname{Re} a$, and c is not zero or a negative integer.

4.14 The Zeros of $\Omega(a, c; z)$, Where a and c Are Real

From (4.68), using Rolle's theorem, we see that, if c is not zero or a negative integer, between two consecutive zeros of $\Omega(a, c; z)$ there lies at least one zero of $\Omega(a+1, c+1; z)$. Similarly, from (4.71), if c is not zero or a negative integer, between two consecutive zeros of $\Omega(a, c; z)$ there lies at least one zero of $\Omega(a, c+1; z)$, if $c \neq a$. The converse of these two statements is not true.

Considering the coefficients of the terms in the power series (4.105), we see, on using (4.81), that if $2a > c > a > 0$, all the coefficients are positive. Thus $\Omega(a, c; z) > 0$ for all positive z if $2a > c > a > 0$.

If $c > 2a > 0$, the coefficients of the lower powers of z are negative, and those of all subsequent powers of z are positive. By an extension of Descartes' rule of signs to a convergent power series, we see that $\Omega(a, c; z)$ has one (and only one) positive zero if $c > 2a > 0$.

Using (4.102) and (4.103), we see that, if $2a > c > a > 0$, $\Omega(a, c; z)$ has one (and only one) negative zero. If $c > 2a > 0$, $\Omega(a, c; z) < 0$ for all negative z.

If $c = 2a > 0$, $\Omega(a, c; z)$ has a zero at $z = 0$ and is positive for $z > 0$, and negative for $z < 0$.

4.15 Asymptotic Expansion of $\Omega(a, c; z)$

From (4.41), putting $u = e^{-i\pi}zv$,

$$\Omega(a, c; z) = \frac{\Gamma(c)}{\Gamma(a)} e^{i\pi(a-c)\varepsilon} e^{z} \Psi(c - a, c; -z)$$

$$- \frac{\Gamma(c)}{\Gamma(c-a)} e^{i\pi a\varepsilon} \Psi(a, c; z) - \frac{2^{3-c}\Gamma(c)}{\Gamma(a)\Gamma(c-a)} z^{-1} e^{(1/2)z} I, \quad (4.146)$$

where

$$I = \int_0^\infty e^{-u}\left(1 - \frac{2u}{z}\right)^{a-1}\left(1 + \frac{2u}{z}\right)^{c-a-1} du, \quad (4.147)$$

$|\arg z| < \pi$, $\arg z \neq 0$, and $\varepsilon = \operatorname{sgn}(\operatorname{Im} z) = 1, -1$, according as $\operatorname{Im} z > 0$, < 0. The arguments of $1 - (2u/z)$ and $1 + (2u/z)$ both have their principal values at the origin.

Using Taylor's expansion we find (as in Whittaker and Watson [*344*, 1935])

$$\left(1 - \frac{2u}{z}\right)^{a-1} = 1 - \frac{a-1}{1!}\frac{2u}{z} + \frac{(a-1)(a-2)}{2!}\left(\frac{2u}{z}\right)^2 + \cdots$$

$$+ (-1)^n \frac{(a-1)(a-2)\cdots(a-n)}{n!}\left(\frac{2u}{z}\right)^n + R_n(u, z)$$

and

$$\left(1 + \frac{2u}{z}\right)^{c-a-1} = 1 + \frac{(c-a-1)}{1!}\frac{2u}{z} + \frac{(c-a-1)(c-a-2)}{2!}\left(\frac{2u}{z}\right)^2 + \cdots$$

$$+ \frac{(c-a-1)(c-a-2)\cdots(c-a-n)}{n!}\left(\frac{2u}{z}\right)^n + r_n(u, z),$$

where

$$R_n(u, z) = \frac{(a-1)(a-2)\cdots(a-n-1)}{n!}\left(1 - \frac{2u}{z}\right)^{a-1} \int_0^{-2u/z} t^n(1+t)^{-a}\, dt$$

and

$$r_n(u, z) = \frac{(c-a-1)(c-a-2)\cdots(c-a-n-1)}{n!}\left(1+\frac{2u}{z}\right)^{c-a-1} \times \int_0^{2u/z} t^n(1+t)^{a-c}\,dt.$$

On substituting in (4.147), multiplying the series, and integrating term by term, we obtain

$$I = \sum_{m=0}^{n} c_m\left(\frac{2}{z}\right)^m + \int_0^\infty e^{-u}\left(1+\frac{2u}{z}\right)^{c-a-1} R_n(u, z)\,du + \int_0^\infty e^{-u}\left[\left(1+\frac{2u}{z}\right)^{a-1} - R_n(u, z)\right] r_n(u, z)\,du, \quad (4.148)$$

where

$$c_m = \left[\frac{d^m}{dh^m}\{(1-h)^{a-1}(1+h)^{c-a-1}\}\right]_{h=0}. \quad (4.149)$$

Now, as shown by Whittaker and Watson [*344*, 1935], both $R_n(u, z)$ and $r_n(u, z)$ are $0(z^{-n-1})$, and the integrals in (4.148) are convergent. Thus the asymptotic expansion of $\Omega(a, c; z)$ for large values of $|z|$ is

$$\Omega(a, c; z) \sim \frac{\Gamma(c)}{\Gamma(a)} e^{i\pi(a-c)\varepsilon} e^z \Psi(c-a, c; -z) - \frac{\Gamma(c)}{\Gamma(c-a)} e^{i\pi a\varepsilon}\Psi(a, c; z) - \frac{2^{3-c}\Gamma(c)}{\Gamma(a)\Gamma(c-a)} z^{-1} e^{(1/2)z} \sum_{m=0}^{\infty} c_m\left(\frac{2}{z}\right)^m, \quad (4.150)$$

$|\arg z| < \pi$, $\arg z \neq 0$, where c_m is given by (4.149).

If both a and $c - a$ are positive integers, the series (4.150) terminates after a finite number of terms and is then exact.

4.16 Indefinite Integrals Connected with $\Omega(a, c; z)$ and $\overline{\Omega}(a, c; z)$

A number of indefinite integrals connected with $\Omega(a, c; z)$ and $\overline{\Omega}(a, c; z)$ can be obtained directly from the differential relations given in §4.7.

Other integrals can be obtained by solving the differential equation

$$z\frac{d^2y}{dz^2} + (c-z)\frac{dy}{dz} - ay = \frac{2^{1-c}\Gamma(c)}{\Gamma(a)\Gamma(c-a)} e^{(1/2)z} \quad (4.151)$$

by the method of variation of parameters (see §1.5). The Wronskian of $\Phi(a, c; z)$ and $\bar{\Phi}(a, c; z)$ is given by (4.13). We find that

$$\Omega(a, c; z) = \frac{2^{1-c}\Gamma(c-1)}{\Gamma(a)\Gamma(c-a)}\left[\Phi(a, c; z)\int e^{-(1/2)z}z^{c-1}\bar{\Phi}(a, c; z)\,dz - \bar{\Phi}(a, c; z)\int e^{-(1/2)z}z^{c-1}\Phi(a, c; z)\,dz\right]. \tag{4.152}$$

Now $x = \Phi(a, c; z)$ is a solution of the differential equation

$$z\frac{d^2x}{dz^2} + (c-z)\frac{dx}{dz} - ax = 0. \tag{4.153}$$

On multiplying (4.151) by $xe^{-z}z^{c-1}$ and (4.153) by $ye^{-z}z^{c-1}$ and subtracting, we obtain

$$e^{-z}z^{c}\left(x\frac{d^2y}{dz^2} - y\frac{d^2x}{dz^2}\right) + e^{-z}z^{c-1}(c-z)\left(x\frac{dy}{dz} - y\frac{dx}{dz}\right) = \frac{2^{1-c}\Gamma(c)}{\Gamma(a)\Gamma(c-a)}xe^{-(1/2)z}z^{c-1},$$

that is,

$$\frac{d}{dz}\left[e^{-z}z^{c}\left(x\frac{dy}{dz} - y\frac{dx}{dz}\right)\right] = \frac{2^{1-c}\Gamma(c)}{\Gamma(a)\Gamma(c-a)}xe^{-(1/2)z}z^{c-1}. \tag{4.154}$$

On integrating (4.154) and putting $x = \Phi(a, c; z)$, we see that

$$\begin{aligned}\int e^{-(1/2)z}z^{c-1}\Phi(a, c; z)\,dz &= \frac{2^{c-1}\Gamma(a)\Gamma(c-a)}{\Gamma(c)}e^{-z}z^{c} \\ &\quad\times[\Phi(a, c; z)\Omega'(a, c; z) - \Omega(a, c; z)\Phi'(a, c; z)] \\ &= \frac{2^{c-1}\Gamma(a+1)\Gamma(c-a)}{\Gamma(c+1)}e^{-z}z^{c}[\Phi(a, c; z)\Omega(a+1, c+1; z) \\ &\quad - \Omega(a, c; z)\Phi(a+1, c+1; z)].\end{aligned} \tag{4.155}$$

Similarly, by solving the differential equation

$$z\frac{d^2y}{dz^2} + (c-z)\frac{dy}{dz} - ay = \frac{2^{c-1}\Gamma(2-c)}{\Gamma(a-c+1)\Gamma(1-a)}e^{(1/2)z}z^{1-c}$$

by the method of variation of parameters, we find

$$\overline{\Omega}(a, c; z) = \frac{2^{c-1}\Gamma(2-c)}{\Gamma(a-c+1)\Gamma(1-a)}\left[\Phi(a, c; z)\int e^{-(1/2)z}\overline{\Phi}(a, c; z)\,dz - \overline{\Phi}(a, c; z)\int e^{-(1/2)z}\Phi(a, c; z)\,dz\right]. \quad (4.156)$$

By a precisely similar analysis to that given above, we obtain

$$\begin{aligned}\int e^{-(1/2)z}\Phi(a, c; z)\,dz &= \frac{2^{1-c}\Gamma(a-c+1)\Gamma(1-a)}{\Gamma(2-c)}\,e^{-z}z^{c} \\ &\quad\times [\Phi(a, c; z)\overline{\Omega}'(a, c; z) - \overline{\Omega}(a, c; z)\Phi'(a, c; z)] \\ &= \frac{2^{1-c}\Gamma(a-c+1)\Gamma(1-a)}{\Gamma(1-c)}\,e^{-z}z^{c}\left[\Phi(a, c; z)\overline{\Omega}(a+1, c+1; z)\right. \\ &\quad \left. - \frac{a}{c(1-c)}\overline{\Omega}(a, c; z)\Phi(a+1, c+1; z)\right] - 2e^{-(1/2)z}\Phi(a, c; z).\end{aligned} \quad (4.157)$$

4.17 Infinite Integrals Connected with $\Omega(a, c; z)$

The formula

$$\int_0^\infty e^{-pz}z^{b-1}\Omega(a, c; kz)\,dz = \Gamma(b)p^{-b}B(b, a; c; kp^{-1})$$
$$(\operatorname{Re} b > 0,\ \operatorname{Re} p > 0,\ \operatorname{Re} p > \operatorname{Re} k,\ |p| > |k|), \quad (4.158)$$

where B is the nonhomogeneous hypergeometric function (defined in Chapter 6), can be proved by expanding Ω as a power series and integrating term by term.

Using the transformation formula for the B function [Eq. (6.47)], (4.158) can be written in the alternative form

$$\int_0^\infty e^{-pz}z^{b-1}\Omega(a, c; kz)\,dz = -\Gamma(b)(p-k)^{-b}B\left[b, c-a; c; \frac{k}{k-p}\right]$$
$$(\operatorname{Re} b > 0,\ \operatorname{Re} p > 0,\ \operatorname{Re} p > \operatorname{Re} k,\ |p-k| > |k|). \quad (4.159)$$

On letting $p \to 0$ in (4.159), and using the formula [Eq. (6.89)],

$$B(a, b; c; 1) = \frac{\Gamma(c)\Gamma(c-a-b)}{\Gamma(c-a)\Gamma(c-b)}\Omega(b, c-a; 0) \qquad [\operatorname{Re} c > \operatorname{Re} b > 0,\ \operatorname{Re}(c-a-b) > 0], \quad (4.160)$$

we obtain, with $h = -k > 0$,

$$\int_0^\infty z^{b-1}\Omega(a, c; -hz)\, dz$$

$$= -h^{-b}\frac{\Gamma(b)\Gamma(c)\Gamma(a-b)}{\Gamma(c-b)\Gamma(a)}\Omega(c-a, c-b; 0)$$

$$= h^{-b}\frac{\Gamma(b)\Gamma(c)\Gamma(a-b)}{\Gamma(c-b)\Gamma(a)}\Omega(a-b, c-b; 0) \qquad (\text{Re}\, a > \text{Re}\, b > 0). \tag{4.161}$$

Equation (4.161) is the Mellin inversion of (4.145).

4.18 The Nonhomogeneous Confluent Hypergeometric Functions $\theta_\sigma(a, c; z)$ and $\Theta_\sigma(a, c; z)$

We consider next the solutions of the nonhomogeneous confluent hypergeometric equation

$$z\frac{d^2y}{dz^2} + (c - z)\frac{dy}{dz} - ay = z^{\sigma-1}, \tag{4.162}$$

where a, c, and σ are constants. As stated above, the associated homogeneous equation has one regular singularity at $z = 0$ and an irregular singular point at infinity. We shall analyze the properties of certain particular integrals of (4.162) in a similar manner to that given in Chapter 3 for the Lommel functions.

Using the method of Frobenius (§1.12), we see that a particular integral of (4.162) is

$$\theta_\sigma(a, c; z) = \frac{z^\sigma}{\sigma(\sigma + c - 1)}\left[1 + \frac{\sigma + a}{(\sigma+1)(\sigma+c)}z + \frac{(\sigma+a)(\sigma+a+1)}{(\sigma+1)(\sigma+2)(\sigma+c)(\sigma+c+1)}z^2 + \cdots\right]$$

$$= z^\sigma \sum_{n=0}^{\infty} \frac{\Gamma(\sigma+a+n)\Gamma(\sigma)\Gamma(\sigma+c-1)}{\Gamma(\sigma+a)\Gamma(\sigma+n+1)\Gamma(\sigma+c+n)} z^n$$

$$= \frac{z^\sigma}{\sigma(\sigma+c-1)}\, {}_2F_2(1, \sigma+a; \sigma+1, \sigma+c; z). \tag{4.163}$$

The series is convergent for all values of z. The complete primitive of (4.162) is then

$$y = C_1\Phi(a, c; z) + C_2\overline{\Phi}(a, c; z) + \theta_\sigma(a, c; z), \tag{4.164}$$

where C_1 and C_2 are arbitrary constants.

The series solution (4.163) is not valid if σ or $\sigma + c - 1$ is zero or a negative integer (since in these cases all the coefficients in the series after a certain value of n become infinite). As shown in §1.12, for these values of σ the particular solution of (4.162) will, in general, contain logarithmic terms.

If $\sigma = m$, a positive integer, (4.163) can be written

$$\theta_m(a, c; z) = \frac{(m-1)!\,\Gamma(m+c-1)\Gamma(a)}{\Gamma(m+a)\Gamma(c)} \sum_{n=0}^{\infty} \frac{\Gamma(m+n+a)\Gamma(c)}{\Gamma(a)\Gamma(m+n+c)} \frac{z^{n+m}}{(n+m)!}, \tag{4.165}$$

and if $\sigma = m + 1 - c$, where m is a positive integer, (4.163) can be written

$$\theta_{m+1-c}(a, c; z) = z^{1-c} \frac{(m-1)!\,\Gamma(m+1-c)\Gamma(a+1-c)}{\Gamma(m+a+1-c)\Gamma(2-c)}$$
$$\times \sum_{n=0}^{\infty} \frac{\Gamma(m+n+a+1-c)\Gamma(2-c)}{\Gamma(a+1-c)\Gamma(m+n+2-c)} \frac{z^{n+m}}{(n+m)!}. \tag{4.166}$$

From (4.163),

$$\theta_{\sigma+1-c}(a, c; z) = z^{1-c}\theta_\sigma(a+1-c, 2-c; z). \tag{4.167}$$

We see also that

$$\theta_\sigma(c, c; z) = \frac{z^\sigma}{\sigma(\sigma+c-1)}\, {}_1F_1(1; \sigma+1; z)$$
$$= \frac{z^\sigma}{\sigma(\sigma+c-1)} \Phi(1, \sigma+1; z)$$
$$= (\sigma+c-1)^{-1} e^z \gamma(\sigma, z), \tag{4.168}$$

where γ is the incomplete gamma function. Similarly,

$$\theta_\sigma(1, c; z) = \frac{z^\sigma}{\sigma(\sigma+c-1)}\, {}_1F_1(1; \sigma+c; z)$$
$$= \frac{z^\sigma}{\sigma(\sigma+c-1)} \Phi(1, \sigma+c; z)$$
$$= \sigma^{-1} e^z z^{1-c} \gamma(\sigma+c-1, z). \tag{4.169}$$

Also, from (4.163),

$$\theta_{-a}(a, c; z) = \frac{z^{-a}}{a(a+1-c)}. \tag{4.170}$$

Consider now the solution of (4.162) expressed as a series of descending powers of z (see §1.13). Such an integral is

$$y = \frac{z^{\sigma-1}}{1-\sigma-a}\left[1 - \frac{(1-\sigma)(2-\sigma-c)}{(2-\sigma-a)z} + \frac{(1-\sigma)(2-\sigma)(2-\sigma-c)(3-\sigma-c)}{(2-\sigma-a)(3-\sigma-a)z^2} - \cdots\right]$$

$$= z^{\sigma-1}\sum_{n=0}^{\infty}(-1)^n\frac{\Gamma(n+1-\sigma)\Gamma(n+2-\sigma-c)\Gamma(1-\sigma-a)}{\Gamma(1-\sigma)\Gamma(2-\sigma-c)\Gamma(n+2-\sigma-a)z^n}. \quad (4.171)$$

If $\sigma = m$, a positive integer, the series terminates after m terms. Equation (4.171) can then be written

$$y = -\frac{(m-1)!\,\Gamma(m+c-1)\Gamma(a)}{\Gamma(m+a)\Gamma(c)}\sum_{n=0}^{m-1}\frac{\Gamma(a+n)\Gamma(c)}{\Gamma(a)\Gamma(c+n)}\frac{z^n}{n!}. \quad (4.172)$$

Similarly, if $\sigma = m + 1 - c$, where m is a positive integer, the series (4.171) terminates after m terms. Equation (4.171) can then be written

$$y = -z^{1-c}\frac{(m-1)!\,\Gamma(m+1-c)\Gamma(a+1-c)}{\Gamma(m+a+1-c)\Gamma(2-c)} \times \sum_{n=0}^{m-1}\frac{\Gamma(a+1-c+n)\Gamma(2-c)}{\Gamma(a+1-c)\Gamma(n+2-c)}\frac{z^n}{n!}. \quad (4.173)$$

Consider the particular integral of (4.162) defined by

$$\Theta_\sigma(a, c; z)$$

$$= \theta_\sigma(a, c; z) - \frac{\Gamma(\sigma)\Gamma(\sigma+c-1)\Gamma(a)\sin[\pi(\sigma+c)]\sin[\pi(\sigma+a)]}{\Gamma(\sigma+a)\Gamma(c)\sin\pi c\,\sin\pi a}\Phi(a, c; z)$$

$$- \frac{\Gamma(\sigma)\Gamma(\sigma+c-1)\Gamma(a+1-c)\sin[\pi(c-a)]\sin\pi\sigma}{\Gamma(\sigma+a)\Gamma(2-c)\sin\pi c\,\sin[\pi(\sigma+a)]}\overline{\Phi}(a, c; z)$$

$$= \theta_\sigma(a, c; z) - \frac{\Gamma(\sigma)\Gamma(\sigma+c-1)\Gamma(1-\sigma-a)}{\sin\pi c}$$

$$\times \left\{\sin[\pi(\sigma+c)]\frac{\Phi(a, c; z)}{\Gamma(c)\Gamma(1-a)} + \sin\pi\sigma\frac{\overline{\Phi}(a, c; z)}{\Gamma(2-c)\Gamma(c-a)}\right\}. \quad (4.174)$$

The functions θ and Θ are directly related to the nonhomogeneous Whittaker functions S and R defined by Buchholz [1953b] (see §5.5). When $c = 1$, the quantity in braces in (4.174) vanishes. $\Theta_\sigma(a, 1; z)$ can be found from (4.174) by using L'Hospital's rule.

When $\sigma = m$, a positive integer,

$$\Theta_m(a, c; z) = \theta_m(a, c; z) - \frac{(m-1)!\,\Gamma(m+c-1)\Gamma(a)}{\Gamma(m+a)\Gamma(c)}\Phi(a, c; z)$$

$$= -\frac{(m-1)!\,\Gamma(m+c-1)\Gamma(a)}{\Gamma(m+a)\Gamma(c)}\sum_{n=0}^{m-1}\frac{\Gamma(a+n)\Gamma(c)}{\Gamma(a)\Gamma(c+n)}\frac{z^n}{n!}, \qquad (4.175)$$

in agreement with (4.172).

Similarly, when $\sigma = m + 1 - c$, where m is a positive integer,

$$\Theta_{m+1-c}(a, c; z)$$

$$= \theta_{m+1-c}(a, c; z) - \frac{(m-1)!\,\Gamma(m+1-c)\Gamma(a+1-c)}{\Gamma(m+a+1-c)\Gamma(2-c)}\overline{\Phi}(a, c; z)$$

$$= -z^{1-c}\frac{(m-1)!\,\Gamma(m+1-c)\Gamma(a+1-c)}{\Gamma(m+a+1-c)\Gamma(2-c)}$$

$$\times\sum_{n=0}^{m-1}\frac{\Gamma(a+1-c+n)\Gamma(2-c)}{\Gamma(a+1-c)\Gamma(n+2-c)}\frac{z^n}{n!}, \qquad (4.176)$$

in agreement with (4.173).

The series in (4.175) and (4.176) are, of course, truncated forms of the series for $\Phi(a, c; z)$ and $\overline{\Phi}(a, c; z)$.

From (4.167) and (4.174),

$$\Theta_{\sigma+1-c}(a, c; z) = z^{1-c}\Theta_\sigma(a+1-c, 2-c; z). \qquad (4.177)$$

We see also, from (4.175), that

$$\Theta_1(a, c; z) = -\frac{1}{a} \qquad (4.178)$$

and, from (4.176),

$$\Theta_{2-c}(a, c; z) = -\frac{z^{1-c}}{a+1-c}. \qquad (4.179)$$

As shown above, when $\sigma = m$ or $m + 1 - c$, $\Theta_\sigma(a, c; z)$ reduces to particular cases of the series (4.171), which terminates for these values of σ. For all other values of σ, the series (4.171) does not terminate and is divergent; as shown in §4.19, the series is an asymptotic expansion of $\Theta_\sigma(a, c; z)$ when $|z|$ is large and $|\arg z| < \frac{3}{2}\pi$.

4.19 Mellin-Barnes Integrals for $\theta_\sigma(a, c; z)$ and $\Theta_\sigma(a, c; z)$

If neither σ nor $\sigma + c - 1$ is zero or a negative integer, the formula

$$\theta_\sigma(a, c; z) = \frac{1}{2\pi i} \frac{\Gamma(\sigma)\Gamma(\sigma + c - 1)}{\Gamma(\sigma + a)} z^\sigma \int_{\gamma - i\infty}^{\gamma + i\infty} \frac{\Gamma(1 + s)\Gamma(-s)\Gamma(\sigma + a + s)}{\Gamma(\sigma + 1 + s)\Gamma(\sigma + c + s)}$$
$$\times (-z)^s\, ds \qquad [-\tfrac{1}{2}\pi < \arg(-z) < \tfrac{1}{2}\pi, 0 > \gamma > -\mathrm{Re}(\sigma + a), 0 > \gamma > -1], \tag{4.180}$$

can be proved in a similar manner to that given in §3.7, by considering a contour integral taken around a contour consisting of the line $s = \gamma$ together with a large semicircle to the right of this, and evaluating the integral as the sum of residues of the integrand at the poles of $\Gamma(-s)$.

Consider next the contour integral

$$I = \frac{z^\sigma}{2\pi i} \int_C \frac{\Gamma(-\sigma - s)\Gamma(1 - \sigma - c - s)}{\Gamma(1 - \sigma - a - s)} \frac{z^s}{\sin \pi s}\, ds$$
$$= \frac{z^\sigma}{2\pi i} \int_C \frac{\Gamma(1 + s)\Gamma(-s)\Gamma(\sigma + a + s)\sin \pi(\sigma + a + s)}{\Gamma(\sigma + 1 + s)\Gamma(\sigma + c + s)\sin \pi(\sigma + s)\sin \pi(\sigma + c + s)} z^s\, ds, \tag{4.181}$$

where $|\arg z| < \frac{3}{2}\pi$, taken around a contour consisting of the line $s = -p + \frac{1}{2}$ together with a semicircle (lying to the right of this line) of large radius $N + \frac{1}{2}$ (where N and p are integers) with center at the point $(-p - \frac{1}{2})$, p being chosen so that both $p - \frac{1}{2} - \sigma$ and $p + \frac{1}{2} - \sigma - c$ are positive.

By a similar analysis to that in §3.7, it can be shown that the contribution to the integral arising from the semicircle tends to zero as $N \to \infty$. Now the integrand has poles at the points

$$-1, -2, \ldots, -(p - 1),$$
$$0, 1, 2, 3, \ldots,$$
$$-\sigma,\ 1 - \sigma,\ 2 - \sigma, \ldots,$$
$$1 - \sigma - c,\ 2 - \sigma - c,\ 3 - \sigma - c, \ldots.$$

On evaluating the residues at these poles we find

$$I = z^\sigma \sum_{n=1}^{p-1} \frac{\Gamma(-\sigma + n)\Gamma(1 - \sigma - c + n)}{\Gamma(1 - \sigma - a + n)} (-1)^n \pi^{-1} z^{-n}$$
$$+ z^\sigma \sum_{n=0}^{\infty} \frac{n!\,\Gamma(\sigma + a + n)\sin \pi(\sigma + a + n)}{\Gamma(\sigma + 1 + n)\Gamma(\sigma + c + n)\sin \pi(\sigma + n)\sin \pi(\sigma + c + n)}$$
$$\times \frac{(-1)^{n-1}}{n!} z^n + \sum_{n=0}^{\infty} \frac{\Gamma(a + n)\sin \pi(a + n)}{n!\,\Gamma(c + n)\sin \pi(c + n)\sin \pi(n - \sigma)} (-1)^{n+1} z^n$$
$$+ \sum_{n=0}^{\infty} \frac{\Gamma(a + n + 1 - c)\sin \pi(a + n + 1 - c)}{n!\,\Gamma(n + 2 - c)\sin \pi(n + 1 - c)\sin \pi(n + 1 - \sigma - c)} (-1)^n z^{n+1-c}$$

$$= -z^{\sigma-1}\sum_{n=0}^{p-2}\frac{\Gamma(n+1-\sigma)\Gamma(n+2-\sigma-c)}{\Gamma(n+2-\sigma-a)}(-1)^n\pi^{-1}z^{-n}$$

$$-\frac{\Gamma(\sigma+a)\sin\pi(\sigma+a)}{\Gamma(\sigma)\Gamma(\sigma+c-1)\sin\pi\sigma\sin\pi(\sigma+c)}\,\theta_\sigma(a,c;z)$$

$$+\frac{\Gamma(a)\sin\pi a}{\Gamma(c)\sin\pi c\sin\pi\sigma}\Phi(a,c;z)+\frac{\Gamma(a+1-c)\sin\pi(c-a)}{\Gamma(2-c)\sin\pi c\sin\pi(\sigma+c)}\overline{\Phi}(a,c;z)$$

$$= -z^{\sigma-1}\sum_{n=0}^{p-2}\frac{\Gamma(n+1-\sigma)\Gamma(n+2-\sigma-c)}{\Gamma(n+2-\sigma-a)}(-1)^n\pi^{-1}z^{-n}$$

$$-\frac{\pi}{\Gamma(\sigma)\Gamma(\sigma+c-1)\Gamma(1-\sigma-a)\sin\pi\sigma\sin\pi(\sigma+c)}\,\Theta_\sigma(a,c;z),$$

using (4.174). Thus

$$\Theta_\sigma(a,c;z)=z^{\sigma-1}\sum_{n=0}^{p-2}(-1)^n\frac{\Gamma(n+1-\sigma)\Gamma(n+2-\sigma-c)\Gamma(1-\sigma-a)}{\Gamma(1-\sigma)\Gamma(2-\sigma-c)\Gamma(n+2-\sigma-a)z^n}$$
$$-\frac{\pi\Gamma(1-\sigma-a)}{\Gamma(1-\sigma)\Gamma(2-\sigma-c)}I_1, \quad (4.182)$$

where

$$I_1=\frac{z^\sigma}{2\pi i}\int_{-\infty i-p+(1/2)}^{\infty i-p+(1/2)}\frac{\Gamma(-\sigma-s)\Gamma(1-\sigma-c-s)}{\Gamma(1-\sigma-a-s)}\frac{z^s}{\sin\pi s}\,ds. \quad (4.183)$$

Again, consider the integral (4.181) taken around a contour C' consisting of the line $s=-p+\frac{1}{2}$ together with a semicircle (lying to the left of this line) of large radius $N+\frac{1}{2}$ with center at the point $(-p-\frac{1}{2})$, where N and p are integers, p being chosen so that both $p-\frac{1}{2}-\sigma$ and $p+\frac{1}{2}-\sigma-c$ are positive. The only poles within this contour are the poles of $\csc \pi s$. Now the integral is convergent when $|\arg z|<\frac{3}{2}\pi$, and we see that it is $0(z^{\sigma-p+(1/2)})$. Thus

$$I_1=0(z^{\sigma-p+(1/2)}) \quad (4.184)$$

and

$$\Theta_\sigma(a,c;z)=z^{\sigma-1}\sum_{n=0}^{p-2}(-1)^n\frac{\Gamma(n+1-\sigma)\Gamma(n+2-\sigma-c)\Gamma(1-\sigma-a)}{\Gamma(1-\sigma)\Gamma(2-\sigma-c)\Gamma(n+2-\sigma-a)z^n}$$
$$+0(z^{\sigma-p+(1/2)}). \quad (4.185)$$

From §1.13, we see that the series (4.171) or (4.185) is an asymptotic expansion of $\Theta_\sigma(a,c;z)$ when $|z|$ is large and $|\arg z|<\frac{3}{2}\pi$.

Equation (4.185) can be written in the alternative form

$$\Theta_\sigma(a, c; z) \sim \frac{z^{\sigma-1}}{1-\sigma-a}\, {}_3F_1\left(1, 1-\sigma, 2-\sigma-c; 2-\sigma-a; \frac{-1}{z}\right). \tag{4.186}$$

Alternatively we see that, if $|\arg z| < \frac{3}{2}\pi$ and $\sigma < 0,\ \sigma + c - 1 < 0$,

$$\begin{aligned}\Theta_\sigma(a, c; z) &= \frac{z^\sigma}{2\pi i}\int_{-\infty i}^{\infty i} \frac{\Gamma(-\sigma-s)\Gamma(1-\sigma-c-s)\Gamma(1-\sigma-a)}{\Gamma(1-\sigma-a-s)\Gamma(1-\sigma)\Gamma(2-\sigma-c)}\frac{\pi z^s}{\sin \pi s}\, ds \\ &= \frac{z^\sigma}{2\pi i}\int_{-\infty i}^{\infty i} \frac{\Gamma(s)\Gamma(1-s)\Gamma(1-\sigma-c-s)\Gamma(1-\sigma-a)}{\Gamma(1-\sigma-a-s)\Gamma(1-\sigma)\Gamma(2-\sigma-c)} z^s\, ds,\end{aligned} \tag{4.187}$$

the contour being indented slightly to pass to the left of the origin. On replacing s by $s - \sigma$, we see that

$$\Theta_\sigma(a, c; z) = \frac{1}{2\pi i}\int_{-\infty i+\sigma}^{\infty i+\sigma} \frac{\Gamma(s-\sigma)\Gamma(1+\sigma-s)\Gamma(1-c-s)\Gamma(1-\sigma-a)}{\Gamma(1-a-s)\Gamma(1-\sigma)\Gamma(2-\sigma-c)} z^s\, ds. \tag{4.188}$$

4.20 Recurrence Formulas and Relations Between Contiguous Functions

From the series (4.163) we see that

$$(\sigma + a)\theta_{\sigma+1}(a, c; z) = \sigma(\sigma + c - 1)\theta_\sigma(a, c; z) - z^\sigma. \tag{4.189}$$

From (4.163) we see too that, as $\sigma \to \infty$,

$$\theta_\sigma(a, c; z) = 0\left(\frac{z^\sigma}{\sigma^2}\right), \tag{4.190}$$

provided neither σ nor $\sigma + c - 1$ is zero or a negative integer. On differentiating (4.163), we find that

$$\frac{d}{dz}\theta_\sigma(a, c; z) = (\sigma - 1)\theta_{\sigma-1}(a + 1, c + 1; z). \tag{4.191}$$

We shall now show that the four contiguous functions $\theta_\sigma(a \pm 1, c; z)$ and $\theta_\sigma(a, c \pm 1; z)$ can be expressed in terms of $\theta_\sigma(a, c; z)$ and its derivative with respect to z.

Let $\delta \equiv z(d/dz)$. Then, from (4.163),

$$(\delta + a)\theta_\sigma(a, c; z) = (\sigma + a)\theta_\sigma(a + 1, c; z). \tag{4.192}$$

Equation (4.162) can be put in the form

$$[\delta(\delta + c - 1) - z(\delta + a)]\theta_\sigma(a, c; z) = z^\sigma. \tag{4.193}$$

On replacing a by $a-1$, we obtain

$$[\delta(\delta+c-1)-z(\delta+a-1)]\theta_\sigma(a-1,c;z)=z^\sigma;$$

that is,

$$(\delta+c-a-z)(\delta+a-1)\theta_\sigma(a-1,c;z)=z^\sigma+(c-a)(a-1)\theta_\sigma(a-1,c;z). \tag{4.194}$$

From (4.192), with $a-1$ instead of a, and (4.194),

$$(\delta+c-a-z)(\sigma+a-1)\theta_\sigma(a,c;z)=z^\sigma+(c-a)(a-1)\theta_\sigma(a-1,c;z). \tag{4.195}$$

From (4.163),

$$(\delta+c-1)\theta_\sigma(a,c;z)=(\sigma+c-2)\theta_\sigma(a,c-1;z). \tag{4.196}$$

From (4.193),

$$[\delta(\delta+c)-z(\delta+a)]\theta_\sigma(a,c+1;z)=z^\sigma;$$

that is,

$$(\delta-z)(\delta+c)\theta_\sigma(a,c+1;z)=z^\sigma-(c-a)z\theta_\sigma(a,c+1;z). \tag{4.197}$$

From (4.196), with $c+1$ instead of c, and (4.197),

$$(\delta-z)(\sigma+c-1)\theta_\sigma(a,c;z)=z^\sigma-(c-a)z\theta_\sigma(a,c+1;z). \tag{4.198}$$

Equations (4.192), (4.195), (4.196), and (4.198) may be rearranged to give

$$\delta\theta_\sigma(a,c;z)=(\sigma+a)\theta_\sigma(a+1,c;z)-a\theta_\sigma(a,c;z), \tag{4.199}$$

$$\delta\theta_\sigma(a,c;z)=(\sigma+a-1)^{-1}[(c-a)(a-1)\theta_\sigma(a-1,c;z)+z^\sigma] + (a-c+z)\theta_\sigma(a,c;z), \tag{4.200}$$

$$\delta\theta_\sigma(a,c;z)=(\sigma+c-1)^{-1}[z^\sigma-(c-a)z\theta_\sigma(a,c+1;z)]+z\theta_\sigma(a,c;z), \tag{4.201}$$

and

$$\delta\theta_\sigma(a,c;z)=(\sigma+c-2)\theta_\sigma(a,c-1;z)-(c-1)\theta_\sigma(a,c;z). \tag{4.202}$$

The six relations between the four contiguous functions $\theta_\sigma(a\pm 1,c;z)$ and $\theta_\sigma(a,c\pm 1;z)$ follow from (4.199) to (4.202), on equating any two values of $\delta\theta_\sigma(a,c;z)$.

From (4.174), on using the relations between $\Phi(a,c;z)$ and its contiguous functions, we find that the equations (4.189) and (4.191) to (4.202) hold if the function θ_σ is replaced throughout by Θ_σ.

4.21 Particular Values of $\Theta_\sigma(a, c; z)$

Consider now the value of $\Theta_\sigma(a, c; z)$ when σ or $\sigma + c - 1$ is zero or a negative integer; as shown in §4.18, the series solution for $\theta_\sigma(a, c; z)$ is then no longer valid. We shall show that $\Theta_\sigma(a, c; z)$ has a finite limit in these cases. The method of analysis is similar to that used in Chapter 3 for the Lommel functions. We shall determine first the value of $\Theta_0(a, c; z)$, $c \neq 1$.

From (4.189), replacing θ by Θ, we see that

$$\Theta_0(a, c; z) = \lim_{\sigma \to 0} \frac{z^\sigma + (\sigma + a)\Theta_{\sigma+1}(a, c; z)}{\sigma(\sigma + c - 1)}. \tag{4.203}$$

Now, from (4.178), both numerator and denominator vanish when $\sigma = 0$. From L'Hospital's rule, using (4.178),

$$\Theta_0(a, c; z) = \frac{1}{c-1}\left[\log z - \frac{1}{a} + a\frac{\partial}{\partial\sigma}\Theta_{\sigma+1}(a, c; z)\right]_{\sigma=0}. \tag{4.204}$$

From (4.174), together with the power series for $\theta_{\sigma+1}(a, c; z)$, we see that (4.204) reduces to

$$\begin{aligned}
&\Theta_0(a, c; z)\\
&= \frac{1}{c-1}\left(\log z - \frac{1}{a}\right) + \sum_{n=0}^{\infty} \frac{\Gamma(a+n+1)\Gamma(c-1)}{\Gamma(a)\Gamma(c+n+1)} \frac{z^{n+1}}{(n+1)!}\\
&\quad \times [\log z + \psi(a+n+1) + \psi(1) + \psi(c) - \psi(a+1)\\
&\qquad\qquad - \psi(n+2) - \psi(c+n+1)]\\
&\quad - \frac{1}{c-1}\Phi(a, c; z)[\psi(1) + \psi(c) - \psi(a+1) + \pi(\cot \pi c + \cot \pi a)]\\
&\quad + \frac{\Gamma(1-a)\{\Gamma(c-1)\}^2}{\Gamma(c-a)}\overline{\Phi}(a, c; z)\\
&= \frac{1}{c-1}\Phi(a, c; z)[\log z + \psi(a+1) - \psi(1) - \psi(c) - \pi(\cot \pi c + \cot \pi a)]\\
&\quad + \frac{\Gamma(1-a)\{\Gamma(c-1)\}^2}{\Gamma(c-a)}\overline{\Phi}(a, c; z) - \frac{1}{a(c-1)}\\
&\quad + \sum_{n=1}^{\infty} \frac{\Gamma(a+n)\Gamma(c-1)}{\Gamma(a)\Gamma(c+n)} \frac{z^n}{n!}[\psi(a+n) + \psi(1) + \psi(c) - \psi(a+1)\\
&\qquad\qquad - \psi(n+1) - \psi(c+n)],
\end{aligned} \tag{4.205}$$

where ψ is the logarithmic derivative of the gamma function.

Now, by analogy with (4.177), we define

$$\begin{aligned}
&\Theta_{1-c}(a, c; z)\\
&= z^{1-c}\Theta_0(a+1-c, 2-c; z)\\
&= \frac{1}{1-c}\,\Phi(a, c; z)[\log z + \psi(a+2-c) - \psi(1) - \psi(2-c)\\
&\quad + \pi\{\cot \pi c + \cot \pi(c-a)\}]\\
&\quad + \frac{\Gamma(c-a)\{\Gamma(1-c)\}^2}{\Gamma(1-a)}\,\Phi(a, c; z) - \frac{1}{(a+1-c)(1-c)}\,z^{1-c}\\
&\quad + \sum_{n=1}^{\infty} \frac{\Gamma(a+1-c+n)\Gamma(1-c)}{\Gamma(a+1-c)\Gamma(2-c+n)}\,\frac{z^{n+1-c}}{n!}\,[\psi(a+1-c+n) + \psi(1)\\
&\quad + \psi(2-c) - \psi(a+2-c) - \psi(n+1) - \psi(2-c+n)]\,. \qquad (4.206)
\end{aligned}$$

$\Theta_{-p}(a, c; z)$ and $\Theta_{-p+1-c}(a, c; z)$ (where p is a positive integer) can be found from (4.205) and (4.206) by repeated use of the recurrence formula (4.189) with θ replaced by Θ. If $c-1$ is a positive integer, (4.206) is nugatory; however, the required solution can be found by using (4.205). Similarly, if $c-1$ is a negative integer, (4.205) is nugatory, the required solution being found from (4.206).

We consider finally the case $c = 1$. From (4.203),

$$\begin{aligned}
&\Theta_0(a, 1; z)\\
&= \frac{1}{2}\left[\frac{\partial^2}{\partial\sigma^2}\{z^\sigma + (\sigma + a)\Theta_{\sigma+1}(a, 1; z)\}\right]_{\sigma=0}\\
&= \frac{1}{2}\left[(\log z)^2 + 2\frac{\partial}{\partial\sigma}\{\Theta_{\sigma+1}(a, 1; z)\} + a\frac{\partial^2}{\partial\sigma^2}\{\Theta_{\sigma+1}(a, 1; z)\}\right]_{\sigma=0}.
\end{aligned} \qquad (4.207)$$

Using (4.174), together with the power series for $\theta_{\sigma+1}(a, 1; z)$, (4.207) can be reduced to an expression of the form

$$\Theta_0(a, 1; z) = \tfrac{1}{2}\Phi(a, 1; z)(\log z)^2 + f_1(z)\log z + f_2(z)\,, \qquad (4.208)$$

where f_i is a power series of the form $\sum_{n=0}^{\infty} c_{ni} z^n$.

As above, $\Theta_{-p}(a, 1; z)$ (where p is a positive integer) can be found from (4.208) by repeated use of the recurrence formula.

4.22 Integrals Connected with $\theta_\sigma(a, c; z)$ and $\Theta_\sigma(a, c; z)$

A number of indefinite integrals connected with $\theta_\sigma(a, c; z)$ and $\Theta_\sigma(a, c; z)$ can be obtained from the differential relations given in §4.20. Other integrals can be obtained by solving the differential equation (4.162) by the method of variation of parameters. We find that

$$\theta_\sigma(a, c; z) = \frac{1}{c-1}\left[\Phi(a, c; z)\int e^{-z}z^{\sigma+c-2}\overline{\Phi}(a, c; z)\,dz \right.$$
$$\left. - \overline{\Phi}(a, c; z)\int e^{-z}z^{\sigma+c-2}\Phi(a, c; z)\,dz\right]. \quad (4.209)$$

In a manner similar to that of §4.16, we can show that

$$\int e^{-z}z^{\sigma+c-2}\Phi(a, c; z)\,dz$$
$$= e^{-z}z^{c}[\Phi(a, c; z)\theta'_\sigma(a, c; z) - \theta_\sigma(a, c; z)\Phi'(a, c; z)]$$
$$= e^{-z}z^{c}\left[(\sigma-1)\Phi(a, c; z)\theta_{\sigma-1}(a+1, c+1; z)\right.$$
$$\left. - \frac{a}{c}\,\theta_\sigma(a, c; z)\Phi(a+1, c+1; z)\right] \quad (4.210)$$

and

$$\int e^{-z}z^{\sigma+c-2}\overline{\Phi}(a, c; z)\,dz$$
$$= e^{-z}z^{c}[\overline{\Phi}(a, c; z)\theta'_\sigma(a, c; z) - \theta_\sigma(a, c; z)\overline{\Phi}'(a, c; z)]$$
$$= e^{-z}z^{c}[(\sigma-1)\overline{\Phi}(a, c; z)\theta_{\sigma-1}(a+1, c+1; z)$$
$$+ (c-1)\theta_\sigma(a, c; z)\overline{\Phi}(a+1, c+1; z)]. \quad (4.211)$$

In (4.210) and (4.211) we can substitute Θ for θ on the right side, the integrals on the left side being indefinite.

The formulas

$$\int_0^1 (1-z)^{\nu-1}\theta_\sigma(a, c; pz)\,dz = \frac{\Gamma(\sigma)\Gamma(\nu)}{\Gamma(\sigma+\nu)}\,p^{-\nu}\theta_{\sigma+\nu}(a-\nu, c-\nu; p)$$
$$[\mathrm{Re}\,\nu > 0,\ \mathrm{Re}\,\sigma > 0,\ \mathrm{Re}(\sigma+c) > 1] \quad (4.212)$$

and

$$\int_0^1 z^{c-1}(1-z)^{\nu-1}\theta_\sigma(a, c; pz)\,dz = \frac{\Gamma(\sigma+c-1)\Gamma(\nu)}{\Gamma(\sigma+c+\nu-1)}\,\theta_\sigma(a, c+\nu; p)$$
$$[\mathrm{Re}\,\nu > 0,\ \mathrm{Re}\,\sigma > 0,\ \mathrm{Re}(\sigma+c) > 1] \quad (4.213)$$

may be proved by expanding $\theta_\sigma(a, c; pz)$ as a power series in z and integrating term by term. Similarly, if $\operatorname{Re} \nu > 0$ and $\operatorname{Re} c > 1$,

$$\int_0^1 (1-z)^{\nu-1}\Phi(a, c; pz)dz = (c-1)p^{-\nu}\theta_\nu(a-\nu, c-\nu; p). \qquad (4.214)$$

The formula

$$\int_0^\infty e^{-bz}z^\nu\theta_\sigma(a, c; pz)\,dz$$

$$= \frac{\Gamma(\nu+\sigma+1)p^\sigma}{\sigma(\sigma+c-1)b^{\nu+\sigma+1}}\,{}_3F_2\left(1, \sigma+a, \nu+\sigma+1; \sigma+1, \sigma+c; \frac{p}{b}\right)$$

$$[\operatorname{Re}\sigma > 0, \operatorname{Re}(\sigma+c) > 1, \operatorname{Re}\nu > -1, \operatorname{Re} b > \operatorname{Re} p] \qquad (4.215)$$

can be proved by expanding $\theta_\sigma(a, c; pz)$ as a power series in z and integrating term by term. In particular, if $\nu = 0$,

$$\int_0^\infty e^{-bz}\theta_\sigma(a, c; pz)\,dz = \frac{\Gamma(\sigma)p^\sigma}{(\sigma+c-1)b^{\sigma+1}}\,F\left(1, \sigma+a; \sigma+c; \frac{p}{b}\right)$$

$$[\operatorname{Re}\sigma > 0, \operatorname{Re}(\sigma+c) > 1, \operatorname{Re} b > \operatorname{Re} p], \qquad (4.216)$$

where F is the hypergeometric function. As shown in §3.13, the hypergeometric function can be expressed in terms of elementary functions for certain values of the parameters.

On letting $b \to 0$ in (4.215), and using the result given in (3.94), we find

$$\int_0^\infty z^\nu\theta_\sigma(a, c; pe^{i\pi}z)\,dz$$

$$= \frac{\Gamma(\nu+\sigma+1)\Gamma(-\nu-\sigma)\Gamma(\sigma)\Gamma(\sigma+c-1)\Gamma(a-\nu-1)}{\Gamma(-\nu)\Gamma(c-\nu-1)\Gamma(\sigma+a)}\,\frac{e^{i\pi\sigma}}{p^{\nu+1}}$$

$$[p > 0, \operatorname{Re}\sigma > 0, \operatorname{Re}(\sigma+c) > 1, \operatorname{Re} a > \operatorname{Re}(\nu+1) > 0,$$

$$0 > \operatorname{Re}(\nu+\sigma) > -1]. \qquad (4.217)$$

4.23 The Nonhomogeneous Confluent Hypergeometric Function $\Lambda_{\rho,\sigma}(a, c; z)$

We consider, finally, the solutions of the nonhomogeneous confluent hypergeometric equation

$$z\frac{d^2y}{dz^2} + (c-z)\frac{dy}{dz} - ay = e^{\rho z}z^{\sigma-1}, \qquad (4.218)$$

where a, c, ρ, and σ are constants. On expanding $e^{\rho z}$ as a power series in z, we see, as in §1.2, that a particular integral of (4.218) is $\Lambda_{\rho,\sigma}(a, c; z)$, where

$$\Lambda_{\rho,\sigma}(a, c; z) = \sum_{n=0}^{\infty} \frac{\theta_{\sigma+n}(a, c; z)\rho^n}{n!}$$

$$= z^{\sigma} \sum_{m=0}^{\infty} \sum_{n=0}^{\infty} \frac{\Gamma(\sigma + a + n + m)\Gamma(\sigma + n)\Gamma(\sigma + c + n - 1)}{\Gamma(\sigma + a + n)\Gamma(\sigma + n + m + 1)\Gamma(\sigma + c + n + m)} \times \frac{z^{n+m}\rho^n}{n!}. \quad (4.219)$$

Using (4.190) it is easily verified that the series in (4.219) is convergent for all values of ρ and z.

On using the power-series expansion of the θ functions, we find that (4.219) can be written in the alternative form

$$\Lambda_{\rho,\sigma}(a, c; z) = z^{\sigma} \sum_{n=0}^{\infty} \frac{\Gamma(\sigma + a + n)\Gamma(\sigma)\Gamma(\sigma + c - 1)}{\Gamma(\sigma + a)\Gamma(\sigma + n + 1)\Gamma(\sigma + c + n)} \times F_{(n+1)}[\sigma, \sigma + c - 1; \sigma + a; \rho]z^n, \quad (4.220)$$

where $F_{(n+1)}$ stands for the first $n + 1$ terms of the hypergeometric series with the given parameters.

From (4.167) and (4.219),

$$\Lambda_{\rho,\sigma+1-c}(a, c; z) = z^{1-c}\Lambda_{\rho,\sigma}(a + 1 - c, 2 - c; z). \quad (4.221)$$

In (4.218) put $u = e^x y$, $z = e^{i\pi}x$. Then

$$x\frac{d^2u}{dx^2} + (c - x)\frac{du}{dx} - (c - a)u = e^{i\pi\sigma}e^{(1-\rho)x}x^{\sigma-1}.$$

On replacing a by $c - a$ in this equation, we see that the equation

$$x\frac{d^2u}{dx^2} + (c - x)\frac{du}{dx} - au = e^{i\pi\sigma}e^{(1-\rho)x}x^{\sigma-1} \quad (4.222)$$

has a particular integral $u = e^x\Lambda_{\rho,\sigma}(c - a, c; e^{i\pi}x)$. Now, from (4.218), the general solution of (4.222) is

$$C_1\Phi(a, c; x) + C_2\overline{\Phi}(a, c; x) + e^{i\pi\sigma}\Lambda_{1-\rho,\sigma}(a, c; x),$$

where C_1 and C_2 are arbitrary constants. On comparing the power series for these two solutions, we find that

$$\Lambda_{1-\rho,\sigma}(a, c; x) = e^{-i\pi\sigma}e^x\Lambda_{\rho,\sigma}(c - a, c; e^{i\pi}x),$$

or, on writing z instead of x,

$$\Lambda_{1-\rho,\sigma}(a, c; z) = e^{-i\pi\sigma}e^z\Lambda_{\rho,\sigma}(c - a, c; e^{i\pi}z). \quad (4.223)$$

From (4.219) we see that

$$\Lambda_{0,\sigma}(a, c; z) = \theta_\sigma(a, c; z), \tag{4.224}$$

and, from (4.223),

$$\Lambda_{1,\sigma}(a, c; z) = e^{-i\pi\sigma} e^z \theta_\sigma(c - a, c; e^{i\pi} z). \tag{4.225}$$

Similarly, on comparing power-series solutions of the equation

$$z \frac{d^2 y}{dz^2} + (c - z)\frac{dy}{dz} - ay = \frac{2^{1-c}\Gamma(c)}{\Gamma(a)\Gamma(c-a)} e^{(1/2)z} \tag{4.226}$$

with the series in (4.219), we find

$$\Lambda_{1/2,1}(a, c; z) = 2^{c-1} \frac{\Gamma(a)\Gamma(c-a)}{\Gamma(c)} [\Omega(a, c; z) - \Omega(a, c; 0)\Phi(a, c; z)]. \tag{4.227}$$

Equation (4.227) can be written in the alternative form

$$\Omega(a, c; z) = \Omega(a, c; 0)\Phi(a, c; z) + \frac{2^{1-c}\Gamma(c)}{\Gamma(a)\Gamma(c-a)} \sum_{n=0}^{\infty} \frac{2^{-n}\theta_{n+1}(a, c; z)}{n!}. \tag{4.228}$$

From (4.221) and (4.227),

$$\Lambda_{1/2,2-c}(a, c; z) = 2^{1-c} \frac{\Gamma(a-c+1)\Gamma(1-a)}{\Gamma(2-c)} \times [\bar{\Omega}(a, c; z) - \Omega(a - c + 1, 2 - c; 0)\bar{\Phi}(a, c; z)]. \tag{4.229}$$

In (4.218), putting $\rho = \frac{1}{2}$, we see that the equation

$$z \frac{d^2 y}{dz^2} + (c - z)\frac{dy}{dz} - ay = e^{(1/2)z} z^{\sigma - 1} \tag{4.230}$$

has a particular solution $\Lambda_{1/2,\sigma}(a, c; z)$. In (4.230), put $u = e^{-(1/2)z} z^\nu y$. Then

$$z \frac{d^2 u}{dz^2} + (c - 2\nu)\frac{du}{dz} + \left[-\frac{1}{4} z + (\tfrac{1}{2}c - a) + \frac{\nu(\nu + 1 - c)}{z}\right] u = z^{\nu+\sigma-1}, \tag{4.231}$$

which has a particular solution $e^{-(1/2)z} z^\nu \Lambda_{1/2,\sigma}(a, c; z)$. If $c = 2a = 2\nu + 1$, (4.231) becomes

$$\frac{d^2 u}{dz^2} + \frac{1}{z}\frac{du}{dz} - \left(\frac{1}{4} + \frac{\nu^2}{z^2}\right) u = z^{\nu+\sigma-2}, \tag{4.232}$$

which, from §3.21, has the particular solution

$$(2e^{-(1/2)i\pi})^{\nu+\sigma} s_{\nu+\sigma-1,\nu}(\tfrac{1}{2} e^{(1/2)i\pi} z),$$

where s is the Lommel function (§3.16). On comparing the solutions of (4.231) and (4.232), expressed as power series in z, we find that

$$\Lambda_{1/2,\sigma}(a, 2a; z)$$
$$= (2e^{-(1/2)i\pi})^{a+\sigma-(1/2)} z^{(1/2)-a} e^{(1/2)z} s_{a+\sigma-(3/2),a-(1/2)}(\tfrac{1}{2}e^{(1/2)i\pi}z). \tag{4.233}$$

4.24 Recurrence Formulas and Relations Between Contiguous Functions

We shall now derive formulas for $\Lambda_{\rho,\sigma}(a, c; z)$ which are generalizations of the formulas given in §4.20.

It is easily verified that $y = e^{\rho z} z^{\sigma}$ is a particular solution of the equation

$$z\frac{d^2y}{dz^2} + (c - z)\frac{dy}{dz} - ay$$
$$= [\rho(\rho - 1)z^2 + \{\rho(2\sigma + c) - \sigma - a\}z + \sigma(\sigma + c - 1)]e^{\rho z}z^{\sigma}. \tag{4.234}$$

Now the general solution of (4.234) can be written

$$\sigma(\sigma + c - 1)\Lambda_{\rho,\sigma}(a, c; z) + [\rho(2\sigma + c) - \sigma - a]\Lambda_{\rho,\sigma+1}(a, c; z)$$
$$+ \rho(\rho - 1)\Lambda_{\rho,\sigma+2}(a, c; z) + C_1\Phi(a, c; z) + C_2\overline{\Phi}(a, c; z),$$

where C_1 and C_2 are arbitrary constants. On comparing the power series for these two solutions we find that

$$\sigma(\sigma + c - 1)\Lambda_{\rho,\sigma}(a, c; z) + [\rho(2\sigma + c) - \sigma - a]\Lambda_{\rho,\sigma+1}(a, c; z)$$
$$+ \rho(\rho - 1)\Lambda_{\rho,\sigma+2}(a, c; z) = e^{\rho z}z^{\sigma}. \tag{4.235}$$

On differentiating (4.219), and using (4.191), we find that

$$\frac{d}{dz}\Lambda_{\rho,\sigma}(a, c; z) = \sum_{n=0}^{\infty}(\sigma + n - 1)\theta_{\sigma+n-1}(a + 1, c + 1; z)\frac{\rho^n}{n!}$$
$$= (\sigma - 1)\sum_{n=0}^{\infty}\theta_{\sigma+n-1}(a + 1, c + 1; z)\frac{\rho^n}{n!}$$
$$+ \rho\sum_{n=1}^{\infty}\theta_{\sigma+n-1}(a + 1, c + 1; z)\frac{\rho^{n-1}}{(n - 1)!};$$

that is,

$$\frac{d}{dz}\Lambda_{\rho,\sigma}(a, c; z) = (\sigma - 1)\Lambda_{\rho,\sigma-1}(a + 1, c + 1; z) + \rho\Lambda_{\rho,\sigma}(a + 1, c + 1; z). \tag{4.236}$$

Similarly, using (4.192) and (4.196), we find

$$(\delta + a)\Lambda_{\rho,\sigma}(a, c; z) = \sum_{n=0}^{\infty} (\sigma + a + n)\theta_{\sigma+n}(a + 1, c; z)\frac{\rho^n}{n!}$$
$$= (\sigma + a)\Lambda_{\rho,\sigma}(a + 1, c; z) + \rho\Lambda_{\rho,\sigma+1}(a + 1, c; z) \tag{4.237}$$

and

$$(\delta + c - 1)\Lambda_{\rho,\sigma}(a, c; z) = \sum_{n=0}^{\infty} (\sigma + c - 2 + n)\theta_{\sigma+n}(a, c - 1; z)\frac{\rho^n}{n!}$$
$$= (\sigma + c - 2)\Lambda_{\rho,\sigma}(a, c - 1; z) + \rho\Lambda_{\rho,\sigma+1}(a, c - 1; z), \tag{4.238}$$

where $\delta \equiv zd/dz$. From (4.237) and (4.238),

$$(a - c + 1)\Lambda_{\rho,\sigma}(a, c; z) = (\sigma + a)\Lambda_{\rho,\sigma}(a + 1, c; z) + \rho\Lambda_{\rho,\sigma+1}(a + 1, c; z)$$
$$-(\sigma + c - 2)\Lambda_{\rho,\sigma}(a, c - 1; z) - \rho\Lambda_{\rho,\sigma+1}(a, c - 1; z). \tag{4.239}$$

4.25 Related Differential Equations

We shall now briefly consider certain second-order differential equations, the solutions of which can be expressed in terms of $\Lambda_{\rho,\sigma}(a, c; z)$.

In (4.218) put $u = e^{-\rho z}y$. Then

$$z\frac{d^2u}{dz^2} + [c + (2\rho - 1)z]\frac{du}{dz} + [c\rho - a + \rho(\rho - 1)z]u = z^{\sigma-1}. \tag{4.240}$$

Finally, in (4.240) put

$$x = \zeta^\alpha u = \zeta^\alpha e^{-\rho z}y, \qquad z = \beta\zeta^\gamma, \tag{4.241}$$

where α, β, and γ are constants. Equation (4.241) is then transformed into

$$\zeta^2\frac{d^2x}{d\zeta^2} + [(1 - 2\alpha - \gamma + \gamma c)\zeta + \beta\gamma(2\rho - 1)\zeta^{\gamma+1}]\frac{dx}{d\zeta}$$
$$+ [\alpha(\alpha + \gamma - \gamma c) + \{\alpha\beta\gamma(1 - 2\rho) + \beta\gamma^2(c\rho - a)\}\zeta^\gamma + \beta^2\gamma^2\rho(\rho - 1)\zeta^{2\gamma}]x$$
$$= \beta^\sigma\gamma^2\zeta^{\alpha+\gamma\sigma}. \tag{4.242}$$

A particular integral of (4.242) is $x = \zeta^\alpha e^{-\beta\rho\zeta^\gamma}\Lambda_{\rho,\sigma}(a, c; \beta\zeta^\gamma)$. The complementary function is

$$\zeta^\alpha e^{-\beta\rho\zeta^\gamma}[C_1\Phi(a, c; \beta\zeta^\gamma) + C_2\overline{\Phi}(a, c; \beta\zeta^\gamma)].$$

Some special cases of this transformation are of interest. In (4.242) put

$\gamma = 1$. Then (4.242) becomes

$$\zeta^2 \frac{d^2x}{d\zeta^2} + [(c - 2\alpha)\zeta + \beta(2\rho - 1)\zeta^2] \frac{dx}{d\zeta}$$
$$+ [\alpha(\alpha + 1 - c) + \{\alpha\beta(1 - 2\rho) + \beta(c\rho - a)\}\zeta + \beta^2\rho(\rho - 1)\zeta^2]x = \beta^\sigma\zeta^{\alpha+\sigma}, \tag{4.243}$$

with a particular integral $x = \zeta^\alpha e^{-\beta\rho\zeta}\Lambda_{\rho,\sigma}(a, c; \beta\zeta)$.

In (4.243) put $\alpha = 0$. Then (4.243) becomes

$$\zeta \frac{d^2x}{d\zeta^2} + [c + \beta(2\rho - 1)\zeta] \frac{dx}{d\zeta} + [\beta(c\rho - a) + \beta^2\rho(\rho - 1)\zeta]x = \beta^\sigma\zeta^{\sigma-1}, \tag{4.244}$$

with a particular integral $x = e^{-\beta\rho\zeta}\Lambda_{\rho,\sigma}(a, c; \beta\zeta)$. Now the general nonhomogeneous linear differential equation of second order, the coefficients of which are linear functions of the dependent variable, can be put in the form

$$(a_0 z + b_0) \frac{d^2y}{dz^2} + (a_1 z + b_1) \frac{dy}{dz} + (a_2 z + b_2)y = f(z). \tag{4.245}$$

This is the nonhomogeneous form of Laplace's linear equation of second order. If $f(z) = C(a_0 z + b_0)^p$, where $a_0 \neq 0$, it is readily seen, by putting $\zeta = z + b_0/a_0$, that (4.245) reduces to an equation of the form

$$\zeta \frac{d^2y}{d\zeta^2} + (A_1\zeta + B_1) \frac{dy}{d\zeta} + (A_2\zeta + B_2)y = k\zeta^p, \tag{4.246}$$

where A_1, A_2, B_1, B_2, k, and p are constants. Comparing this equation with (4.244) we see that the solution of (4.246) can be expressed in terms of the nonhomogeneous confluent hypergeometric function $\Lambda_{\rho,\sigma}(a, c; \beta\zeta)$. A_1, A_2, B_1, B_2, and p can be related to the five parameters a, c, β, ρ, and σ.

Similarly, the solution of the nonhomogeneous equation

$$z^2 \frac{d^2y}{dz^2} + (Az^2 + Bz) \frac{dy}{dz} + (Lz^2 + Mz + N)y = z^P$$

or (4.247)

$$\frac{d^2y}{dz^2} + \left(A + \frac{B}{z}\right) \frac{dy}{dz} + \left(L + \frac{M}{z} + \frac{N}{z^2}\right)y = z^{P-2},$$

where A, B, L, M, N, and P are constants, follows immediately by comparing (4.247) with (4.243). A, B, L, M, N, and P can be related to the six parameters a, c, α, β, ρ, and σ.

More generally, the solution of the nonhomogeneous equation

$$z^2\frac{d^2y}{dz^2}+(Az^{S+1}+Bz)\frac{dy}{dz}+(Lz^{2S}+Mz^S+N)y=z^P$$

or (4.248)

$$\frac{d^2y}{dz^2}+\left(Az^{S-1}+\frac{B}{z}\right)\frac{dy}{dz}+\left(Lz^{2S-2}+Mz^{S-2}+\frac{N}{z^2}\right)y=z^{P-2}$$

follows immediately from that of (4.242), the constants A, B, L, M, N, P, and S being related to the seven parameters a, c, α, β, γ, ρ, and σ.

In particular, from (4.242), with $\gamma = 2$, the equation

$$\frac{d^2x}{d\zeta^2}+\left[2\beta(2\rho-1)\zeta+\frac{2c-2\alpha-1}{\zeta}\right]\frac{dx}{d\zeta}$$
$$+\left[4\beta^2\rho(\rho-1)\zeta^2+\{2\alpha\beta(1-2\rho)+4\beta(c\rho-a)\}+\frac{\alpha(\alpha+2-2c)}{\zeta^2}\right]x$$
$$=4\beta^\sigma\zeta^{\alpha+2\sigma-2} \qquad (4.249)$$

has a particular integral $x=\zeta^\alpha e^{-\beta\rho\zeta^2}\Lambda_{\rho,\sigma}(a, c; \beta\zeta^2)$.

In (4.249) put $\alpha = 0$. Then (4.249) becomes

$$\frac{d^2x}{d\zeta^2}+\left[2\beta(2\rho-1)\zeta+\frac{2c-1}{\zeta}\right]\frac{dx}{d\zeta}+[4\beta^2\rho(\rho-1)\zeta^2+4\beta(c\rho-a)]x$$
$$=4\beta^\sigma\zeta^{2\sigma-2} \qquad (4.250)$$

with a particular integral $x=e^{-\beta\rho\zeta^2}\Lambda_{\rho,\sigma}(a, c; \beta\zeta^2)$.

In (4.242) put $\gamma=-1$. Then (4.242) becomes

$$\zeta^2\frac{d^2x}{d\zeta^2}+[(2-2\alpha-c)\zeta-\beta(2\rho-1)]\frac{dx}{d\zeta}$$
$$+[\alpha(\alpha+c-1)+\{\alpha\beta(2\rho-1)+\beta(c\rho-a)\}\zeta^{-1}+\beta^2\rho(\rho-1)\zeta^{-2}]x$$
$$=\beta^\sigma\zeta^{\alpha-\sigma}, \qquad (4.251)$$

with a particular integral $x=\zeta^\alpha e^{-\beta\rho/\zeta}\Lambda_{\rho,\sigma}(a, c; \beta/\zeta)$.

In (4.243) put $\alpha=\frac{1}{2}c$, $\beta=1$, and $\rho=\frac{1}{2}$. Then (4.243) becomes

$$\frac{d^2x}{d\zeta^2}+\left[-\frac{1}{4}+\frac{\frac{1}{2}c-a}{\zeta}+\frac{\frac{1}{2}c(1-\frac{1}{2}c)}{\zeta^2}\right]x=\zeta^{\sigma+(1/2)c-2}, \qquad (4.252)$$

with a particular integral $x=\zeta^{(1/2)c}e^{-(1/2)\zeta}\Lambda_{1/2,\sigma}(a, c; \zeta)$.

In (4.249) put $\alpha=c-1$, $\beta=e^{(1/2)i\pi}$, $\rho=\frac{1}{2}$, and $\tau=e^{(1/2)i\pi}(a-\frac{1}{2}c)$. Then

(4.249) becomes

$$\frac{d^2x}{d\zeta^2} + \frac{1}{\zeta}\frac{dx}{d\zeta} + \left[\zeta^2 - 4\tau - \frac{(c-1)^2}{\zeta^2}\right]x = 4e^{(1/2)i\pi\sigma}\zeta^{c+2\sigma-3}, \qquad (4.253)$$

with a particular integral $x = \zeta^{c-1}e^{-(1/2)i\zeta^2}\Lambda_{1/2,\sigma}(\frac{1}{2}c - i\tau, c; i\zeta^2)$.

In (4.250), put $\beta = \frac{1}{2}$, $\rho = \frac{1}{2}$, and $c = \frac{1}{2}$. Then (4.250) becomes

$$\frac{d^2x}{d\zeta^2} + (\tfrac{1}{2} - 2a - \tfrac{1}{4}\zeta^2)x = 2^{2-\sigma}\zeta^{2\sigma-2}, \qquad (4.254)$$

with a particular integral $x = e^{-\zeta^2/4}\Lambda_{1/2,\sigma}(a, \frac{1}{2}; \frac{1}{2}\zeta^2)$.

Equations (4.252), (4.253), and (4.254) are nonhomogeneous equations which correspond, respectively, to Whittaker's confluent hypergeometric equation, the equation for the functions of the paraboloid of revolution, and the equation for the parabolic cylinder functions. These three equations are dealt with in Chapter 5.

PROBLEMS

1. Show that, if Re $c >$ Re $a > 0$,

$$\Phi(a, c; z) = \frac{\Gamma(c)}{\Gamma(a)\Gamma(c-a)}\int_0^1 f\,dt$$

and

$$\Omega(a, c; z) = \frac{\Gamma(c)}{\Gamma(a)\Gamma(c-a)}\left[\int_{1/2}^1 f\,dt - \int_0^{1/2} f\,dt\right],$$

where

$$f = e^{zt}t^{a-1}(1-t)^{c-a-1}.$$

2. Obtain the power series for $\Omega(a, c; z)$ by using the result of Problem 1 and expanding f in powers of z.

3. Verify the relations between functions contiguous to $\Omega(a, c; z)$ by comparing coefficients of like powers of z.

4. By repeated application of the relations between contiguous functions, prove that any three functions of the form $\Omega(a+m, c+n; z)$, where m and n are integers, are connected by a linear relation in which the coefficients are polynomials in z.

5. Show, by differentiating term by term, that

$$\frac{d}{dz}\,\Omega(a, c; z) = \frac{a}{c}\,\Omega(a+1, c+1; z).$$

6. Prove that

$$\Omega(a, a+1; 0) = 1 - 2^{1-a} \qquad (a > 0).$$

7. Show, by numerical integration or otherwise, that the values of $\Omega(a, c; 0)$ are as follows:

$$\Omega(\tfrac{1}{2}, \tfrac{3}{4}; 0) = 0.36623,$$

$$\Omega(\tfrac{3}{4}, 1; 0) = 0.56110,$$

$$\Omega(\tfrac{3}{4}, \tfrac{5}{4}; 0) = 0.24243,$$

$$\Omega(1, \tfrac{5}{4}; 0) = 0.68179,$$

$$\Omega(1, \tfrac{3}{2}; 0) = 0.41421,$$

$$\Omega(1, \tfrac{7}{4}; 0) = 0.18921.$$

Verify that the values of $\Omega(\tfrac{1}{4}m, \tfrac{1}{4}n; 0)$, where m and n are any positive integers $(n > m)$, can be found by using the six results given above together with the contiguity relations and the transformation formula.

8. Show that, if a is a positive constant, $\Omega(a, c; 0)$ decreases monotonically to -1 as c increases to infinity, $c - a$ being positive.

9. Show that, if $c - a$ is a positive constant, $\Omega(a, c; 0)$ increases monotonically to 1 as c increases to infinity, a being positive.

10. Prove that $e^{-z}\Omega(a, c; z)$ is a particular solution of the differential equation

$$z\frac{d^2y}{dz^2} + (c+z)\frac{dy}{dz} + (c-a)y = \frac{2^{1-c}\Gamma(c)}{\Gamma(a)\Gamma(c-a)}e^{-(1/2)z}.$$

11. Deduce the power series for $\Omega(a, c; z)$ directly from the differential equation

$$z\frac{d^2y}{dz^2} + (c-z)\frac{dy}{dz} - ay = \frac{2^{1-c}\Gamma(c)}{\Gamma(a)\Gamma(c-a)}e^{(1/2)z}.$$

12. Two Fresnel's integrals are

$$C(x) = (2\pi)^{-(1/2)}\int_0^x t^{-(1/2)}\cos t\,dt$$

and

$$S(x) = (2\pi)^{-(1/2)}\int_0^x t^{-(1/2)}\sin t\,dt.$$

Show that

$$\Omega(\tfrac{1}{2}, \tfrac{3}{2}; -xe^{-(1/2)i\pi}) + \Omega(\tfrac{1}{2}, \tfrac{3}{2}; -xe^{(1/2)i\pi}) = (2\pi/x)^{1/2}[C(x) - 2C(\tfrac{1}{2}x)]$$

and

$$\Omega(\tfrac{1}{2}, \tfrac{3}{2}; -xe^{-(1/2)i\pi}) - \Omega(\tfrac{1}{2}, \tfrac{3}{2}; -xe^{(1/2)i\pi}) = i(2\pi/x)^{1/2}[S(x) - 2S(\tfrac{1}{2}x)].$$

13. Show that, if $2a > c > a > 1$, $\Omega(a-1, c-1; z)$ increases monotonically to infinity as z increases from zero to infinity.

14. Show that

$$\int e^{-z} z\Omega(a, c; z)\, dz = -\frac{c-1}{c-a-1} ze^{-z}\Omega(a, c-1; z) - \frac{(c-1)(c-2)}{(c-a-1)(c-a-2)} e^{-z}\Omega(a, c-2; z).$$

15. Prove that, if $\operatorname{Re} p > 0$, $\operatorname{Re}(p-k) > 0$, and $|p| > |k|$,

$$\int_0^\infty e^{-pz}\Omega(1, 2; kz)\, dz = \frac{1}{k}\left[2 \log\left(1 - \frac{k}{2p}\right) - \log\left(1 - \frac{k}{p}\right)\right].$$

16. The generalized hypergeometric function ${}_2F_2(a_1, a_2; b_1, b_2; z)$ satisfies the differential equation

$$\{\delta(\delta + b_1 - 1)(\delta + b_2 - 1) - z(\delta + a_1)(\delta + a_2)\}u = 0,$$

where $\delta \equiv z d/dz$.

Show that $z^{-\sigma}\theta_\sigma(a, c; z)$ satisfies a third-order differential equation of this form. Hence derive an expression for $\theta_\sigma(a, c; z)$ in terms of the generalized hypergeometric function ${}_2F_2$.

17. Verify that $y = -1/a$ is a particular solution of the differential equation satisfied by $\theta_1(a, c; z)$.

18. Determine the form of $f(z)$ so that $y = z^\sigma$ is a particular solution of the differential equation

$$z\frac{d^2y}{dz^2} + (c - z)\frac{dy}{dz} - ay = f(z).$$

Hence show that

$$(\sigma + a)\theta_{\sigma+1}(a, c; z) = \sigma(\sigma - c - 1)\theta_\sigma(a, c; z) - z^\sigma.$$

19. Show that $\Theta_\sigma(a, c; z)$ is the only particular integral of (4.162) which (a) is a continuous function of σ and c, and (b) is represented by a terminating power series if σ or $\sigma + c - 1$ is a positive integer.

20. Obtain the series solution for $\Theta_\sigma(a, c; z)$ directly from the differential equation.

21. Prove that, if $1 > \operatorname{Re} \sigma > 0$ and $\operatorname{Re}(\sigma + c) > 1$,

$$\int_0^1 (1 - z)^{-\sigma}\theta_\sigma(a, c; pz)\, dz = \frac{\pi p^{\sigma-1}}{\sin \pi\sigma} \frac{\Phi(a + \sigma - 1, c + \sigma - 1; p) - 1}{a + \sigma - 1}.$$

22. Prove that, if $\operatorname{Re}\sigma > 0$, $\operatorname{Re} c > 0$, $\operatorname{Re}(\sigma + c) > 1$, and $\operatorname{Re} b > \operatorname{Re} p$,

$$\int_0^\infty e^{-bz} z^{c-1} \theta_\sigma(a, c; pz)\, dz = \frac{\Gamma(\sigma + c - 1)p^\sigma}{\sigma b^{\sigma+c}} F\left(1, \sigma + a; \sigma + 1; \frac{p}{b}\right).$$

23. By comparing coefficients of powers of z, show that

$$\Omega(a, c; z) = \Omega(a, c; 0)\Phi(a, c; z) + \frac{2^{1-c}\Gamma(c)}{\Gamma(a)\Gamma(c-a)} \sum_{n=0}^{\infty} \frac{2^{-n}\theta_{n+1}(a, c; z)}{n!}.$$

24. Use the substitution $u = y^{1-k}$ to show that the solution of the nonlinear differential equation

$$yz\frac{d^2y}{dz^2} = kz\left(\frac{dy}{dz}\right)^2 - (c - z)y\frac{dy}{dz} + \frac{a}{1-k}y^2 + \frac{z^{\sigma-1}y^{k+1}}{1-k}$$

is

$$y = [C_1\Phi(a, c; z) + C_2\Phi(a, c; z) + \Theta_\sigma(a, c; z)]^{1/(1-k)},$$

where C_1 and C_2 are arbitrary constants.

CHAPTER 5

Nonhomogeneous Whittaker and Parabolic Functions

5.1 Introduction

In Chapter 4 the properties of solutions of certain nonhomogeneous linear differential equations were considered, these equations having as their associated homogeneous equation the confluent hypergeometric equation

$$z\frac{d^2y}{dz^2}+(c-z)\frac{dy}{dz}-ay=0, \tag{5.1}$$

where a and c are constants.

We now briefly consider the properties of certain nonhomogeneous equations which have as their associated homogeneous equation Whittaker's form of the confluent hypergeometric equation

$$\frac{d^2y}{dz^2}+\left(-\frac{1}{4}+\frac{\kappa}{z}+\frac{\frac{1}{4}-\mu^2}{z^2}\right)y=0, \tag{5.2}$$

where κ and μ are constants.

In particular we consider, in §5.3, the function $A_{\kappa,\mu}(z)$, which is a particular integral of the equation

$$\frac{d^2y}{dz^2}+\left(-\frac{1}{4}+\frac{\kappa}{z}+\frac{\frac{1}{4}-\mu^2}{z^2}\right)y=\frac{2^{-2\mu}\Gamma(2\mu+1)}{\Gamma(\mu-\kappa+\frac{1}{2})\Gamma(\mu+\kappa+\frac{1}{2})}z^{\mu-(1/2)} \tag{5.3}$$

and, in §5.4, the function $N_{\kappa,\mu}^{(\nu)}(z)$, which is a particular integral of the equation

$$\frac{d^2y}{dz^2}+\left(-\frac{1}{4}+\frac{\kappa}{z}+\frac{\frac{1}{4}-\mu^2}{z^2}\right)y=z^{\nu-(1/2)}, \tag{5.4}$$

where ν is a constant.

In §5.6 we show that the particular integrals of the nonhomogeneous equation for the functions of the paraboloid of revolution

$$\frac{d^2y}{dz^2}+\frac{1}{z}\frac{dy}{dz}+\left(z^2-4\tau-\frac{p^2}{z^2}\right)y=-\frac{2^{2-p}e^{\pi i(p-1)/4}\Gamma(p+1)}{\Gamma(\frac{1}{2}p+\frac{1}{2}-i\tau)\Gamma(\frac{1}{2}p+\frac{1}{2}+i\tau)}z^p \tag{5.5}$$

and

$$\frac{d^2y}{dz^2} + \frac{1}{z}\frac{dy}{dz} + \left(z^2 - 4\tau - \frac{p^2}{z^2}\right)y = -4e^{\pi i(\sigma-1)/4}z^\sigma \tag{5.6}$$

can be related to those of (5.3) and (5.4).

Finally, in §§5.7 to 5.15, we discuss the properties of certain other related functions, namely, $F_\nu^{(0)}(z)$, $F_\nu^{(1)}(z)$, and $G_\nu^{(\sigma)}(z)$, which are particular integrals of the nonhomogeneous equations

$$\frac{d^2y}{dz^2} + (\nu + \tfrac{1}{2} - \tfrac{1}{4}z^2)y = \frac{4\pi^{1/2}}{\Gamma(-\tfrac{1}{2}\nu)\Gamma(\tfrac{1}{2} + \tfrac{1}{2}\nu)}, \tag{5.7}$$

$$\frac{d^2y}{dz^2} + (\nu + \tfrac{1}{2} - \tfrac{1}{4}z^2)y = \frac{(2\pi)^{1/2}}{\Gamma(\tfrac{1}{2} - \tfrac{1}{2}\nu)\Gamma(1 + \tfrac{1}{2}\nu)}z, \tag{5.8}$$

and

$$\frac{d^2y}{dz^2} + (\nu + \tfrac{1}{2} - \tfrac{1}{4}z^2)y = z^\sigma, \tag{5.9}$$

where ν and σ are constants, the associated homogenenous equation being Weber's equation.

As shown in Chapter 11, these functions are related to solutions of Poisson's equation in terms of parabolic coordinates.

5.2 Whittaker's Form of the Confluent Hypergeometric Equation

The theory of the Whittaker functions, which satisfy the confluent hypergeometric equation (5.2), is fully set out in Whittaker and Watson [1935]. We shall here briefly summarize various properties of these functions.

As is well known, the solutions of (5.2) can be expressed in terms of the confluent hypergeometric functions defined in Chapter 4. If 2μ is not an integer, two independent solutions of (5.2) are the Whittaker functions $M_{\kappa,\mu}(z)$ and $M_{\kappa,-\mu}(z)$, defined by

$$M_{\kappa,\mu}(z) = e^{-(1/2)z}z^{(1/2)+\mu}\Phi(\tfrac{1}{2} - \kappa + \mu, 1 + 2\mu; z) \tag{5.10}$$

and

$$\begin{aligned} M_{\kappa,-\mu}(z) &= e^{-(1/2)z}z^{(1/2)-\mu}\Phi(\tfrac{1}{2} - \kappa - \mu, 1 - 2\mu; z) \\ &= e^{-(1/2)z}z^{(1/2)+\mu}\overline{\Phi}(\tfrac{1}{2} - \kappa + \mu, 1 + 2\mu; z), \end{aligned} \tag{5.11}$$

where Φ and $\overline{\Phi}$ are confluent hypergeometric functions defined in §4.2.

When $\kappa = 0$, as shown by Erdélyi [5, 1953b], these solutions can be expressed in terms of modified Bessel functions (see §3.2). Thus

$$M_{0,\mu}(z) = 2^{2\mu}\Gamma(\mu + 1)z^{1/2}I_\mu(\tfrac{1}{2}z). \tag{5.12}$$

Two other solutions of (5.2) are

$$W_{\kappa,\mu}(z) = e^{-(1/2)z}z^{(1/2)+\mu}\Psi(\tfrac{1}{2} - \kappa + \mu, 1 + 2\mu; z)$$

and (5.13)

$$W_{\kappa,-\mu}(z) = e^{-(1/2)z}z^{(1/2)-\mu}\Psi(\tfrac{1}{2} - \kappa - \mu, 1 - 2\mu; z),$$

where Ψ is another confluent hypergeometric function defined in §4.2. $M_{\kappa,\mu}(z)$ and $W_{\kappa,\mu}(z)$ are many-valued functions of z. We restrict the values considered to those in the z plane with a cut along the negative real axis.

The corresponding integral representations of these functions follows immediately from those given for Φ and Ψ in §4.2. Thus, if $\operatorname{Re}(\mu \pm \kappa) > -\frac{1}{2}$,

$$M_{\kappa,\mu}(z) = \frac{2^{1-2\mu}\Gamma(2\mu + 1)}{\Gamma(\frac{1}{2} - \kappa + \mu)\Gamma(\frac{1}{2} + \kappa + \mu)} z^{\mu+(1/2)} \int_0^1 (1 - t^2)^{\mu-(1/2)}$$

$$\times \cosh\left[\tfrac{1}{2}zt - \kappa \log \frac{1 + t}{1 - t}\right] dt \tag{5.14}$$

and, if $\operatorname{Re}(\mu - \kappa) > -\frac{1}{2}$ and $\operatorname{Re} z > 0$,

$$W_{\kappa,\mu}(z) = \frac{1}{\Gamma(\frac{1}{2} - \kappa + \mu)} e^{-(1/2)z}z^{\mu+(1/2)} \int_0^\infty e^{-zt}t^{-(1/2)-\kappa+\mu}(1 + t)^{-(1/2)+\kappa+\mu}\, dt. \tag{5.15}$$

5.3 Generalized Modified Struve Function $A_{\kappa,\mu}(z)$

By analogy with (5.10) we define the function $A_{\kappa,\mu}(z)$ by the equation

$$A_{\kappa,\mu}(z) = e^{-(1/2)z}z^{(1/2)+\mu}\Omega(\tfrac{1}{2} - \kappa + \mu, 1 + 2\mu; z), \tag{5.16}$$

where Ω is the generalized modified Struve function defined in §4.3. From (4.47),

$$A_{\kappa,-\mu}(z) = e^{-(1/2)z}z^{(1/2)+\mu}\overline{\Omega}(\tfrac{1}{2} - \kappa + \mu, 1 + 2\mu; z). \tag{5.17}$$

As in the case of $M_{\kappa,\mu}(z)$ and $W_{\kappa,\mu}(z)$, we consider the values of these functions in the z plane with a cut along the negative real axis.

Using the transformation formulas for Ω (§4.9), we find that

$$A_{\kappa,\mu}(z) = -e^{i\pi\varepsilon[\mu+(1/2)]}A_{-\kappa,\mu}(-z), \tag{5.18}$$

where $\varepsilon = \operatorname{sgn}(\operatorname{Im} z) = 1, -1$, according as $\operatorname{Im} z > 0, < 0$. This corresponds to Kummer's transformation formula for $M_{\kappa,\mu}(z)$.

When $\kappa = 0$, from (4.34),

$$A_{0,\mu}(z) = 2^{2\mu}\Gamma(\mu + 1)z^{1/2}L_\mu(\tfrac{1}{2}z), \tag{5.19}$$

where $L_\mu(\frac{1}{2}z)$ is the modified Struve function (see §3.14).

The corresponding integral representations of these functions follow immediately from those for Ω in §4.3. Thus, if $\mathrm{Re}(\mu \pm \kappa) > -\frac{1}{2}$,

$$A_{\kappa,\mu}(z) = \frac{2^{1-2\mu}\Gamma(2\mu+1)}{\Gamma(\frac{1}{2}-\kappa+\mu)\Gamma(\frac{1}{2}+\kappa+\mu)} z^{\mu+(1/2)} \int_0^1 (1-t^2)^{\mu-(1/2)} \times \sinh\left[\tfrac{1}{2}zt - \kappa \log \frac{1+t}{1-t}\right] dt. \tag{5.20}$$

From (5.16), using the differential equation for Ω (4.70), we see that $A_{\kappa,\mu}(z)$ satisfies the nonhomogeneous linear differential equation

$$\frac{d^2y}{dz^2} + \left(-\frac{1}{4} + \frac{\kappa}{z} + \frac{\frac{1}{4}-\mu^2}{z^2}\right)y = \frac{2^{-2\mu}\Gamma(2\mu+1)}{\Gamma(\mu-\kappa+\frac{1}{2})\Gamma(\mu+\kappa+\frac{1}{2})} z^{\mu-(1/2)}. \tag{5.21}$$

The associated homogeneous equation is Whittaker's form of the confluent hypergeometric equation (5.2), which has one regular singularity at $z = 0$ and an irregular singular point at infinity. The complete primitive of (5.21) is $C_1 M_{\kappa,\mu}(z) + C_2 M_{\kappa,-\mu}(z) + A_{\kappa,\mu}(z)$.

By differentiating (5.21), it can be shown that $A_{\kappa,\mu}(z)$ is a solution of the homogeneous third-order equation

$$\frac{d^3y}{dz^3} - \frac{\mu-\frac{1}{2}}{z}\frac{d^2y}{dz^2} + \left(-\frac{1}{4} + \frac{\kappa}{z} + \frac{\frac{1}{4}-\mu^2}{z^2}\right)\frac{dy}{dz} + \left[\frac{2\mu-1}{8z} - \frac{\kappa(2\mu+1)}{2z^2} - \frac{(\frac{1}{4}-\mu^2)(\frac{3}{2}+\mu)}{z^3}\right]y = 0. \tag{5.22}$$

The other solutions of (5.22) are $M_{\kappa,\mu}(z)$ and $M_{\kappa,-\mu}(z)$.

The expansion of $A_{\kappa,\mu}(z)$ as a power series in z follows immediately from that given for Ω in §4.10. We find

$$A_{\kappa,\mu}(z) = e^{-(1/2)z} z^{(1/2)+\mu} \sum_{n=0}^{\infty} \frac{\Gamma(\frac{1}{2}-\kappa+\mu+n)\Gamma(1+2\mu)}{\Gamma(\frac{1}{2}-\kappa+\mu)\Gamma(1+2\mu+n)} \times \Omega(\tfrac{1}{2}-\kappa+\mu, 1+2\mu; 0)\frac{z^n}{n!}. \tag{5.23}$$

The corresponding series for $M_{\kappa,\mu}(z)$ is

$$M_{\kappa,\mu}(z) = e^{-(1/2)z} z^{(1/2)+\mu} \sum_{n=0}^{\infty} \frac{\Gamma(\frac{1}{2}-\kappa+\mu+n)\Gamma(1+2\mu)}{\Gamma(\frac{1}{2}-\kappa+\mu)\Gamma(1+2\mu+n)} \frac{z^n}{n!}. \tag{5.24}$$

The asymptotic expansion of $A_{\kappa,\mu}(z)$ for large values of $|z|$ is obtained from that for Ω given in §4.15. We find, on using (5.13), that

$$A_{\kappa,\mu}(z) \sim \frac{\Gamma(1+2\mu)}{\Gamma(\frac{1}{2}-\kappa+\mu)} e^{-i\pi\kappa\varepsilon} W_{-\kappa,\mu}(-z) - \frac{\Gamma(1+2\mu)}{\Gamma(\frac{1}{2}+\kappa+\mu)} e^{i\pi[(1/2)-\kappa+\mu]\varepsilon} W_{\kappa,\mu}(z)$$

$$- \frac{2^{2-2\mu}\Gamma(1+2\mu)}{\Gamma(\frac{1}{2}-\kappa+\mu)\Gamma(\frac{1}{2}+\kappa+\mu)} z^{\mu-(1/2)} \sum_{n=0}^{\infty} c_n \left(\frac{2}{z}\right)^n, \tag{5.25}$$

where $|\arg z| < \pi$, $\arg z \neq 0$, $\varepsilon = \operatorname{sgn}(\operatorname{Im} z) = 1, -1$, according as $\operatorname{Im} z > 0$, < 0, and

$$c_n = \left[\frac{d^n}{dh^n}\{(1+h)^{\mu+\kappa-(1/2)}(1-h)^{\mu-\kappa-(1/2)}\}\right]_{h=0}.$$

A number of integrals involving $A_{\kappa,\mu}(z)$ can be derived from the integrals involving $\Omega(a, c; z)$ given in §§4.16 and 4.17.

5.4 The Nonhomogeneous Whittaker Function $N_{\kappa,\mu}^{(\nu)}(z)$

We consider next the solution of the nonhomogeneous equation

$$\frac{d^2y}{dz^2} + \left(-\frac{1}{4} + \frac{\kappa}{z} + \frac{\frac{1}{4}-\mu^2}{z^2}\right) y = z^{\nu-(1/2)}, \tag{5.26}$$

where κ, μ, and ν are constants.

Using the method of Frobenius (§1.12), we see that a particular integral of (5.26) is

$$N_{\kappa,\mu}^{(\nu)}(z) = z^{\nu+(3/2)} \sum_{n=0}^{\infty} a_n z^n, \tag{5.27}$$

where

$$a_0 = [(\nu+1)^2 - \mu^2]^{-1}, \qquad a_1 = -\kappa[\{(\nu+1)^2 - \mu^2\}\{(\nu+2)^2 - \mu^2\}]^{-1},$$

and

$$[(\nu+n+1)^2 - \mu^2]a_n + \kappa a_{n-1} - \tfrac{1}{4}a_{n-2} = 0 \qquad (n \geq 2).$$

The complete primitive of (5.26) is then

$$y = C_1 M_{\kappa,\mu}(z) + C_2 M_{\kappa,-\mu}(z) + N_{\kappa,\mu}^{(\nu)}(z), \tag{5.28}$$

where C_1 and C_2 are arbitrary constants.

The series solution (5.27) is not valid if $\nu \pm \mu$ is a negative integer (since, in that case, all the coefficients in the series after a certain value of n become infinite). As shown in §1.12, for these values of ν, the particular solution of (5.26) will, in general, contain logarithmic terms. From (5.27),

$$N_{\kappa,-\mu}^{(\nu)}(z) = N_{\kappa,\mu}^{(\nu)}(z). \tag{5.29}$$

As shown in §4.25, a particular solution of (5.26) is

$$y = e^{-(1/2)z} z^{(1/2)+\mu} \Lambda_{1/2,1+\nu-\mu}(\tfrac{1}{2} - \kappa + \mu, 1 + 2\mu; z).$$

On expanding this expression as a power series in z and comparing it with (5.27), we find that

$$N_{\kappa,\mu}^{(\nu)}(z) = e^{-(1/2)z} z^{(1/2)+\mu} \Lambda_{1/2,1+\nu-\mu}(\tfrac{1}{2} - \kappa + \mu, 1 + 2\mu; z), \tag{5.30}$$

that is, from (4.220),

$$N_{\kappa,\mu}^{(\nu)}(z) = e^{-(1/2)z} z^{\nu+(3/2)} \sum_{n=0}^{\infty} \frac{\Gamma(\frac{3}{2} - \kappa + \nu + n)\Gamma(1 + \nu - \mu)\Gamma(1 + \nu + \mu)}{\Gamma(\frac{3}{2} - \kappa + \nu)\Gamma(2 + \nu - \mu + n)\Gamma(2 + \nu + \mu + n)}$$
$$\times F_{(n+1)}(1 + \nu - \mu, 1 + \nu + \mu; \tfrac{3}{2} - \kappa + \nu; \tfrac{1}{2})z^n, \tag{5.31}$$

where $F_{(n+1)}$ stands for the first $n+1$ terms of the hypergeometric series with the given parameters.

From (5.30) we see that

$$N_{\kappa,\mu}^{(\mu)}(z) = \frac{2^{2\mu}\Gamma(\mu + \kappa + \frac{1}{2})\Gamma(\mu - \kappa + \frac{1}{2})}{\Gamma(2\mu + 1)}$$
$$\times [A_{\kappa,\mu}(z) - \Omega(\tfrac{1}{2} - \kappa + \mu, 1 + 2\mu; 0)M_{\kappa,\mu}(z)] \tag{5.32}$$

and

$$N_{0,\mu}^{(\nu)}(z) = (2e^{-(1/2)i\pi})^{\nu+1} z^{1/2} s_{\nu,\mu}(\tfrac{1}{2}e^{(1/2)i\pi}z), \tag{5.33}$$

where s is the Lommel function (§3.16).

5.5 The Nonhomogeneous Whittaker Functions R and S

Buchholz [1953b] considered the solution of the nonhomogeneous equation

$$\frac{d^2y}{dz^2} + \left(-\frac{1}{4} + \frac{\kappa}{z} + \frac{\frac{1}{4} - \mu^2}{z^2}\right)y = \frac{1}{\Gamma(\nu - \mu)\Gamma(\nu + \mu)} e^{-(1/2)z} z^{\nu-(3/2)}. \tag{5.34}$$

It can readily be shown that two particular solutions of this equation are

$$\frac{1}{\Gamma(\nu - \mu)\Gamma(\nu + \mu)} e^{-(1/2)z} z^{(1/2)+\mu} \theta_{\nu-\mu}(\tfrac{1}{2} - \kappa + \mu, 1 + 2\mu; z)$$

and

$$\frac{1}{\Gamma(\nu - \mu)\Gamma(\nu + \mu)} e^{-(1/2)z} z^{(1/2)+\mu} \Theta_{\nu-\mu}(\tfrac{1}{2} - \kappa + \mu, 1 + 2\mu; z),$$

where the functions θ and Θ were defined in §4.18. These two solutions are identically equal to the Buchholz functions S and R, allowing for the difference in notation.

5.6 The Equations for the Functions of the Paraboloid of Revolution

Nonhomogeneous equations of the form

$$\frac{d^2y}{dz^2}+\frac{1}{z}\frac{dy}{dz}+\left(z^2-4\tau-\frac{p^2}{z^2}\right)y=-\frac{2^{2-p}e^{\pi i(p-1)/4}\Gamma(p+1)}{\Gamma(\frac{1}{2}p+\frac{1}{2}-i\tau)\Gamma(\frac{1}{2}p+\frac{1}{2}+i\tau)}z^p \quad (5.35)$$

and

$$\frac{d^2y}{dz^2}+\frac{1}{z}\frac{dy}{dz}+\left(z^2-4\tau-\frac{p^2}{z^2}\right)y=-4e^{\pi i(\sigma-1)/4}z^\sigma \quad (5.36)$$

(where p, τ, and σ are constants) occur in the solution of Lorenz's equation in terms of the coordinates of the paraboloid of revolution (see Chapter 11).

It is easily verified that a particular solution of (5.35) is

$$y=z^{-1}A_{i\tau,(1/2)p}(iz^2)=e^{i\pi(p+1)/4}e^{-(1/2)iz^2}z^p\Omega(\tfrac{1}{2}p+\tfrac{1}{2}-i\tau,\,p+1;\,iz^2), \quad (5.37)$$

where A is the generalized modified Struve function defined in §5.3.

Similarly, we find that a particular solution of (5.36) is

$$y=z^{-1}N^{[(1/2)\sigma]}_{i\tau,(1/2)p}(iz^2)$$
$$=e^{i\pi(p+1)/4}e^{-(1/2)iz^2}z^p\Lambda_{1/2,1+(1/2)\sigma-(1/2)p}(\tfrac{1}{2}p+\tfrac{1}{2}-i\tau,\,p+1;\,iz^2), \quad (5.38)$$

where N is the nonhomogeneous Whittaker function defined in §5.4.

When $p=\pm\frac{1}{2}$, the solutions of (5.35) and (5.36) can be expressed in terms of the nonhomogeneous parabolic cylinder function $G_\nu^{(\sigma)}(z)$ (see §5.16).

5.7 The Equation for the Parabolic Cylinder Functions

We consider now the properties of certain functions which satisfy the nonhomogeneous differential equations

$$\frac{d^2y}{dz^2}+(\nu+\tfrac{1}{2}-\tfrac{1}{4}z^2)y=\frac{4\pi^{1/2}}{\Gamma(-\frac{1}{2}\nu)\Gamma(\frac{1}{2}+\frac{1}{2}\nu)}, \quad (5.39)$$

$$\frac{d^2y}{dz^2}+(\nu+\tfrac{1}{2}-\tfrac{1}{4}z^2)y=\frac{(2\pi)^{1/2}}{\Gamma(\frac{1}{2}-\frac{1}{2}\nu)\Gamma(1+\frac{1}{2}\nu)}z, \quad (5.40)$$

and

$$\frac{d^2y}{dz^2}+(\nu+\tfrac{1}{2}-\tfrac{1}{4}z^2)y=z^\sigma, \quad (5.41)$$

where ν and σ are constants. The associated homogeneous equation is

Weber's equation,

$$\frac{d^2y}{dz^2} + (\nu + \tfrac{1}{2} - \tfrac{1}{4}z^2)y = 0\,, \tag{5.42}$$

which has the point $z = 0$ as an ordinary point, and an irregular singular point at infinity.

5.8 The Parabolic Cylinder Functions $D_\nu(z)$, $E_\nu^{(0)}(z)$, and $E_\nu^{(1)}(z)$

Weber's equation (5.42) has as its solution the parabolic cylinder functions $D_\nu(\pm z)$ and $D_{-\nu-1}(\pm iz)$. The properties of $D_\nu(z)$ are discussed in detail by Whittaker and Watson [1935], Buchholz [1953a], and Erdélyi [1953b]. It is shown that

$$\begin{aligned} D_\nu(z) &= 2^{\nu/2+1/4}z^{-1/2}W_{\nu/2+1/4,-1/4}(\tfrac{1}{2}z^2) \\ &= 2^{\nu/2}e^{-z^2/4}\Psi(-\tfrac{1}{2}\nu, \tfrac{1}{2}; \tfrac{1}{2}z^2) \\ &= 2^{\nu/2-1/2}e^{-z^2/4}z\Psi\left(\frac{1}{2} - \frac{\nu}{2}, \frac{3}{2}; \frac{1}{2}z^2\right), \end{aligned} \tag{5.43}$$

where W is the Whittaker function defined in §5.2, and Ψ is the confluent hypergeometric function defined in §4.2.

Two other solutions of (5.42) are (Buchholz [*40*, 1953a])

$$\begin{aligned} E_\nu^{(0)}(z) &= 2^{3/4}z^{-1/2}M_{\nu/2+1/4,-1/4}(\tfrac{1}{2}z^2) \\ &= 2^{1/2}e^{-z^2/4}\Phi(-\tfrac{1}{2}\nu, \tfrac{1}{2}; \tfrac{1}{2}z^2) \end{aligned} \tag{5.44}$$

and

$$\begin{aligned} E_\nu^{(1)}(z) &= 2^{7/4}z^{-1/2}M_{\nu/2+1/4,-1/4}(\tfrac{1}{2}z^2) \\ &= 2ze^{-z^2/4}\Phi(\tfrac{1}{2} - \tfrac{1}{2}\nu, \tfrac{3}{2}; \tfrac{1}{2}z^2) \\ &= 2^{3/2}e^{-z^2/4}\overline{\Phi}(-\tfrac{1}{2}\nu, \tfrac{1}{2}; \tfrac{1}{2}z^2), \end{aligned} \tag{5.45}$$

where M is the Whittaker function defined in §5.2, and Φ and $\overline{\Phi}$ are the confluent hypergeometric functions defined in §4.2.

Using the relations between Φ and Ψ given in Erdélyi [1953a], we find that

$$D_\nu(z) = 2^{\nu/2-1/2}\pi^{1/2}\left[\frac{E_\nu^{(0)}(z)}{\Gamma(\tfrac{1}{2} - \tfrac{1}{2}\nu)} - \frac{E_\nu^{(1)}(z)}{\Gamma(-\tfrac{1}{2}\nu)}\right] \qquad (|\arg z| < \tfrac{3}{4}\pi). \tag{5.46}$$

From (5.44) and (5.45),

$$E_\nu^{(0)}(z) = \frac{(2\pi)^{1/2}}{\Gamma(-\tfrac{1}{2}\nu)}\, e^{-z^2/4} \sum_{n=0}^{\infty} \frac{\Gamma(-\tfrac{1}{2}\nu + n)}{\Gamma(\tfrac{1}{2} + n)} \frac{(\tfrac{1}{2}z^2)^n}{n!} \tag{5.47}$$

and

$$E_\nu^{(1)}(z) = \frac{\pi^{1/2}}{\Gamma(\frac{1}{2} - \frac{1}{2}\nu)} z e^{-z^2/4} \sum_{n=0}^{\infty} \frac{\Gamma(\frac{1}{2} - \frac{1}{2}\nu + n)}{\Gamma(\frac{3}{2} + n)} \frac{(\frac{1}{2}z^2)^n}{n!}. \tag{5.48}$$

We see that $E_\nu^{(0)}(z)$ is an even function of z and $E_\nu^{(1)}(z)$ is an odd function of z. $E_\nu^{(0)}(z)$ and $E_\nu^{(1)}(z)$ thus form a pair of independent solutions of (5.42). The Wronskian of $E_\nu^{(0)}(z)$ and $E_\nu^{(1)}(z)$ is

$$E_\nu^{(0)}(z) \frac{d}{dz} [E_\nu^{(1)}(z)] - E_\nu^{(1)}(z) \frac{d}{dz} [E_\nu^{(0)}(z)] = 2^{3/2}. \tag{5.49}$$

When $\nu = -\frac{1}{2}$, the functions $E_\nu^{(0)}(z)$ and $E_\nu^{(1)}(z)$ can be expressed in terms of modified Bessel functions (see §3.2). Thus

$$E_{-(1/2)}^{(0)}(z) = 2^{-1/4}\Gamma(\tfrac{3}{4}) z^{1/2} I_{-1/4}(\tfrac{1}{4}z^2)$$

and

$$E_{-(1/2)}^{(1)}(z) = 2^{-1/4}\Gamma(\tfrac{1}{4}) z^{1/2} I_{1/4}(\tfrac{1}{4}z^2). \tag{5.50}$$

From (5.46) and (5.50),

$$D_{-(1/2)}(z) = (z/2\pi)^{1/2} K_{1/4}(\tfrac{1}{4}z^2), \tag{5.51}$$

where K is the modified Bessel function of the third kind (see §3.2).

Using the transformation formulas for Φ we find

$$E_\nu^{(0)}(z) = E_\nu^{(0)}(-z) = E_{-\nu-1}^{(0)}(iz) = E_{-\nu-1}^{(0)}(-iz) \tag{5.52}$$

and

$$E_\nu^{(1)}(z) = -E_\nu^{(1)}(-z) = -iE_{-\nu-1}^{(1)}(iz) = iE_{-\nu-1}^{(1)}(-iz). \tag{5.53}$$

5.9 The Nonhomogeneous Parabolic Cylinder Functions $F_\nu^{(0)}(z)$ and $F_\nu^{(1)}(z)$

Consider now the solution of the nonhomogeneous equations (5.39) and (5.40). It is readily verified that a particular integral of (5.39) is

$$\begin{aligned} F_\nu^{(0)}(z) &= 2^{3/4} z^{-(1/2)} A_{\nu/2+1/4,-1/4}(\tfrac{1}{2}z^2) \\ &= 2^{1/2} e^{-z^2/4} \Omega(-\tfrac{1}{2}\nu, \tfrac{1}{2}; \tfrac{1}{2}z^2) \\ &= z e^{-z^2/4} \overline{\Omega}(\tfrac{1}{2} - \tfrac{1}{2}\nu, \tfrac{3}{2}; \tfrac{1}{2}z^2) \end{aligned} \tag{5.54}$$

and that a particular integral of (5.40) is

$$\begin{aligned} F_\nu^{(1)}(z) &= 2^{7/4} z^{-(1/2)} A_{\nu/2+1/4,1/4}(\tfrac{1}{2}z^2) \\ &= 2^{3/2} e^{-z^2/4} \overline{\Omega}(-\tfrac{1}{2}\nu, \tfrac{1}{2}; \tfrac{1}{2}z^2) \\ &= 2z e^{-z^2/4} \Omega(\tfrac{1}{2} - \tfrac{1}{2}\nu, \tfrac{3}{2}; \tfrac{1}{2}z^2), \end{aligned} \tag{5.55}$$

where A, Ω, and $\bar{\Omega}$ are the generalized modified Struve functions defined in §5.3 and in §4.3. We see that the F functions bear the same relation to Ω as the E functions bear to Φ.

Using the power series for Ω given in §4.10, we see that

$$F_\nu^{(0)}(z) = \frac{(2\pi)^{1/2}}{\Gamma(-\frac{1}{2}\nu)} e^{-z^2/4} \sum_{n=0}^{\infty} \frac{\Gamma(-\frac{1}{2}\nu + n)}{\Gamma(\frac{1}{2} + n)} \Omega(-\tfrac{1}{2}\nu + n, \tfrac{1}{2} + n; 0) \frac{(\frac{1}{2}z^2)^n}{n!} \tag{5.56}$$

and

$$F_\nu^{(1)}(z) = \frac{\pi^{1/2}}{\Gamma(\frac{1}{2} - \frac{1}{2}\nu)} z e^{-z^2/4} \sum_{n=0}^{\infty} \frac{\Gamma(\frac{1}{2} - \frac{1}{2}\nu + n)}{\Gamma(\frac{3}{2} + n)} \times \Omega(\tfrac{1}{2} - \tfrac{1}{2}\nu + n, \tfrac{3}{2} + n; 0) \frac{(\frac{1}{2}z^2)^n}{n!}. \tag{5.57}$$

As shown in §4.8,

$$\Omega(a, c; 0) = \frac{\Gamma(c)}{\Gamma(a)\Gamma(c-a)} [B_{1/2}(c-a, a) - B_{1/2}(a, c-a)], \tag{5.58}$$

where $B_{1/2}$ is the incomplete beta function (see Problem 5, Chapter 1).

We see that $F_\nu^{(0)}(z)$ is an even function of z and $F_\nu^{(1)}(z)$ is an odd function of z. When $c = 2a$, $\Omega(a, c; x)$ can be expressed in terms of the modified Struve function $L_{a-(1/2)}(\frac{1}{2}x)$ (see §3.14). Thus

$$F_{-(1/2)}^{(0)}(z) = 2^{-1/4}\Gamma(\tfrac{3}{4}) z^{1/2} L_{-1/4}(\tfrac{1}{4}z^2)$$

and (5.59)

$$F_{-(1/2)}^{(1)}(z) = 2^{-1/4}\Gamma(\tfrac{1}{4}) z^{1/2} L_{1/4}(\tfrac{1}{4}z^2).$$

Using the transformation formulas for Ω given in §4.9, we find

$$F_\nu^{(0)}(z) = F_\nu^{(0)}(-z) = -F_{-\nu-1}^{(0)}(iz) = -F_{-\nu-1}^{(0)}(-iz) \tag{5.60}$$

and

$$F_\nu^{(1)}(z) = -F_\nu^{(1)}(-z) = iF_{-\nu-1}^{(1)}(iz) = -iF_{-\nu-1}^{(1)}(-iz). \tag{5.61}$$

5.10 Recurrence Relations for $F_\nu^{(0)}(z)$ and $F_\nu^{(1)}(z)$

These can be obtained by using the formulas relating Ω, $\bar{\Omega}$, and their derivatives given in §4.7, together with (5.60) and (5.61). Thus

$$\frac{d}{dz}[e^{z^2/4} F_\nu^{(0)}(z)] = -2^{1/2} \nu z \Omega(1 - \tfrac{1}{2}\nu, \tfrac{3}{2}; \tfrac{1}{2}z^2) = -2^{-1/2} \nu e^{z^2/4} F_{\nu-1}^{(1)}(z);$$

that is,

$$\frac{d}{dz}[F_\nu^{(0)}(z)] + \tfrac{1}{2}zF_\nu^{(0)}(z) = -2^{-(1/2)}\nu F_{\nu-1}^{(1)}(z). \tag{5.62}$$

Similarly,

$$\frac{d}{dz}[e^{z^2/4}F_\nu^{(1)}(z)] = 2^{1/2}z\bar{\Omega}(1 - \tfrac{1}{2}\nu, \tfrac{3}{2}; \tfrac{1}{2}z^2) - \frac{2^{3/2}\pi^{1/2}}{\Gamma(\frac{1}{2} - \frac{1}{2}\nu)\Gamma(1 + \frac{1}{2}\nu)}e^{z^2/4}$$

$$= 2^{1/2}e^{z^2/4}F_{\nu-1}^{(0)}(z) - \frac{2^{3/2}\pi^{1/2}}{\Gamma(\frac{1}{2} - \frac{1}{2}\nu)\Gamma(1 + \frac{1}{2}\nu)}e^{z^2/4};$$

that is,

$$\frac{d}{dz}[F_\nu^{(1)}(z)] + \tfrac{1}{2}zF_\nu^{(1)}(z) = 2^{1/2}F_{\nu-1}^{(0)}(z) - \frac{2^{3/2}\pi^{1/2}}{\Gamma(\frac{1}{2} - \frac{1}{2}\nu)\Gamma(1 + \frac{1}{2}\nu)}. \tag{5.63}$$

Again, from (5.60),

$$\frac{d}{dz}[e^{-z^2/4}F_\nu^{(0)}(z)] = -\frac{d}{dz}[e^{-z^2/4}F_{-\nu-1}^{(0)}(iz)]$$

$$= -i\frac{d}{d(iz)}[e^{i^2z^2/4}F_{-\nu-1}^{(0)}(iz)];$$

that is, using (5.62),

$$\frac{d}{dz}[e^{-z^2/4}F_\nu^{(0)}(z)] = -i2^{-(1/2)}(\nu + 1)e^{-z^2/4}F_{-\nu-2}^{(1)}(iz)$$

$$= -2^{-(1/2)}(\nu + 1)e^{-z^2/4}F_{\nu+1}^{(1)}(z);$$

that is,

$$\frac{d}{dz}[F_\nu^{(0)}(z)] - \tfrac{1}{2}zF_\nu^{(0)}(z) = -2^{-(1/2)}(\nu + 1)F_{\nu+1}^{(1)}(z). \tag{5.64}$$

Similarly, from (5.60),

$$\frac{d}{dz}[e^{-z^2/4}F_\nu^{(1)}(z)] = i\frac{d}{dz}[e^{-z^2/4}F_{-\nu-1}^{(1)}(iz)] = -\frac{d}{d(iz)}[e^{i^2z^2/4}F_{-\nu-1}^{(1)}(iz)];$$

that is, using (5.63),

$$\frac{d}{dz}[e^{-z^2/4}F_\nu^{(1)}(z)] = -2^{1/2}e^{-z^2/4}F_{-\nu-2}^{(0)}(iz) + \frac{2^{3/2}\pi^{1/2}}{\Gamma(\frac{1}{2} - \frac{1}{2}\nu)\Gamma(1 + \frac{1}{2}\nu)}e^{-z^2/4}$$

$$= 2^{1/2}e^{-z^2/4}F_{\nu+1}^{(0)}(z) + \frac{2^{3/2}\pi^{1/2}}{\Gamma(\frac{1}{2} - \frac{1}{2}\nu)\Gamma(1 + \frac{1}{2}\nu)}e^{-z^2/4};$$

that is,

$$\frac{d}{dz}[F_\nu^{(1)}(z)] - \tfrac{1}{2}zF_\nu^{(1)}(z) = 2^{1/2}F_{\nu+1}^{(0)}(z) + \frac{2^{3/2}\pi^{1/2}}{\Gamma(\frac{1}{2}-\frac{1}{2}\nu)\Gamma(1+\frac{1}{2}\nu)}. \tag{5.65}$$

From (5.62) and (5.64),

$$(\nu+1)F_{\nu+1}^{(1)}(z) - 2^{1/2}zF_\nu^{(0)}(z) - \nu F_{\nu-1}^{(1)}(z) = 0. \tag{5.66}$$

From (5.63) and (5.65),

$$F_{\nu+1}^{(0)}(z) + 2^{-(1/2)}zF_\nu^{(1)}(z) - F_{\nu-1}^{(0)}(z) = -\frac{4\pi^{1/2}}{\Gamma(\frac{1}{2}-\frac{1}{2}\nu)\Gamma(1+\frac{1}{2}\nu)}. \tag{5.67}$$

From (5.66) and (5.67),

$$(\nu+1)F_{\nu+2}^{(0)}(z) + (z^2-2\nu-1)F_\nu^{(0)}(z) + \nu F_{\nu-2}^{(0)}(z) = -\frac{16\pi^{1/2}}{\Gamma(-\frac{1}{2}\nu)\Gamma(\frac{1}{2}+\frac{1}{2}\nu)}, \tag{5.68}$$

and

$$(\nu+2)F_{\nu+2}^{(1)}(z) + (z^2-2\nu-1)F_\nu^{(1)}(z) + (\nu-1)F_{\nu-2}^{(1)}(z) = -\frac{2^{5/2}\pi^{1/2}z}{\Gamma(\frac{1}{2}-\frac{1}{2}\nu)\Gamma(1+\frac{1}{2}\nu)}. \tag{5.69}$$

5.11 Degenerate Cases of $F_\nu^{(0)}(z)$ and $F_\nu^{(1)}(z)$

When ν is an integer, the right side of one of the equations (5.39) or (5.40) vanishes, and the corresponding F function can be expressed in terms of the E functions. If ν is a nonnegative integer, the E functions can be expressed in terms of Hermite polynomials.

Using the formulas given in §4.11, we see that, if ν is zero or an even positive integer,

$$F_\nu^{(0)}(z) = -E_\nu^{(0)}(z) = -2^{(1/2)(1-\nu)}\pi^{-(1/2)}\Gamma(\tfrac{1}{2}-\tfrac{1}{2}\nu)D_\nu(z);$$

if ν is an odd negative integer,

$$F_\nu^{(0)}(z) = E_\nu^{(0)}(z) = 2^{1+\nu/2}\pi^{-(1/2)}\Gamma(1+\tfrac{1}{2}\nu)D_{-\nu-1}(iz);$$

if ν is an odd positive integer,

$$F_\nu^{(1)}(z) = -E_\nu^{(1)}(z) = 2^{(1/2)(1-\nu)}\pi^{-(1/2)}\Gamma(-\tfrac{1}{2}\nu)D_\nu(z);$$

if ν is an even negative integer,

$$F_\nu^{(1)}(z) = E_\nu^{(1)}(z) = i2^{1+\nu/2}\pi^{-(1/2)}\Gamma(\tfrac{1}{2}+\tfrac{1}{2}\nu)D_{-\nu-1}(iz).$$

In these cases, a particular solution of

$$\frac{d^2y}{dz^2} + (\nu + \tfrac{1}{2} - \tfrac{1}{4}z^2)y = 1$$

and

$$\frac{d^2y}{dz^2} + (\nu + \tfrac{1}{2} - \tfrac{1}{4}z^2)y = z$$

can be found by the method given in §4.11.

5.12 The Zeros of $F_\nu^{(0)}(z)$ and $F_\nu^{(1)}(z)$, Where ν Is Real

From (4.62) and (4.64), using Rolle's theorem, we see that, if $\nu \neq 0$ or -1, between two consecutive zeros of $F_\nu^{(0)}(z)$ there lies at least one zero of $F_{\nu-1}^{(1)}(z)$ and at least one zero of $F_{\nu+1}^{(1)}(z)$. The converse is not true. From (5.66), at a zero of $F_\nu^{(0)}(z)$, $(\nu+1)F_{\nu+1}^{(1)}(z)$ and $\nu F_{\nu-1}^{(1)}(z)$ have the same sign. From (5.62) and (5.64), at a positive value of z which is a maximum or minimum of $F_\nu^{(0)}(z)$, $F_\nu^{(0)}(z)$ and $(\nu+1)F_{\nu+1}^{(1)}(z)$ have the same sign and $\nu F_{\nu-1}^{(1)}(z)$ is of opposite sign.

Other properties of the zeros of $F_\nu^{(0)}(z)$ and $F_\nu^{(1)}(z)$ follow from those of the zeros of Ω, given in §4.14. Thus, if $-1 < \nu < -\frac{1}{2}$, $F_\nu^{(0)}(z)$ is positive for all real z; if $-\frac{1}{2} < \nu < 0$, $F_\nu^{(0)}(z)$ has one positive and one (numerically equal) negative zero. If $\nu = -\frac{1}{2}$, $F_\nu^{(0)}(z)$ has a zero at $z = 0$.

If $-2 < \nu \leqslant -\frac{1}{2}$, $F_\nu^{(1)}(z)$ is positive for all real nonzero values of z; if $-\frac{1}{2} < \nu < 1$, $F_\nu^{(1)}(z)$ has one positive zero and one (numerically equal) negative zero (apart from the point $z = 0$).

5.13 Asymptotic Expansion of $F_\nu^{(0)}(z)$ and $F_\nu^{(1)}(z)$

The asymptotic expansion of $F_\nu^{(0)}(z)$ and $F_\nu^{(1)}(z)$ for large values of $|z|$ is obtained from that for Ω given in §4.15. We find, on using (5.43), that

$$F_\nu^{(0)}(z) \sim \frac{2^{1+\nu/2}\pi^{1/2}}{\Gamma(-\frac{1}{2}\nu)} e^{-(1/2)i\pi(1+\nu)\varepsilon} D_{-\nu-1}(e^{-(1/2)i\pi\varepsilon}z) - \frac{2^{(1-\nu)/2}\pi^{1/2}}{\Gamma(\frac{1}{2}+\frac{1}{2}\nu)} \times e^{-(1/2)i\pi\nu\varepsilon} D_\nu(z) - \frac{16\pi^{1/2}}{\Gamma(-\frac{1}{2}\nu)\Gamma(\frac{1}{2}+\frac{1}{2}\nu)} \frac{1}{z^2} \sum_{n=0}^{\infty} c_n \left(\frac{2}{z}\right)^{2n} \tag{5.70}$$

and

$$F_\nu^{(1)}(z) \sim \frac{2^{1+\nu/2}\pi^{1/2}}{\Gamma(\frac{1}{2}-\frac{1}{2}\nu)} e^{-(1/2)i\pi(1+\nu)\varepsilon} D_{-\nu-1}(e^{-(1/2)i\pi\varepsilon}z) - \frac{2^{(1-\nu)/2}\pi^{1/2}}{\Gamma(1+\frac{1}{2}\nu)} \times e^{(1/2)i\pi(1-\nu)\varepsilon} D_\nu(z) - \frac{2^{5/2}\pi^{1/2}}{\Gamma(\frac{1}{2}-\frac{1}{2}\nu)\Gamma(1+\frac{1}{2}\nu)} \frac{1}{z} \sum_{n=0}^{\infty} d_n \left(\frac{2}{z}\right)^{2n}, \tag{5.71}$$

where $|\arg z| < \frac{1}{2}\pi$, $\varepsilon = \operatorname{sgn}(\operatorname{Im} z) = 1, -1$, according as $\operatorname{Im} z > 0$, < 0, and

$$c_n = \left[\frac{d^n}{dh^n}\{(1+h)^{-(1/2)+(1/2)\nu}(1-h)^{-1-(1/2)\nu}\}\right]_{h=0},$$

$$d_n = \left[\frac{d^n}{dh^n}\{(1+h)^{(1/2)\nu}(1-h)^{-(1/2)-(1/2)\nu}\}\right]_{h=0}.$$

Asymptotic expansions of $F_\nu^{(0)}(z)$ and $F_\nu^{(1)}(z)$ for other values of arg z can be obtained by repeated use of (5.60) and (5.61), together with (5.70) and (5.71).

A number of integrals involving $F_\nu^{(0)}(z)$ and $F_\nu^{(1)}(z)$ can be derived from the integrals involving $\Omega(a, c; z)$ given in §§4.16 and 4.17.

5.14 The Nonhomogeneous Parabolic Cylinder Function $G_\nu^\sigma(z)$

We consider next the solution of the nonhomogeneous equation

$$\frac{d^2y}{dz^2} + (\nu + \tfrac{1}{2} - \tfrac{1}{4}z^2)y = z^\sigma, \tag{5.72}$$

where ν and σ are constants.

Using the method of Frobenius (§1.12), we see that the particular integral of (5.72) is

$$G_\nu^{(\sigma)}(z) = z^{\sigma+2}\sum_{n=0}^{\infty} a_n z^{2n}, \tag{5.73}$$

where

$$a_0 = [(\sigma+2)(\sigma+1)]^{-1}, \quad a_1 = -(\nu+\tfrac{1}{2})[(\sigma+4)(\sigma+3)(\sigma+2)(\sigma+1)]^{-1},$$

and

$$(\sigma+2n+2)(\sigma+2n+1)a_n + (\nu+\tfrac{1}{2})a_{n-1} - \tfrac{1}{4}a_{n-2} = 0 \qquad (n \geq 2).$$

The complete primitive of (5.73) is then

$$y = C_1E_\nu^{(0)}(z) + C_2E_\nu^{(1)}(z) + G_\nu^{(\sigma)}(z). \tag{5.74}$$

where C_1 and C_2 are arbitrary constants.

The series solution is not valid if σ is a negative integer (since, in that case, all the coefficients in the series after a certain value of n become infinite). As shown in §1.12, for these values of σ, the particular solution of (5.72) will, in general, contain logarithmic terms.

As shown in §4.25, a particular solution of (5.72) is

$$y = 2^{(1/2)\sigma-1}e^{-z^2/4}\Lambda_{1/2,(1/2)\sigma+1}(-\tfrac{1}{2}\nu, \tfrac{1}{2}; \tfrac{1}{2}z^2).$$

On expanding this expression as a power series in z and comparing it with (5.73) we find that

$$G_\nu^{(\sigma)}(z) = 2^{(1/2)\sigma-1}e^{-z^2/4}\Lambda_{1/2,(1/2)\sigma+1}(-\tfrac{1}{2}\nu, \tfrac{1}{2}; \tfrac{1}{2}z^2)$$
$$= 2^{(1/2)(\sigma-3)}ze^{-z^2/4}\Lambda_{1/2,(1/2)\sigma+(1/2)}(\tfrac{1}{2}-\tfrac{1}{2}\nu, \tfrac{3}{2}; \tfrac{1}{2}z^2); \quad (5.75)$$

that is, from (4.220),

$$G_\nu^{(\sigma)}(z) = \tfrac{1}{4}z^{\sigma+2}\sum_{n=0}^{\infty}\frac{\Gamma(\frac{1}{2}\sigma-\frac{1}{2}\nu+n+1)\Gamma(\frac{1}{2}\sigma+1)\Gamma(\frac{1}{2}\sigma+\frac{1}{2})}{\Gamma(\frac{1}{2}\sigma-\frac{1}{2}\nu+1)\Gamma(\frac{1}{2}\sigma+n+2)\Gamma(\frac{1}{2}\sigma+n+\frac{3}{2})}$$
$$\times F_{(n+1)}[\tfrac{1}{2}\sigma+1, \tfrac{1}{2}\sigma+\tfrac{1}{2}; \tfrac{1}{2}\sigma-\tfrac{1}{2}\nu+1; \tfrac{1}{4}](\tfrac{1}{2}z^2)^n, \quad (5.76)$$

where $F_{(n+1)}$ stands for the first $n+1$ terms of the hypergeometric series with the given parameters.

From (5.30) and (5.75), we see that

$$G_\nu^{(\sigma)}(z) = 2^{\lambda-(1/2)}z^{-1/2}N^{(\lambda)}_{\nu/2+1/4,-1/4}(\tfrac{1}{2}z^2), \quad (5.77)$$

where $\lambda = \tfrac{1}{2}\sigma - \tfrac{1}{4}$.

From (5.75), we see that

$$G_\nu^{(0)}(z) = 2^{-(3/2)}\pi^{-(1/2)}\Gamma(-\tfrac{1}{2}\nu)\Gamma(\tfrac{1}{2}+\tfrac{1}{2}\nu)e^{-z^2/4}$$
$$\times [\Omega(-\tfrac{1}{2}\nu, \tfrac{1}{2}; \tfrac{1}{2}z^2) - \Omega(-\tfrac{1}{2}\nu, \tfrac{1}{2}; 0)\Phi(-\tfrac{1}{2}\nu, \tfrac{1}{2}; \tfrac{1}{2}z^2)]; \quad (5.78)$$

that is, using (5.44) and (5.54),

$$G_\nu^{(0)}(z) = \tfrac{1}{4}\pi^{-(1/2)}\Gamma(-\tfrac{1}{2}\nu)\Gamma(\tfrac{1}{2}+\tfrac{1}{2}\nu)[F_\nu^{(0)}(z) - \Omega(-\tfrac{1}{2}\nu, \tfrac{1}{2}; 0)E_\nu^{(0)}(z)]. \quad (5.79)$$

Similarly,

$$G_\nu^{(1)}(z) = (2/\pi)^{1/2}\Gamma(\tfrac{1}{2}-\tfrac{1}{2}\nu)\Gamma(1+\tfrac{1}{2}\nu)ze^{-z^2/4}$$
$$\times [\Omega(\tfrac{1}{2}-\tfrac{1}{2}\nu, \tfrac{3}{2}; \tfrac{1}{2}z^2) - \Omega(\tfrac{1}{2}-\tfrac{1}{2}\nu, \tfrac{3}{2}; 0)\Phi(\tfrac{1}{2}-\tfrac{1}{2}\nu, \tfrac{3}{2}; \tfrac{1}{2}z^2)]; \quad (5.80)$$

that is, using (5.45) and (5.55),

$$G_\nu^{(1)}(z) = (2\pi)^{-(1/2)}\Gamma(\tfrac{1}{2}-\tfrac{1}{2}\nu)\Gamma(1+\tfrac{1}{2}\nu)[F_\nu^{(1)}(z) - \Omega(\tfrac{1}{2}-\tfrac{1}{2}\nu, \tfrac{3}{2}; 0)E_\nu^{(1)}(z)]. \quad (5.81)$$

When $\nu = -\tfrac{1}{2}$, from (5.33) and (5.77),

$$G_{-(1/2)}^{(\sigma)}(z) = 2^{\lambda-(1/2)}e^{-i\pi/4}z^{1/2}s_{\lambda,-1/4}(\tfrac{1}{4}e^{(1/2)i\pi}z^2), \quad (5.82)$$

where $\lambda = \tfrac{1}{2}\sigma - \tfrac{1}{4}$.

From (5.73), we see that

$$G_\nu^{(\sigma)}(ze^{i\pi}) = e^{i\pi\sigma}G_\nu^{(\sigma)}(z)$$

and

$$G_{-\nu-1}^{(\sigma)}(ze^{(1/2)i\pi}) = -e^{(1/2)i\pi\sigma}G_\nu^{(\sigma)}(z). \tag{5.83}$$

5.15 Recurrence Relations for $G_\nu^{(\sigma)}(z)$

These can be obtained by using the recurrence formulas given for Λ in §4.24. Thus

$$(\sigma+2)(\sigma+1)G_\nu^{(\sigma)}(z) + (\nu+\tfrac{1}{2})G_\nu^{(\sigma+2)}(z) - \tfrac{1}{4}G_\nu^{(\sigma+4)}(z) = z^{\sigma+2}. \tag{5.84}$$

Also

$$\begin{aligned}\frac{d}{dz}[e^{z^2/4}G_\nu^{(\sigma)}(z)] &= 2^{(1/2)\sigma-1}\frac{d}{dz}[\Lambda_{1/2,(1/2)\sigma+1}(-\tfrac{1}{2}\nu, \tfrac{1}{2}; \tfrac{1}{2}z^2)] \\ &= 2^{(1/2)\sigma-2}z[\sigma\Lambda_{1/2,(1/2)\sigma}(1-\tfrac{1}{2}\nu, \tfrac{3}{2}; \tfrac{1}{2}z^2) \\ &\quad + \Lambda_{1/2,(1/2)\sigma+1}(1-\tfrac{1}{2}\nu, \tfrac{3}{2}; \tfrac{1}{2}z^2)] \\ &= e^{z^2/4}[\sigma G_{\nu-1}^{(\sigma-1)}(z) + \tfrac{1}{2}G_{\nu-1}^{(\sigma+1)}(z)];\end{aligned}$$

that is,

$$\frac{d}{dz}[G_\nu^{(\sigma)}(z)] + \tfrac{1}{2}zG_\nu^{(\sigma)}(z) = \sigma G_{\nu-1}^{(\sigma-1)}(z) + \tfrac{1}{2}G_{\nu-1}^{(\sigma+1)}(z). \tag{5.85}$$

Similarly, from (5.83),

$$\begin{aligned}\frac{d}{dz}[e^{-z^2/4}G_\nu^{(\sigma)}(z)] &= -e^{-(1/2)i\pi\sigma}\frac{d}{dz}[e^{-z^2/4}G_{-\nu-1}^{(\sigma)}(iz)] \\ &= -e^{-(1/2)i\pi(\sigma-1)}\frac{d}{d(iz)}[e^{i^2z^2/4}G_{-\nu-1}^{(\sigma)}(iz)];\end{aligned}$$

that is, using (5.85),

$$\begin{aligned}\frac{d}{dz}[e^{-z^2/4}G_\nu^{(\sigma)}(z)] &= -e^{-(1/2)i\pi(\sigma-1)}e^{-z^2/4}[\sigma G_{-\nu-2}^{(\sigma-1)}(iz) + \tfrac{1}{2}G_{-\nu-2}^{(\sigma+1)}(iz)] \\ &= e^{-z^2/4}[\sigma G_{\nu+1}^{(\sigma-1)}(z) - \tfrac{1}{2}G_{\nu+1}^{(\sigma+1)}(z)];\end{aligned}$$

that is,

$$\frac{d}{dz}[G_\nu^{(\sigma)}(z)] - \tfrac{1}{2}zG_\nu^{(\sigma)}(z) = \sigma G_{\nu+1}^{(\sigma-1)}(z) - \tfrac{1}{2}G_{\nu+1}^{(\sigma+1)}(z). \tag{5.86}$$

From (5.85) and (5.86),

$$zG_\nu^{(\sigma)}(z) = \sigma[G_{\nu-1}^{(\sigma-1)}(z) - G_{\nu+1}^{(\sigma-1)}(z)] + \tfrac{1}{2}[G_{\nu-1}^{(\sigma+1)}(z) + G_{\nu+1}^{(\sigma+1)}(z)] \tag{5.87}$$

and

$$\frac{d}{dz}[G_\nu^{(\sigma)}(z)] = \tfrac{1}{2}\sigma[G_{\nu-1}^{(\sigma-1)}(z) + G_{\nu+1}^{(\sigma-1)}(z)] + \tfrac{1}{4}[G_{\nu-1}^{(\sigma+1)}(z) - G_{\nu+1}^{(\sigma+1)}(z)]. \quad (5.88)$$

Again, from (4.239), with $\rho = \frac{1}{2}$, $a = -\frac{1}{2}\nu$, and $c = \frac{3}{2}$,

$$(\sigma - \tfrac{1}{2})\Lambda_{1/2,\sigma}(-\tfrac{1}{2}\nu, \tfrac{1}{2}; z) + \tfrac{1}{2}\Lambda_{1/2,\sigma+1}(-\tfrac{1}{2}\nu, \tfrac{1}{2}; z) = (\tfrac{1}{2}\nu + \tfrac{1}{2})\Lambda_{1/2,\sigma}(-\tfrac{1}{2}\nu, \tfrac{3}{2}; z)$$
$$+ (\sigma - \tfrac{1}{2}\nu)\Lambda_{1/2,\sigma}(1 - \tfrac{1}{2}\nu, \tfrac{3}{2}; z)$$
$$+ \tfrac{1}{2}\Lambda_{1/2,\sigma+1}(1 - \tfrac{1}{2}\nu, \tfrac{3}{2}; z). \quad (5.89)$$

Replacing σ by $\frac{1}{2}\sigma + 1$ and using (5.75), we obtain

$$z[(\sigma + 1)G_\nu^{(\sigma)}(z) + \tfrac{1}{2}G_\nu^{(\sigma+2)}(z)] = (\nu + 1)G_{\nu+1}^{(\sigma+1)}(z) + (\sigma + 2 - \nu)G_{\nu-1}^{(\sigma+1)}(z)$$
$$+ \tfrac{1}{2}G_{\nu-1}^{(\sigma+3)}(z). \quad (5.90)$$

5.16 Related Differential Equations

We shall now briefly consider a certain class of second-order differential equations, the solutions of which can be expressed in terms of $G_\nu^{(\sigma)}(z)$.

In the equation

$$\frac{d^2y}{dz^2} + (\nu + \tfrac{1}{2} - \tfrac{1}{4}z^2)y = z^\sigma \quad (5.91)$$

put

$$x = \zeta^\alpha y, \qquad z = \beta\zeta^\gamma, \quad (5.92)$$

where α, β, and γ are constants.

Equation (5.91) is then transformed into

$$\zeta^2\frac{d^2x}{d\zeta^2} + (1 - 2\alpha - \gamma)\zeta\frac{dx}{d\zeta} + [\alpha(\alpha + \gamma) + \beta^2\gamma^2(\nu + \tfrac{1}{2})\zeta^{2\gamma} - \tfrac{1}{4}\beta^4\gamma^2\zeta^{4\gamma}]x$$
$$= \beta^{\sigma+2}\gamma^2\zeta^{\alpha+\sigma\gamma+2\gamma}. \quad (5.93)$$

A particular integral of (5.93) is $x = \zeta^\alpha G_\nu^{(\sigma)}(\beta\zeta^\gamma)$. The complementary function is

$$\zeta^\alpha[C_1E_\nu^{(0)}(\beta\zeta^\gamma) + C_2E_\nu^{(1)}(\beta\zeta^\gamma)].$$

Some special cases of this transformation are of interest. In (5.93) put $\gamma = 1$. Then (5.93) becomes

$$\frac{d^2x}{d\zeta^2} - \frac{2\alpha}{\zeta}\frac{dx}{d\zeta} + \left[\frac{\alpha(\alpha + 1)}{\zeta^2} + \beta^2(\nu + \tfrac{1}{2}) - \tfrac{1}{4}\beta^4\zeta^2\right]x = \beta^{\sigma+2}\zeta^{\alpha+\sigma}, \quad (5.94)$$

with a particular integral $x = \zeta^\alpha G_\nu^{(\sigma)}(\beta\zeta)$.

In (5.94) put $\alpha = 0$. Then (5.94) becomes

$$\frac{d^2x}{d\zeta^2} + [\beta^2(\nu + \tfrac{1}{2}) - \tfrac{1}{4}\beta^4\zeta^2]x = \beta^{\sigma+2}\zeta^{\sigma}, \tag{5.95}$$

with a particular integral $x = G_\nu^{(\sigma)}(\beta\zeta)$.

In (5.94), put $\alpha = -\frac{1}{2}$. Then (5.94) becomes

$$\frac{d^2x}{d\zeta^2} + \frac{1}{\zeta}\frac{dx}{d\zeta} - \frac{1}{4}\left[\frac{1}{\zeta^2} - 4\beta^2(\nu + \tfrac{1}{2}) + \beta^4\zeta^2\right]x = \beta^{\sigma+2}\zeta^{\sigma-(1/2)}, \tag{5.96}$$

with a particular integral $x = \zeta^{-1/2}G_\nu^{(\sigma)}(\beta\zeta)$.

In (5.94), put $\alpha = -1$. Then (5.94) becomes

$$\frac{d^2x}{d\zeta^2} + \frac{2}{\zeta}\frac{dx}{d\zeta} + [\beta^2(\nu + \tfrac{1}{2}) - \tfrac{1}{4}\beta^4\zeta^2]x = \beta^{\sigma+2}\zeta^{\sigma-1}, \tag{5.97}$$

with a particular integral $x = \zeta^{-1}G_\nu^{(\sigma)}(\beta\zeta)$.

In (5.93), put $\alpha = \frac{1}{2}(1 - \gamma)$. Then (5.93) becomes

$$\zeta^2\frac{d^2x}{d\zeta^2} + [\tfrac{1}{4}(1 - \gamma^2) + \beta^2\gamma^2(\nu + \tfrac{1}{2})\zeta^{2\gamma} - \tfrac{1}{4}\beta^4\gamma^2\zeta^{4\gamma}]x = \beta^{\sigma+2}\gamma^2\zeta^{(1/2)+\sigma\gamma+3\gamma/2}, \tag{5.98}$$

with a particular integral $x = \zeta^{(1-\gamma)/2}G_\nu^{(\sigma)}(\beta\zeta^\gamma)$.

In (5.93) put $\alpha = 0$. Then (5.93) becomes

$$\frac{d^2x}{d\zeta^2} + \frac{1-\gamma}{\zeta}\frac{dx}{d\zeta} + [\beta^2\gamma^2(\nu + \tfrac{1}{2})\zeta^{2\gamma-2} - \tfrac{1}{4}\beta^4\gamma^2\zeta^{4\gamma-2}]x = \beta^{\sigma+2}\gamma^2\zeta^{\sigma\gamma+2\gamma-2}, \tag{5.99}$$

with a particular integral $x = G_\nu^{(\sigma)}(\beta\zeta^\gamma)$.

In (5.93) put $\alpha = -\gamma$. Then (5.93) becomes

$$\frac{d^2x}{d\zeta^2} + \frac{1+\gamma}{\zeta}\frac{dx}{d\zeta} + [\beta^2\gamma^2(\nu + \tfrac{1}{2})\zeta^{2\gamma-2} - \tfrac{1}{4}\beta^4\gamma^2\zeta^{4\gamma-2}]x = \beta^{\sigma+2}\gamma^2\zeta^{\sigma\gamma+\gamma-2}, \tag{5.100}$$

with a particular integral $x = \zeta^{-\gamma}G_\nu^{(\sigma)}(\beta\zeta^\gamma)$.

In (5.100), put $\gamma = \frac{1}{2}$. Then (5.100) becomes

$$\frac{d^2x}{d\zeta^2} + \frac{3}{2\zeta}\frac{dx}{d\zeta} + \left[\frac{\beta^2(\nu + \frac{1}{2})}{4\zeta} - \frac{1}{16}\beta^4\right]x = \tfrac{1}{4}\beta^{\sigma+2}\zeta^{(1/2)\sigma-(3/2)}, \tag{5.101}$$

with a particular integral $x = \zeta^{-1/2}G_\nu^{(\sigma)}(\beta\zeta^{1/2})$.

In (5.100), put $\gamma = -1$. Then (5.100) becomes

$$\zeta^4 \frac{d^2x}{d\zeta^2} + \left[\beta^2(\nu + \tfrac{1}{2}) - \frac{1}{4}\frac{\beta^2}{\zeta^2}\right]x = \beta^{\sigma+2}\zeta^{1-\sigma}, \tag{5.102}$$

with a particular integral $x = \zeta G_\nu^{(\sigma)}(\beta/\zeta)$.

PROBLEMS

1. By differentiating the integral representation (5.20) for $A_{\kappa,\mu}(z)$, show that $A_{\kappa,\mu}(z)$ satisfies the differential equation

$$\frac{d^2y}{dz^2} + \left(-\frac{1}{4} + \frac{\kappa}{z} + \frac{\frac{1}{4} - \mu^2}{z^2}\right)y = \frac{2^{-2\mu}\Gamma(2\mu + 1)}{\Gamma(\mu - \kappa + \frac{1}{2}\Gamma(\mu + \kappa + \frac{1}{2})} z^{\mu-(1/2)}.$$

2. Obtain the power series for $A_{\kappa,\mu}(z)$ from the integral representation (5.20).

3. Show that, if $\operatorname{Re}(\mu + \nu) > -\frac{1}{2}$ and $\operatorname{Re} p > \frac{1}{2}|\operatorname{Re} a|$,

$$\int_0^\infty e^{-pt}t^{\nu-1}A_{\kappa,\mu}(at)dt = a^{\mu+(1/2)}(p + \tfrac{1}{2}a)^{-\mu-\nu-(1/2)}\Gamma(\mu + \nu + \tfrac{1}{2})$$

$$\times B[\mu + \nu + \tfrac{1}{2}, \mu - \kappa + \tfrac{1}{2}; 2\mu + 1; a/(p + \tfrac{1}{2}a)],$$

where B is the nonhomogeneous hypergeometric function (defined in Chapter 6).

4. By comparing coefficients of powers of z, show that

$$N_{0,\mu}^{(\nu)}(z) = (2e^{-(1/2)i\pi})^{\nu+1}z^{1/2}s_{\nu,\mu}(\tfrac{1}{2}e^{(1/2)i\pi}z).$$

5. Derive the series solutions for $F_\nu^{(0)}(z)$ and $F_\nu^{(1)}(z)$ directly from the differential equation.

6. Determine the recurrence relations for $F_\nu^{(0)}(z)$ and $F_\nu^{(1)}(z)$ from their power-series expansions.

7. Obtain the power-series solutions of

$$\frac{d^2y}{dz^2} + (\nu + \tfrac{1}{2} - \tfrac{1}{4}z^2)y = 1,$$

and

$$\frac{d^2y}{dz^2} + (\nu + \tfrac{1}{2} - \tfrac{1}{4}z^2)y = z.$$

Show that the first equation has a particular integral which is an even function of z, and the second equation has one which is an odd function of z.

8. Use the substitution $u=y^{1-k}$ to show that the solution of the nonlinear differential equation

$$y\frac{d^2y}{dz^2}=k\left(\frac{dy}{dz}\right)^2+(\tfrac{1}{4}z^2-\nu-\tfrac{1}{2})\frac{y^2}{1-k}+\frac{z^\sigma y^{k+1}}{1-k}$$

is

$$y=[C_1E_\nu^{(0)}(z)+C_2E_\nu^{(1)}(z)+G_\nu^{(\sigma)}(z)]^{1/(1-k)},$$

where C_1 and C_2 are arbitrary constants.

CHAPTER 6

Nonhomogeneous Hypergeometric Functions

6.1 Introduction

In this chapter we consider the properties of the solutions of certain nonhomogeneous linear differential equations which have as their associated homogeneous equation the hypergeometric equation

$$z(1-z)\frac{d^2y}{dz^2}+[c-(a+b+1)z]\frac{dy}{dz}-aby=0, \tag{6.1}$$

where a, b, and c are constants.

We consider first the nonhomogeneous hypergeometric function $B(a, b; c; z)$, defined in §6.3 (see also Babister [1961]). $B(a, b; c; z)$ bears the same relation to the generalized modified Struve function Ω (defined in Chapter 4) as the hypergeometric function $F(a, b; c; z)$ does to the confluent hypergeometric function Φ. As shown in §6.5, $B(a, b; c; z)$ is a particular integral of the nonhomogeneous equation

$$z(1-z)\frac{d^2y}{dz^2}+[c-(a+b+1)z]\frac{dy}{dz}-aby=a\,\frac{2^{1-c}\Gamma(c)}{\Gamma(b)\Gamma(c-b)}\,(1-\tfrac{1}{2}z)^{-a-1}. \tag{6.2}$$

In §6.2 we summarize various properties of (6.1) and in the following sections we discuss in detail the properties of $B(a, b; c; z)$. As in Chapter 4, we find it convenient to define this function in terms of certain contour integrals (see §1.14).

In §§6.16 to 6.21, we discuss the properties of the nonhomogeneous hypergeometric functions $f_\sigma(a, b; c; z)$ and $F_\sigma(a, b; c; z)$, which satisfy the equation

$$z(1-z)\frac{d^2y}{dz^2}+[c-(a+b+1)z]\frac{dy}{dz}-aby=z^{\sigma-1}, \tag{6.3}$$

and those of $C_{\rho,\sigma}^{(\tau)}(a, b; c; z)$, which satisfy the equation

$$z(1-z)\frac{d^2y}{dz^2}+[c-(a+b+1)z]\frac{dy}{dz}-aby=z^{\sigma-1}(1-\rho z)^{\tau-1}. \tag{6.4}$$

In §6.22 and in Chapter 7, we consider the solutions of some differential equations (such as the nonhomogeneous Legendre equation) which are related to (6.4).

6.2 Some Properties of the Hypergeometric Function

The theory of the hypergeometric function $F(a, b; c; z)$ is fully set out in Erdélyi [1953a], Poole [1936], Whittaker and Watson [1935], and Klein [1933]. We shall here briefly summarize various properties of this function.

If c is not an integer, two independent solutions of (6.1) are

$$y_1 = F(a, b; c; z) = \frac{\Gamma(c)}{\Gamma(a)\Gamma(b)} \sum_{n=0}^{\infty} \frac{\Gamma(a+n)\Gamma(b+n)}{\Gamma(c+n)} \frac{z^n}{n!} \tag{6.5}$$

and

$$y_2 = z^{1-c}F(a-c+1, b-c+1; 2-c; z). \tag{6.6}$$

As shown by Kummer, there are 24 functions of the type

$$z^{\lambda}(1-z)^{\mu}F(a', b'; c'; z')$$

which are solutions of the hypergeometric equation (6.1), where λ, μ, a', b', and c' are linear functions of a, b, and c and where z' is one of the variables

$$z, \quad 1-z, \quad \frac{1}{z}, \quad \frac{1}{1-z}, \quad \frac{z}{z-1}, \quad \frac{z-1}{z},$$

provided that none of the quantities c, $c-a-b$, and $b-a$ is an integer. Any three of these solutions are linearly related.

The Wronskian of y_1 and y_2 is

$$W(y_1, y_2) = y_1 Dy_2 - y_2 Dy_1 = (1-c)z^{-c}(1-z)^{c-a-b-1}, \tag{6.7}$$

where $D \equiv d/dz$. When $c = 1$, $y_1 = y_2$, and the solutions are no longer independent.

When $c - 1$ is a negative integer, $F(a, b; c; z)$ is infinite. Similarly, when $c - 1$ is a positive integer, y_2 is infinite. Thus, when c is an integer, one solution of (6.1) is given by y_1 or y_2, and the second solution will contain logarithmic terms.

Consider next the solution of (6.1) in terms of contour integrals. As shown by Poole [*107*, 1936], these contour integrals can be of the form

$$\frac{1}{2\pi i}\int_C t^{b-1}(t-1)^{c-b-1}(zt-1)^{-a}\,dt$$

where the contour C must satisfy the condition

$$[t^{b-1}(t-1)^{c-b-1}(zt-1)^{-a}]_C = 0. \tag{6.8}$$

Thus the solutions of (6.1) can be expressed in terms of the simple loop integrals

$$y_1 = \frac{1}{2\pi i}\int_I^{(0+)} t^{b-1}(t-1)^{c-b-1}(zt-1)^{-a}\,dt, \tag{6.9}$$

$$y_2 = \frac{1}{2\pi i}\int_I^{(1+)} t^{b-1}(t-1)^{c-b-1}(zt-1)^{-a}\,dt, \tag{6.10}$$

and

$$y_3 = \frac{1}{2\pi i}\int_I^{(1/z+)} t^{b-1}(t-1)^{c-b-1}(zt-1)^{-a}\,dt, \tag{6.11}$$

where I is some convenient point in the t plane such that (6.8) is satisfied. If $\mathrm{Re}(c-a) < 2$, the integrands tend to zero as $|t| \to \infty$. Then, if

$$\arg z = \theta \qquad (-\pi < \theta < \pi),$$

we shall take I as the point at infinity having argument $\pi - \theta$, and

$$\arg t = \arg(t-1) = \arg(t - z^{-1}) = -\pi - \theta$$

at the start of the contours. The contours for y_1 and y_2 are shown in Figure 6.1.

From Erdélyi [1953a] and Poole [1936], four solutions of (6.1) are

$$F(a, b; c; z)$$
$$= i(2\pi)^{-1}e^{i\pi(b-a)}\Gamma(1-b)\Gamma(c)\Gamma(1+b-c)y_4, \tag{6.12}$$

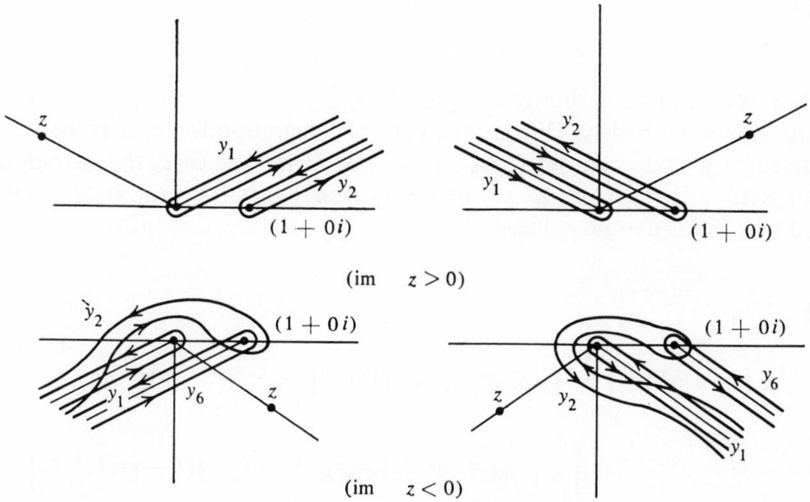

Figure 6.1 Contours for y_1, y_2, and y_6.

$$z^{1-c}F(a-c+1, b-c+1; 2-c; z)$$
$$= e^{-i\pi a}\Gamma(a)\Gamma(2-c)[\Gamma(a+1-c)]^{-1}y_5, \tag{6.13}$$

$$F(a, b; a+b+1-c; 1-z)$$
$$= -e^{i\pi(c-a-b)}\Gamma(1-b)\Gamma(a+b+1-c)[\Gamma(a+1-c)]^{-1}y_1, \tag{6.14}$$

$$z^{-a}F(a, a+1-c; a+1-b; z^{-1})$$
$$= e^{i\pi(b+c-2a)}\Gamma(a+1-b)\Gamma(b+1-c)[\Gamma(a+1-c)]^{-1}y_2 \qquad (\operatorname{Im} z > 0), \tag{6.15}$$

and

$$z^{-a}F(a, a+1-c; a+1-b; z^{-1})$$
$$= e^{i\pi(b-c)}\Gamma(a+1-b)\Gamma(b+1-c)[\Gamma(a+1-c)]^{-1}y_6 \qquad (\operatorname{Im} z < 0), \tag{6.16}$$

where

$$y_4 = \frac{1}{2\pi i}\int_I^{(1+,0+,1-,0-)} t^{b-1}(t-1)^{c-b-1}(zt-1)^{-a}\,dt$$
$$= y_2[1-e^{2\pi ib}] - y_1[1-e^{2\pi i(c-b)}], \tag{6.17}$$

$$y_5 = \frac{1}{2\pi i}\int_I^{(0+,1+)} t^{b-1}(t-1)^{c-b-1}(zt-1)^{-a}\,dt$$
$$= y_1 + y_2 e^{2\pi ib} \tag{6.18}$$

and

$$y_6 = y_1[1-e^{2\pi i(c-b)}] + y_2 e^{2\pi ib}. \tag{6.19}$$

The contour for y_6 is shown in Figure 6.1.

As shown by Erdélyi [1953a], the path of integration for y_4 may be contracted to a finite contour $(1+, 0+, 1-, 0-)$; in that case, the restriction that $\operatorname{Re}(c-a) < 2$ is no longer necessary. Finally, putting $t = \frac{1}{2}(1+s)$, we find that (6.17) can be reduced to

$$y_4 = i\,\frac{2^{-c}}{\pi}\,e^{i\pi(a-b-c)}$$
$$\times\Bigg[(1-e^{2i\pi b})\int_0^{(1+)}(1+s)^{b-1}(1-s)^{c-b-1}[1-\tfrac{1}{2}(1+s)z]^{-a}\,ds$$
$$-\{1-e^{2i\pi(c-b)}\}\int_0^{(-1+)}(1+s)^{b-1}(1-s)^{c-b-1}[1-\tfrac{1}{2}(1+s)z]^{-a}\,ds\Bigg], \tag{6.20}$$

where the arguments of $1+s$, $1-s$, and $1-\frac{1}{2}(1+s)z$ all have their principal values at the start of the contours, and z^{-1} is not a real number between 0 and 1.

For $\operatorname{Re} c > \operatorname{Re} b > 0$, the contours of integration in (6.20) may be replaced by portions of the real axis. We find that

$$F(a, b; c; z) = 2^{1-c}\frac{\Gamma(c)}{\Gamma(b)\Gamma(c-b)}\int_0^1 (1-s^2)^{(1/2)c-1}$$

$$\times\left\{\left(\frac{1+s}{1-s}\right)^{b-(1/2)c}[1-\tfrac{1}{2}(1+s)z]^{-a} + \left(\frac{1-s}{1+s}\right)^{b-(1/2)c}[1-\tfrac{1}{2}(1-s)z]^{-a}\right\} ds. \tag{6.21}$$

This can be simplified to give Euler's integral,

$$F(a, b; c; z) = \frac{\Gamma(c)}{\Gamma(b)\Gamma(c-b)}\int_0^1 t^{b-1}(1-t)^{c-b-1}(1-tz)^{-a}\,dt. \tag{6.22}$$

The corresponding formula for the confluent hypergeometric function can be deduced immediately, if we put $z = x/a$ and let $a \to \infty$. Then

$$\lim_{a\to\infty} F\left(a, b; c; \frac{x}{a}\right) = \Phi(b, c; x) \tag{6.23}$$

and (6.21) reduces to

$$\Phi(b, c; x) = 2^{2-c}\frac{\Gamma(c)}{\Gamma(b)\Gamma(c-b)}e^{(1/2)x}\int_0^1 (1-s^2)^{(1/2)c-1}$$

$$\times \cosh\left[\tfrac{1}{2}xs + (b-\tfrac{1}{2}c)\log\frac{1+s}{1-s}\right] ds \tag{6.24}$$

in agreement with the result of §4.2.

6.3 Nonhomogeneous Hypergeometric Function $B(a, b; c; z)$

Consider the function $B(a, b; c; z)$ defined by

$$B(a, b; c; z) = i(2\pi)^{-1}e^{i\pi(b-a)}\Gamma(1-b)\Gamma(c)\Gamma(1+b-c)v, \tag{6.25}$$

where

$$v = i\frac{2^{-c}}{\pi}e^{i\pi(a-b-c)}\left[(1-e^{2i\pi b})\int_0^{(1+)}(1+s)^{b-1}(1-s)^{c-b-1}[1-\tfrac{1}{2}(1+s)z]^{-a}ds\right.$$

$$\left. + \{1-e^{2i\pi(c-b)}\}\int_0^{(-1+)}(1+s)^{b-1}(1-s)^{c-b-1}[1-\tfrac{1}{2}(1+s)z]^{-a}\,ds\right], \tag{6.26}$$

where the arguments of $1+s$, $1-s$, and $1-\frac{1}{2}(1+s)z$ all have their principal values at the start of the contours, and z^{-1} is not a real number between 0 and 1.

From (6.12) and (6.25),

$$\frac{B(a,b;c;z)}{F(a,b;c;z)}=\frac{v}{y_4}.$$

For $\operatorname{Re} c > \operatorname{Re} b > 0$, the contours of integration in (6.26) may be replaced by portions of the real axis. We find that

$$B(a,b;c;z)=2^{1-c}\frac{\Gamma(c)}{\Gamma(b)\Gamma(c-b)}\int_0^1 (1-s^2)^{(1/2)c-1}$$
$$\times\left\{\left(\frac{1+s}{1-s}\right)^{b-(1/2)c}\left[1-\tfrac{1}{2}(1+s)z\right]^{-a}-\left(\frac{1-s}{1+s}\right)^{b-(1/2)c}\left[1-\tfrac{1}{2}(1-s)z\right]^{-a}\right\}ds. \tag{6.27}$$

Put $z=x/a$ and let $a\to\infty$. The right side of (6.27) reduces to

$$2^{2-c}\frac{\Gamma(c)}{\Gamma(b)\Gamma(c-b)}e^{(1/2)x}\int_0^1 (1-s^2)^{(1/2)c-1}\sinh\left[\tfrac{1}{2}xs+(b-\tfrac{1}{2}c)\log\frac{1+s}{1-s}\right]ds,$$

which, from (4.32), is equal to $\Omega(b,c;x)$, where Ω is the generalized modified Struve function. Thus

$$\lim_{a\to\infty} B\left(a,b;c;\frac{x}{a}\right)=\Omega(b,c;x). \tag{6.28}$$

Using (6.20) and (6.26) we find

$$F(a,b;c;z)+B(a,b;c;z)=2^{2-c}\frac{\Gamma(c)}{\Gamma(b)\Gamma(c-b)}$$
$$\times\int_0^1 (1+s)^{b-1}(1-s)^{c-b-1}\left[1-\tfrac{1}{2}(1+s)z\right]^{-a}ds \qquad (\operatorname{Re} c>\operatorname{Re} b); \tag{6.29}$$

that is, on putting $t=\frac{1}{2}(1+s)$,

$$F(a,b;c;z)+B(a,b;c;z)=\frac{2\Gamma(c)}{\Gamma(b)\Gamma(c-b)}$$
$$\times\int_{1/2}^1 t^{b-1}(1-t)^{c-b-1}(1-tz)^{-a}\,dt \qquad (\operatorname{Re} c>\operatorname{Re} b). \tag{6.30}$$

Similarly, we find

$$F(a, b; c; z) - B(a, b; c; z) = 2^{2-c} \frac{\Gamma(c)}{\Gamma(b)\Gamma(c-b)} \times \int_0^1 (1-s)^{b-1}(1+s)^{c-b-1}[1 - \tfrac{1}{2}(1-s)z]^{-a}\, ds \qquad (\operatorname{Re} b > 0); \tag{6.31}$$

that is, on putting $t = \frac{1}{2}(1-s)$,

$$F(a, b; c; z) - B(a, b; c; z) = \frac{2\Gamma(c)}{\Gamma(b)\Gamma(c-b)} \times \int_0^{1/2} t^{b-1}(1-t)^{c-b-1}(1-tz)^{-a}\, dt \qquad (\operatorname{Re} b > 0). \tag{6.32}$$

From (6.26), putting $t = \frac{1}{2}(1+s)$, we see that

$$v = \frac{1}{2\pi i}\left[(1 - e^{2i\pi b}) \int_{1/2}^{(1+)} t^{b-1}(t-1)^{c-b-1}(zt-1)^{-a}\, dt + \{1 - e^{2i\pi(c-b)}\} \int_{1/2}^{(0+)} t^{b-1}(t-1)^{c-b-1}(zt-1)^{-a}\, dt\right], \tag{6.33}$$

where $\arg t = -2\pi$ and $\arg(t-1) = -\pi$ at the start of the contours. At that point, $\arg(t - z^{-1})$ is chosen so that it tends to $-\pi - \theta$ as z tends to zero (with argument θ).

Using (6.9), (6.10), and (6.19), we see, by deforming the contours, that, if $\operatorname{Re}(c-a) < 2$, (6.33) can be put in the form

$$v = \frac{1}{2\pi i}\left[(1 - e^{2i\pi b})\left\{\int_{1/2}^{I} X\, dt + 2\pi i y_2 - e^{2i\pi(c-b)} \int_{1/2}^{I} X\, dt\right\} + \{1 - e^{2i\pi(c-b)}\}\left\{\int_{1/2}^{I} X\, dt + 2\pi i y_1 - e^{2i\pi b} \int_{1/2}^{I} X\, dt\right\}\right] \qquad (\operatorname{Im} z > 0), \tag{6.34}$$

$$v = \frac{1}{2\pi i}\left[(1 - e^{2i\pi b})\left\{\int_{1/2}^{I} X\, dt + 2\pi i e^{-2i\pi b} y_6 - e^{2i\pi(c-b)} \int_{1/2}^{I} X\, dt\right\} + \{1 - e^{2i\pi(c-b)}\}\left\{\int_{1/2}^{I} X\, dt + 2\pi i e^{-2i\pi b} y_1 - e^{2i\pi b} \int_{1/2}^{I} X\, dt\right\}\right] \qquad (\operatorname{Im} z < 0), \tag{6.35}$$

where

$$X = t^{b-1}(t-1)^{c-b-1}(zt-1)^{-a}$$

and the contours for y_1, y_2, and y_6 are given above.

The integrals $\int_{1/2}^{I} X\,dt$ can be taken along a line through $t = \frac{1}{2}$ having argument $\pi - \theta$, where $\arg z = \theta$ $(-\pi < \theta < \pi)$.

Putting $t = r + \frac{1}{2}$, we find that

$$\int_{1/2}^{I} X\,dt = e^{2i\pi(a-c)} \int_0^{\infty \exp(i\pi - i\theta)} (r + \tfrac{1}{2})^{b-1}(r - \tfrac{1}{2})^{c-b-1}\{z(r + \tfrac{1}{2}) - 1\}^{-a}\,dr, \tag{6.36}$$

where the arguments of $r + \frac{1}{2}$ and $r - \frac{1}{2}$ are to be taken as 0 and π at the origin, and $\arg(r + \frac{1}{2} - z^{-1})$ is chosen so that, at the origin, it tends to $\pi - \theta$ as z tends to zero (with argument θ).

From (6.25) and (6.34) to (6.36), using (6.14) to (6.16), we find that

$$\begin{aligned} B(a, b; c; z) &= e^{i\pi(a+b-c)\varepsilon} \frac{\Gamma(c)\Gamma(a+1-c)}{\Gamma(b)\Gamma(a+1-b)} z^{-a} F(a, a+1-c; a+1-b; z^{-1}) \\ &\quad - e^{i\pi b\varepsilon} \frac{\Gamma(c)\Gamma(a+1-c)}{\Gamma(c-b)\Gamma(a+b+1-c)} F(a, b; a+b+1-c; 1-z) \\ &\quad - 2e^{i\pi(a+b-c)} \frac{\Gamma(c)}{\Gamma(b)\Gamma(c-b)} \\ &\quad \times \int_0^{\infty \exp(i\pi - i\theta)} (r + \tfrac{1}{2})^{b-1}(r - \tfrac{1}{2})^{c-b-1}\{z(r + \tfrac{1}{2}) - 1\}^{-a}\,dr, \end{aligned}$$

$$[\operatorname{Re}(c-a) < 2], \tag{6.37}$$

where $\varepsilon = \operatorname{sgn}(\operatorname{Im} z) = 1, -1$, according as $\operatorname{Im} z > 0, < 0$.

6.4 An Alternative Integral Relation for $B(a, b; c; z)$

We shall now obtain an alternative integral relation for $B(a, b; c; z)$ by the method used in §4.4.

When z is real $(0 < z < 1)$ and $\operatorname{Re}(c-a) < 1$, the contours for the two integrals in (6.33) can be deformed as shown in Figure 6.2, part of each contour being a semicircle of large radius. Then, if $\operatorname{Re}(c-a) < 1$, the contribution from the semicircles vanishes as their radius increases to infinity, and we find that

$$\begin{aligned} v = \frac{1}{2\pi i}\Bigg[&(1 - e^{2\pi ib})\left\{\int_{1/2}^{(1/2)-\infty i} X\,dt + 2\pi i e^{-2\pi ib} y_5 - e^{2\pi i(c-b)} \int_{1/2}^{(1/2)+\infty i} X\,dt\right\} \\ &+ \{1 - e^{2\pi i(c-b)}\}\left\{\int_{1/2}^{(1/2)+\infty i} X\,dt - e^{2\pi ib} \int_{1/2}^{(1/2)-\infty i} X\,dt\right\}\Bigg]; \end{aligned}$$

that is,

$$v = (e^{-2\pi ib} - 1)y_5 + \frac{1}{2\pi i}[1 - 2e^{2\pi ib} + e^{2\pi ic}] \int_{1/2}^{(1/2)-\infty i} X\, dt$$
$$+ \frac{1}{2\pi i}[1 - 2e^{2\pi i(c-b)} + e^{2\pi ic}] \int_{1/2}^{(1/2)+\infty i} X\, dt. \quad (6.38)$$

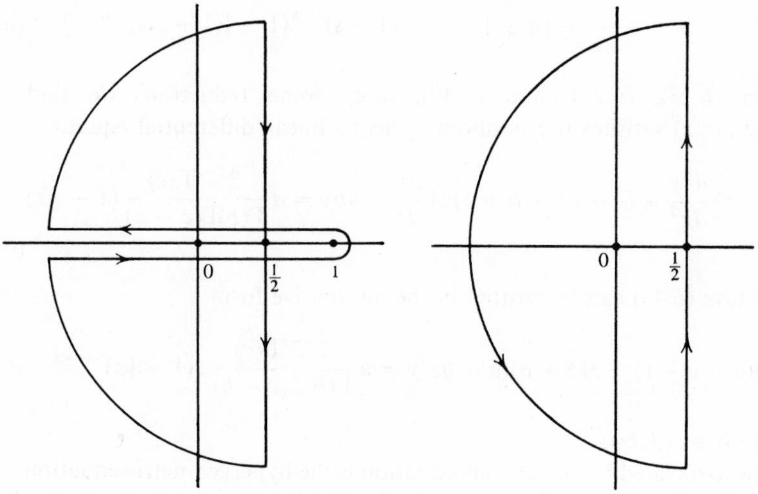

Figure 6.2.

Equation (6.38) can be simplified to give

$$v = (e^{-2\pi ib} - 1)y_5 - i\pi^{-1}e^{i\pi(a-b)} \operatorname{Re} Z(a, b; c; z), \quad (6.39)$$

where

$$Z(a, b; c; z) = ie^{-i\pi[b-(1/2)c]}\{e^{2\pi ib} - 2 + e^{-2\pi i(c-b)}\}$$
$$\times \int_0^\infty (s - \tfrac{1}{2}i)^{b-1}(s + \tfrac{1}{2}i)^{c-b-1}(1 - \tfrac{1}{2}z - isz)^{-a}\, ds. \quad (6.40)$$

From (6.13), (6.25), and (6.40), if $0 < z < 1$ and $\operatorname{Re}(c - a) < 1$,

$$B(a, b; c; z)$$
$$= \frac{\Gamma(c)\Gamma(a+1-c)\Gamma(b+1-c)}{\Gamma(a)\Gamma(b)\Gamma(2-c)} z^{1-c}F(a - c + 1, b - c + 1; 2 - c; z)$$
$$+ (2\pi^2)^{-1}\Gamma(1-b)\Gamma(c)\Gamma(1+b-c)[\operatorname{Re} Z(a, b; c; z)]. \quad (6.41)$$

6.5 Differential Equation Satisfied by $B(a, b; c; z)$

As in Erdélyi [*60*, 1953a], it can be shown that

$$\left\{z(1-z)\frac{\partial^2}{\partial z^2} + [c-(a+b+1)z]\frac{\partial}{\partial z} - ab\right\}$$
$$\times [(1+s)^{b-1}(1-s)^{c-b-1}\{1-\tfrac{1}{2}(1+s)z\}^{-a}]$$
$$= -\tfrac{1}{2}a\frac{\partial}{\partial s}[(1+s)^b(1-s)^{c-b}\{1-\tfrac{1}{2}(1+s)z\}^{-a-1}]. \quad (6.42)$$

From (6.25), (6.26), and (6.42), after some reduction, we find that $B(a, b; c; z)$ satisfies the nonhomogeneous linear differential equation

$$z(1-z)\frac{d^2y}{dz^2} + [c-(a+b+1)z]\frac{dy}{dz} - aby = a\frac{2^{1-c}\Gamma(c)}{\Gamma(b)\Gamma(c-b)}(1-\tfrac{1}{2}z)^{-a-1}. \quad (6.43)$$

Equation (6.43) can be written in the alternative form

$$[\delta(\delta-c-1) - z(\delta+a)(\delta+b)]y = a\frac{2^{1-c}\Gamma(c)}{\Gamma(b)\Gamma(c-b)}z(1-\tfrac{1}{2}z)^{-a-1}, \quad (6.44)$$

where $\delta \equiv z(d/dz)$.

The associated homogeneous equation is the hypergeometric equation (6.1), which has regular singularities at $z = 0$ and 1, and a regular singular point at infinity. The complete primitive of (6.43) is

$$C_1F(a, b; c; z) + C_2z^{1-c}F(a-c+1, b-c+1; 2-c; z) + B(a, b; c; z),$$

where C_1 and C_2 are arbitrary constants.

Differentiating (6.26) with respect to z, we obtain

$$\frac{dB(a, b; c; z)}{dz} = \frac{ab}{c}B(a+1, b+1; c+1; z) \quad (6.45)$$

and

$$\frac{d^nB(a, b; c; z)}{dz^n} = \frac{\Gamma(a+n)\Gamma(b+n)\Gamma(c)}{\Gamma(a)\Gamma(b)\Gamma(c+n)}B(a+n, b+n; c+n; z). \quad (6.46)$$

These formulas can be used, in conjunction with Taylor's series, to express $B(a, b; c; z)$ as a power series in z (see §6.8).

From (6.25) and (6.26),

$$B(a, b; c; z) = -(1-z)^{-a}B[a, c-b; c; z/(z-1)]. \quad (6.47)$$

Thus $(1-z)^{-a}B[a, c-b; c; z/(z-1)]$ is a particular integral of the equation

$$z(1-z)\frac{d^2y}{dz^2}+[c-(a+b+1)z]\frac{dy}{dz}-aby=-a\frac{2^{1-c}\Gamma(c)}{\Gamma(b)\Gamma(c-b)}(1-\tfrac{1}{2}z)^{-a-1}.$$

There are 24 functions of the type

$$z^{\lambda}(1-z)^{\mu}B(a',b';c';z'),$$

which correspond to Kummer's 24 solutions of the hypergeometric equation (see §6.2). These functions are particular integrals of nonhomogeneous equations of the form

$$z(1-z)\frac{d^2y}{dz^2}+[c-(a+b+1)z]\frac{dy}{dz}-aby=f(z).$$

The 24 functions, grouped in pairs according to (6.47), are given in Table 6.1, together with the corresponding values of $f(z)$.

6.6 Relations for Contiguous Functions

The six functions $B(a\pm 1,b;c;z)$, $B(a,b\pm 1;c;z)$, and $B(a,b;c\pm 1;z)$ are said to be contiguous to $B(a,b;c;z)$. We shall now show that these six functions can be expressed in terms of $B(a,b;c;z)$ and its derivative with respect to z (cf. Poole [*92*, 1936]).

From (6.12), (6.20), (6.25), and (6.26),

$$B(a,b;c;z)+F(a,b;c;z)=\frac{i}{\pi}2^{1-c}e^{i\pi(b-c)}\frac{\Gamma(c)\Gamma(1+b-c)}{\Gamma(b)}I(a,b;\ c;z), \tag{6.48}$$

where

$$I(a,b;c;z)=\int_0^{(1+)}(1+s)^{b-1}(1-s)^{c-b-1}[1-\tfrac{1}{2}(1+s)z]^{-a}\,ds. \tag{6.49}$$

From (6.49),

$$I(a+1,b;c;z)=I(a,b;c;z)+\tfrac{1}{2}zI(a+1,b+1;c+1;z) \tag{6.50}$$

and

$$2I(a,b;c-1;z)=I(a,b;c;z)+I(a,b+1;c;z). \tag{6.51}$$

Integrating (6.49) by parts, we obtain

$$\begin{aligned} bI(a,b;c;z)={}&\{e^{2i\pi(c-b)}-1\}(1-\tfrac{1}{2}z)^{-a}\\ &+(c-b-1)\int_0^{(1+)}(1+s)^{b}(1-s)^{c-b-2}[1-\tfrac{1}{2}(1+s)z]^{-a}\,ds\\ &-\tfrac{1}{2}az\int_0^{(1+)}(1+s)^{b}(1-s)^{c-b-1}[1-\tfrac{1}{2}(1+s)z]^{-a-1}\,ds; \end{aligned}$$

TABLE 6.1

B function	$f(z)$
$B(a, b; c; z)$ $(1-z)^{-a}B[a, c-b; c; z/(z-1)]$	$\pm a \dfrac{2^{a-c+2}\Gamma(c)}{\Gamma(b)\Gamma(c-b)}(2-z)^{-a-1}$
$(1-z)^{c-a-b}B(c-a, c-b; c; z)$ $(1-z)^{-b}B[c-a, b; c; z/(z-1)]$	$\pm (c-a) \dfrac{2^{2-a}\Gamma(c)}{\Gamma(c-b)\Gamma(b)}$ $\times (2-z)^{a-c-1}(1-z)^{c-a-b}$
$z^{1-c}B(b+1-c, a+1-c; 2-c; z)$ $z^{1-c}(1-z)^{c-b-1}B[b+1-c, 1-a; 2-c; z/(z-1)]$	$\pm (b+1-c) \dfrac{2^{b+1}\Gamma(2-c)}{\Gamma(a+1-c)\Gamma(1-a)}$ $\times (2-z)^{c-b-2}z^{1-c}$
$z^{1-c}(1-z)^{c-a-b}B(1-b, 1-a; 2-c; z)$ $z^{1-c}(1-z)^{c-a-1}B[1-b, a+1-c; 2-c; z/(z-1)]$	$\pm (1-b) \dfrac{2^{c-b+1}\Gamma(2-c)}{\Gamma(1-a)\Gamma(a+1-c)}$ $\times (2-z)^{b-2}(1-z)^{c-a-b}z^{1-c}$
$B(a, b; a+b+1-c; 1-z)$ $z^{-a}B(a, a+1-c; a+b+1-c; 1-z^{-1})$	$\pm a \dfrac{2^{c-b+1}\Gamma(a+b+1-c)}{\Gamma(b)\Gamma(a+1-c)}(1+z)^{-a-1}$
$z^{1-c}B(b+1-c, a+1-c; a+b+1-c; 1-z)$ $z^{-b}B(b+1-c, b; a+b+1-c; 1-z^{-1})$	$\pm (b+1-c) \dfrac{2^{2-a}\Gamma(a+b+1-c)}{\Gamma(a+1-c)\Gamma(b)}$ $\times (1+z)^{c-b-2}z^{1-c}$

$(1-z)^{c-a-b}B(c-a, c-b; c+1-a-b; 1-z)$ $z^{a-c}(1-z)^{c-a-b}B(c-a, 1-a; c+1-a-b; 1-z^{-1})$	$\pm (c-a)\dfrac{2^{b+1}\Gamma(c+1-a-b)}{\Gamma(c-b)\Gamma(1-a)}$ $\times (1+z)^{a-c-1}(1-z)^{c-a-b}$
$z^{1-c}(1-z)^{c-a-b}B(1-b, 1-a; c+1-a-b; 1-z)$ $z^{b-c}(1-z)^{c-a-b}B(1-b, c-b; c+1-a-b; 1-z^{-1})$	$\pm (1-b)\dfrac{2^{a-c+2}\Gamma(c+1-a-b)}{\Gamma(1-a)\Gamma(c-b)}$ $\times (1+z)^{b-2}(1-z)^{c-a-b}z^{1-c}$
$(-z)^{-a}B(a, a+1-c; a+1-b; z^{-1})$ $(1-z)^{-a}B[a, c-b; a+1-b; (1-z)^{-1}]$	$\pm a\dfrac{2^{b+1}\Gamma(a+1-b)}{\Gamma(a+1-c)\Gamma(c-b)}(1-2z)^{-a-1}$
$(-z)^{b-c}(1-z)^{c-a-b}B(1-b, c-b; a+1-b; z^{-1})$ $(-z)^{1-c}(1-z)^{c-a-1}$ $\times B[1-b, a+1-c; a+1-b; (1-z)^{-1}]$	$\pm (1-b)\dfrac{2^{2-a}\Gamma(a+1-b)}{\Gamma(c-b)\Gamma(a+1-c)}$ $\times (1-2z)^{b-2}(1-z)^{c-a-b}(-z)^{1-c}$
$(-z)^{-b}B(b+1-c, b; b+1-a; z^{-1})$ $(-z)^{1-c}(1-z)^{c-b-1}$ $\times B[b+1-c, 1-a; b+1-a; (1-z)^{-1}]$	$\pm (b+1-c)\dfrac{2^{a-c+2}\Gamma(b+1-a)}{\Gamma(b)\Gamma(1-a)}$ $\times (1-2z)^{c-b-2}(-z)^{1-c}$
$(-z)^{a-c}(1-z)^{c-a-b}B(c-a, 1-a; b+1-a; z^{-1})$ $(1-z)^{-b}B[c-a, b; b+1-a; (1-z)^{-1}]$	$\pm (c-a)\dfrac{2^{c-b+1}\Gamma(b+1-a)}{\Gamma(1-a)\Gamma(b)}$ $\times (1-2z)^{a-c-1}(1-z)^{c-a-b}$

that is,

$$bI(a, b; c; z) + (b - c + 1)I(a; b + 1; c; z) + \tfrac{1}{2}azI(a + 1, b + 1; c + 1; z) = \{e^{2i\pi(c-b)} - 1\}(1 - \tfrac{1}{2}z)^{-a}. \quad (6.52)$$

From (6.50) to (6.52), using (6.48) and the recurrence formulas for F given in Erdélyi [1953a], we obtain

$$B(a + 1, b; c; z) = B(a, b; c; z) + bc^{-1}zB(a + 1, b + 1; c + 1; z), \quad (6.53)$$

$$(c - 1)B(a, b; c - 1; z) = (c - b - 1)B(a, b; c; z) + bB(a, b + 1; c; z), \quad (6.54)$$

and

$$B(a, b + 1; c; z) = B(a, b; c; z) + ac^{-1}zB(a + 1, b + 1; c + 1; z) + \frac{2^{2-c}\Gamma(c)}{\Gamma(b + 1)\Gamma(c - b)}(1 - \tfrac{1}{2}z)^{-a}. \quad (6.55)$$

As in Poole [1936], for conciseness, we shall denote $B(a + 1, b; c; z)$ and $B(a - 1, b; c; z)$ by B_{a+}, B_{a-}, and similarly for the other four functions which are contiguous to $B(a, b; c; z)$.

From (6.45) and (6.53),

$$aB_{a+} = (\delta + a)B, \quad (6.56)$$

where $\delta \equiv z(d/dz)$. The operator δ is used in this sense in the following analysis. Now, from (6.44),

$$[\delta(\delta + c - 1) - z(\delta + a - 1)(\delta + b)]B_{a-} = (a - 1)\frac{2^{1-c}\Gamma(c)}{\Gamma(b)\Gamma(c - b)}z(1 - \tfrac{1}{2}z)^{-a};$$

that is,

$$[\delta + c - a - z(\delta + b)](\delta + a - 1)B_{a-} = (a - 1)\frac{2^{1-c}\Gamma(c)}{\Gamma(b)\Gamma(c - b)}z(1 - \tfrac{1}{2}z)^{-a} + (c - a)(a - 1)B_{a-}. \quad (6.57)$$

From (6.56), with $a - 1$ instead of a, and (6.57),

$$(c - a)B_{a-} = [(1 - z)\delta + c - a - bz]B - \frac{2^{1-c}\Gamma(c)}{\Gamma(b)\Gamma(c - b)}z(1 - \tfrac{1}{2}z)^{-a}. \quad (6.58)$$

From (6.45) and (6.55),

$$bB_{b+} = (\delta + b)B + \frac{2^{2-c}\Gamma(c)}{\Gamma(b)\Gamma(c - b)}(1 - \tfrac{1}{2}z)^{-a}. \quad (6.59)$$

Now, from (6.44),

$$[\delta(\delta + c - 1) - z(\delta + a)(\delta + b - 1)]B_{b-} = a\,\frac{2^{1-c}\Gamma(c)}{\Gamma(b-1)\Gamma(c-b+1)}\,z(1-\tfrac{1}{2}z)^{-a-1};$$

that is,

$$[\delta + c - b - z(\delta + a)](\delta + b - 1)B_{b-} = a\,\frac{2^{1-c}\Gamma(c)}{\Gamma(b-1)\Gamma(c-b+1)}\,z(1-\tfrac{1}{2}z)^{-a-1} + (c-b)(b-1)B_{b-}. \quad (6.60)$$

From (6.59), with $b - 1$ instead of b, and (6.60),

$$(c-b)B_{b-} = [(1-z)\delta + c - b - az]B - \frac{2^{2-c}\Gamma(c)}{\Gamma(b)\Gamma(c-b)}(1-\tfrac{1}{2}z)^{-a}. \quad (6.61)$$

From (6.54) and (6.59),

$$(c-1)B_{c-} = (\delta + c - 1)B + \frac{2^{2-c}\Gamma(c)}{\Gamma(b)\Gamma(c-b)}(1-\tfrac{1}{2}z)^{-a}. \quad (6.62)$$

Now, from (6.44),

$$[\delta(\delta + c) - z(\delta + a)(\delta + b)]B_{c+} = a\,\frac{2^{-c}\Gamma(c+1)}{\Gamma(b)\Gamma(c+1-b)}\,z(1-\tfrac{1}{2}z)^{-a-1};$$

that is,

$$[\delta - z(\delta + a + b - c)](\delta + c)B_{c+} = a\,\frac{2^{-c}\Gamma(c+1)}{\Gamma(b)\Gamma(c+1-b)}\,z(1-\tfrac{1}{2}z)^{-a-1} + (c-a)(c-b)zB_{c+}. \quad (6.63)$$

From (6.62), with $c + 1$ instead of c, and (6.63),

$$(c-a)(c-b)zB_{c+} = c[(1-z)\delta + z(c-a-b)]B - \frac{2^{1-c}\Gamma(c+1)}{\Gamma(b)\Gamma(c-b)}\,z(1-\tfrac{1}{2}z)^{-a}. \quad (6.64)$$

Equations (6.56), (6.58), (6.59), (6.61), (6.62), and (6.64) may be rearranged to give

$$\delta B = a(B_{a+} - B), \quad (6.65)$$

$$\delta B = b(B_{b+} - B) - \frac{2^{2-c}\Gamma(c)}{\Gamma(b)\Gamma(c-b)}(1-\tfrac{1}{2}z)^{-a}, \quad (6.66)$$

$$\delta B = (c-1)(B_{c-} - B) - \frac{2^{2-c}\Gamma(c)}{\Gamma(b)\Gamma(c-b)}(1-\tfrac{1}{2}z)^{-a}, \tag{6.67}$$

$$(1-z)\delta B = (c-a)B_{a-} + (a-c+bz)B + \frac{2^{1-c}\Gamma(c)}{\Gamma(b)\Gamma(c-b)}z(1-\tfrac{1}{2}z)^{-a}, \tag{6.68}$$

$$(1-z)\delta B = (c-b)B_{b-} + (b-c+az)B + \frac{2^{2-c}\Gamma(c)}{\Gamma(b)\Gamma(c-b)}(1-\tfrac{1}{2}z)^{-a}, \tag{6.69}$$

and

$$c(1-z)\delta B = (c-a)(c-b)zB_{c+} + c(a+b-c)zB + \frac{2^{1-c}\Gamma(c+1)}{\Gamma(b)\Gamma(c-b)}z(1-\tfrac{1}{2}z)^{-a}. \tag{6.70}$$

The 15 relations between the six contiguous functions (corresponding to Gauss's relations for the hypergeometric function) follow from (6.65) to (6.70), on equating any two values of δB. By repeated use of these relations, $B(a+l, b+m; c+n; z)$, where l, m, and n are integers, can be expressed in terms of $B(a, b; c; z)$ and one of its contiguous functions, together with a function of z (provided that neither c nor $c+n$ are zero or negative integers).

By repeated application of (6.56) we find

$$\frac{\Gamma(a+n)}{\Gamma(a)}B(a+n, b; c; z) = (\delta+a+n-1)(\delta+a+n-2)\cdots \times(\delta+a)B(a, b; c; z), \tag{6.71}$$

where n is a positive integer. Now, from the properties of the operator δ given in §2.7,

$$F(\delta+m)V = z^{-m}F(\delta)[z^m V], \tag{6.72}$$

where F is any polynomial in δ ($=z d/dz$) and V is a function of z. From (6.71) and (6.72), with $m = a+n-1$,

$$\begin{aligned}\frac{\Gamma(a+n)}{\Gamma(a)}B(a+n, b; c; z) &= z^{1-a-n}\delta(\delta-1)\cdots \\ &\quad\times(\delta-n+1)[z^{a+n-1}B(a, b; c; z)] \\ &= z^{1-a}\frac{d^n}{dz^n}[z^{a+n-1}B(a, b; c; z)];\end{aligned}$$

that is

$$\frac{d^n}{dz^n}[z^{a+n-1}B(a, b; c; z)] = \frac{\Gamma(a+n)}{\Gamma(a)}z^{a-1}B(a+n, b; c; z). \tag{6.73}$$

From (6.68) and 6.70)

$$c(1-z)B - cB_{a-} + (c-b)zB_{c+} = 0\,;$$

that is, replacing a by $a+1$ and using (6.56),

$$\frac{a}{c}(c-b)B(a+1, b; c+1; z) = aB(a, b; c; z) - (1-z)\frac{dB(a, b; c; z)}{dz}. \tag{6.74}$$

On putting $u = 1 - z$, and $\theta = u(d/du)$, we obtain

$$\frac{a}{c}(c-b)B(a+1, b; c+1; 1-u) = (\theta + a)B(a, b; c; 1-u)\,,$$

and thus, by analogy with (6.71) to (6.73),

$$\frac{\Gamma(a+n)\Gamma(c-b+n)\Gamma(c)}{\Gamma(c+n)\Gamma(a)\Gamma(c-b)}B(a+n, b; c+n; 1-u)$$

$$= (\theta + a + n - 1)(\theta + a + n - 2)\cdots(\theta + a)B(a, b; c; 1-u)$$

$$= u^{1-a}\frac{d^n}{du^n}[u^{a+n-1}B(a, b; c; 1-u)]\,;$$

that is,

$$\frac{d^n}{dz^n}[(1-z)^{a+n-1}B(a, b; c; z)] = (-1)^n\frac{\Gamma(a+n)\Gamma(c-b+n)\Gamma(c)}{\Gamma(c+n)\Gamma(a)\Gamma(c-b)}(1-z)^{a-1} \times B(a+n, b; c+n; z)\,. \tag{6.75}$$

6.7 Particular Values of $B(a, b; c; z)$

DETERMINATION OF $B(a, b; c; 0)$

From (6.27), for $\operatorname{Re} c > \operatorname{Re} b > 0$,

$$B(a, b; c; 0) = \frac{\Gamma(c)}{\Gamma(b)\Gamma(c-b)}[B_{1/2}(c-b, b) - B_{1/2}(b, c-b)]\,, \tag{6.76}$$

where

$$B_{1/2}(c-b, b) = 2^{1-c}\int_0^1 (1+u)^{b-1}(1-u)^{c-b-1}\,du$$

$$= \int_0^{1/2} t^{c-b-1}(1-t)^{b-1}\,dt\,, \tag{6.77}$$

on putting $t = \frac{1}{2}(1-u)$. $B_{1/2}$ is the incomplete beta function (see Problem 5, Chapter 1).

On comparing (6.76) with the corresponding result for Ω [(4.78)], we see that, for Re $c >$ Re $b > 0$,

$$B(a, b; c; 0) = \Omega(b, c; 0). \tag{6.78}$$

We note that the value of $B(a, b; c; 0)$ depends only on the parameters b and c.

From (6.76),

$$B(a, b; c; 0) = -B(a', c - b; c; 0) \qquad (\text{Re}\, c > \text{Re}\, b > 0). \tag{6.79}$$

Using (6.47), we see that (6.79) applies for all values of a, a', and b, and for all values of c except zero or negative integral values.

If $c = 2b$, from (6.76) and (6.77), for Re $b > 0$,

$$B(a, b; 2b; 0) = \Omega(b, 2b; 0) = 0. \tag{6.80}$$

As shown in §4.8, (6.80) applies for all values of $2b$, except zero or negative integral values.

The properties of $\Omega(b, c; 0)$ were discussed in §4.8. In particular it was shown that, for real values of b and c,

$$1 > \Omega(b, c; 0) > 0 \qquad \text{if} \quad 2b > c > b > 0 \tag{6.81}$$

and

$$0 > \Omega(b, c; 0) > -1 \qquad \text{if} \quad c > 2b > 0. \tag{6.82}$$

Equations (6.76) and (6.77) only hold for Re $c >$ Re $b > 0$. For values of b and c outside this range, $B(a, b; c; 0)$ can be found by using the relations between contiguous Ω functions given in §4.8.

SPECIAL VALUES OF $B(a, b; c; 0)$

We shall consider first the values of $B(a, b; c; 0)$ when either b or $c - b$ (but not both) is zero or a negative integer. In these cases, (6.2) reduces to the hypergeometric equation.

When b is zero or a negative integer, from (6.20) and (6.26),

$$v = -y_4$$

and

$$B(a, b; c; z) = -F(a, b; c; z). \tag{6.83}$$

Then

$$B(a, b; c; 0) = -1. \tag{6.84}$$

When $c - b$ is zero or a negative integer, from (6.20) and (6.26),

$$v = y_4$$

and

$$B(a, b; c; z) = F(a, b; c; z). \tag{6.85}$$

Then

$$B(a, b; c; 0) = 1. \tag{6.86}$$

Equations (6.83) to (6.86) are not valid when c is zero or a negative integer.

Considered as a function of c, we see from (6.25) that $B(a, b; c; z)$ has poles at the poles of $\Gamma(c)$, that is, at $c = 0, -1, -2, \ldots$ (if b or $c - b$ is also a negative integer, the function is indeterminate). However, $B(a, b; c; z)/\Gamma(c)$ is an entire function of a, b, c, and z (if z^{-1} is not a real number between 0 and 1); this is considered further in §6.9. As shown in §6.9, when b is an integer,

$$\lim_{c \to 1-n} \frac{B(a, b; c; 0)}{\Gamma(c)} = 0 \qquad (n = 1, 2, \ldots). \tag{6.87}$$

DETERMINATION OF $B(a, b; c; z)$ FOR CERTAIN NONZERO VALUES OF z

It is possible to express $B(a, b; c; z)$ in terms of incomplete beta functions for certain nonzero values of z.

From (6.27), for $\operatorname{Re} c > \operatorname{Re} b > 0$ and $\operatorname{Re}(c - a - b) > 0$,

$$B(a, b; c; 1) = \frac{\Gamma(c)}{\Gamma(b)\Gamma(c-b)} [B_{1/2}(c - a - b, b) - B_{1/2}(b, c - a - b)] \tag{6.88}$$

where $B_{1/2}$ is the incomplete beta function [see (6.77)]. From (6.76) and (6.88), we see that, for $\operatorname{Re} c > \operatorname{Re} b > 0$ and $\operatorname{Re}(c - a - b) > 0$,

$$\begin{aligned} B(a, b; c; 1) &= \frac{\Gamma(c)\Gamma(c-a-b)}{\Gamma(c-a)\Gamma(c-b)} B(a, b; c - a; 0) \\ &= \frac{\Gamma(c)\Gamma(c-a-b)}{\Gamma(c-a)\Gamma(c-b)} \Omega(b, c - a; \nu) \\ &= -\frac{\Gamma(c)\Gamma(c-a-b)}{\Gamma(c-a)\Gamma(c-b)} \Omega(c - a - b, c - a; 0). \end{aligned} \tag{6.89}$$

The corresponding formula for $F(a, b; c; 1)$ is

$$F(a, b; c; 1) = \frac{\Gamma(c)\Gamma(c-a-b)}{\Gamma(c-a)\Gamma(c-b)}. \tag{6.90}$$

Now, if $\operatorname{Re}(c - a - b) > 0$ and c is not zero or a negative integer, from (6.25) and (6.26), both sides of (6.89) are entire functions of a, b, and c. Thus the only restrictions on (6.89) are that $\operatorname{Re}(c - a - b) > 0$ and $c \neq 0, -1, -2, \ldots$.

Consider next the case of $z = -1$. From (6.30) and (6.32),

$$F(a, b; c; -1) + B(a, b; c; -1)$$
$$= \frac{2\Gamma(c)}{\Gamma(b)\Gamma(c-b)} \int_{1/2}^{1} t^{b-1}(1-t)^{c-b-1}(1+t)^{-a}\,dt \qquad (\operatorname{Re} c > \operatorname{Re} b) \tag{6.91}$$

and

$$F(a, b; c; -1) - B(a, b; c; -1)$$
$$= \frac{2\Gamma(c)}{\Gamma(b)\Gamma(c-b)} \int_{0}^{1/2} t^{b-1}(1-t)^{c-b-1}(1+t)^{-a}\,dt \qquad (\operatorname{Re} b > 0). \tag{6.92}$$

In (6.91) and (6.92), put $u = t^2$. Then, if $a = 1 + b - c$, we see that

$$F(1+b-c, b; c; -1) + B(1+b-c, b; c; -1)$$
$$= \frac{\Gamma(c)}{\Gamma(b)\Gamma(c-b)} \int_{1/4}^{1} (1-u)^{c-b-1} u^{(1/2)b-1}\,du \tag{6.93}$$

and

$$F(1+b-c, b; c; -1) - B(1+b-c, b; c; c; -1)$$
$$= \frac{\Gamma(c)}{\Gamma(b)\Gamma(c-b)} \int_{0}^{1/4} (1-u)^{c-b-1} u^{(1/2)b-1}\,du. \tag{6.94}$$

From (6.93) and (6.94) we see that, for these values of the parameters, B and F can be expressed in terms of incomplete beta functions. Thus

$$B(1+b-c, b; c; -1)$$
$$= \frac{\Gamma(c)}{2\Gamma(b)\Gamma(c-b)} [B_{3/4}(c-b, \tfrac{1}{2}b) - B_{1/4}(\tfrac{1}{2}b, c-b)] \quad (\operatorname{Re} c > \operatorname{Re} b > 0), \tag{6.95}$$

where

$$B_x(p, q) = \int_0^x u^{p-1}(1-u)^{q-1}\,du = \int_{1-x}^{1} u^{q-1}(1-u)^{p-1}\,du. \tag{6.96}$$

The corresponding formula for F is

$$F(1+b-c, b; c; -1) = \frac{\Gamma(c)}{2\Gamma(b)\Gamma(c-b)} B_1(\tfrac{1}{2}b, c-b) = \frac{\Gamma(c)\Gamma(\tfrac{1}{2}b)}{2\Gamma(b)\Gamma(c-\tfrac{1}{2}b)};$$

that is,

$$F(1+b-c, b; c; -1) = \frac{2^{-b}\Gamma(c)\Gamma(\tfrac{1}{2})}{\Gamma(\tfrac{1}{2}b+\tfrac{1}{2})\Gamma(c-\tfrac{1}{2}b)}. \tag{6.97}$$

Consider next the case $z = -1$, $a = 2 + b - c$. Putting $u = t^2$ in (6.91) and (6.92), we see that, if $\operatorname{Re}(c-1) > \operatorname{Re} b > 0$,

$$F(2 + b - c, b; c; -1) + B(2 + b - c, b; c; -1)$$
$$= \frac{\Gamma(c)}{\Gamma(b)\Gamma(c-b)} \int_{1/4}^{1} (1-u)^{c-b-2}(u^{(1/2)b-1} - u^{(1/2)b-(1/2)})\, du \quad (6.98)$$

and

$$F(2 + b - c, b; c; -1) - B(2 + b - c; b; c, -1)$$
$$= \frac{\Gamma(c)}{\Gamma(b)\Gamma(c-b)} \int_{0}^{1/4} (1-u)^{c-b-2}(u^{(1/2)b-1} - u^{(1/2)b-(1/2)})\, du. \quad (6.99)$$

Using (6.96) we find that

$$B(2 + b - c, b; c; -1) = \frac{\Gamma(c)}{2\Gamma(b)\Gamma(c-b)} [B_{3/4}(c - b - 1, \tfrac{1}{2}b)$$
$$-B_{3/4}(c - b - 1, \tfrac{1}{2}b + \tfrac{1}{2}) - B_{1/4}(\tfrac{1}{2}b, c - b - 1) + B_{1/4}(\tfrac{1}{2}b + \tfrac{1}{2}, c - b - 1)]. \quad (6.100)$$

By using the relations between contiguous functions of B, given in §6.6, we see from (6.95) and (6.100) that $B(m + b - c, b; c; -1)$ can be expressed in terms of incomplete beta functions, where m is any integer, provided that $\operatorname{Re}(c-1) > \operatorname{Re} b > 0$.

From (6.91) and (6.92), if $b = 1$, putting $u = \tfrac{1}{2}(1-t)$, we see that

$$F(a, 1; c; -1) + B(a, 1; c; -1) = 2^{c-a}(c-1) \int_0^{1/4} u^{c-2}(1-u)^{-a}\, du \qquad (\operatorname{Re} c > 1) \quad (6.101)$$

and

$$F(a, 1; c; -1) - B(a, 1; c; -1) = 2^{c-a}(c-1) \int_{1/4}^{1/2} u^{c-2}(1-u)^{-a}\, du. \quad (6.102)$$

From (6.96), (6.101), and (6.102), we obtain

$$B(a, 1; c; -1) = 2^{c-a-1}(c-1)[2B_{1/4}(c-1, 1-a) - B_{1/2}(c-1, 1-a)] \qquad (\operatorname{Re} c > 1). \quad (6.103)$$

The corresponding formula for F is

$$F(a, 1; c; -1) = 2^{c-a-1}(c-1)B_{1/2}(c-1, 1-a). \quad (6.104)$$

Now, from (6.83), if c is not zero or a negative integer,

$$B(a, 0; c; -1) = -F(a, 0; c; -1) = -1. \quad (6.105)$$

By using the relations between contiguous functions of B given in §6.6, we see from (6.103) and (6.105) that $B(a, m; c; -1)$ can be expressed in terms of incomplete beta functions, where m is any integer, provided that $\operatorname{Re} c > 1$.

Using the transformation formula (6.47) together with (6.95), we see that, if $\operatorname{Re} c > \operatorname{Re} b > 0$,

$$B(1 + b - c, c - b; c; \tfrac{1}{2}) = -\frac{2^{b-c}\Gamma(c)}{\Gamma(b)\Gamma(c-b)}[B_{3/4}(c-b, \tfrac{1}{2}b) - B_{1/4}(\tfrac{1}{2}b, c-b)].$$

This can be written in the form

$$B(a, 1-a; c; \tfrac{1}{2}) = -\frac{2^{a-1}\Gamma(c)}{\Gamma(a+c-1)\Gamma(1-a)}\{B_{3/4}[1-a, \tfrac{1}{2}(a+c-1)] - B_{1/4}[\tfrac{1}{2}(a+c-1), 1-a]\} \quad [\operatorname{Re} c > \operatorname{Re}(1-a) > 0]. \quad (6.106)$$

Similarly, from (6.47) and (6.100), if $\operatorname{Re}(c-1) > \operatorname{Re} b > 0$,

$$B(2 + b - c, c - b; c; \tfrac{1}{2}) = -\frac{2^{b-c+1}\Gamma(c)}{\Gamma(b)\Gamma(c-b)}[B_{3/4}(c-b-1, \tfrac{1}{2}b) - B_{3/4}(c-b-1, \tfrac{1}{2}b+\tfrac{1}{2}) - B_{1/4}(\tfrac{1}{2}b, c-b-1) + B_{1/4}(\tfrac{1}{2}b+\tfrac{1}{2}, c-b-1)].$$

This can be written

$$B(a, 2-a; c; \tfrac{1}{2}) = -\frac{2^{a-1}\Gamma(c)}{\Gamma(a+c-2)\Gamma(2-a)}\{B_{3/4}[1-a, \tfrac{1}{2}(a+c-2)] - B_{3/4}[1-a, \tfrac{1}{2}(a+c-1)] - B_{1/4}[\tfrac{1}{2}(a+c-2), 1-a] + B_{1/4}[\tfrac{1}{2}(a+c-1), 1-a]\} \quad [\operatorname{Re}(c-1) > \operatorname{Re}(1-a) > 0]. \quad (6.107)$$

Again, from (6.47) and (6.103),

$$B(a, c-1; c; \tfrac{1}{2}) = -2^{c-1}(c-1)[2B_{1/4}(c-1, 1-a) - B_{1/2}(c-1, 1-a)] \quad (\operatorname{Re} c > 1). \quad (6.108)$$

6.8 Power Series for $B(a, b; c; z)$

The expansion of $B(a, b; c; z)$ as a power series in z can be found by means of a Taylor's series expansion, using (6.45) and (6.46). We find that, if c is not zero or a negative integer,

$$B(a, b; c; z) = B(a, b; c; 0) + \frac{ab}{c}B(a+1, b+1; c+1; 0)\frac{z}{1!} + \frac{a(a+1)b(b+1)}{c(c+1)}B(a+2, b+2; c+2; 0)\frac{z^2}{2!} + \cdots;$$

that is, from (6.78),

$$B(a, b; c; z) = \Omega(b, c; 0) + \frac{ab}{c}\Omega(b+1, c+1; 0)\frac{z}{1!} + \frac{a(a+1)b(b+1)}{c(c+1)}\Omega(b+2, c+2; 0)\frac{z^2}{2!} + \cdots. \tag{6.109}$$

Now, from §4.10, if Re $c >$ Re b,

$$\lim_{n\to\infty} \Omega(b+n, c+n; 0) = 1,$$

and thus, if c is not zero or a negative integer, the series (6.109) converges absolutely for all values of $|z| < 1$ (Re $c >$ Re b). Consider next the case Re $c >$ Re b, $|z| = 1$. The coefficient of z^n in the series in (6.109) is

$$\frac{\Gamma(a+n)\Gamma(b+n)\Gamma(c)}{\Gamma(a)\Gamma(b)\Gamma(c+n)\Gamma(n+1)}\Omega(b+n, c+n; 0) = \frac{\Gamma(c)}{\Gamma(a)\Gamma(b)} n^{a+b-c-1}[1 + 0(n^{-1})]$$

for large n, and thus, as in the case of the hypergeometric series, the series (6.109) is absolutely convergent for $|z| = 1$, if Re $c >$ Re b and Re $c >$ Re $(a + b)$, where c is not zero or a negative integer. From (6.109) we see that, in general, $B(a, b; c; z)$ does not equal $B(b, a; c; z)$.

The corresponding series for $F(a, b; c; z)$ is

$$\begin{aligned} F(a, b; c; z) &= F(a, b; c; 0) + \frac{ab}{c}F(a+1, b+1; c+1; 0)\frac{z}{1!} \\ &\quad + \frac{a(a+1)b(b+1)}{c(c+1)}F(a+2, b+2; c+2; 0)\frac{z^2}{2!} + \cdots \\ &= 1 + \frac{ab}{c}z + \frac{a(a+1)b(b+1)}{c(c+1)}\frac{z^2}{2!} + \cdots \\ &= \sum_{n=0}^{\infty}\frac{\Gamma(a+n)\Gamma(b+n)\Gamma(c)}{\Gamma(a)\Gamma(b)\Gamma(c+n)}\frac{z^n}{n!}. \end{aligned} \tag{6.110}$$

From (6.109) and (6.110),

$$B(a, b; c; z) - B(a, b; c; 0)F(a, b; c; z) = \sum_{n=1}^{\infty}\frac{\Gamma(a+n)\Gamma(b+n)\Gamma(c)}{\Gamma(a)\Gamma(b)\Gamma(c+n)}[\Omega(b+n, c+n; 0) - \Omega(b, c; 0)]\frac{z^n}{n!};$$

that is, from (4.107),

$$B(a, b; c; z) - B(a, b; c; 0)F(a, b; c; z)$$
$$= \frac{2^{1-c}\Gamma(c)}{\Gamma(b+1)\Gamma(c-b)} \sum_{n=1}^{\infty} \frac{\Gamma(a+n)\Gamma(b+n)\Gamma(c)}{\Gamma(a)\Gamma(b)\Gamma(c+n)} F_{(n)}(1, c; b+1; \tfrac{1}{2}) \frac{z^n}{n!}, \tag{6.111}$$

where $F_{(n)}$ stands for the first n terms of the hypergeometric series with the given parameters.

The coefficients of the power series (6.109) can be expressed in terms of incomplete beta functions. From (6.76) and (6.109), for $\operatorname{Re} c > \operatorname{Re} b > 0$,

$$B(a, b; c; z) = \frac{\Gamma(c)}{\Gamma(a)\Gamma(b)\Gamma(c-b)} \sum_{n=0}^{\infty} \Gamma(a+n)$$
$$\times [B_{1/2}(c-b, b+n) - B_{1/2}(b+n, c-b)] \frac{z^n}{n!}. \tag{6.112}$$

From (6.109) and (6.110), using (6.29) and (6.31), we find that

$$F(a, b; c; z) + B(a, b; c; z) = 2 \frac{\Gamma(c)}{\Gamma(a)\Gamma(b)\Gamma(c-b)}$$
$$\times \sum_{n=0}^{\infty} \Gamma(a+n) B_{1/2}(c-b, b+n) \frac{z^n}{n!} \qquad (\operatorname{Re} c > \operatorname{Re} b) \tag{6.113}$$

and

$$F(a, b; c; z) - B(a, b; c; z) = 2 \frac{\Gamma(c)}{\Gamma(a)\Gamma(b)\Gamma(c-b)}$$
$$\times \sum_{n=0}^{\infty} \Gamma(a+n) B_{1/2}(b+n, c-b) \frac{z^n}{n!} \qquad (\operatorname{Re} b > 0). \tag{6.114}$$

Now, for all real values of p and q, $B_{1/2}(p, q)$ is positive. Thus, for $0 \leqslant z < 1$,

$$|F(a, b; c; z)| \geqslant |B(a, b; c; z)| \qquad (c > b > 0, a > 0). \tag{6.115}$$

Using (6.47) and the corresponding formula for F, we see that (6.115) applies also for all negative values of z (for $c > b > 0$, $a > 0$).

More generally, if a, b, c, and z are all real ($z < 1$), we see from (6.29) that, if $c > b$, the sign of $\{F(a, b; c; z) + B(a, b; c; z)\}$ is the same as that of $\Gamma(c)/\Gamma(b)$. Similarly, from (6.31), if a, b, c, and z are all real ($z < 1$) and $b > 0$, the sign of $\{F(a, b; c; z) - B(a, b; c; z)\}$ is the same as that of $\Gamma(c)/\Gamma(c-b)$.

Using the results of §4.8, we find, from (6.109), that, if $\operatorname{Re} c \to \infty$ while a and b are constant, and $|z| < 1$,

$$B(a, b; c; z) \to -\left[\lim_{c \to \infty} F(a, b; c; z)\right] = -1 + 0(|c|^{-1}). \tag{6.116}$$

Similarly, if $\operatorname{Re} c \to \infty$ while a and $c - b$ are constant ($\operatorname{Re} c > \operatorname{Re} b > 0$), and $\operatorname{Re} z < \frac{1}{2}$, from (6.47) and (6.109),

$$B(a, b; c; z) = -(1 - z)^{-a}\left\{\lim_{c\to\infty} B\left[a, c - b; c; \frac{z}{z - 1}\right]\right\}$$

$$= (1 - z)^{-a}[1 + 0(|c|^{-1})]. \tag{6.117}$$

If $|a| \to \infty$ while b, c, and z are constant, $0 < |z| < 1$, and $c \neq 0, -1, -2, \ldots$, we find (as in Erdélyi [77, 1953a])

$$B(a, b; c; z) = \left[\sum_{n=0}^{\infty} \frac{\Gamma(b + n)\Gamma(c)}{\Gamma(b)\Gamma(c + n)} \Omega(b + n, c + n; 0) \frac{(az)^n}{n!}\right][1 + 0(|a|^{-1})]$$

$$= \left[\lim_{a\to\infty} \Omega(b, c; az)\right][1 + 0(|a|^{-1})]. \tag{6.118}$$

The asymptotic expansion of $\Omega(b, c; az)$ for large values of a can then be found from §4.15, for $|\arg az| < \pi$, $\arg az \neq 0$.

The asymptotic expansion of $B(a, b; c; z)$ for large values of z is given in §6.13.

6.9 Degenerate Cases of $B(a, b; c; z)$

When a is zero or a negative integer, and c is not zero or a negative integer, the power series (6.109) terminates and $B(a, b; c; z)$ is a polynomial of degree $(-a)$. In particular,

$$B(0, b; c; z) = \Omega(b, c; 0). \tag{6.119}$$

When b is zero or a negative integer, and c is not zero or a negative integer, the power series (6.109) terminates and, as shown in §6.7,

$$B(a, b; c; z) = -F(a, b; c; z).$$

In particular,

$$B(a, 0; c; z) = -1. \tag{6.120}$$

When $b = 1 - n$ (n being a positive integer), a particular solution of

$$z(1 - z)\frac{d^2y}{dz^2} + [c - (a + b + 1)z]\frac{dy}{dz} - aby = a\frac{2^{1-c}\Gamma(c)}{\Gamma(c - b)}(1 - \tfrac{1}{2}z)^{-a-1}$$

is

$$\lim_{b\to 1-n} \Gamma(b)[B(a, b; c; z) + F(a, b; c; z)].$$

The power series for the latter function can be found from (6.113), for Re $c >$ Re b.

Similarly, as shown in §6.7, when $c - b$ is zero or a negative integer, and c is not zero or a negative integer,

$$B(a, b; c; z) = F(a, b; c; z)$$

$$= (1 - z)^{-a} F\left[a, c - b; c; \frac{z}{z - 1}\right],$$

where the latter hypergeometric series can be expressed as a finite series in terms of $z/(z - 1)$. In particular,

$$B(a, b; b; z) = (1 - z)^{-a}. \tag{6.121}$$

When $c - b = 1 - n$ (n being a positive integer), a particular solution of

$$z(1 - z)\frac{d^2y}{dz^2} + [c - (a + b + 1)z]\frac{dy}{dz} - aby = a\frac{2^{1-c}\Gamma(c)}{\Gamma(b)}(1 - \tfrac{1}{2}z)^{-a-1}$$

is

$$\lim_{c-b \to 1-n} \Gamma(c - b)[B(a, b; c; z) - F(a, b; c; z)].$$

The power series for the latter function can be found from (6.114), for Re $b > 0$.

As shown in §6.7, $B(a, b; c; z)$ has poles at $c = 0, -1, -2, \ldots$. We shall now show that, when $c = 1 - n$ (n being a negative integer), $\lim_{c \to 1-n} B(a, b; c; z)/\Gamma(c)$ can be expressed in terms of $\bar{B}(a, b; 1 - n, z)$, where

$$\bar{B}(a, b; c; z) = z^{1-c}B(a - c + 1, b - c + 1; 2 - c; z). \tag{6.122}$$

From Table 6.1 we see that $\bar{B}(a, b; c; z)$ is a particular solution of the equation

$$z(1 - z)\frac{d^2y}{dz^2} + [c - (a + b + 1)z]\frac{dy}{dz} - aby$$

$$= (a - c + 1)\frac{2^{c-1}\Gamma(2 - c)}{\Gamma(b - c + 1)\Gamma(1 - b)}(1 - \tfrac{1}{2}z)^{c-a-2}z^{1-c}. \tag{6.123}$$

From (6.122),

$$B(a, b; 1; z) = \bar{B}(a, b; 1; z). \tag{6.124}$$

Now, from (6.54) and (6.55), with $c + 1$ instead of c,

$$cB(a, b; c; z) = (c - b)B(a, b; c + 1; z) + bB(a, b + 1; c + 1; z) \tag{6.125}$$

and

$$B(a, b+1; c+1; z)$$
$$= B(a, b; c+1; z) + a(c+1)^{-1} z B(a+1, b+1; c+2; z)$$
$$+ \frac{2^{1-c}\Gamma(c+1)}{\Gamma(b+1)\Gamma(c-b+1)} (1 - \tfrac{1}{2}z)^{-a}. \quad (6.126)$$

From (6.125) and (6.126),

$$\frac{B(a, b; c; z)}{\Gamma(c)} = \frac{cB(a, b; c+1; z)}{\Gamma(c+1)} + \frac{abzB(a+1, b+1; c+2; z)}{\Gamma(c+2)}$$
$$+ \frac{2^{1-c}}{\Gamma(b)\Gamma(c-b+1)} (1 - \tfrac{1}{2}z)^{-a}.$$

Thus

$$\lim_{c \to 0} \frac{B(a, b; c; z)}{\Gamma(c)} = abzB(a+1, b+1; 2; z) + \frac{2}{\Gamma(b)\Gamma(1-b)} (1 - \tfrac{1}{2}z)^{-a}; \quad (6.127)$$

that is, from (6.122),

$$\lim_{c \to 0} \frac{B(a, b; c; z)}{\Gamma(c)} = ab\bar{B}(a, b; 0; z) + \frac{2}{\Gamma(b)\Gamma(1-b)} (1 - \tfrac{1}{2}z)^{-a}. \quad (6.128)$$

Now, from (6.67) and (6.70), eliminating δB, we obtain

$$(1-z)\frac{B(a, b; c-1; z)}{\Gamma(c-1)} - [c - 1 + (a + b - 2c + 1)z]\frac{B(a, b; c; z)}{\Gamma(c)}$$
$$- (a-c)(b-c)z\frac{B(a, b; c+1; z)}{\Gamma(c+1)} = \frac{2^{2-c}}{\Gamma(b)\Gamma(c-b)} (1 - \tfrac{1}{2}z)^{1-a}. \quad (6.129)$$

Also, from (6.2) and (6.46),

$$(a+1)(b+1)z(1-z)\frac{B(a+2, b+2; c+2; z)}{\Gamma(c+2)}$$
$$+ [c - (a+b+1)z]\frac{B(a+1, b+1; c+1; z)}{\Gamma(c+1)} - \frac{B(a, b; c; z)}{\Gamma(c)}$$
$$= \frac{2^{1-c}}{\Gamma(b+1)\Gamma(c-b)} (1 - \tfrac{1}{2}z)^{-a-1}. \quad (6.130)$$

From (6.130), on replacing a, b, c by $a - c$, $b - c$, $1 - c$, respectively, we obtain

$$(a-c+1)(b-c+1)z(1-z)\frac{B(a-c+2,b-c+2;3-c;z)}{\Gamma(3-c)}$$
$$+[1-c-(a+b-2c+1)z]\frac{B(a-c+1,b-c+1;2-c;z)}{\Gamma(2-c)}$$
$$-\frac{B(a-c,b-c;1-c;z)}{\Gamma(1-c)}=\frac{2^c}{\Gamma(b-c+1)\Gamma(1-b)}(1-\tfrac{1}{2}z)^{c-a-1};$$

that is, using (6.122),

$$(1-z)\frac{\Gamma(a-c+2)\Gamma(b-c+2)}{\Gamma(a)\Gamma(b)\Gamma(3-c)}\bar{B}(a,b;c-1;z)$$
$$-[c-1+(a+b-2c+1)z]\frac{\Gamma(a-c+1)\Gamma(b-c+1)}{\Gamma(a)\Gamma(b)\Gamma(2-c)}\bar{B}(a,b;c;z)$$
$$-(a-c)(b-c)z\frac{\Gamma(a-c)\Gamma(b-c)}{\Gamma(a)\Gamma(b)\Gamma(1-c)}\bar{B}(a,b;c+1;z)=\frac{2^c\Gamma(a-c+1)}{\Gamma(a)\Gamma(b)\Gamma(1-b)}$$
$$\times(1-\tfrac{1}{2}z)^{c-a-1}z^{1-c}. \quad (6.131)$$

From (6.129) and (6.131), using (6.124) and (6.127), we find that

$$\lim_{c\to 1-n}\frac{B(a,b;c;z)}{\Gamma(c)}=\frac{\Gamma(a+n)\Gamma(b+n)}{\Gamma(a)\Gamma(b)\Gamma(n+1)}\bar{B}(a,b;c;z)$$
$$+\frac{g_n(z)}{\Gamma(b)\Gamma(1-b)}(1-\tfrac{1}{2}z)^{1-a-n}(1-z)^{1-n} \qquad (n=0,1,2,\ldots), \quad (6.132)$$

where $g_0=0$, $g_1=2$, and

$$g_n+[n-1-(a+b+2n-3)z](1-\tfrac{1}{2}z)g_{n-1}$$
$$-(a+n-2)(b+n-2)z(1-z)(1-\tfrac{1}{2}z)^2g_{n-2}$$
$$=\left[2^n\frac{\Gamma(1-b)}{\Gamma(2-n-b)}(1-\tfrac{1}{2}z)^n-2^{2-n}\frac{\Gamma(a+n-1)}{\Gamma(a)}z^{n-1}\right](1-z)^{n-2}.$$
$$(n\geqslant 2).$$

We see that $g_n(z)$ is a polynomial in z of degree $2n-2$ $(n\geqslant 1)$. Alternatively, from (6.122),

$$\lim_{c\to 1-n}\frac{B(a,b;c;z)}{\Gamma(c)}=\frac{\Gamma(a+n)\Gamma(b+n)}{\Gamma(a)\Gamma(b)}\frac{z^n}{n!}B(a+n,b+n;n+1;z)$$
$$+\frac{g_n(z)}{\Gamma(b)\Gamma(1-b)}(1-\tfrac{1}{2}z)^{1-a-n}(1-z)^{1-n} \qquad (n=0,1,2,\ldots). \quad (6.133)$$

6.10 Other Particular Cases of $B(a, b; c; z)$

In §6.9 we considered certain degenerate cases of $B(a, b; c; z)$. We shall now consider other particular cases in which $B(a; b; c; z)$ can be expressed in terms of simple functions.

If $c = 2b$, $B(a, b; c; z)$ can be expressed in terms of the nonhomogeneous Legendre function $R_\nu^\mu(z)$, defined in Chapter 7. As will be shown in §7.6,

$$B\left(a, b; 2b; \frac{2}{1+z}\right)$$
$$= 2^b \pi^{-(1/2)} e^{i\pi(b-a)} \Gamma(b + \tfrac{1}{2})[\Gamma(a)]^{-1}(z+1)^{(1/2)(a+b)}(z-1)^{(1/2)(b-a)} \times R_{b-1}^{a-b}(z). \quad (6.134)$$

The corresponding relation for $F(a, b; c; z)$ is (Erdélyi, [*132*, 1953a])

$$F\left(a, b; 2b; \frac{2}{1+z}\right)$$
$$= 2^b \pi^{-(1/2)} e^{i\pi(b-a)} \Gamma(b + \tfrac{1}{2})[\Gamma(a)]^{-1}(z+1)^{(1/2)(a+b)}(z-1)^{(1/2)(b-a)} \times Q_{b-1}^{a-b}(z). \quad (6.135)$$

As will be shown in §7.8, if $c = 2b$, $B(a, b; c; z)$ is directly related to the nonhomogeneous hypergeometric function $f_\sigma\{\tfrac{1}{2}a, \tfrac{1}{2} + \tfrac{1}{2}a; b + \tfrac{1}{2}; z^2/(2-z)^2\}$ (the latter function is defined in §6.16).

If $c = 2b = 1$, from (6.30) and (6.32),

$$F(a, \tfrac{1}{2}; 1; z) + B(a, \tfrac{1}{2}; 1; z) = \frac{2}{\pi}\int_{1/2}^{1} \frac{(1-tz)^{-a}}{[t(1-t)]^{1/2}}\, dt$$
$$= \frac{4}{\pi}\int_{(1/4)\pi}^{(1/2)\pi} (1 - z\sin^2\theta)^{-a}\, d\theta \quad (6.136)$$

and

$$F(a, \tfrac{1}{2}; 1; z) - B(a, \tfrac{1}{2}; 1; z) = \frac{2}{\pi}\int_{0}^{1/2} \frac{(1-tz)^{-a}}{[t(1-t)]^{1/2}}\, dt$$
$$= \frac{4}{\pi}\int_{0}^{(1/4)\pi} (1 - z\sin^2\theta)^{-a}\, d\theta, \quad (6.137)$$

on putting $t = \sin^2\theta$.

Now the elliptic integrals of the first and second kinds are

$$F(\phi, k) = \int_0^\phi (1 - k^2\sin^2\theta)^{-(1/2)}\, d\theta \quad (6.138)$$

and

$$E(\phi, k) = \int_0^{\phi} (1 - k^2 \sin^2 \theta)^{1/2} \, d\theta \,. \tag{6.139}$$

From (6.136) to (6.139) we see that

$$B(\tfrac{1}{2}, \tfrac{1}{2}; 1; z^2) = \frac{2}{\pi} [F(\tfrac{1}{2}\pi, z) - 2F(\tfrac{1}{4}\pi, z)] \tag{6.140}$$

and

$$B(-\tfrac{1}{2}, \tfrac{1}{2}; 1; z^2) = \frac{2}{\pi} [E(\tfrac{1}{2}\pi, z) - 2E(\tfrac{1}{4}\pi, z)] \,. \tag{6.141}$$

If $c = b + 1$, from (6.30)

$$\begin{aligned} F(a, b; b+1; z) + B(a, b; b+1; z) &= 2b \int_{1/2}^{1} t^{b-1}(1 - tz)^{-a} \, dt \\ &= 2bz^{-b} \int_{(1/2)z}^{z} u^{b-1}(1 - u)^{-a} \, du \,, \end{aligned} \tag{6.142}$$

on putting $u = tz$; that is, in terms of the incomplete beta function, given by (6.96),

$$\begin{aligned} &F(a, b; b+1; z) + B(a, b; b+1; z) \\ &\qquad = 2bz^{-b}[B_z(b, 1 - a) - B_{(1/2)z}(b, 1 - a)] \,. \end{aligned} \tag{6.143}$$

Similarly, from (6.32), if $\operatorname{Re} b > 0$,

$$\begin{aligned} F(a, b; b+1; z) - B(a, b; b+1; z) &= 2b \int_0^{1/2} t^{b-1}(1 - tz)^{-a} \, dt \\ &= 2bz^{-b} \int_0^{(1/2)z} u^{b-1}(1 - u)^{-a} \, du \,, \end{aligned} \tag{6.144}$$

on putting $u = tz$; that is, in terms of the incomplete beta function,

$$F(a, b; b+1; z) - B(a, b; b+1; z) = 2bz^{-b} B_{(1/2)z}(b, 1 - a) \,. \tag{6.145}$$

From (6.143) and (6.145),

$$B(a, b; b+1; z) = bz^{-b}[B_z(b, 1 - a) - 2B_{(1/2)z}(b, 1 - a)] \qquad (\operatorname{Re} b > 0) \,. \tag{6.146}$$

Using (6.121) and the recurrence formulas for B, we see that, when $c - b$ is any positive integer, $B(a, b; c; z)$ can be expressed in terms of incomplete beta functions.

From (6.47) and (6.146),

$$B\left[a, 1; b+1; \frac{z}{z-1}\right] = -bz^{-b}(1-z)^a[B_z(b, 1-a) - 2B_{(1/2)z}(b, 1-a)];$$

that is, replacing $b+1$ by c and $z/(z-1)$ by z,

$$B(a, 1; c; z) = -(c-1)(-z)^{1-c}(1-z)^{c-a-1} \times [B_\zeta(c-1, 1-a) - 2B_{(1/2)\zeta}(c-1, 1-a)] \quad (\operatorname{Re} c > 1), \tag{6.147}$$

where $\zeta = -z/(1-z)$. Using (6.120) and the recurrence formulas for B, we see that when b is any positive integer, $B(a, b; c; z)$ can be expressed in terms of incomplete beta functions.

For particular values of the parameters a, b, and c, the incomplete beta functions can be expressed in terms of elementary functions. Thus

$$B_x(1, 0) = \int_0^x \frac{du}{1-u} = -\log(1-x), \tag{6.148}$$

$$B_x(\tfrac{1}{2}, \tfrac{1}{2}) = \int_0^x \frac{du}{\sqrt{u(1-u)}} = 2\sin^{-1}\sqrt{x}, \tag{6.149}$$

$$B_x(\tfrac{1}{2}, 0) = \int_0^x \frac{du}{(1-u)\sqrt{u}} = \log\frac{1+\sqrt{x}}{1-\sqrt{x}}. \tag{6.150}$$

From (6.146) and (6.148),

$$B(1, 1; 2; z) = z^{-1}[2\log(1-\tfrac{1}{2}z) - \log(1-z)]. \tag{6.151}$$

From (6.146) and (6.149),

$$B(\tfrac{1}{2}, \tfrac{1}{2}; \tfrac{3}{2}; z^2) = z^{-1}\left[\sin^{-1}z - 2\sin^{-1}\left(\frac{z}{\sqrt{2}}\right)\right]. \tag{6.152}$$

From (6.146) and (6.150),

$$B(1, \tfrac{1}{2}, \tfrac{3}{2}, z^2) = \tfrac{1}{2}z^{-1}\left[\log\frac{1+z}{1-z} - 2\log\frac{1+z/\sqrt{2}}{1-z/\sqrt{2}}\right]. \tag{6.153}$$

To evaluate $B(1, \frac{1}{2}; \frac{3}{2}; -z^2)$, we return to equations (6.142) and (6.144). From (6.142),

$$F(1, \tfrac{1}{2}; \tfrac{3}{2}; -z^2) + B(1, \tfrac{1}{2}; \tfrac{3}{2}; -z^2) = \int_{1/2}^1 \frac{dt}{(1+tz^2)\sqrt{t}} = \frac{1}{z}\int_{(1/2)z^2}^{z^2} \frac{dv}{(1+v)\sqrt{v}}, \tag{6.154}$$

on putting $v = tz^2$. Similarly, from (6.144),

$$F(1, \tfrac{1}{2}; \tfrac{3}{2}; -z^2) - B(1, \tfrac{1}{2}; \tfrac{3}{2}; -z^2) = \int_0^{1/2} \frac{dt}{(1 + tz^2)\sqrt{t}}$$

$$= \frac{1}{z} \int_0^{(1/2)z^2} \frac{dv}{(1 + v)\sqrt{v}}, \qquad (6.155)$$

on putting $v = tz^2$. Now

$$\int_0^x \frac{dv}{(1 + v)\sqrt{v}} = 2 \tan^{-1} \sqrt{x}. \qquad (6.156)$$

From (6.154) to (6.156),

$$B(1, \tfrac{1}{2}; \tfrac{3}{2}; -z^2) = z^{-1}\left[\tan^{-1} z - 2 \tan^{-1}\left(\frac{z}{\sqrt{2}}\right)\right]. \qquad (6.157)$$

6.11 Mellin-Barnes Integral for $B(a, b; c; z)$

Consider the integral

$$I(z) = \int_C \frac{\Gamma(a + s)\Gamma(b + s)\Gamma(-s)}{\Gamma(c + s)} [\Omega(b + s, c + s; 0) - 1](-z)^s \, ds$$

$$(\operatorname{Re} a > 0, \operatorname{Re} b > 0, c \neq 0, -1, -2, \ldots). \qquad (6.158)$$

The contour C consists of the line $s = 0$ together with the semicircle (center at the origin) of large radius $N + \frac{1}{2}$ lying to the right of this line, where N is an integer. We shall now show that the part of the integral arising from the semicircle vanishes as $N \to \infty$.

In a similar way to that given in §4.13, we find that (6.158) can be written

$$I(z) = -\frac{1}{\Gamma(c - b)} \int_C \Gamma(a + s)\Gamma(-s)(-z)^s J(s) \, ds, \qquad (6.159)$$

where

$$J(s) = \int_0^1 \left(\frac{1 + u}{2}\right)^{c-b-1} \left(\frac{1 - u}{2}\right)^{b+s-1} du < K \frac{2^{1-\operatorname{Re}(b+s)}}{\operatorname{Re}(b + s)} \qquad [\operatorname{Re}(b + s) > 0],$$

where K is a constant which does not depend upon s. Put

$$s = (N + \tfrac{1}{2})e^{i\theta} = \xi + i\eta$$

and

$$-z = Re^{i\psi}.$$

Using the results of §4.13, together with the asymptotic expansion of the gamma function, we find that, on the semicircle,

$$|\Gamma(a+s)\Gamma(-s)(-z)^s| = 0\exp[(a-1)\log N - \pi|\eta| + \xi\log R - \eta\psi].$$

Thus the integrand tends to zero sufficiently rapidly to ensure that the contribution from the semicircle is zero as $N \to \infty$ if $\log R$ is negative and if $|\psi| \leqslant \pi - \delta$, where δ is any positive quantity; that is, if $|z| < 1$ and $|\arg(-z)| < \pi$.

Now, in (6.156), the integrand has simple poles at $s = 0, 1, 2, 3, \ldots$. Thus

$$\int_{-i\infty}^{i\infty} \frac{\Gamma(a+s)\Gamma(b+s)\Gamma(-s)}{\Gamma(c+s)} [\Omega(b+s, c+s; 0) - 1](-z)^s\, ds$$

$$= 2\pi i \sum_{n=0}^{\infty} \frac{\Gamma(a+n)\Gamma(b+n)}{\Gamma(c+n)} [\Omega(b+n, c+n; 0) - 1]\frac{z^n}{n!}. \quad (6.160)$$

Now, from Erdélyi [*62*, 1953a] if $|\arg(-z)| < \pi$, and a and b are not equal to zero or a negative integer,

$$\int_{-i\infty}^{i\infty} \frac{\Gamma(a+s)\Gamma(b+s)\Gamma(-s)}{\Gamma(c+s)} (-z)^s\, ds = 2\pi i \frac{\Gamma(a)\Gamma(b)}{\Gamma(c)} F(a, b; c; z). \quad (6.161)$$

From (6.160) and (6.161), using (6.109) and (6.110), we obtain the Mellin-Barnes integral for $B(a, b; c; z)$:

$$B(a, b; c; z) = \frac{1}{2\pi i}\frac{\Gamma(c)}{\Gamma(a)\Gamma(b)} \int_{-i\infty}^{i\infty} \frac{\Gamma(a+s)\Gamma(b+s)\Gamma(-s)}{\Gamma(c+s)}$$

$$\times\, \Omega(b+s, c+s; 0)(-z)^s\, ds, \quad (6.162)$$

where $|z| < 1$, $|\arg(-z)| < \pi$, $\operatorname{Re} a > 0$, $\operatorname{Re} b > 0$, and c is not zero or a negative integer.

6.12 The Zeros of $B(a, b; c; z)$, Where a, b, and c Are Real

From (6.45), using Rolle's theorem, we see that, if c is not zero or a negative integer, between two consecutive zeros of $B(a, b; c; z)$ there lies at least one zero of $B(a+1, b+1; c+1; z)$. Similarly, from (6.73), if neither a nor c are zero or negative integers, between two consecutive zeros (which are both positive or both negative) of $B(a, b; c; z)$ there lies at least one zero of $B(a+1, b; c; z)$. Again, from (6.75), if none of a, c, or $c-b$ are zero or negative integers, between two zeros of $B(a, b; c; z)$, both less than $z = 1$, there lies at least one zero of $B(a+1, b; c+1; z)$. The converse of these statements is not true.

Considering the coefficients of the terms in the power series (6.109), we see, on using the results of §4.8, that if $a > 0$ and $2b > c > b > 0$, all the coefficients are positive. Thus $B(a, b; c; z) > 0$ for $0 \leqslant z \leqslant 1$ if $a > 0$ and $2b > c > b > 0$. If $a > 0$ and $c > 2b > 0$, the coefficients of the lower powers of z are negative, and those of all subsequent powers of z are positive. By an extension of Descartes' rule of signs to a convergent power series, we see that $B(a, b; c; z)$ cannot have more than one zero in the range $0 < z < 1$ if $a > 0$ and $c > 2b > 0$. More generally, we find, from (6.89), that if $c > a + b$ ($c \neq 0, -1, -2, \ldots$), $B(a, b; c; z)$ will have an even or odd number of zeros between 0 and 1 according as

$$\frac{\Gamma(c)\Omega(b, c-a; 0)}{\Gamma(c-a)\Gamma(c-b)\Omega(b, c; 0)} > \quad \text{or} \quad < 0 .$$

In particular, from (6.80) and (6.89), we see that

$$B(a, b; a + 2b; 1) = 0 . \tag{6.163}$$

Using (6.47) we see that, if $a > 0$ and $2b > c > b > 0$, $B(a, b; c; z)$ has one (and only one) negative zero. If $a > 0$ and $c > 2b > 0$, $B(a, b; c; z) < 0$ for $z < 0$.

If $a > 0$ and $c = 2b > 0$, $B(a, b; c; z)$ has a zero at $z = 0$ and is positive for $1 \geqslant z > 0$ and negative for $z < 0$.

6.13 Asymptotic Expansion of $B(a, b; c; z)$

From (6.12), (6.20), (6.25), and (6.26),

$$B(a, b; c; z) + F(a, b; c; z) = -2^{a-c}\pi^{-2}e^{-i\pi c}(1 - e^{2i\pi b})\Gamma(1-b)\Gamma(c) \times \Gamma(1 + b - c)(-z)^{-a}I , \tag{6.164}$$

where

$$I = \int_0^{(1+)} (1+s)^{b-a-1}(1-s)^{c-b-1}\left[1 - \frac{2}{z(1+s)}\right]^{-a} ds , \tag{6.165}$$

where the arguments of $1 + s$, $1 - s$, and $1 - 2[z(1+s)]^{-1}$ all have their principal values at the start of the contour and z^{-1} is not a real number between 0 and 1.

Using Taylor's expansion, we find (as in §4.15),

$$\left[1 - \frac{2}{z(1+s)}\right]^{-a} = 1 + \frac{a}{1!}\left[\frac{2}{z(1+s)}\right] + \frac{a(a+1)}{2!}\left[\frac{2}{z(1+s)}\right]^2 + \cdots + \frac{a(a+1)\cdots(a+n-1)}{n!}\left[\frac{2}{z(1+s)}\right]^n + R_n(s, z), \tag{6.166}$$

where

$$R_n(s, z) = \frac{a(a+1)\cdots(a+n)}{n!}\left[1 - \frac{2}{z(1+s)}\right]^{-a}\int_0^{-2/[z(1+s)]} t^n(1+t)^{a-1}\, dt .$$

From (6.165) and (6.166),

$$I = \sum_{m=0}^{n} \frac{\Gamma(a+m)}{\Gamma(a)\cdot m!}\left(\frac{2}{z}\right)^m \int_0^{(1+)} (1+s)^{b-a-m-1}(1-s)^{c-b-1}\,ds$$

$$+ \int_0^{(1+)} (1+s)^{b-a-1}(1-s)^{c-b-1}R_n(s,z)\,ds. \quad (6.167)$$

Now, as shown by Whittaker and Watson [*344*, 1935], $R_n(s, z)$ is $0(z^{-n-1})$ and the final contour integral in (6.167) is thus $0(z^{-n-1})$. Also, from §§4.2 and 4.3, replacing a by b, and putting $z = 0$,

$$\Omega(b, c; 0) + \Phi(b, c; 0)$$
$$= -2^{-c}\pi^{-2}e^{-i\pi c}(1-e^{2i\pi b})\Gamma(1-b)\Gamma(c)\Gamma(1+b-c)J(b,c), \quad (6.168)$$

where

$$J(b, c) = \int_0^{(1+)} (1+u)^{b-1}(1-u)^{c-b-1}\,du. \quad (6.169)$$

Thus, from (6.167) and (6.168),

$$I = \sum_{m=0}^{n} \frac{\Gamma(a+m)}{\Gamma(a)\cdot m!}\left(\frac{2}{z}\right)^m J(b-a-m, c-a-m) + 0(z^{-n-1});$$

that is, using (6.164) and (6.168), and remembering that $\Phi(b, c; 0) = 1$, we obtain the asymptotic expansion of $B(a, b; c; z)$ for large values of $|z|$ in the form

$$B(a, b; c; z) \sim -F(a, b; c; z) + (-z)^{-a}\sum_{m=0}^{\infty} \frac{\Gamma(a+m)\Gamma(b-a-m)\Gamma(c)}{\Gamma(a)\Gamma(b)\Gamma(c-a-m)\cdot m!}$$
$$\times [1 + \Omega(b-a-m, c-a-m; 0)]\left(\frac{1}{z}\right)^m, \quad (6.170)$$

where z^{-1} is not a real number between 0 and 1.

Now, as shown by Erdélyi [*63*, 1953a],

$$F(a, b; c; z) = \frac{\Gamma(b-a)\Gamma(c)}{\Gamma(b)\Gamma(c-a)}(-z)^{-a}F(a, a+1-c; a+1-b; z^{-1})$$
$$+ \frac{\Gamma(a-b)\Gamma(c)}{\Gamma(a)\Gamma(c-b)}(-z)^{-b}F(b, b+1-c; b+1-a; z^{-1}). \quad (6.171)$$

From (6.170) and (6.171) we obtain, after some simplification,

$$B(a, b; c; z) \sim -\frac{\Gamma(a-b)\Gamma(c)}{\Gamma(a)\Gamma(c-b)}(-z)^{-b}F(b, b+1-c; b+1-a; z^{-1})$$
$$+ (-z)^{-a}\sum_{m=0}^{\infty} \frac{\Gamma(a+m)\Gamma(b-a-m)\Gamma(c)}{\Gamma(a)\Gamma(b)\Gamma(c-a-m)\cdot m!}\Omega(b-a-m, c-a-m; 0)\left(\frac{1}{z}\right)^m.$$
$$(6.172)$$

If a is a negative integer, the factor $\Gamma(a+m)/\Gamma(a)$ in the summation is to be taken as $a(a+1)(a+2)\cdots(a+m-1)$. In this case, the series in (6.170) and (6.172) terminate after a finite number of terms, and are then exact.

6.14 Indefinite Integrals Connected with $B(a, b; c; z)$

A number of indefinite integrals connected with $B(a, b; c; z)$ can be obtained directly from the differential relations given in §§6.5 and 6.6. Other integrals can be obtained by solving the differential equation

$$z(1-z)\frac{d^2y}{dz^2} + [c-(a+b+1)]\frac{dy}{dz} - aby = a\frac{2^{1-c}\Gamma(c)}{\Gamma(b)\Gamma(c-b)}(1-\tfrac{1}{2}z)^{-a-1} \tag{6.173}$$

by the method of variation of parameters (see §1.5). The Wronskian corresponding to the solutions $F(a, b; c; z)$ and $z^{1-c}F(a-c+1, b-c+1; 2-c; z)$ is given by (6.7). We find that

$$\begin{aligned} B(a, b; c; z) & \\ &= a\frac{2^{1-c}\Gamma(c-1)}{\Gamma(b)\Gamma(c-b)}[F(a, b; c; z) \\ &\quad\times\int(1-z)^{a+b-c}(1-\tfrac{1}{2}z)^{-a-1}F(a-c+1, b-c+1; 2-c; z)\,dz \\ &\quad - z^{1-c}F(a-c+1, b-c+1; 2-c; z) \\ &\quad\times\int z^{c-1}(1-z)^{a+b-c}(1-\tfrac{1}{2}z)^{-a-1}F(a, b; c; z)\,dz]. \end{aligned} \tag{6.174}$$

Now $x = F(a, b; c; z)$ is a solution of the differential equation

$$z(1-z)\frac{d^2x}{dz^2} + [c-(a+b+1)z]\frac{dx}{dz} - abx = 0. \tag{6.175}$$

On multiplying (6.173) by $xz^{c-1}(1-z)^{a+b-c}$ and (6.175) by $yz^{c-1}(1-z)^{a+b-c}$ and subtracting, we obtain

$$\begin{aligned} z^c(1-z)^{a+b-c+1}\left(x\frac{d^2y}{dz^2} - y\frac{d^2x}{dz^2}\right) + [c-(a+b+1)z]z^{c-1}(1-z)^{a+b-c} & \\ \times\left(x\frac{dy}{dz} - y\frac{dx}{dz}\right) = a\frac{2^{1-c}\Gamma(c)}{\Gamma(b)\Gamma(c-b)}z^{c-1}(1-z)^{a+b-c}(1-\tfrac{1}{2}z)^{-a-1}x; & \end{aligned}$$

that is,

$$\frac{d}{dz}\left[z^c(1-z)^{a+b-c+1}\left(x\frac{dy}{dz}-y\frac{dx}{dz}\right)\right]=a\frac{2^{1-c}\Gamma(c)}{\Gamma(b)\Gamma(c-b)}z^{c-1}(1-z)^{a+b-c}$$
$$\times(1-\tfrac{1}{2}z)^{-a-1}x. \quad (6.176)$$

On integrating (6.176) and putting $x = F(a, b; c; z)$, we see that

$$\int z^{c-1}(1-z)^{a+b-c}(2-z)^{-a-1}F(a,b;c;z)\,dz$$
$$=\frac{2^{c-a-2}\Gamma(b)\Gamma(c-b)}{a\Gamma(c)}z^c(1-z)^{a+b-c+1}$$
$$\times[F(a,b;c;z)B'(a,b;c;z)-B(a,b;c;z)F'(a,b;c;z)]$$
$$=\frac{2^{c-a-2}\Gamma(b+1)\Gamma(c-b)}{\Gamma(c+1)}z^c(1-z)^{a+b-c+1}$$
$$\times[F(a,b;c;z)B(a+1,b+1;c+1;z)$$
$$-B(a,b;c;z)F(a+1,b+1;c+1;z)]. \quad (6.177)$$

Similar integrals can be found by using the differential equations given in Table 6.1. Thus

$$\int(1+z)^{b-2}F(a,b;c;z)\,dz$$
$$=\frac{2^{c-a-2}\Gamma(1-a)\Gamma(c-b)}{(1-b)\Gamma(c+1-a-b)}z^c(1-z)^{a+b-c+1}$$
$$\times\Bigg[F(a,b;c;z)\frac{d}{dz}\{z^{1-c}(1-z)^{c-a-b}$$
$$\times B(1-b,1-a;c+1-a-b;1-z)\}-z^{1-c}(1-z)^{c-a-b}$$
$$\times B(1-b,1-a;c+1-a-b;1-z)\frac{d}{dz}F(a,b;c;z)\Bigg]$$
$$=\frac{2^{c-a-2}\Gamma(1-a)\Gamma(c-b)}{(1-b)\Gamma(c+1-a-b)}\Bigg\{F(a,b;c;z)\Bigg[\{1-c-(1-a-b)z\}$$
$$\times B(1-b,1-a;c+1-a-b;1-z)$$
$$-\frac{(1-b)(1-a)}{c+1-a-b}z(1-z)B(2-b,2-a;c+2-a-b;1-z)\Bigg]$$
$$-\frac{ab}{c}z(1-z)B(1-b,1-a;c+1-a-b;1-z)$$
$$\times F(a+1,b+1;c+1;z)\Bigg\}. \quad (6.178)$$

6.15 Definite Integrals Connected with $B(a, b; c; z)$

The formula

$$\int_0^s z^{\rho-1}(s-z)^{\sigma-1}B(a,b;c;kz)\,dz = \frac{\Gamma(\rho)\Gamma(\sigma)}{\Gamma(\rho+\sigma)} s^{\rho+\sigma-1}{}_3B_2(a,\rho,b;\rho+\sigma,c;ks), \tag{6.179}$$

where (see Chapter 8)

$${}_3B_2(a,\rho,b;\rho+\sigma,c;ks) = \sum_{n=0}^{\infty} \frac{\Gamma(a+n)\Gamma(\rho+n)\Gamma(b+n)\Gamma(\rho+\sigma)\Gamma(c)}{\Gamma(a)\Gamma(\rho)\Gamma(b)\Gamma(\rho+\sigma+n)\Gamma(c+n)} \times \Omega(b+n, c+n; 0)\frac{(ks)^n}{n!}, \tag{6.180}$$

and $\operatorname{Re}\rho > 0$, $\operatorname{Re}\sigma > 0$, and $|ks| < 1$, can be proved by expanding B as a power series and integrating term by term. In particular, putting $\sigma = a - \rho$, we obtain

$$\int_0^s z^{\rho-1}(s-z)^{a-\rho-1}B(a,b;c;kz)\,dz = \frac{\Gamma(\rho)\Gamma(a-\rho)}{\Gamma(a)} s^{a-1}B(\rho,b;c;ks). \tag{6.181}$$

Now if $\operatorname{Re} a > \operatorname{Re}\rho > 0$ and $c \neq 0, -1, -2, \ldots$, both sides of (6.181) are analytic functions of k provided that $(ks)^{-1}$ is not a real number between 0 and 1, and thus, by the principle of analytic continuation, (6.181) is true for this more extensive range of ks.

Now, using (6.47), (6.181) may be written in the alternative form

$$\int_0^s z^{\rho-1}\left(1-\frac{z}{s}\right)^{a-\rho-1} B(a,b;c;kz)\,dz = -\frac{\Gamma(\rho)\Gamma(a-\rho)}{\Gamma(a)}\left(\frac{s}{1-ks}\right)^{\rho} \times B\left(\rho, c-b; c; \frac{ks}{ks-1}\right). \tag{6.182}$$

On letting $s \to \infty$ we obtain, with $h = -k > 0$,

$$\begin{aligned}\int_0^\infty z^{\rho-1}B(a,b;c;-hz)\,dz &= -h^{-\rho}\frac{\Gamma(\rho)\Gamma(a-\rho)}{\Gamma(a)}B(\rho,c-b;c;1)\\ &= h^{-\rho}\frac{\Gamma(a-\rho)\Gamma(b-\rho)\Gamma(c)\Gamma(\rho)}{\Gamma(a)\Gamma(b)\Gamma(c-\rho)}\Omega(b-\rho,c-\rho;0)\end{aligned}$$

$$(\operatorname{Re} a > \operatorname{Re}\rho > 0,\ \operatorname{Re} b > \operatorname{Re}\rho,\ \operatorname{Re} c > 0). \tag{6.183}$$

Equation (6.183) is the Mellin inversion of (6.162).

6.16 The Nonhomogeneous Functions $f_\sigma(a, b; c; z)$ and $F_\sigma(a, b; c; z)$

We consider next the solutions of the nonhomogeneous hypergeometric equation

$$z(1-z)\frac{d^2y}{dz^2} + [c-(a+b+1)z]\frac{dy}{dz} - aby = z^{\sigma-1}, \tag{6.184}$$

where a, b, c, and σ are constants. As stated above, the associated homogeneous equation has regular singularities at $z = 0$ and 1 and a regular singular point at infinity. We shall analyze the properties of certain particular integrals of (6.184) in a similar manner to that given in §4.18 for the functions $\theta_\sigma(a, c; z)$ and $\Theta_\sigma(a, c; z)$.

Using the method of Frobenius (§1.12), we see that a particular integral of (6.184) is

$$\begin{aligned} f_\sigma(a, b; c; z) &= \frac{z^\sigma}{\sigma(\sigma+c-1)}\left[1 + \frac{(\sigma+a)(\sigma+b)}{(\sigma+1)(\sigma+c)} z \right. \\ &\quad \left. + \frac{(\sigma+a)(\sigma+a+1)(\sigma+b)(\sigma+b+1)}{(\sigma+1)(\sigma+2)(\sigma+c)(\sigma+c+1)} z^2 + \cdots\right] \\ &= z^\sigma \sum_{n=0}^{\infty} \frac{\Gamma(\sigma+a+n)\Gamma(\sigma+b+n)\Gamma(\sigma)\Gamma(\sigma+c-1)}{\Gamma(\sigma+a)\Gamma(\sigma+b)\Gamma(\sigma+n+1)\Gamma(\sigma+c+n)} z^n \\ &= \frac{z^\sigma}{\sigma(\sigma+c-1)}\, {}_3F_2(1, \sigma+a, \sigma+b; \sigma+1, \sigma+c; z). \end{aligned} \tag{6.185}$$

The series converges when $|z| < 1$; it converges when $|z| = 1$ provided that $\mathrm{Re}(c-a-b) > 0$. The complete primitive of (6.184) is

$$y = C_1 F(a, b; c; z) + C_2 z^{1-c} F(a-c+1, b-c+1; 2-c; z) + f_\sigma(a, b; c; z), \tag{6.186}$$

where C_1 and C_2 are arbitrary constants.

The series solution (6.185) is not valid if σ or $\sigma + c - 1$ is zero or a negative integer (since in these cases all the coefficients in the series after a certain value of n become infinite). As shown in §1.12, for these values of σ the particular solution of (6.184) will, in general, contain logarithmic terms.

If $\sigma = m$, a positive integer, (6.185) can be written

$$\begin{aligned} f_m(a, b; c; z) &= \frac{(m-1)!\,\Gamma(m+c-1)\Gamma(a)\Gamma(b)}{\Gamma(m+a)\Gamma(m+b)\Gamma(c)} \\ &\quad \times \sum_{n=0}^{\infty} \frac{\Gamma(m+n+a)\Gamma(m+n+b)\Gamma(c)}{\Gamma(a)\Gamma(b)\Gamma(m+n+c)} \frac{z^{n+m}}{(n+m)!} \end{aligned} \tag{6.187}$$

and, if $\sigma = m + 1 - c$, where m is a positive integer, (6.185) can be written

$$f_{m+1-c}(a, b; c; z) = z^{1-c} \frac{(m-1)!\,\Gamma(m+1-c)\Gamma(a+1-c)\Gamma(b+1-c)}{\Gamma(m+a+1-c)\Gamma(m+b+1-c)\Gamma(2-c)}$$

$$\times \sum_{n=0}^{\infty} \frac{\Gamma(m+n+a+1-c)\Gamma(m+n+b+1-c)\Gamma(2-c)}{\Gamma(a+1-c)\Gamma(b+1-c)\Gamma(m+n+2-c)} \frac{z^{n+m}}{(n+m)!}. \tag{6.188}$$

From (6.185),

$$f_{\sigma+1-c}(a, b; c; z) = z^{1-c} f_\sigma(a+1-c, b+1-c; 2-c; z). \tag{6.189}$$

We see also that

$$f_\sigma(a, b; c; z) = f_\sigma(b, a; c; z) \tag{6.190}$$

and

$$f_\sigma(a, c; c; z) = \frac{z^\sigma}{\sigma(\sigma+c-1)} F(1, \sigma+a; \sigma+1; z)$$

$$= (\sigma+c-1)^{-1}(1-z)^{-a} B_z(\sigma, a), \tag{6.191}$$

where B is the incomplete beta function. Similarly,

$$f_\sigma(1, b; c; z) = \frac{z^\sigma}{\sigma(\sigma+c-1)} F(1, \sigma+b; \sigma+c; z)$$

$$= \sigma^{-1} z^{1-c} (1-z)^{c-b-1} B_z(\sigma+c-1, b-c+1). \tag{6.192}$$

If $\sigma + a$ or $\sigma + b$ is zero or a negative integer, the series (6.185) terminates. In particular,

$$f_{-a}(a, b; c; z) = \frac{z^{-a}}{a(a+1-c)}. \tag{6.193}$$

Also, from (6.185),

$$\lim_{a \to \infty} \left\{ a^\sigma f_\sigma\left(a, b; c; \frac{x}{a}\right) \right\} = \theta_\sigma(b, c; x). \tag{6.194}$$

If $c = \frac{1}{2}$, $f_\sigma(a, b; c; z^2)$ can be expressed in terms of the nonhomogeneous Legendre function $s^\mu_{\nu,\sigma}(z)$ defined in Chapter 7. As will be shown in §7.16,

$$f_\sigma(a, b; \tfrac{1}{2}; z^2) = 4(z^2-1)^{(1-2a-2b)/4} s^{b+a-(1/2)}_{b-a-(1/2),\sigma}(z). \tag{6.195}$$

In §6.17 we consider the analytic continuation of $f_\sigma(a, b; c; z)$ beyond the region $|z| < 1$.

Consider now the solution of (6.184) expressed as a series of descending powers of z (see §1.13). Such a particular integral is

$$\begin{aligned}
F_\sigma(a, b; c; z) &\\
&= -\frac{z^{\sigma-1}}{(1-\sigma-a)(1-\sigma-b)}\left[1+\frac{(1-\sigma)(2-\sigma-c)}{(2-\sigma-a)(2-\sigma-b)z}\right.\\
&\quad\left.+\frac{(1-\sigma)(2-\sigma)(2-\sigma-c)(3-\sigma-c)}{(2-\sigma-a)(3-\sigma-a)(2-\sigma-b)(3-\sigma-b)z^2}+\cdots\right]\\
&= -z^{\sigma-1}\sum_{n=0}^{\infty}\frac{\Gamma(n+1-\sigma)\Gamma(n+2-\sigma-c)\Gamma(1-\sigma-a)\Gamma(1-\sigma-b)}{\Gamma(1-\sigma)\Gamma(2-\sigma-c)\Gamma(n+2-\sigma-a)\Gamma(n+2-\sigma-b)z^n}\\
&= -\frac{z^{\sigma-1}}{(1-\sigma-a)(1-\sigma-b)}\\
&\quad\times {}_3F_2\left(1, 1-\sigma, 2-\sigma-c; 2-\sigma-a, 2-\sigma-b; \frac{1}{z}\right). \qquad (6.196)
\end{aligned}$$

The series converges if $|z| > 1$; it converges when $|z| = 1$ provided that $\operatorname{Re}(c - a - b) > 0$.

If $\sigma = m$, a positive integer, the series terminates after m terms. Equation (6.196) can then be written

$$F_m(a, b; c; z) = -\frac{(m-1)!\,\Gamma(m+c-1)\Gamma(a)\Gamma(b)}{\Gamma(m+a)\Gamma(m+b)\Gamma(c)}\sum_{n=0}^{m-1}\frac{\Gamma(a+n)\Gamma(b+n)\Gamma(c)}{\Gamma(a)\Gamma(b)\Gamma(c+n)}\frac{z^n}{n!}. \qquad (6.197)$$

Similarly, if $\sigma = m + 1 - c$, where m is a positive integer, the series (6.196) terminates after m terms. Equation (6.196) can then be written

$$\begin{aligned}
F_{m+1-c}(a, b; c; z) &= -\frac{(m-1)!\,\Gamma(m+1-c)\Gamma(a+1-c)\Gamma(b+1-c)}{\Gamma(m+a+1-c)\Gamma(m+b+1-c)\Gamma(2-c)}\\
&\quad\times\sum_{n=0}^{m-1}\frac{\Gamma(a+1-c+n)\Gamma(b+1-c+n)\Gamma(2-c)}{\Gamma(a+1-c)\Gamma(b+1-c)\Gamma(n+2-c)}\frac{z^{n+1-c}}{n!}. \qquad (6.198)
\end{aligned}$$

The series in (6.197) and (6.198) are, of course, truncated forms of the series for $F(a, b; c; z)$ and $z^{1-c}F(a-c+1, b-c+1; 2-c; z)$.

From (6.196),

$$F_{\sigma+1-c}(a, b; c; z) = z^{1-c}F_{\sigma}(a + 1 - c, b + 1 - c; 2 - c; z). \quad (6.199)$$

We also see that

$$F_{\sigma}(a, b; c; z) = F_{\sigma}(b, a; c; z) \quad (6.200)$$

and

$$\begin{aligned} F_{\sigma}(a, c; c; z) &= -\frac{z^{\sigma-1}}{(1-\sigma-a)(1-\sigma-c)} F\left(1, 1-\sigma; 2-\sigma-a; \frac{1}{z}\right) \\ &= (\sigma + c - 1)^{-1}(z-1)^{-a}B_{1/z}(1-\sigma-a, a). \end{aligned} \quad (6.201)$$

Similarly,

$$\begin{aligned} F_{\sigma}(1, b; c; z) &= \frac{z^{\sigma-1}}{\sigma(1-\sigma-b)} F\left(1, 2-\sigma-c; 2-\sigma-b; \frac{1}{z}\right) \\ &= \sigma^{-1}z^{1-c}(z-1)^{c-b-1}B_{1/z}(1-\sigma-b, 1+b-c). \end{aligned} \quad (6.202)$$

Also, from (6.196),

$$F_1(a, b; c; z) = -\frac{1}{ab} \quad (6.203)$$

and

$$F_{2-c}(a, b; c; z) = -\frac{z^{1-c}}{(a+1-c)(b+1-c)}. \quad (6.204)$$

On comparing (6.196) with (4.186), we see that

$$\lim_{a\to\infty}\left\{a^{\sigma}F_{\sigma}\left(a, b; c; \frac{x}{a}\right)\right\} = \Theta_{\sigma}(b, c; x). \quad (6.205)$$

More generally, from (6.185) and (6.196),

$$\begin{aligned} F_{\sigma}(a, b; c; z) &= -z^{-a}f_{1-\sigma-a}\left(a, a+1-c; a+1-b; \frac{1}{z}\right) \\ &= -z^{-b}f_{1-\sigma-b}\left(b, b+1-c; b+1-a; \frac{1}{z}\right), \end{aligned} \quad (6.206)$$

and, conversely,

$$f_\sigma(a, b; c; z) = -z^{-a}F_{1-\sigma-a}\left(a, a+1-c; a+1-b; \frac{1}{z}\right)$$

$$= -z^{-b}F_{1-\sigma-b}\left(b, b+1-c; b+1-a; \frac{1}{z}\right). \qquad (6.207)$$

If $c = \frac{1}{2}$, $F_\sigma(a, b; c; z^2)$ can be expressed in terms of the nonhomogeneous Legendre function $S^{\mu}_{\nu,\sigma}(z)$ defined in Chapter 7. As will be shown in §7.16,

$$F_\sigma(a, b; \tfrac{1}{2}; z^2) = 4(z^2-1)^{(1-2a-2b)/4}S^{b+a-(1/2)}_{b-a-(1/2),\sigma}(z). \qquad (6.208)$$

In §6,17, we shall derive a direct relation between $f_\sigma(a, b; c; z)$ and $F_\sigma(a, b; c; z)$.

6.17 Mellin-Barnes Integral and Analytic Continuation for $f_\sigma(a, b; c; z)$

If none of σ, $\sigma + a$, $\sigma + b$, $\sigma + c - 1$ is zero or a negative integer, the formula

$$f_\sigma(a, b; c; z) = \frac{1}{2\pi i}\frac{\Gamma(\sigma)\Gamma(\sigma+c-1)}{\Gamma(\sigma+a)\Gamma(\sigma+b)}$$

$$\times z^\sigma \int_{-i\infty}^{i\infty} \frac{\Gamma(\sigma+a+s)\Gamma(\sigma+b+s)\Gamma(1+s)\Gamma(-s)}{\Gamma(\sigma+1+s)\Gamma(\sigma+c+s)}(-z)^s\,ds, \qquad (6.209)$$

in which the path of integration is indented if necessary to separate the poles of $\Gamma(s)$ from those of $\Gamma(\sigma+a+s)$, $\Gamma(\sigma+b+s)$ and $\Gamma(1+s)$, can be proved (for the case $|z|<1$) by considering a contour integral taken around a contour consisting of the line $s=0$ together with a large semicircle to the right of this, and evaluating the integral as the sum of the residues at the poles of $\Gamma(-s)$.

The integral in (6.209) defines an analytic function of z which is one-valued in the region $|\arg(-z)| < \pi$. The relation (6.209) can now be taken as the definition of $f_\sigma(a, b; c; z)$, thus enabling us to give a meaning to the analytic continuation of $f_\sigma(a, b; c; z)$ throughout the region $|\arg(-z)| < \pi$.

Consider now the same integrand to be taken around a contour consisting of the line $s=0$ together with a large semicircle to the left of this. As in the previous case, the contribution from the semicircle vanishes as the radius tends to infinity. On evaluating the sum of the residues at the poles of $\Gamma(1+s)$, $\Gamma(\sigma+a+s)$ and $\Gamma(\sigma+b+s)$, we find that, if $\sigma+a$, $\sigma+b$ and $a-b$ are not integers,

$$\frac{\Gamma(\sigma+a)\Gamma(\sigma+b)}{\Gamma(\sigma)\Gamma(\sigma+c-1)}\,z^{-\sigma}f_\sigma(a,b;c;z)$$

$$= -\sum_{n=1}^{\infty}\frac{\Gamma(\sigma+a+n)\Gamma(\sigma+b+n)}{\Gamma(\sigma+1-n)\Gamma(\sigma+c-n)z^n}$$

$$+(-z)^{-\sigma-a}\sum_{n=0}^{\infty}\frac{\Gamma(b-a-n)\Gamma(1-\sigma-a-n)\Gamma(\sigma+a+n)}{\Gamma(1-a-n)\Gamma(c-a-n)n!\,z^n}$$

$$+(-z)^{-\sigma-b}\sum_{n=0}^{\infty}\frac{\Gamma(a-b-n)\Gamma(1-\sigma-b-n)\Gamma(\sigma+b+n)}{\Gamma(1-b-n)\Gamma(c-b-n)n!\,z^n}$$

$$= -\frac{\Gamma(\sigma+a)\Gamma(1-\sigma-a)\Gamma(\sigma+b)\Gamma(1-\sigma-b)}{\Gamma(\sigma+1)\Gamma(-\sigma)\Gamma(\sigma+c)\Gamma(1-\sigma-c)}$$

$$\times\sum_{n=1}^{\infty}\frac{\Gamma(n-\sigma)\Gamma(n+1-\sigma-c)}{\Gamma(n+1-\sigma-a)\Gamma(n+1-\sigma-b)z^n}$$

$$+\frac{\Gamma(b-a)\Gamma(1+a-b)\Gamma(\sigma+a)\Gamma(1-\sigma-a)}{\Gamma(a)\Gamma(1-a)\Gamma(c-a)\Gamma(1-c+a)}(-z)^{-\sigma-a}$$

$$\times\sum_{n=0}^{\infty}\frac{\Gamma(a+n)\Gamma(1+a-c+n)}{\Gamma(1+a-b+n)n!\,z^n}$$

$$+\frac{\Gamma(a-b)\Gamma(1+b-a)\Gamma(\sigma+b)\Gamma(1-\sigma-b)}{\Gamma(b)\Gamma(1-b)\Gamma(c-b)\Gamma(1-c+b)}(-z)^{-\sigma-b}$$

$$\times\sum_{n=0}^{\infty}\frac{\Gamma(b+n)\Gamma(1+b-c+n)}{\Gamma(1+b-a+n)n!\,z^n};$$

that is, on simplifying and using (6.196),

$$z^{-\sigma}f_\sigma(a,b;c;z)$$

$$= z^{-\sigma}F_\sigma(a,b;c;z)+A_1(-z)^{-\sigma-a}F(a,1+a-c;1+a-b;z^{-1})$$

$$+B_1(-z)^{-\sigma-b}F(b,1+b-c;1+b-a;z^{-1}), \quad (6.210)$$

where

$$A_1=\frac{\Gamma(b-a)\Gamma(\sigma)\Gamma(1-\sigma-a)\Gamma(\sigma+c-1)}{\Gamma(1-a)\Gamma(c-a)\Gamma(\sigma+b)},$$

$$B_1=\frac{\Gamma(a-b)\Gamma(\sigma)\Gamma(1-\sigma-b)\Gamma(\sigma+c-1)}{\Gamma(1-b)\Gamma(c-b)\Gamma(\sigma+a)},$$

$|\arg(-z)|<\pi$, and σ, $\sigma+c-1$ are not zero or negative integers, and $\sigma+a$, $\sigma+b$, $a-b$ are not integers.

Equation (6.210) can be written in the alternative form

$$f_\sigma(a, b; c; z)$$
$$= F_\sigma(a, b; c; z) + A_1 e^{-i\pi(\sigma+a)\varepsilon} z^{-a} F(a, 1+a-c; 1+a-b; z^{-1})$$
$$+ B_1 e^{-i\pi(\sigma+b)\varepsilon} z^{-b} F(b, 1+b-c; 1+b-a; z^{-1}), \quad (6.211)$$

where $\varepsilon = \operatorname{sgn}(\operatorname{Im} z) = 1, -1$, according as $\operatorname{Im} z >, <0$.

On replacing z by $1/z$ in (6.211) we obtain (with the same definition of ε),

$$f_\sigma(a, b; c; 1/z)$$
$$= F_\sigma(a, b; c; 1/z) + A_1 e^{i\pi(\sigma+a)\varepsilon} z^a F(a, 1+a-c; 1+a-b; z)$$
$$+ B_1 e^{i\pi(\sigma+b)\varepsilon} z^b F(b, 1+b-c; 1+b-a; z);$$

that is, using (6.206) and (6.207),

$$z^a F_{1-\sigma-a}(a, a+1-c; a+1-b; z) = z^a f_{1-\sigma-a}(a, a+1-c; a+1-b; z)$$
$$- A_1 e^{i\pi(\sigma+a)\varepsilon} z^a F(a, a+1-c; 1+a-b; z) - B_1 e^{i\pi(\sigma+b)\varepsilon} z^b$$
$$\times F(b, b+1-c; 1+b-a; z).$$

This can be written in the alternative form

$$F_\sigma(a, b; c; z) = f_\sigma(a, b; c; z) + A_2 e^{-i\pi\sigma\varepsilon} F(a, b; c; z)$$
$$- B_2 e^{-i\pi(\sigma+c)\varepsilon} z^{1-c} F(a-c+1, b-c+1; 2-c; z), \quad (6.212)$$

where

$$A_2 = \frac{\Gamma(1-c)\Gamma(\sigma)\Gamma(1-\sigma-a)\Gamma(1-\sigma-b)}{\Gamma(1-a)\Gamma(1-b)\Gamma(2-\sigma-c)},$$

$$B_2 = \frac{\Gamma(c-1)\Gamma(\sigma+c-1)\Gamma(1-\sigma-a)\Gamma(1-\sigma-b)}{\Gamma(c-a)\Gamma(c-b)\Gamma(1-\sigma)},$$

and $|\arg(-z)| < \pi$.

6.18 Recurrence Formulas and Relations for Contiguous Functions

From the series (6.185) we see that

$$(\sigma+a)(\sigma+b) f_{\sigma+1}(a, b; c; z) = \sigma(\sigma+c-1) f_\sigma(a, b; c; z) - z^\sigma. \quad (6.213)$$

From (6.185) we see that, as $\sigma \to \infty$,

$$f_\sigma(a, b; c; z) = 0\left(\frac{z^\sigma}{\sigma^2}\right) \qquad (|z| < 1), \quad (6.214)$$

provided that neither σ nor $\sigma + c - 1$ is zero or a negative integer. On differentiating (6.185) we find that

$$\frac{d}{dz} f_\sigma(a, b; c; z) = (\sigma - 1) f_{\sigma-1}(a + 1, b + 1; c + 1; z). \tag{6.215}$$

By the same analysis as that given in §6.6, it can be shown that the six contiguous functions $f_\sigma(a \pm 1, b; c; z)$, $f_\sigma(a, b \pm 1; c; z)$, $f_\sigma(a, b; c \pm 1; z)$ can be expressed in terms of $f_\sigma(a, b; c; z)$ and its derivative with respect to z. For conciseness we shall denote $f_\sigma(a+1, b; c; z)$ and $f_\sigma(a-1, b, c, z)$ by f_{a+}, f_{a-}, and similarly for the other contiguous functions, it being understood that in these cases all the functions have the same parameter σ.

Let $\delta \equiv z(d/dz)$. Then, from (6.185),

$$(\delta + a) f = (\sigma + a) f_{a+}, \tag{6.216}$$

$$(\delta + b) f = (\sigma + b) f_{b+}, \tag{6.217}$$

and

$$(\delta + c - 1) f = (\sigma + c - 2) f_{c-}. \tag{6.218}$$

Using the analysis of §6.6, we find

$$(c - a)(a - 1) f_{a-} = (\sigma + a - 1)[(1 - z)\delta + c - a - bz] f - z^\sigma, \tag{6.219}$$

$$(c - b)(b - 1) f_{b-} = (\sigma + b - 1)[(1 - z)\delta + c - b - az] f - z^\sigma, \tag{6.220}$$

and

$$(c - a)(c - b) z f_{c+} = (\sigma + c - 1)[(1 - z)\delta + z(c - a - b)] f - z^\sigma. \tag{6.221}$$

Equations (6.216) to (6.221) may be rearranged to give

$$\delta f = (\sigma + a) f_{a+} - a f, \tag{6.222}$$

$$\delta f = (\sigma + b) f_{b+} - b f, \tag{6.223}$$

$$\delta f = (\sigma + c - 2) f_{c-} - (c - 1) f, \tag{6.224}$$

$$(\sigma + a - 1)(1 - z)\delta f = (c - a)(a - 1) f_{a-} + (\sigma + a - 1)(a - c + bz) f + z^\sigma, \tag{6.225}$$

$$(\sigma + b - 1)(1 - z)\delta f = (c - b)(b - 1) f_{b-} + (\sigma + b - 1)(b - c + az) f + z^\sigma, \tag{6.226}$$

and

$$(\sigma + c - 1)(1 - z)\delta f = (c - a)(c - b) z f_{c+} + (\sigma + c - 1)(a + b - c) z f + z^\sigma. \tag{6.227}$$

The 15 relations between the six contiguous functions follow from (6.222) to (6.227) on equating any two values of δf. Using (6.196) we find that equations (6.213) and (6.215) to (6.227) hold if the function f_σ is replaced throughout by F_σ.

6.19 Integrals Connected with $f_\sigma(a, b; c; z)$ and $F_\sigma(a, b; c; z)$

A number of indefinite integrals connected with $f_\sigma(a, b; c; z)$ and $F_\sigma(a, b; c; z)$ can be obtained from the differential relations given in §6.18. Other integrals can be obtained by solving the differential equation (6.184) by the method of variation of parameters. We find that

$$f_\sigma(a, b; c; z) = \frac{1}{c-1}\Big[F(a, b; c; z)\int z^{\sigma-1}(1-z)^{a+b-c} \times F(a-c+1, b-c+1; 2-c; z)\,dz - z^{1-c}F(a-c+1, b-c+1; 2-c; z) \times \int z^{\sigma+c-2}(1-z)^{a+b-c}F(a, b; c; z)\,dz\Big]. \qquad (6.228)$$

In a manner similar to that of §6.14, we can show that

$$\int z^{\sigma+c-2}(1-z)^{a+b-c}F(a, b; c; z)\,dz = z^c(1-z)^{a+b-c+1} \times [F(a, b; c; z)f_\sigma'(a, b; c; z) - f_\sigma(a, b; c; z)F'(a, b; c; z)]$$
$$= z^c(1-z)^{a+b-c+1}[(\sigma-1)F(a, b; c; z)f_{\sigma-1}(a+1, b+1; c+1; z) - abc^{-1}f_\sigma(a, b; c; z)F(a+1, b+1; c+1; z)]. \qquad (6.229)$$

In (6.229) we can substitute F_σ for f_σ on the right side, the integral on the left side being indefinite.

The formulas

$$\int_0^1 (1-z)^{\nu-1}f_\sigma(a, b; c; pz)\,dz = \frac{\Gamma(\sigma)\Gamma(\nu)}{\Gamma(\sigma+\nu)}p^{-\nu}f_{\sigma+\nu}(a-\nu, b-\nu; c-\nu; p),$$
$$[\operatorname{Re}\nu > 0,\ \operatorname{Re}\sigma > 0,\ \operatorname{Re}(\sigma+c) > 1,\ |p| < 1] \qquad (6.230)$$

and

$$\int_0^1 z^{c-1}(1-z)^{\nu-1}f_\sigma(a, b, c; pz)dz = \frac{\Gamma(\sigma+c-1)\Gamma(\nu)}{\Gamma(\sigma+c+\nu-1)}f_\sigma(a, b; c+\nu; p)$$
$$[\operatorname{Re}\nu > 0,\ \operatorname{Re}\sigma > 0,\ \operatorname{Re}(\sigma+c) > 1,\ |p| < 1] \qquad (6.231)$$

may be proved by expanding $f_\sigma(a, b, c, pz)$ as a power series in z and integrating term by term.

Similarly, if $\operatorname{Re} \nu > 0$, $\operatorname{Re} c > 1$, and $|p| < 1$,

$$\int_0^1 (1-z)^{\nu-1} F(a, b; c; pz)\, dz = (c-1)p^{-\nu} f_\nu(a-\nu, b-\nu; c-\nu; p). \quad (6.232)$$

The formula

$$\int_0^s z^{\rho-1}(s-z)^{\nu-1} f_\sigma(a, b; c; pz)\, dz = \frac{\Gamma(\rho+\sigma)\Gamma(\nu)}{\sigma(\sigma+c-1)\Gamma(\rho+\sigma+\nu)} p^\sigma s^{\rho+\sigma+\nu-1}$$
$$\times\, {}_4F_3(1, \sigma+a, \sigma+b, \rho+\sigma; \sigma+1, \sigma+c, \rho+\sigma+\nu; ps)$$

$$[\operatorname{Re} \sigma > 0, \operatorname{Re}(\sigma+c) > 1, \operatorname{Re} \nu > 0, \operatorname{Re} \rho > 0, |ps| < 1] \quad (6.233)$$

can be proved by expanding $f_\sigma(a, b; c; pz)$ as a power series in z and integrating term by term.

The Mellin inversion of (6.209) gives

$$\int_0^\infty z^{\rho-1}\left[\frac{f_\sigma(a, b; c; -z)}{(-z)^\sigma}\right] dz$$
$$= \frac{\Gamma(\sigma)\Gamma(\sigma+c-1)\Gamma(\sigma+a-\rho)\Gamma(\sigma+b-\rho)\Gamma(\rho)\Gamma(1-\rho)}{\Gamma(\sigma+a)\Gamma(\sigma+b)\Gamma(\sigma+1-\rho)\Gamma(\sigma+c-\rho)}, \quad (6.234)$$

where $\operatorname{Re} \sigma > 0$, $\operatorname{Re}(\sigma+c) > 1$, $\operatorname{Re}(\sigma+a) > \operatorname{Re} \rho$, $\operatorname{Re}(\sigma+b) > \operatorname{Re} \rho$, and $1 > \operatorname{Re} \rho > 0$.

6.20 The Nonhomogeneous Hypergeometric Function $C_{\rho,\sigma}^{(\tau)}(a, b; c; z)$

We consider, finally, the solution of the nonhomogeneous hypergeometric equation

$$z(1-z)\frac{d^2y}{dz^2} + [c-(a+b+1)z]\frac{dy}{dz} - aby = z^{\sigma-1}(1-\rho z)^{\tau-1}, \quad (6.235)$$

where a, b, c, ρ, σ, and τ are constants. On expanding $(1-\rho z)^{\tau-1}$ as a power series in z, we see, as in §1.12, that a particular integral of (6.235) is $C_{\rho,\sigma}^{(\tau)}(a, b; c; z)$, where

$$C_{\rho,\sigma}^{(\tau)}(a, b; c; z)$$
$$= \sum_{n=0}^\infty \frac{\Gamma(n+1-\tau)\rho^n}{\Gamma(1-\tau)\cdot n!} f_{\sigma+n}(a, b; z)$$
$$= z^\sigma \sum_{m=0}^\infty \sum_{n=0}^\infty \frac{\Gamma(n+1-\tau)\Gamma(\sigma+a+n+m)\Gamma(\sigma+b+n+m) \times \Gamma(\sigma+n)\Gamma(\sigma+c+n-1)\rho^n z^{n+m}}{\Gamma(1-\tau)\Gamma(\sigma+a+n)\Gamma(\sigma+b+n) \times \Gamma(\sigma+n+m+1)\Gamma(\sigma+c+n+m)\cdot n!}.$$
$$(6.236)$$

From (6.214) it is easily verified that the series in (6.236) is convergent if both $|z| < 1$ and $|\rho z| < 1$. On using the power-series expansion of the f functions, we find that (6.236) can be written in the alternative form

$$C_{\rho,\sigma}^{(\tau)}(a, b; c; z) = z^\sigma \sum_{n=0}^{\infty} \frac{\Gamma(\sigma + a + n)\Gamma(\sigma + b + n)\Gamma(\sigma)\Gamma(\sigma + c - 1)}{\Gamma(\sigma + a)\Gamma(\sigma + b)\Gamma(\sigma + n + 1)\Gamma(\sigma + c + n)}$$
$$\times\, {}_3F_{2,(n+1)}[1 - \tau, \sigma, \sigma + c - 1; \sigma + a, \sigma + b; \rho]z^n, \tag{6.237}$$

where ${}_3F_{2,(n+1)}$ stands for the first $n + 1$ terms of the generalized hypergeometric series with the given parameters. For certain values of the parameters, the hypergeometric series can be simplified. Thus

$$C_{\rho,\sigma}^{(1-a-\sigma)}(a, b; c; z) = z^\sigma \sum_{n=0}^{\infty} \frac{\Gamma(\sigma + a + n)\Gamma(\sigma + b + n)\Gamma(\sigma)\Gamma(\sigma + c - 1)}{\Gamma(\sigma + a)\Gamma(\sigma + b)\Gamma(\sigma + n + 1)\Gamma(\sigma + c + n)}$$
$$\times\, {}_2F_{1,(n+1)}[\sigma, \sigma + c - 1; \sigma + b; \rho]z^n. \tag{6.238}$$

From (6.238) and (4.220),

$$\lim_{a\to\infty} \left\{a^\sigma C_{\rho,\sigma}^{(1-a-\sigma)}\left(a, b; c; \frac{x}{a}\right)\right\} = \Lambda_{\rho,\sigma}(b, c; x). \tag{6.239}$$

From (6.189) and (6.236),

$$C_{\rho,\sigma+1-c}^{(\tau)}(a, b; c; z) = z^{1-c} C_{\rho,\sigma}^{(\tau)}(a + 1 - c, b + 1 - c; 2 - c; z). \tag{6.240}$$

We see also that

$$C_{\rho,\sigma}^{(\tau)}(a, b; c; z) = C_{\rho,\sigma}^{(\tau)}(b, a; c; z). \tag{6.241}$$

In (6.235) put $u = (1 - x)^{-a}y$, $z = e^{i\pi}x/(1 - x)$. Then

$$x(1 - x)\frac{d^2u}{dx^2} + [c - (a + c - b + 1)x]\frac{du}{dx} - a(c - b)u$$
$$= e^{i\pi\sigma}x^{\sigma-1}(1 - x)^{1-a-\sigma-\tau}[1 - (1 - \rho)x]^{\tau-1}.$$

On replacing b by $c - b$ in this equation and putting $\tau = 1 - a - \sigma$, we see that the equation

$$x(1 - x)\frac{d^2u}{dx^2} + [c - (a + b + 1)x]\frac{du}{dx} - abu = e^{i\pi\sigma}x^{\sigma-1}[1 - (1 - \rho)x]^{-a-\sigma} \tag{6.242}$$

has a particular integral

$$u = (1 - x)^{-a} C_{\rho,\sigma}^{(1-a-\sigma)}\left(a, c - b; c; \frac{e^{i\pi}x}{1 - x}\right).$$

Now, from (6.235), the general solution of (6.242) is

$$C_1F(a, b; c; x) + C_2x^{1-c}F(a-c+1, b-c+1; 2-c; x) + e^{i\pi\sigma}C_{1-\rho,\sigma}^{(1-a-\sigma)}(a, b; c; x).$$

On comparing the power series (in ascending powers of x) for these two solutions, we find that

$$C_{1-\rho,\sigma}^{(1-a-\sigma)}(a, b; c; x) = e^{-i\pi\sigma}(1-x)^{-a}C_{\rho,\sigma}^{(1-a-\sigma)}\left(a, c-b; c; \frac{e^{i\pi}x}{1-x}\right),$$

or, on writing z instead of x,

$$C_{1-\rho,\sigma}^{(1-a-\sigma)}(a, b; c; z) = e^{-i\pi\sigma}(1-z)^{-a}C_{\rho,\sigma}^{(1-a-\sigma)}\left(a, c-b; c; \frac{e^{i\pi}z}{1-z}\right). \tag{6.243}$$

From (6.236) we see that

$$C_{0,\sigma}^{(\tau)}(a, b; c; z) = f_\sigma(a, b; c; z), \tag{6.244}$$

and, from (6.111) and (6.238),

$$C_{1/2,1}^{(-a)}(a, b; c; z) = 2^{c-1}\frac{\Gamma(b)\Gamma(c-b)}{a\Gamma(c)}[B(a, b; c; z) - \Omega(b, c; 0)F(a, b; c; z)]. \tag{6.245}$$

Equation (6.245) can be written in the alternative form

$$B(a, b; c; z) = \Omega(b, c; 0)F(a, b; c; z) + a\frac{2^{1-c}\Gamma(c)}{\Gamma(b)\Gamma(c-b)} \times \sum_{n=0}^{\infty}\frac{\Gamma(a+1+n)2^{-n}}{\Gamma(a+1)\cdot n!}f_{n+1}(a, b; c; z). \tag{6.246}$$

If $c = \frac{1}{2}$, $C_{1,\sigma}^{(\tau)}(a, b; c; z^2)$ can be expressed in terms of the nonhomogeneous Legendre function $t_{\nu,\sigma}^{\mu,\tau}(z)$, defined in Chapter 7. As will be shown in §7.20,

$$C_{1,\sigma}^{(\tau)}(a, b; \tfrac{1}{2}; z^2) = 4e^{i\pi\varepsilon(1-\tau)}(z^2-1)^{(1-2a-2b)/4}t_{b-a-(1/2),\sigma}^{b+a-(1/2),\tau}(z), \tag{6.247}$$

where $\varepsilon = \operatorname{sgn}(\operatorname{Im} z) = 1, -1$, according as $\operatorname{Im} z >, <0$.

6.21 Recurrence Formulas and Relations Between Contiguous Functions

We shall now derive formulas for $C_{\rho,\sigma}^{(\tau)}(a, b; c; z)$ which are generalizations of the formulas given in §6.18. We see that

$$z^{\sigma-1}(1-\rho z)^{\tau-1} = z^{\sigma-1}(1-\rho z)^{\tau-2} - \rho z^\sigma(1-\rho z)^{\tau-2}. \tag{6.248}$$

The three terms in (6.248) are of the same form as the right side of (6.235). On solving the three corresponding nonhomogeneous equations and expressing their solutions as power series in z, we find

$$C_{\rho,\sigma}^{(\tau)}(a, b; c; z) = C_{\rho,\sigma}^{(\tau-1)}(a, b; c; z) - \rho C_{\rho,\sigma+1}^{(\tau-1)}(a, b; c; z). \quad (6.249)$$

Using (6.249), we see that any function $C_{\rho,\sigma}^{(\tau)}(a, b; c; z)$ can be expressed in terms of $n+1$ functions of the form $C_{\rho,\sigma+m}^{(\tau-n)}(a, b; c; z)$, $m = 0$ to n. Alternatively, we see from (6.249) that any function $C_{\rho,\sigma}^{(\tau)}(a, b; c; z)$ can be expressed in terms of $n + 1$ functions of the form $C_{\rho,\sigma-n}^{\tau+m}(a, b; c; z)$, $m = 0$ to n.

From (6.239) and (6.249), with $\tau = 1 - a - \sigma$,

$$\lim_{a\to\infty} \left\{a^\sigma C_{\rho,\sigma}^{-a-\sigma}\left(a, b; c; \frac{x}{a}\right)\right\} = \Lambda_{\rho,\sigma}(b, c; x).$$

More generally, by repeated application of (6.249), we find that, if n is zero or a positive integer,

$$\lim_{a\to\infty} \left\{a^\sigma C_{\rho,\sigma}^{1-n-a-\sigma}\left(a, b; c; \frac{x}{a}\right)\right\} = \Lambda_{\rho,\sigma}(b, c; x). \quad (6.250)$$

It is easily verified that $y = z^\sigma(1-\rho z)^{\tau+1}$ is a particular solution of the equation

$$z(1 - z)\frac{d^2y}{dz^2} + [c - (a + b + 1)z]\frac{dy}{dz} - aby = z^{\sigma-1}(1 - \rho z)^{\tau-1}$$
$$\times [\sigma(\sigma + c - 1) - \{\sigma(\sigma + 2\rho[\sigma + \tau + c] + a + b) + c\rho(\tau + 1) + ab\}z$$
$$+ \{\sigma(2\sigma + \rho\sigma + \rho + 2 + 2\tau + 2\rho\tau + c\rho + 2a + 2b)$$
$$+ (\rho\tau + c\rho + a + b + 1)(\tau + 1) + 2ab\}\rho z^2$$
$$- \{\sigma^2 + (a + b + 2\tau + 2)\sigma + (\tau + a + 1)(\tau + b + 1)\}\rho^2 z^3]. \quad (6.251)$$

Now the general solution of (6.251) can be written in the form

$$\sigma(\sigma + c - 1)C_{\rho,\sigma}^{(\tau)}(a, b; c; z) - \{\sigma(\sigma + 2\rho[\sigma + \tau + c] + a + b)$$
$$+ c\rho(\tau + 1) + ab\}C_{\rho,\sigma+1}^{(\tau)}(a, b; c; z) + \{\sigma(2\sigma + \rho\sigma + \rho + 2 + 2\tau + 2\rho\tau$$
$$+ c\rho + 2a + 2b) + (\rho\tau + c\rho + a + b + 1)(\tau + 1) + 2ab\}$$
$$\times \rho C_{\rho,\sigma+2}^{(\tau)}(a, b; c; z) - \{\sigma^2 + (a + b + 2\tau + 2)\sigma$$
$$+ (\tau + a + 1)(\tau + b + 1)\}\rho^2 C_{\rho,\sigma+3}^{(\tau)}(a, b; c; z)$$
$$+ C_1 F(a, b; c; z) + C_2 z^{1-c} F(a - c + 1, b - c + 1; 2 - c; z),$$

where C_1 and C_2 are arbitrary constants. On comparing the power series for these two solutions in ascending powers of z, we find that

$$\begin{aligned}
&\sigma(\sigma+c-1)C^{(\tau)}_{\rho,\sigma}(a, b; c; z) - \{\sigma(\sigma+2\rho[\sigma+\tau+c]+a+b) \\
&\quad + c\rho(\tau+1)+ab\}C^{(\tau)}_{\rho,\sigma+1}(a, b; c; z) + \{\sigma(2\sigma+\rho\sigma+\rho+2+2\tau+2\rho\tau \\
&\quad + c\rho+2a+2b)+(\rho\tau+c\rho+a+b+1)(\tau+1)+2ab\} \\
&\quad \times \rho C^{(\tau)}_{\rho,\sigma+2}(a, b; c; z) - \{\sigma^2+(a+b+2\tau+2)\sigma \\
&\quad + (\tau+a+1)(\tau+b+1)\}\rho^2 C^{(\tau)}_{\rho,\sigma+3}(a, b; c; z) = z^\sigma(1-\rho z)^{\tau+1}. \quad (6.252)
\end{aligned}$$

On putting $z = x/a$ and $\tau = -2-a-\sigma$ and using (6.250), we find that as $a \to \infty$, (6.252) reduces to

$$\begin{aligned}
&\sigma(\sigma+c-1)\Lambda_{\rho,\sigma}(b, c; x) + [\rho(2\sigma+c)-\sigma-b]\Lambda_{\rho,\sigma+1}(b, c; x) \\
&\qquad + \rho(\rho-1)\Lambda_{\rho,\sigma+2}(b, c; x) = e^{\rho x}x^\sigma, \quad (6.253)
\end{aligned}$$

in agreement with (4.235).

On differentiating (6.236) and using (6.215), we find that

$$\begin{aligned}
&\frac{d}{dz}C^{(\tau)}_{\varrho,\sigma}(a, b; c; z) \\
&\quad = \sum_{n=0}^{\infty}(\sigma+n-1)\frac{\Gamma(n+1-\tau)\rho^n}{\Gamma(1-\tau)\cdot n!}f_{\sigma+n-1}(a+1, b+1; c+1; z) \\
&\quad = (\sigma-1)\sum_{n=0}^{\infty}\frac{\Gamma(n+1-\tau)\rho^n}{\Gamma(1-\tau)\cdot n!}f_{\sigma+n-1}(a+1, b+1; c+1; z) \\
&\qquad + \rho(1-\tau)\sum_{n=1}^{\infty}\frac{\Gamma(n+1-\tau)\rho^{n-1}}{\Gamma(2-\tau)(n-1)!}f_{\sigma+n-1}(a+1, b+1; c+1; z)
\end{aligned}$$

that is,

$$\begin{aligned}
&\frac{d}{dz}C^{(\tau)}_{\rho,\sigma}(a, b; c; z) = (\sigma-1)C^{(\tau)}_{\rho,\sigma-1}(a+1, b+1; c+1; z) \\
&\qquad + \rho(1-\tau)C^{(\tau-1)}_{\rho,\sigma}(a+1, b+1; c+1; z). \quad (6.254)
\end{aligned}$$

Using (6.216) we find

$$\begin{aligned}
&(\delta+a)C^{(\tau)}_{\rho,\sigma}(a, b; c; z) \\
&\quad = \sum_{n=0}^{\infty}(\sigma+a+n)\frac{\Gamma(n+1-\tau)\rho^n}{\Gamma(1-\tau)\cdot n!}f_{\sigma+n}(a+1, b; c; z) \\
&\quad = (\sigma+a)C^{(\tau)}_{\rho,\sigma}(a+1, b; c; z) + \rho(1-\tau)C^{(\tau-1)}_{\rho,\sigma+1}(a+1, b; c; z), \quad (6.255)
\end{aligned}$$

where $\delta \equiv z\,d/dz$. Similarly,

$$(\delta + b)C_{\rho,\sigma}^{(\tau)}(a, b; c; z) = (\sigma + b)C_{\rho,\sigma}^{(\tau)}(a, b+1; c; z) + \rho(1-\tau)C_{\rho,\sigma+1}^{(\tau-1)}(a, b+1; c; z). \quad (6.256)$$

Using (6.218), we find

$$(\delta + c - 1)C_{\rho,\sigma}^{(\tau)}(a, b; c; z) = \sum_{n=0}^{\infty} (\sigma + c + n - 2)\frac{\Gamma(n+1-\tau)\rho^n}{\Gamma(1-\tau)\cdot n!} f_{\sigma+n}(a, b; c-1; z)$$
$$= (\sigma + c - 2)C_{\rho,\sigma}^{(\tau)}(a, b; c-1; z) + \rho(1-\tau)C_{\rho,\sigma+1}^{(\tau-1)}(a, b; c-1; z). \quad (6.257)$$

6.22 Related Differential Equations

We shall now briefly consider two classes of second-order differential equations, the solution of which can be expressed in terms of $C_{\rho,\sigma}^{(\tau)}(a, b; c; z)$.

In (6.235) put $u = (1-\rho z)^{\alpha} y$, $z = \beta\zeta$, where α and β are constants. Equation (6.235) is then transformed into

$$\zeta(1-\beta\zeta)(1-\rho\beta\zeta)^2 \frac{d^2u}{d\zeta^2} + (1-\rho\beta\zeta)[c + (2\rho\alpha - c\rho - a - b - 1)\beta\zeta + (a+b+1-2\alpha)\rho\beta^2\zeta^2]\frac{du}{d\zeta} + [c\rho\alpha - ab + \{\rho\alpha(\alpha+1-c) + 2ab - (a+b+1)\alpha\}\rho\beta\zeta - (\alpha-a)(\alpha-b)\rho^2\beta^2\zeta^2]\beta u = \beta^{\sigma}\zeta^{\sigma-1}(1-\rho\beta\zeta)^{\tau+\alpha+1}. \quad (6.258)$$

A particular integral of (6.258) is $u = (1-\rho\beta\zeta)^{\alpha} C_{\rho,\sigma}^{(\tau)}(a, b; c; \beta\zeta)$. The complementary function is

$$C_1(1-\rho\beta\zeta)^{\alpha}F(a, b; c; \beta\zeta) + C_2\zeta^{1-c}(1-\rho\beta\zeta)^{\alpha}F(a-c+1, b-c+1; 2-c; \beta\zeta).$$

Some special cases of this transformation are of interest. If $\alpha = -1$, (6.258) becomes

$$\zeta(1-\beta\zeta)(1-\rho\beta\zeta)\frac{d^2u}{d\zeta^2} + [c - (2\rho + c\rho + a + b + 1)\beta\zeta + (a+b+3)\rho\beta^2\zeta^2]\frac{du}{d\zeta} - [c\rho + ab - (1+a)(1+b)\rho\beta\zeta]\beta u = \beta^{\sigma}\zeta^{\sigma-1}(1-\rho\beta\zeta)^{\tau-1}, \quad (6.259)$$

with a particular integral $u = (1 - \rho\beta\zeta)^{-1}C_{\rho,\sigma}^{(\tau)}(a, b; c; \beta\zeta)$. If $\alpha = a$, (6.258) becomes

$$\zeta(1-\beta\zeta)(1-\rho\beta\zeta)^2\frac{d^2u}{d\zeta^2} + (1-\rho\beta\zeta)[c + (2\rho a - c\rho - a - b - 1)\beta\zeta + (b + 1 - a)\rho\beta^2\zeta^2]\frac{du}{d\zeta} + [ac\rho - ab + \{\rho a(a + 1 - c) + (b - a - 1)a\}\rho\beta\zeta]\beta u = \beta^\sigma\zeta^{\sigma-1}(1-\rho\beta\zeta)^{\tau+a+1}, \tag{6.260}$$

with a particular integral $u = (1-\rho\beta\zeta)^a C_{\rho,\sigma}^{(\tau)}(a, b; c; \beta\zeta)$.

The second class of related differential equations is obtained by putting $u = z^\alpha(1-z)^\gamma y$ in (6.235) and letting

$$\begin{aligned} a &= \alpha + \beta + \gamma, \\ b &= \alpha + \beta' + \gamma, \\ c &= 1 + \alpha - \alpha', \end{aligned} \tag{6.261}$$

and

$$c - b = \alpha + \beta + \gamma'.$$

We note that

$$\alpha + \alpha' + \beta + \beta' + \gamma + \gamma' = 1. \tag{6.262}$$

The resulting differential equation is

$$z^2(1-z)^2\frac{d^2u}{dz^2} - z(1-z)\{(\alpha + \alpha' - 1) + (\beta + \beta' + 1)z\}\frac{du}{dz} + \{\alpha\alpha' - (\alpha\alpha' + \beta\beta' - \gamma\gamma')z + \beta\beta' z^2\}u = z^{\alpha+\sigma}(1-z)^{\gamma+1}(1-\rho z)^{\tau-1};$$

that is, using (6.262),

$$\frac{d^2u}{dz^2} + \left\{\frac{1-\alpha-\alpha'}{z} + \frac{1-\gamma-\gamma'}{z-1}\right\}\frac{du}{dz} + \left\{-\frac{\alpha\alpha'}{z} + \frac{\gamma\gamma'}{z-1} + \beta\beta'\right\}\frac{u}{z(z-1)} = z^{\alpha+\sigma-2}(1-z)^{\gamma-1}(1-\rho z)^{\tau-1} \tag{6.263}$$

with a particular integral $u = z^\alpha(1-z)^\gamma C_{\rho,\sigma}^{(\tau)}(a, b; c; z)$, where a, b, and c are given by (6.261). The complementary function is

$$C_1 z^\alpha(1-z)^\gamma F(a, b; c; z) + C_2 z^{\alpha+1-c}(1-z)^\gamma F(a - c + 1, b - c + 1; 2 - c; z).$$

We see that (6.263) has regular singularities at $z = 0$, 1, and at infinity.

Making the substitution

$$z = \frac{w - w_1}{w - w_2}\,\frac{w_3 - w_2}{w_3 - w_1},$$

that is, (6.264)

$$w = \frac{w_2(w_1 - w_3)z - w_1(w_2 - w_3)}{(w_1 - w_3)z - (w_2 - w_3)},$$

where w_1, w_2, and w_3 are constants, (6.263) becomes

$$\frac{d^2u}{dw^2} + \left\{\frac{1-\alpha-\alpha'}{w - w_1} + \frac{1-\beta-\beta'}{w - w_2} + \frac{1-\gamma-\gamma'}{w - w_3}\right\}\frac{du}{dw} + \left\{\frac{\alpha\alpha'(w_1 - w_2)(w_1 - w_3)}{w - w_1}\right.$$

$$\left. + \frac{\beta\beta'(w_2 - w_1)(w_2 - w_3)}{w - w_2} + \frac{\gamma\gamma'(w_3 - w_1)(w_3 - w_2)}{w - w_3}\right\}$$

$$\times \frac{u}{(w - w_1)(w - w_2)(w - w_3)} = k^{\tau-1}\frac{(w_3 - w_2)^{\alpha+\sigma}(w_2 - w_1)^{\gamma+1}}{(w_3 - w_1)^{\alpha+\gamma+\sigma-1}}$$

$$\times \frac{(w - w_0)^{\tau-1}(w - w_1)^{\alpha+\sigma-2}(w - w_3)^{\gamma-1}}{(w - w_2)^{\alpha+\gamma+\sigma+\tau}}, \qquad (6.265)$$

where

$$w_0 = \frac{w_2(w_1 - w_3) - w_1(w_2 - w_3)\rho}{w_1 - w_3 - (w_2 - w_3)\rho};$$

that is,

$$\rho = \frac{(w_0 - w_2)(w_3 - w_1)}{(w_0 - w_1)(w_3 - w_2)} \qquad (6.266)$$

and

$$k = 1 - \rho\,\frac{w_3 - w_2}{w_3 - w_1} = \frac{w_2 - w_1}{w_0 - w_1}.$$

Equation (6.265) has a particular integral

$$u = \frac{(w_3 - w_2)^{\alpha}(w_2 - w_1)^{\gamma}}{(w_3 - w_1)^{\alpha+\gamma}}\,\frac{(w - w_1)^{\alpha}(w - w_3)^{\gamma}}{(w - w_2)^{\alpha+\gamma}}\,C^{(\tau)}_{\rho,\sigma}(a, b; c; z),$$

where z is given by (6.264), ρ by (6.266), and α, α', etc., satisfy (6.262).

Thus the equation

$$\frac{d^2u}{dw^2}+\left\{\frac{1-\alpha-\alpha'}{w-w_1}+\frac{1-\beta-\beta'}{w-w_2}+\frac{1-\gamma-\gamma'}{w-w_3}\right\}\frac{du}{dw}+\left\{\frac{\alpha\alpha'(w_1-w_2)(w_1-w_3)}{w-w_1}\right.$$
$$\left.+\frac{\beta\beta'(w_2-w_1)(w_2-w_3)}{w-w_2}+\frac{\gamma\gamma'(w_3-w_1)(w_3-w_2)}{w-w_3}\right\}$$
$$\times\frac{u}{(w-w_1)(w-w_2)(w-w_3)}=\frac{(w-w_0)^{\tau-1}(w-w_1)^{\alpha+\sigma-2}(w-w_3)^{\gamma-1}}{(w-w_2)^{\alpha+\gamma+\sigma+\tau}} \tag{6.267}$$

has a particular integral

$$u=k^{1-\tau}\frac{(w_3-w_1)^{\sigma-1}}{(w_3-w_2)^{\sigma}(w_2-w_1)}\frac{(w-w_1)^{\alpha}(w-w_3)^{\gamma}}{(w-w_2)^{\alpha+\gamma}}C^{(\tau)}_{\rho,\sigma}(a,b;c;z),$$

where z is given by (6.264), ρ by (6.266), and α, α', etc., satisfy (2.262).

Letting $w_2\to\infty$, from (6.264),

$$z=\frac{w-w_1}{w_3-w_1},$$

that is, (6.268)

$$w=(w_3-w_1)z+w_1,$$

we see, from (6.263) that the equation

$$\frac{d^2u}{dw^2}+\left\{\frac{1-\alpha-\alpha'}{w-w_1}+\frac{1-\gamma-\gamma'}{w-w_3}\right\}\frac{du}{dw}+\left\{-\frac{\alpha\alpha'(w_3-w_1)}{w-w_1}+\frac{\gamma\gamma'(w_3-w_1)}{w-w_3}+\beta\beta'\right\}$$
$$\times\frac{u}{(w-w_1)(w-w_3)}=\rho^{\tau-1}\frac{(w_0-w)^{\tau-1}(w-w_1)^{\alpha+\sigma-2}(w_3-w)^{\gamma-1}}{(w_3-w_1)^{\sigma+\tau-2}}, \tag{6.269}$$

where

$$w_0=w_1+\frac{w_3-w_1}{\rho},$$

has a particular integral $u=(w-w_1)^{\alpha}(w_3-w)^{\gamma}C^{(\tau)}_{\rho,\sigma}(a,b;c;z)$, where z is given by (6.264) and α, α', etc., satisfy (6.262). In particular, if $w_1=0$ and $w_3=K$ (a constant), we see from (6.269) that the equation

$$w(K-w)\frac{d^2u}{dw^2}+\{(1-\alpha-\alpha')K-(1+\beta+\beta')w\}\frac{du}{dw}$$
$$+\left\{\frac{\alpha\alpha'K}{w}+\frac{\gamma\gamma'K}{K-w}-\beta\beta'\right\}u=K^{2-\sigma-\tau}w^{\alpha+\sigma-1}(K-w)^{\gamma}(K-\rho w)^{\tau-1} \tag{6.270}$$

has a particular integral $u = w^{\alpha}(K-w)^{\gamma}C_{\rho,\sigma}^{(\tau)}(a, b; c; w/K)$, where a, b, and c are given by (6.261) and α, α', etc., satisfy (6.262).

Putting $w = \zeta^{\varepsilon}$ in (6.270), where ε is a constant, we see that the equation

$$\zeta(K-\zeta^{\varepsilon})\frac{d^2u}{d\zeta^2} + \{(1-[\alpha+\alpha']\varepsilon)K - (1+[\beta+\beta']\varepsilon)\zeta^{\varepsilon}\}\frac{du}{d\zeta}$$

$$+\left\{\frac{\alpha\alpha' K}{\zeta} + \frac{\gamma\gamma' K\zeta^{\varepsilon-1}}{K-\zeta^{\varepsilon}} - \beta\beta'\zeta^{\varepsilon-1}\right\}\varepsilon^2 u$$

$$= \varepsilon^2 K^{2-\sigma-\tau}\zeta^{\alpha\varepsilon+\sigma\varepsilon-1}(K-\zeta^{\varepsilon})^{\gamma}(K-\rho\zeta^{\varepsilon})^{\tau-1} \qquad (6.271)$$

has a particular integral $u = \zeta^{\alpha\varepsilon}(K-\zeta^{\varepsilon})^{\gamma}C_{\rho,\sigma}^{(\tau)}(a, b; c; \zeta^{\varepsilon}/K)$. Thus, if $K = 1$ and $\varepsilon = 2$, the equation

$$(1-\zeta^2)\frac{d^2u}{d\zeta^2} + \left\{\frac{1-2\alpha-2\alpha'}{\zeta} - (1+2\beta+2\beta')\zeta\right\}\frac{du}{d\zeta} + 4\left\{\frac{\alpha\alpha'}{\zeta^2} + \frac{\gamma\gamma'}{1-\zeta^2} - \beta\beta'\right\}u$$

$$= 4\zeta^{2\alpha+2\sigma-2}(1-\zeta^2)^{\gamma}(1-\rho\zeta^2)^{\tau-1} \qquad (6.272)$$

has a particular integral $u = \zeta^{2\alpha}(1-\zeta^2)^{\gamma}C_{\rho,\sigma}^{(\tau)}(a, b; c; \zeta^2)$. In particular, putting $\alpha = 0$, $\alpha' = \frac{1}{2}$, $\beta = \frac{1}{2}(\nu+1)$, $\beta' = -\frac{1}{2}\nu$, $\gamma = \frac{1}{2}\mu$, and $\gamma' = -\frac{1}{2}\mu$, we see that the equation

$$(1-\zeta^2)\frac{d^2u}{d\zeta^2} - 2\zeta\frac{du}{d\zeta} + \{\nu(\nu+1) - \mu^2(1-\zeta^2)^{-1}\}u$$

$$= 4\zeta^{2\sigma-2}(1-\zeta^2)^{(1/2)\mu}(1-\rho\zeta^2)^{\tau-1} \qquad (6.273)$$

has a particular integral

$$u = (1-\zeta^2)^{(1/2)\mu}C_{\rho,\sigma}^{(\tau)}(\tfrac{1}{2}\mu+\tfrac{1}{2}\nu+\tfrac{1}{2}, \tfrac{1}{2}\mu-\tfrac{1}{2}\nu; \tfrac{1}{2}; \zeta^2).$$

If $w_1 = -1$ and $w_3 = 1$, we see from (6.269) that the equation

$$(1-w^2)\frac{d^2u}{dw^2} + \{\gamma+\gamma'-\alpha-\alpha'-(1+\beta+\beta')w\}\frac{du}{dw}$$

$$+\left\{\frac{2\alpha\alpha'}{1+w} + \frac{2\gamma\gamma'}{1-w} - \beta\beta'\right\}u$$

$$= -2^{1-\sigma}[1-\tfrac{1}{2}\rho(1+w)]^{\tau-1}(1+w)^{\alpha+\sigma-1}(1-w)^{\gamma} \qquad (6.274)$$

has a particular integral $u = (1+w)^{\alpha}(1-w)^{\gamma}C_{\rho,\sigma}^{(\tau)}[a, b; c; \frac{1}{2}(1+w)]$, where a, b, and c are given by (6.261) and α, α', etc., satisfy (6.262).

In particular, putting $\alpha = \gamma = \frac{1}{2}\mu$, $\alpha' = \gamma' = -\frac{1}{2}\mu$, $\beta = \nu+1$, and $\beta' = -\nu$, we see that the equation

$$(1-w^2)\frac{d^2u}{dw^2} - 2w\frac{du}{dw} + \{\nu(\nu+1) - \mu^2(1-w^2)^{-1}\}u$$
$$= -2^{1-\sigma}[1-\tfrac{1}{2}\rho(1+w)]^{\tau-1}(1+w)^{(1/2)\mu+\sigma-1}(1-w)^{(1/2)\mu} \quad (6.275)$$

has a particular integral

$$u = (1+w)^{(1/2)\mu}(1-w)^{(1/2)\mu}C_{\rho,\sigma}^{(\tau)}[\mu+\nu+1, \mu-\nu; \mu+1; \tfrac{1}{2}(1+w)].$$

Again, letting $w_1 \to \infty$, from (6.264),

$$z = \frac{w_3 - w_2}{w - w_2},$$

that is, (6.276)

$$w = w_2 + \frac{w_3 - w_2}{z},$$

we see from (6.263) that the equation

$$\frac{d^2u}{dw^2} + \left\{\frac{1-\beta-\beta'}{w-w_2} + \frac{1-\gamma-\gamma'}{w-w_3}\right\}\frac{du}{dw} + \left\{\alpha\alpha' - \frac{\beta\beta'(w_3-w_2)}{w-w_2} + \frac{\gamma\gamma'(w_3-w_2)}{w-w_3}\right\}$$
$$\times \frac{u}{(w-w_2)(w-w_3)} = \frac{(w_3-w_2)^\sigma(w-w_0)^{\tau-1}(w-w_3)^{\gamma-1}}{(w-w_2)^{\alpha+\gamma+\sigma+\tau}}, \quad (6.277)$$

where $w_0 = w_2 + (w_3 - w_2)\rho$, has a particular integral

$$u = \frac{(w-w_3)^\gamma}{(w-w_2)^{\alpha+\gamma}}\, C_{\rho,\sigma}^{(\tau)}(a, b; c; z),$$

where z is given by (6.276) and α, α', etc., satisfy (6.262). If $w_2 = -1$ and $w_3 = 1$, we see from (6.277), that the equation

$$(1-w^2)\frac{d^2u}{dw^2} + \{\gamma+\gamma'-\beta-\beta'-(1+\alpha+\alpha')w\}\frac{du}{dw}$$
$$+\left\{-\alpha\alpha' + \frac{2\beta\beta'}{1+w} + \frac{2\gamma\gamma'}{1-w}\right\}u$$
$$= -2^\sigma(w+1-2\rho)^{\tau-1}(w+1)^{1-\alpha-\gamma-\sigma-\tau}(w-1)^\gamma \quad (6.278)$$

has a particular integral

$$u = (w+1)^{-\alpha-\gamma}(w-1)^\gamma C_{\rho,\sigma}^{(\tau)}\left(a, b; c; \frac{2}{1+w}\right),$$

where a, b, and c are given by (6.261) and α, α', etc., satisfy (6.262).

In particular, putting $\alpha = \nu + 1$, $\alpha' = -\nu$, $\beta = \gamma = \frac{1}{2}\mu$, and $\beta' = \gamma' = -\frac{1}{2}\mu$, we see that the equation

$$(1 - w^2)\frac{d^2u}{dw^2} - 2w\frac{du}{dw} + \{\nu(\nu + 1) - \mu^2(1 - w^2)^{-1}\}u$$
$$= -2^{\sigma}(w + 1 - 2\rho)^{\tau-1}(w + 1)^{-(1/2)\mu-\nu-\sigma-\tau}(w - 1)^{(1/2)\mu} \quad (6.279)$$

has a particular integral

$$u = (w + 1)^{-(1/2)\mu-\nu-1}(w - 1)^{(1/2)\mu}C_{\rho,\sigma}^{(\tau)}\left(\mu + \nu + 1, \nu + 1; 2\nu + 2; \frac{2}{1 + w}\right).$$

Equations (6.267), (6.273), (6.275), and (6.279) are nonhomogeneous equations, the first of which corresponds to Riemann's equation and the others to Legendre's equation. These equations will be dealt with in Chapter 7.

PROBLEMS

1. Show that, if $\operatorname{Re} c > \operatorname{Re} b > 0$,

$$F(a, b; c; z) = \Gamma(c)[\Gamma(b)\Gamma(c - b)]^{-1} \int_0^1 f\, dt$$

and

$$B(a, b; c; z) = \Gamma(c)[\Gamma(b)\Gamma(c - b)]^{-1}\left[\int_{1/2}^1 f\, dt - \int_0^{1/2} f\, dt\right],$$

where

$$f = t^{b-1}(1 - t)^{c-b-1}(1 - tz)^{-a}.$$

Hence show that

$$\lim_{a\to\infty} B\left(a, b; c; \frac{x}{a}\right) = \Omega(b, c; x).$$

2. Obtain the power series for $B(a, b; c; z)$ by using the result of Problem 1 and expanding $(1 - tz)^{-a}$ in a binomial series.

3. Use the result of Problem 1 to show that

$$\frac{dB(a, b; c; z)}{dz} = \frac{ab}{c} B(a + 1, b + 1; c + 1; z).$$

4. Verify the relations between functions contiguous to $B(a, b; c; z)$ by comparing coefficients of like powers of z.

5. By repeated applications of the relations between contiguous functions, prove that, if l, m, and n are integers, $B(a+l, b+m; c+n; z)$ can be expressed as a linear combination of $B(a, b; c; z)$ and one of its contiguous functions, with coefficients which are rational functions of a, b, c, z (provided that neither c nor $c+n$ are zero or negative integers).

6. Use the result of Problem 1 to show that

$$B(a+1, b; c; z) = B(a, b; c; z) + bc^{-1}zB(a+1, b+1; c+1; z).$$

7. Prove that

$$\frac{d}{dz}[z^{c-1}B(a, b; c; z)]$$
$$= (c-1)z^{c-2}\left[B(a, b; c-1; z) - \frac{2^{2-c}\Gamma(c-1)}{\Gamma(b)\Gamma(c-b)}(1-\tfrac{1}{2}z)^{-a}\right].$$

8. Prove that

$$\frac{d}{dz}[(1-z)^{a+b-c}B(a, b; c; z)]$$
$$= (1-z)^{a+b-c-1}\left[\frac{(c-a)(c-b)}{c}B(a, b; c+1; z) + \frac{2^{1-c}\Gamma(c)}{\Gamma(b)\Gamma(c-b)}(1-\tfrac{1}{2}z)^{-a}\right].$$

9. Prove that

$$B(a, b; c; 1) = \frac{(c-a)(c-b)}{c(c-a-b)}B(a, b; c+1; 1) + \frac{2^{1-c+a}\Gamma(c)}{(c-a-b)\Gamma(b)\Gamma(c-b)}.$$

10. Prove that

$$\lim_{m\to\infty} B(a, b; c+m; 1) = -1.$$

11. Prove that

$$(a+1)F(-a, 1; b+2; -1) + (b+1)F(-b, 1; a+2; -1)$$
$$= 2^{a+b+1}(a+1)(b+1)B(a+1, b+1)$$

and

$$(a+1)B(-a, 1; b+2; -1) + (b+1)B(-b, 1; a+2; -1)$$
$$= 2^{a+b+1}(a+1)(b+1)[2B_{1/4}(a+1, b+1) + 2B_{1/4}(b+1, a+1) - B(a+1, b+1)].$$

12. Derive the series solution for $B(a, b; c; z)$ (a) from the result of Problem 3, and (b) directly from the differential equation.

13. Show that $B(a, b; c; z) \equiv B(b, a; c; z)$ only if $a = b$.

14. Show that

$$\int zB(a+1, b+1; c+1; z)\,dz = \frac{cz}{(a-1)b} B(a, b; c; z) - \frac{c(c-1)}{a(a-1)b(b-1)} B(a, b-1; c-1; z).$$

15. The generalized hypergeometric function ${}_3F_2(a_1, a_2, a_3; b_1, b_2; z)$ satisfies the differential equation

$$\{\delta(\delta + b_1 - 1)(\delta + b_2 - 1) - z(\delta + a_1)(\delta + a_2)(\delta + a_3)\}u = 0,$$

where $\delta \equiv z d/dz$. Show that $z^{-\sigma} f_\sigma(a, b; c; z)$ satisfies a third-order differential equation of this form. Hence derive an expression for $f_\sigma(a, b, c; z)$ in terms of the generalized hypergeometric function ${}_3F_2$.

16. Determine the validity of the series solution (6.196) for $F_\sigma(a, b; c; z)$ if $\sigma + a$ or $\sigma + b$ is a positive integer.

17. Verify that $y = -1/ab$ is a particular solution of the differential equation satisfied by $f_1(a, b; c; z)$.

18. Determine the form of $f(z)$ so that $y = z^\sigma$ is a particular solution of the differential equation

$$z(1-z)\frac{d^2y}{dz^2} + [c - (a+b+1)z]\frac{dy}{dz} - aby = f(z).$$

Hence show that

$$(\sigma + a)(\sigma + b) f_{\sigma+1}(a, b; c; z) = \sigma(\sigma + c - 1) f_\sigma(a, b; c; z) - z^\sigma.$$

Verify that the relation holds if f is replaced throughout by F.

19. Determine the contiguity relations for $F_\sigma(a, b; c; z)$ directly from the power series.

20. By comparing coefficients of powers of z, show that

$$B(a, b; c; z) = \Omega(b, c; 0)F(a, b; c; z) + a\frac{2^{1-c}\Gamma(c)}{\Gamma(b)\Gamma(c-b)} \times \sum_{n=0}^{\infty} \frac{\Gamma(a+1+n)2^{-n}}{\Gamma(a+1)\cdot n!} f_{n+1}(a, b; c; z).$$

21. Use the substitution $u = y^{1-k}$ to show that the solution of the nonlinear differential equation

$$y\frac{d^2y}{dz^2} = k\left(\frac{dy}{dz}\right)^2 + \frac{1}{z(1-z)} \times \left[\{(a+b+1)z - c\}y\frac{dy}{dz} + \frac{ab}{1-k}y^2 + \frac{z^{\sigma-1}y^{k+1}}{1-k}\right]$$

is

$$y = [C_1F(a, b; c; z) + C_2z^{1-c}F(a-c+1, b-c+1; 2-c; z) + F_\sigma(a, b; c; z)]^{1/(1-k)},$$

where C_1 and C_2 are arbitrary constants.

CHAPTER 7

Nonhomogeneous Riemann and Legendre Functions

7.1 Introduction

In Chapter 6 the properties of solutions of certain nonhomogeneous linear differential equations were considered, the equations having as their associated homogeneous equation the hypergeometric equation

$$z(1-z)\frac{d^2y}{dz^2}+[c-(a+b+1)z]\frac{dy}{dz}-aby=0, \tag{7.1}$$

where a, b, and c are constants.

We now briefly consider the properties of certain nonhomogeneous equations which have as their associated homogeneous equation Riemann's equation,

$$\begin{aligned}\frac{d^2u}{dw^2}&+\left\{\frac{1-\alpha-\alpha'}{w-w_1}+\frac{1-\beta-\beta'}{w-w_2}+\frac{1-\gamma-\gamma'}{w-w_3}\right\}\frac{du}{dw}+\left\{\frac{\alpha\alpha'(w_1-w_2)(w_1-w_3)}{w-w_1}\right.\\&\left.+\frac{\beta\beta'(w_2-w_1)(w_2-w_3)}{w-w_2}+\frac{\gamma\gamma'(w_3-w_1)(w_3-w_2)}{w-w_3}\right\}\\&\times\frac{u}{(w-w_1)(w-w_2)(w-w_3)}=0,\end{aligned} \tag{7.2}$$

where w_1, w_2, w_3, α, α', β, β', γ, and γ' are constants and

$$\alpha+\alpha'+\beta+\beta'+\gamma+\gamma'=1. \tag{7.3}$$

For conciseness we shall sometimes write (7.2) in the alternative form

$$p_w\begin{pmatrix}w_1 & w_2 & w_3\\ \alpha & \beta & \gamma\\ \alpha' & \beta' & \gamma'\end{pmatrix}u=0, \tag{7.4}$$

where p_w is a *differential operator* with the given parameters. The symbol

$$P\begin{Bmatrix}w_1 & w_2 & w_3\\ \alpha & \beta & \gamma & w\\ \alpha' & \beta' & \gamma'\end{Bmatrix} \tag{7.5}$$

is used to denote the complete set of solutions of (7.2).

In §7.2 we summarize various properties of Riemann's equation and the Riemann P function. In §§7.3 and 7.4 we consider the properties of the solutions of the equation

$$P_w\begin{pmatrix} w_1 & w_2 & w_3 \\ \alpha & \beta & \gamma \\ \alpha' & \beta' & \gamma' \end{pmatrix} u = \frac{(w-w_0)^{\tau-1}(w-w_1)^{\alpha+\sigma-2}(w-w_3)^{\gamma-1}}{(w-w_2)^{\alpha+\gamma+\sigma+\tau}}, \tag{7.6}$$

where w_0, σ, and τ are constants.

In §§7.6 to 7.15 we consider in detail a particular case of (7.6)—the nonhomogeneous Legendre equation

$$(1-z^2)\frac{d^2y}{dz^2} - 2z\frac{dy}{dz} + [\nu(\nu+1) - \mu^2(1-z^2)^{-1}]y$$
$$= -e^{i\pi\mu}\frac{2^{-\nu}\Gamma(\mu+\nu+2)}{\Gamma(\nu+1)} z^{-\mu-\nu-2}(z^2-1)^{(1/2)\mu}, \tag{7.7}$$

having as a particular integral the nonhomogeneous Legendre function $R_\nu^\mu(z)$ defined in §7.6. $R_\nu^\mu(z)$ bears the same relation to the nonhomogeneous hypergeometric function $B(a, b; c; z)$ (defined in Chapter 6) as the Legendre function of the second kind $Q_\nu^\mu(z)$ does to the hypergeometric function $F(a, b; c; z)$.

In §§7.16 to 7.22 we discuss the properties of the nonhomogeneous Legendre functions $s_{\nu,\sigma}^\mu(z)$ and $S_{\nu,\sigma}^\mu(z)$ which satisfy the equation

$$(1-z^2)\frac{d^2y}{dz^2} - 2z\frac{dy}{dz} + [\nu(\nu+1) - \mu^2(1-z^2)^{-1}]y = z^{2\sigma-2}(z^2-1)^{(1/2)\mu} \tag{7.8}$$

and the function $t_{\nu,\sigma}^{\mu,\tau}(z)$ which satisfies the equation

$$(1-z^2)\frac{d^2y}{dz^2} - 2z\frac{dy}{dz} + [\nu(\nu+1) - \mu^2(1-z^2)^{-1}]y$$
$$= z^{2\sigma-2}(z^2-1)^{(1/2)\mu+\tau-1}. \tag{7.9}$$

As will be shown in Chapter 11 these functions are related to the solutions of Poisson's equation in terms of spherical polar coordinates.

7.2 Riemann's Equation and Riemann's *P* Function

Riemann's equation (7.2) and the properties of the Riemann P functions (7.4) which satisfy it are fully set out in Poole [1936], Whittaker and Watson [1935], and Erdélyi [1953a]. We shall here briefly summarize these results.

Riemann's equation (7.2) is a homogeneous linear differential equation of second order with three, and only three, singularities, at w_1, w_2, and w_3.

These singularities are regular and thus the equation is of the Fuchsian class (see §1.11). When the power-series solution is obtained in the form

$$u = (w - w_1)^c\{a_0 + a_1(w - w_1) + a_2(w - w_1)^2 + \cdots\}, \qquad (7.10)$$

the roots of the indicial equation are α and α'. α and α' are called the *exponents* belonging to $w = w_1$; similarly, β and β' are the exponents for $w = w_2$ and γ and γ' are the exponents for $w = w_3$. From (7.3), the sum of the six exponents is unity. If one or more of the exponent differences $\alpha - \alpha'$, $\beta - \beta'$, and $\gamma - \gamma'$ are integers, then one or more of the series (7.10) may involve logarithmic terms.

From (7.2) and (7.5) we see that the meaning of the P symbol is unaltered if the first three columns are interchanged in any manner, or if the two exponents (α, α'), or (β, β') or (γ, γ'), are interchanged. Also, as shown in the above references,

$$\left(\frac{w - w_1}{w - w_2}\right)^r \left(\frac{w - w_3}{w - w_2}\right)^s P\begin{Bmatrix} w_1 & w_2 & w_3 & \\ \alpha & \beta & \gamma & w \\ \alpha' & \beta' & \gamma' & \end{Bmatrix} = P\begin{Bmatrix} w_1 & w_2 & w_3 & \\ \alpha + r & \beta - r - s & \gamma + s & w \\ \alpha' + r & \beta' - r - s & \gamma' + s & \end{Bmatrix} \qquad (7.11)$$

and

$$P\begin{Bmatrix} z_1 & z_2 & z_3 & \\ \alpha & \beta & \gamma & z \\ \alpha' & \beta' & \gamma' & \end{Bmatrix} = P\begin{Bmatrix} w_1 & w_2 & w_3 & \\ \alpha & \beta & \gamma & w \\ \alpha' & \beta' & \gamma' & \end{Bmatrix}, \qquad (7.12)$$

where r and s are constants and

$$z = \frac{Aw + B}{Cw + D}, \quad z_n = \frac{Aw_n + B}{Cw_n + D} \quad (n = 1 \text{ to } 3), \qquad (7.13)$$

A, B, C, and D being arbitrary constants such that $AD - BC \neq 0$.

From (7.11) and (7.12),

$$P\begin{Bmatrix} w_1 & w_2 & w_3 & \\ \alpha & \beta & \gamma & w \\ \alpha' & \beta' & \gamma' & \end{Bmatrix} = \left(\frac{w - w_1}{w - w_2}\right)^\alpha \left(\frac{w - w_3}{w - w_2}\right)^\gamma$$

$$\times P\begin{Bmatrix} 0 & \infty & 1 & \\ 0 & \alpha + \beta + \gamma & 0 & \dfrac{(w - w_1)(w_3 - w_2)}{(w - w_2)(w_3 - w_1)} \\ \alpha' - \alpha & \alpha + \beta' + \gamma & \gamma' - \gamma & \end{Bmatrix}. \qquad (7.14)$$

Now, from (7.1), (7.2), and (7.5), we see that the complete set of solutions of the hypergeometric equation is defined by

$$P\begin{Bmatrix} 0 & \infty & 1 & \\ 0 & a & 0 & z \\ 1 - c & b & c - a - b & \end{Bmatrix}; \qquad (7.15)$$

thus, from (7.14) and (7.15), the solution of Riemann's equation (7.2) can always be expressed in terms of that of the hypergeometric equation (7.1).

7.3 The Nonhomogeneous Riemann Equation and the Differential Operator p

We consider next the nonhomogeneous equation (7.6), which has Riemann's equation (7.2) as its associated homogeneous equation. As stated in §7.1, it is convenient to use the differential operator p, where

$$p_w\begin{pmatrix} w_1 & w_2 & w_3 \\ \alpha & \beta & \gamma \\ \alpha' & \beta' & \gamma' \end{pmatrix} u \equiv \frac{d^2u}{dw^2} + \left\{\frac{1-\alpha-\alpha'}{w-w_1} + \frac{1-\beta-\beta'}{w-w_2} + \frac{1-\gamma-\gamma'}{w-w_3}\right\}\frac{du}{dw}$$
$$+ \left\{\frac{\alpha\alpha'(w_1-w_2)(w_1-w_3)}{w-w_1} + \frac{\beta\beta'(w_2-w_1)(w_2-w_3)}{w-w_2}\right.$$
$$\left. + \frac{\gamma\gamma'(w_3-w_1)(w_3-w_2)}{w-w_3}\right\}\frac{u}{(w-w_1)(w-w_2)(w-w_3)} \tag{7.16}$$

and

$$\alpha + \alpha' + \beta + \beta' + \gamma + \gamma' = 1. \tag{7.17}$$

We see that the operator p is unaltered if any of its three columns are interchanged in any manner, or if the two exponents (α, α'), or (β, β') or (γ, γ'), are interchanged.

By analogy with the properties of the P function given in §7.2, we find that

$$p_w\begin{pmatrix} w_1 & w_2 & w_3 \\ \alpha & \beta & \gamma \\ \alpha' & \beta' & \gamma' \end{pmatrix}\left[\left(\frac{w-w_1}{w-w_2}\right)^{-r}\left(\frac{w-w_3}{w-w_2}\right)^{-s} y\right]$$
$$= \left(\frac{w-w_1}{w-w_2}\right)^{-r}\left(\frac{w-w_3}{w-w_2}\right)^{-s} p_w\begin{pmatrix} w_1 & w_2 & w_3 \\ \alpha+r & \beta-r-s & \gamma+s \\ \alpha'+r & \beta'-r-s & \gamma'+s \end{pmatrix} y \tag{7.18}$$

and

$$p_z\begin{pmatrix} z_1 & z_2 & z_3 \\ \alpha & \beta & \gamma \\ \alpha' & \beta' & \gamma' \end{pmatrix} y = \left(\frac{dw}{dz}\right)^2 p_w\begin{pmatrix} w_1 & w_2 & w_3 \\ \alpha & \beta & \gamma \\ \alpha' & \beta' & \gamma' \end{pmatrix} y$$
$$= \frac{(Cw+D)^4}{(AD-BC)^2}\, p_w\begin{pmatrix} w_1 & w_2 & w_3 \\ \alpha & \beta & \gamma \\ \alpha' & \beta' & \gamma' \end{pmatrix} y, \tag{7.19}$$

where r and s are constants and z, z_1, z_2, and z_3 are given by (7.13).

From (7.18) and (7.19),

$$p_w\begin{pmatrix} w_1 & w_2 & w_3 \\ \alpha & \beta & \gamma \\ \alpha' & \beta' & \gamma' \end{pmatrix}\left[\left(\frac{w-w_1}{w-w_2}\right)^\alpha\left(\frac{w-w_3}{w-w_2}\right)^\gamma y\right]$$

$$= \frac{(w_2-w_1)^2(w_2-w_3)^2}{(w_3-w_1)^2}\frac{(w-w_1)^\alpha(w-w_3)^\gamma}{(w-w_2)^{\alpha+\gamma+4}}$$

$$\times\, p_z\begin{pmatrix} 0 & \infty & 1 \\ 0 & \alpha+\beta+\gamma & 0 \\ \alpha'-\alpha & \alpha+\beta'+\gamma & \gamma'-\gamma \end{pmatrix} y, \qquad (7.20)$$

where

$$z = \frac{(w-w_1)(w_3-w_2)}{(w-w_2)(w_3-w_1)} \qquad (7.21)$$

and α, α', β, β', γ, and γ' satisfy (7.17). Now, from (7.16), we see that

$$z(1-z)p_z\begin{pmatrix} 0 & \infty & 1 \\ 0 & a & 0 \\ 1-c & b & c-a-b \end{pmatrix} y$$

$$\equiv z(1-z)\frac{d^2y}{dz^2} + [c-(a+b+1)z]\frac{dy}{dz} - aby. \qquad (7.22)$$

We see that the differential operator on the right side of (7.20) can be identified with that in (7.22) by putting

$$\alpha' = 1 - c + \alpha,$$

$$\beta = a - \alpha - \gamma,$$

$$\beta' = b - \alpha - \gamma, \qquad (7.23)$$

and

$$\gamma' = c - a - b + \gamma.$$

Consider now the nonhomogeneous Riemann equation derived in §6.22,

$$p_w\begin{pmatrix} w_1 & w_2 & w_3 \\ \alpha & \beta & \gamma \\ \alpha' & \beta' & \gamma' \end{pmatrix} u = \frac{(w-w_0)^{\tau-1}(w-w_1)^{\alpha+\sigma-2}(w-w_3)^{\gamma-1}}{(w-w_2)^{\alpha+\gamma+\sigma+\tau}}, \qquad (7.24)$$

where w_0, σ, and τ are constants. From (7.20) and (7.22), we see that the solution of (7.24) can always be expressed in terms of that of the nonhomogeneous hypergeometric equation

$$p_z\begin{pmatrix} 0 & \infty & 1 \\ 0 & \alpha+\beta+\gamma & 0 \\ \alpha'-\alpha & \alpha+\beta'+\gamma & \gamma'-\gamma \end{pmatrix} y$$

$$= \frac{(w_3-w_1)^2}{(w_2-w_1)^2(w_2-w_3)^2}\left(\frac{w-w_0}{w-w_2}\right)^{\tau-1}\left(\frac{w-w_1}{w-w_2}\right)^{\sigma-2}\left(\frac{w-w_2}{w-w_3}\right)$$

$$= \frac{(w_0-w_2)^{\tau-1}(w_3-w_1)^{\sigma+\tau-2}}{(w_1-w_2)^{\tau}(w_3-w_2)^{\sigma+\tau-1}}\frac{z^{\sigma-2}(z-z_0)^{\tau-1}}{z-1}$$

$$= k^{1-\tau}\frac{(w_3-w_1)^{\sigma-1}}{(w_3-w_2)^{\sigma}(w_2-w_1)}\frac{z^{\sigma-2}(1-\rho z)^{\tau-1}}{1-z}, \tag{7.25}$$

where

$$u = \left(\frac{w-w_1}{w-w_2}\right)^{\alpha}\left(\frac{w-w_3}{w-w_2}\right)^{\gamma} y, \tag{7.26}$$

$$k = \frac{w_2-w_1}{w_0-w_1}, \tag{7.27}$$

$$\rho = \frac{1}{z_0} = \frac{(w_0-w_2)(w_3-w_1)}{(w_0-w_1)(w_3-w_2)}, \tag{7.28}$$

and z is given by (7.21).

Now, as shown in §6.20, $C_{\rho,\sigma}^{(\tau)}(a, b; c; z)$ is a particular integral of the equation

$$p_z\begin{pmatrix} 0 & \infty & 1 \\ 0 & a & 0 \\ 1-c & b & c-a-b \end{pmatrix} y = \frac{z^{\sigma-2}(1-\rho z)^{\tau-1}}{1-z}. \tag{7.29}$$

From (7.25) and (7.29), the solution of the nonhomogeneous Riemann equation (7.24) can always be expressed in terms of that of the nonhomogeneous hypergeometric equation

$$z(1-z)\frac{d^2y}{dz^2} + [c-(a+b+1)z]\frac{dy}{dz} - aby = z^{\sigma-1}(1-\rho z)^{\tau-1}. \tag{7.30}$$

By interchanging the two exponents (α, α'), or (β, β') or (γ, γ'), on both sides of (7.24), we see that the solutions of the resulting four equations can be expressed in terms of $C_{\rho,\sigma}^{(\tau)}(a', b'; c'; z)$ where a', b', and c' are linearly related to a, b, and c. Similarly, by interchanging the three columns of the p operator on the left side of (7.24) and making corresponding changes to the parameters on the right side of that equation, we see that the solutions of the resulting six equations can be expressed in terms of $C_{\rho',\sigma}^{(\tau)}(a'', b''; c''; z')$, where a'', b'', and c'' are linearly related to a, b, and c, and z' is one of the following six functions:

$$z, \quad 1-z, \quad \frac{1}{z}, \quad \frac{1}{1-z}, \quad \frac{z}{z-1}, \quad \frac{z-1}{z}.$$

$\rho' = 1/z_0'$ is obtained from (7.28). We thus see that $4 \times 6 = 24$ (in general, different) nonhomogeneous equations can be obtained from (7.24), all these equations having solutions which can be expressed in terms of $C^{(\tau)}_{\rho',\sigma}(A, B; C; z')$. These 24 equations are generalizations of those given in Table 6.1.

7.4 Riemann's Equation and Legendre's Equation

We consider now two important particular cases for which solutions of Riemann's equation can be expressed in terms of those of Legendre's equation.

From (7.18) and (7.19),

$$p_w\begin{pmatrix} w_1 & w_2 & w_3 \\ \alpha & \beta & \gamma \\ \alpha' & \beta' & \gamma' \end{pmatrix}\left[\left(\frac{w-w_1}{w-w_2}\right)^{(1/2)\alpha+(1/2)\alpha'-(1/2)}\left(\frac{w-w_3}{w-w_2}\right)^{(1/2)\gamma+(1/2)\gamma'} y\right]$$

$$= 4\frac{(w_1-w_2)^2(w_1-w_3)^2}{(w_3-w_2)^2}\frac{(w-w_2)^{(1/2)\beta+(1/2)\beta'}(w-w_3)^{(1/2)\gamma+(1/2)\gamma'}}{(w-w_1)^{(9/2)-(1/2)\alpha-(1/2)\alpha'}}$$

$$\times\, p_z\begin{pmatrix} \infty & -1 & 1 \\ \frac{1}{2}+\frac{1}{2}\alpha-\frac{1}{2}\alpha' & \frac{1}{2}\beta-\frac{1}{2}\beta' & \frac{1}{2}\gamma-\frac{1}{2}\gamma' \\ \frac{1}{2}-\frac{1}{2}\alpha+\frac{1}{2}\alpha' & \frac{1}{2}\beta'-\frac{1}{2}\beta & \frac{1}{2}\gamma'-\frac{1}{2}\gamma \end{pmatrix} y \tag{7.31}$$

where

$$z = 1 + 2\frac{(w-w_3)(w_1-w_2)}{(w-w_1)(w_2-w_3)}. \tag{7.32}$$

Now

$$(1-z^2)p_z\begin{pmatrix} \infty & -1 & 1 \\ \nu+1 & \frac{1}{2}\mu & \frac{1}{2}\mu \\ -\nu & -\frac{1}{2}\mu & -\frac{1}{2}\mu \end{pmatrix} y$$

$$\equiv (1-z^2)\frac{d^2y}{dz^2} - 2z\frac{dy}{dz} + [\nu(\nu+1) - \mu^2(1-z^2)^{-1}]y. \tag{7.33}$$

We see that the differential operator on the right side of (7.31) can be identified with that in (7.33) by putting

$$\alpha - \alpha' = 2\nu + 1$$

and (7.34)

$$\beta - \beta' = \gamma - \gamma' = \mu.$$

In addition, α, α', β, β', γ, and γ' must satisfy (7.17). It follows that any Riemann P function of the form

$$P\begin{Bmatrix} w_1 & w_2 & w_3 & \\ \alpha & \beta & \gamma & w \\ \alpha' & \beta - \mu & \gamma - \mu & \end{Bmatrix} \tag{7.35}$$

can be expressed in terms of Legendre functions, the latter functions satisfying the equation

$$(1 - z^2)\frac{d^2y}{dz^2} - 2z\frac{dy}{dz} + [\nu(\nu+1) - \mu^2(1 - z^2)^{-1}]y = 0\,. \tag{7.36}$$

Consider now the nonhomogeneous equation (7.24), with $\beta' = \beta - \mu$, $\gamma' = \gamma - \mu$, that is,

$$p_w\begin{pmatrix} w_1 & w_2 & w_3 \\ \alpha & \beta & \gamma \\ \alpha' & \beta - \mu & \gamma - \mu \end{pmatrix} u = \frac{(w - w_0)^{\tau-1}(w - w_1)^{\alpha+\sigma-2}(w - w_3)^{\gamma-1}}{(w - w_2)^{\alpha+\gamma+\sigma+\tau}}\,, \tag{7.37}$$

where w_0, σ, and τ are constants. From (7.31) and (7.33), we see that the solution of (7.37) can always be expressed in terms of that of the nonhomogeneous equation

$$p_z\begin{pmatrix} \infty & -1 & 1 \\ \frac{1}{2} + \frac{1}{2}\alpha - \frac{1}{2}\alpha' & \frac{1}{2}\mu & \frac{1}{2}\mu \\ \frac{1}{2} - \frac{1}{2}\alpha + \frac{1}{2}\alpha' & -\frac{1}{2}\mu & -\frac{1}{2}\mu \end{pmatrix} y = \frac{(w_3 - w_2)^2}{4(w_1 - w_2)^2(w_1 - w_3)^2}\left(\frac{w - w_0}{w - w_2}\right)^{\tau-1}$$
$$\times \left(\frac{w - w_1}{w - w_2}\right)^{(5/2)+(1/2)\alpha-(1/2)\alpha'+\sigma}\left(\frac{w - w_3}{w - w_2}\right)^{(1/2)\mu-1};$$

that is, putting $\alpha - \alpha' = 2\nu + 1$, and using (7.32), we see that the solution of (7.37) can be expressed in terms of that of the nonhomogeneous Legendre equation

$$p_z\begin{pmatrix} \infty & -1 & 1 \\ \nu + 1 & \frac{1}{2}\mu & \frac{1}{2}\mu \\ -\nu & -\frac{1}{2}\mu & -\frac{1}{2}\mu \end{pmatrix} y$$
$$= 2^{\nu+\sigma+\tau}\frac{(w_0 - w_3)^{\tau-1}(w_1 - w_3)^{(1/2)\mu+\nu+\sigma}}{(w_1 - w_2)^{1+(1/2)\mu}(w_2 - w_3)^{\nu+\sigma+\tau}}$$
$$\times \frac{(z-1)^{(1/2)\mu-1}}{(z+1)^{(1/2)\mu+\nu+\sigma+\tau+1}}\left(\frac{z - z_0}{1 - z_0}\right)^{\tau-1}$$
$$= 2^{\nu+\sigma+1}k^{1-\tau}\frac{(w_1 - w_3)^{(1/2)\mu+\nu+\sigma}}{(w_1 - w_2)^{1+(1/2)\mu}(w_2 - w_3)^{\nu+\sigma+1}}$$
$$\times \frac{(z-1)^{(1/2)\mu-1}(z + 1 - 2\rho)^{\tau-1}}{(z+1)^{(1/2)\mu+\nu+\sigma+\tau+1}} \tag{7.38}$$

where

$$u = \left(\frac{w - w_1}{w - w_2}\right)^{(1/2)\alpha + (1/2)\alpha' - (1/2)} \left(\frac{w - w_3}{w - w_2}\right)^{\gamma - (1/2)\mu} y, \tag{7.39}$$

$$k = \frac{w_2 - w_1}{w_0 - w_1}, \tag{7.40}$$

$$\rho = \tfrac{1}{2}(z_0 + 1) = \frac{(w_0 - w_2)(w_3 - w_1)}{(w_0 - w_1)(w_3 - w_2)}, \tag{7.41}$$

and z is given by (7.32).

Now, as was shown in (6.279), the equation

$$P_z\begin{pmatrix} \infty & -1 & 1 \\ \nu + 1 & \tfrac{1}{2}\mu & \tfrac{1}{2}\mu \\ -\nu & -\tfrac{1}{2}\mu & -\tfrac{1}{2}\mu \end{pmatrix} y = \frac{(z-1)^{(1/2)\mu - 1}(z + 1 - 2\rho)^{\tau - 1}}{(z+1)^{(1/2)\mu + \nu + \sigma + \tau + 1}} \tag{7.42}$$

has a particular integral

$$y = 2^{-\sigma}(z+1)^{-(1/2)\mu - \nu - 1}(z-1)^{(1/2)\mu} C^{(\tau)}_{\rho,\sigma}\left(\mu + \nu + 1, \nu + 1; 2\nu + 2; \frac{2}{1+z}\right). \tag{7.43}$$

From (7.38) and (7.43) we see that the solution of the nonhomogeneous Riemann equation (7.37) can always be expressed in terms of that of the nonhomogeneous Legendre equation

$$(1 - z^2)\frac{d^2y}{dz^2} - 2z\frac{dy}{dz} + [\nu(\nu+1) - \mu^2(1 - z^2)^{-1}]y$$
$$= -(z + 1 - 2\rho)^{\tau - 1}(z+1)^{-(1/2)\mu - \nu - \sigma - \tau}(z-1)^{(1/2)\mu}. \tag{7.44}$$

Another relation between solutions of Riemann's equation and those of Legendre's equation is obtained from the identity

$$P_{\zeta^2}\begin{pmatrix} 0 & \infty & 1 \\ 0 & \beta & \gamma \\ \tfrac{1}{2} & \beta' & \gamma' \end{pmatrix} y \equiv \frac{1}{4\zeta^2} P_\zeta\begin{pmatrix} \infty & -1 & 1 \\ 2\beta & \gamma & \gamma \\ 2\beta' & \gamma' & \gamma' \end{pmatrix} y, \tag{7.45}$$

in which $\beta + \beta' + \gamma + \gamma' = \tfrac{1}{2}$. The operator on the left side of (7.45) can be identified with that in (7.29), if $c = \tfrac{1}{2}$. The operator on the right side of (7.45) can be identified with that in (7.33) on writing $\beta = \tfrac{1}{2}(\nu + 1)$, $\beta' = -\tfrac{1}{2}\nu$, and $\gamma = -\gamma' = \tfrac{1}{2}\mu$.

Consider now the nonhomogeneous equation (7.24) with $\alpha' = \alpha + \tfrac{1}{2}$; that is,

$$P_w\begin{pmatrix} w_1 & w_2 & w_3 \\ \alpha & \beta & \gamma \\ \alpha + \tfrac{1}{2} & \beta' & \gamma' \end{pmatrix} u = \frac{(w - w_0)^{\tau - 1}(w - w_1)^{\alpha + \sigma - 2}(w - w_3)^{\gamma - 1}}{(w - w_2)^{\alpha + \gamma + \sigma + \tau}}, \tag{7.46}$$

where w_0, σ, and τ are constants. From (7.25) and (7.45), we see that, on putting $z = v^2$, the solution of (7.46) can always be expressed in terms of that of the nonhomogeneous equation

$$P_v\begin{pmatrix} \infty & -1 & 1 \\ 2(\alpha+\beta+\gamma) & 0 & 0 \\ 2(\alpha+\beta'+\gamma) & \gamma'-\gamma & \gamma'-\gamma \end{pmatrix} y = 4k^{1-\tau}\frac{(w_3-w_1)^{\sigma-1}}{(w_3-w_2)^{\sigma}(w_2-w_1)}\frac{v^{2\sigma-2}(1-\rho v^2)^{\tau-1}}{1-v^2}, \qquad (7.47)$$

where y, k, and ρ are given by (7.26) to (7.28).

From (7.18) and (7.47), with $r = \gamma - \gamma'$, $s = \frac{1}{2}(\gamma' - \gamma)$, we obtain

$$P_v\begin{pmatrix} \infty & -1 & 1 \\ \frac{1}{2}+\beta-\beta' & \frac{1}{2}\gamma-\frac{1}{2}\gamma' & \frac{1}{2}\gamma-\frac{1}{2}\gamma' \\ \frac{1}{2}-\beta+\beta' & \frac{1}{2}\gamma'-\frac{1}{2}\gamma & \frac{1}{2}\gamma'-\frac{1}{2}\gamma \end{pmatrix} x = 4k^{1-\tau}\frac{(w_3-w_1)^{\sigma-1}}{(w_3-w_2)^{\sigma}(w_2-w_1)} v^{2\sigma-2} \times (1-v^2)^{(1/2)(\gamma-\gamma')-1}(1-\rho v^2)^{\tau-1}, \qquad (7.48)$$

where $x = (1-v^2)^{(1/2)(\gamma-\gamma')}y$. Thus, putting $\beta - \beta' = v + \frac{1}{2}$ and $\gamma - \gamma' = \mu$, we see that the solution of (7.46) can be expressed in terms of that of the nonhomogeneous Legendre equation

$$P_v\begin{pmatrix} \infty & -1 & 1 \\ v+1 & \frac{1}{2}\mu & \frac{1}{2}\mu \\ -v & -\frac{1}{2}\mu & -\frac{1}{2}\mu \end{pmatrix} x = 4k^{1-\tau}\frac{(w_3-w_1)^{\sigma-1}}{(w_3-w_2)^{\sigma}(w_2-w_1)} v^{2\sigma-2}(1-v^2)^{(1/2)\mu-1} \times (1-\rho v^2)^{\tau-1}. \qquad (7.49)$$

Now, as shown in (6.273), the equation

$$P_v\begin{pmatrix} \infty & -1 & 1 \\ v+1 & \frac{1}{2}\mu & \frac{1}{2}\mu \\ -v & -\frac{1}{2}\mu & -\frac{1}{2}\mu \end{pmatrix} x = v^{2\sigma-2}(1-v^2)^{(1/2)\mu-1}(1-\rho v^2)^{\tau-1}$$

has a particular integral

$$x = \tfrac{1}{4}(1-v^2)^{(1/2)\mu}C^{(\tau)}_{\rho,\sigma}(\tfrac{1}{2}\mu+\tfrac{1}{2}v+\tfrac{1}{2}, \tfrac{1}{2}\mu-\tfrac{1}{2}v; \tfrac{1}{2}; v^2). \qquad (7.50)$$

From (7.49) and (7.50) we see that the solution of the nonhomogeneous Riemann equation (7.46) can always be expressed in terms of that of the nonhomogeneous Legendre equation

$$(1-z^2)\frac{d^2y}{dz^2} - 2z\frac{dy}{dz} + [v(v+1) - \mu^2(1-z^2)^{-1}]y = z^{2\sigma-2}(1-z^2)^{(1/2)\mu}(1-\rho z^2)^{\tau-1}. \qquad (7.51)$$

We shall now consider the properties of certain functions which satisfy the nonhomogeneous differential equations

$$(1-z^2)\frac{d^2y}{dz^2} - 2z\frac{dy}{dz} + [\nu(\nu+1) - \mu^2(1-z^2)^{-1}]y = -e^{i\pi\mu}\frac{2^{-\nu}\Gamma(\mu+\nu+2)}{\Gamma(\nu+1)} z^{-\mu-\nu-2}(z^2-1)^{(1/2)\mu}, \quad (7.52)$$

$$(1-z^2)\frac{d^2y}{dz^2} - 2z\frac{dy}{dz} + [\nu(\nu+1) - \mu^2(1-z^2)^{-1}]y = z^{2\sigma-2}(z^2-1)^{(1/2)\mu} \quad (7.53)$$

and

$$(1-z^2)\frac{d^2y}{dz^2} - 2z\frac{dy}{dz} + [\nu(\nu+1) - \mu^2(1-z^2)^{-1}]y = z^{2\sigma-2}(z^2-1)^{(1/2)\mu+\tau-1}. \quad (7.54)$$

Equation (7.52) is a particular case of (7.44), and (7.53) and (7.54) follow from (7.51).

The associated homogeneous equation is Legendre's equation

$$(1-z^2)\frac{d^2y}{dz^2} - 2z\frac{dy}{dz} + [\nu(\nu+1) - \mu^2(1-z^2)^{-1}]y = 0, \quad (7.55)$$

which has three regular singularities (at $z = -1$, 1, and ∞). The solutions of (7.55) are called *Legendre functions.*

7.5 Some Properties of Legendre Functions

The theory of Legendre functions is fully set out in Hobson [1931], Whittaker and Watson [1935], and Erdélyi [1953a]. We shall here briefly summarize various properties of these functions, which are solutions of Legendre's differential equation (7.55).

On making the substitution $y = (z^2-1)^{(1/2)\mu}u$, (7.55) becomes

$$(1-z^2)\frac{d^2u}{dz^2} - 2(\mu+1)z\frac{du}{dz} + (\nu-\mu)(\nu+1+\mu)u = 0. \quad (7.56)$$

Finally, putting $\zeta = z^2$, (7.56) becomes

$$\zeta(1-\zeta)\frac{d^2u}{d\zeta^2} + [\tfrac{1}{2} - (\mu+\tfrac{3}{2})\zeta]\frac{du}{d\zeta} + \tfrac{1}{4}(\nu-\mu)(\nu+1+\mu)u = 0. \quad (7.57)$$

Comparing (7.1) and (7.57), we see that (7.57) is identical with the hypergeometric equation if $a = \frac{1}{2}\mu - \frac{1}{2}\nu$, $b = \frac{1}{2} + \frac{1}{2}\mu + \frac{1}{2}\nu$, and $c = \frac{1}{2}$. Thus, from

§6.2, two independent solutions of (7.55) are

$$y_1 = (z^2 - 1)^{(1/2)\mu} F(\tfrac{1}{2}\mu - \tfrac{1}{2}\nu, \tfrac{1}{2} + \tfrac{1}{2}\mu + \tfrac{1}{2}\nu; \tfrac{1}{2}; z^2) \tag{7.58}$$

and

$$y_2 = z(z^2 - 1)^{(1/2)\mu} F(\tfrac{1}{2} + \tfrac{1}{2}\mu - \tfrac{1}{2}\nu, 1 + \tfrac{1}{2}\mu + \tfrac{1}{2}\nu; \tfrac{3}{2}; z^2), \tag{7.59}$$

where $|z| < 1$.

Similarly, we find that another pair of solutions of (7.55) is

$$y_3 = z^{-\nu-\mu-1}(z^2 - 1)^{(1/2)\mu} F(\tfrac{1}{2} + \tfrac{1}{2}\nu + \tfrac{1}{2}\mu, 1 + \tfrac{1}{2}\nu + \tfrac{1}{2}\mu; \nu + \tfrac{3}{2}; z^{-2}) \tag{7.60}$$

and

$$y_4 = z^{\nu-\mu}(z^2 - 1)^{(1/2)\mu} F(-\tfrac{1}{2}\nu + \tfrac{1}{2}\mu, \tfrac{1}{2} - \tfrac{1}{2}\nu + \tfrac{1}{2}\mu; \tfrac{1}{2} - \nu; z^{-2}), \tag{7.61}$$

where $|z| > 1$; another pair of solutions is

$$y_5 = (z + 1)^{-(1/2)\mu-\nu-1}(z - 1)^{(1/2)\mu} F\left(1 + \nu + \mu, 1 + \nu; 2 + 2\nu; \frac{2}{1 + z}\right) \tag{7.62}$$

and

$$y_6 = (z + 1)^{-(1/2)\mu+\nu}(z - 1)^{(1/2)\mu} F\left(-\nu + \mu, -\nu; -2\nu; \frac{2}{1 + z}\right), \tag{7.63}$$

where $|z + 1| > 2$.

The Legendre functions $P_\nu^\mu(z)$ and $Q_\nu^\mu(z)$ are given by (Erdélyi [1953a]).

$$\begin{aligned} P_\nu^\mu(z) &= \frac{2^\mu \pi^{1/2} e^{-i\mu\pi\varepsilon}}{\Gamma(\frac{1}{2} - \frac{1}{2}\nu - \frac{1}{2}\mu)\Gamma(1 + \frac{1}{2}\nu - \frac{1}{2}\mu)} y_1 - \frac{2^{\mu+1}\pi^{1/2} e^{-i\mu\pi\varepsilon}}{\Gamma(\frac{1}{2} + \frac{1}{2}\nu - \frac{1}{2}\mu)\Gamma(-\frac{1}{2}\nu - \frac{1}{2}\mu)} y_2 \\ &= \frac{2^{-\nu-1}\pi^{-(1/2)}\Gamma(-\frac{1}{2} - \nu)}{\Gamma(-\nu - \mu)} y_3 + \frac{2^\nu \pi^{-(1/2)}\Gamma(\frac{1}{2} + \nu)}{\Gamma(1 + \nu - \mu)} y_4 \\ &= \frac{2^{\nu+1}\Gamma(-1 - 2\nu)}{\Gamma(-\nu)\Gamma(-\nu - \mu)} y_5 + \frac{2^{-\nu}\Gamma(1 + 2\nu)}{\Gamma(1 + \nu)\Gamma(1 + \nu - \mu)} y_6, \end{aligned} \tag{7.64}$$

and

$$\begin{aligned} Q_\nu^\mu(z) &= e^{i\mu\pi} 2^\mu \pi^{1/2} \left[\frac{e^{-(1/2)i\varepsilon\pi(\mu+\nu+1)}\Gamma(\frac{1}{2} + \frac{1}{2}\nu + \frac{1}{2}\mu)}{2\Gamma(1 + \frac{1}{2}\nu - \frac{1}{2}\mu)} y_1 \right. \\ &\quad \left. + \frac{e^{-(1/2)i\varepsilon\pi(\mu+\nu)}\Gamma(1 + \frac{1}{2}\nu + \frac{1}{2}\mu)}{\Gamma(\frac{1}{2} + \frac{1}{2}\nu - \frac{1}{2}\mu)} y_2 \right] \\ &= e^{i\mu\pi} 2^{-\nu-1} \pi^{1/2} \Gamma(1 + \nu + \mu)[\Gamma(\nu + \tfrac{3}{2})]^{-1} y_3 \\ &= e^{i\mu\pi} 2^{-\nu-1} \pi^{1/2} \Gamma(1 + \nu + \mu)[\Gamma(\nu + \tfrac{3}{2})]^{-1} y_5, \end{aligned} \tag{7.65}$$

where $\varepsilon = \operatorname{sgn}(\operatorname{Im} z) = 1, -1$, according as $\operatorname{Im} z >, < 0$.

$P_\nu^\mu(z)$ and $Q_\nu^\mu(z)$ are the Legendre functions of the first and second kind, respectively. To make them one-valued we consider the z plane with a cut along the real axis from $z = 1$ to $-\infty$. Other solutions of (7.55) are

$$P_\nu^{\pm\mu}(\pm z),\, Q_\nu^{\pm\mu}(\pm z),\, P_{-\nu-1}^{\pm\mu}(\pm z),\, Q_{-\nu-1}^{\pm\mu}(\pm z).$$

The Wronskian of $P_\nu^\mu(z)$ and $Q_\nu^\mu(z)$ is

$$P_\nu^\mu(z)\frac{d}{dz}[Q_\nu^\mu(z)] - Q_\nu^\mu(z)\frac{d}{dz}[P_\nu^\mu(z)] = \frac{e^{i\pi\mu}\Gamma(1+\mu+\nu)}{(1-z^2)\Gamma(1+\nu-\mu)}. \tag{7.66}$$

Consider next the solution of (7.56) in terms of contour integrals. As shown by Hobson [*183*, 1931], these contour integrals can be of the form

$$\int_C (t^2-1)^\nu (t-z)^{-\mu-\nu-1}\,dt,$$

provided the contour C is suitably chosen. Thus solutions of (7.56) can be expressed in terms of the simple loop integrals

$$u_1 = \frac{1}{2\pi i}\int_0^{(-1+)} (t^2-1)^\nu (t-z)^{-\mu-\nu-1}\,dt, \tag{7.67}$$

$$u_2 = \frac{1}{2\pi i}\int_0^{(1+)} (t^2-1)^\nu (t-z)^{-\mu-\nu-1}\,dt \tag{7.68}$$

and

$$u_3 = \frac{1}{2\pi i}\int_0^{(z+)} (t^2-1)^\nu (t-z)^{-\mu-\nu-1}\,dt. \tag{7.69}$$

If $\arg z = \theta$ $(-\pi < \theta < \pi)$, we take

$$\arg(t+1) = -2\pi,$$
$$\arg(t-1) = \pi \tag{7.70}$$

and

$$\arg(t-z) = \theta - \pi$$

at the start of the contours. For the present we assume that z is not a real number between $+1$ and $-\infty$.

As shown by Hobson [*195*, 1931], one solution of (7.55) is given by

$$Q_\nu^\mu(z) = 2^{-\nu-1}e^{-i\nu\pi}\Gamma(-\nu)\Gamma(\mu+\nu+1)(z^2-1)^{(1/2)\mu}u_4, \tag{7.71}$$

where

$$u_4 = \frac{1}{2\pi i}\int^{(-1+,1-)} (t^2-1)^\nu (t-z)^{-\mu-\nu-1}\,dt$$
$$= u_1 - u_2, \tag{7.72}$$

in which $\arg(z-1)$ and $\arg(z+1)$ both tend to zero as z tends to any real number greater than 1.

For Re $\nu > -1$, the contours of integration in (7.72) may be replaced by portions of the real axis. We find that

$$Q_\nu^\mu(z) = -2^{-\nu-1}e^{-i\nu\pi}\frac{\Gamma(\mu+\nu+1)}{\Gamma(\nu+1)}(z^2-1)^{(1/2)\mu}\int_{-1}^{1}(1-t^2)^\nu(t-z)^{-\mu-\nu-1}\,dt$$

$$= 2^{-\nu-1}e^{i\mu\pi}\frac{\Gamma(\mu+\nu+1)}{\Gamma(\nu+1)}(z^2-1)^{(1/2)\mu}\int_{-1}^{1}(1-t^2)^\nu(z-t)^{-\mu-\nu-1}\,dt, \tag{7.73}$$

where $\arg(z-t)=\theta$ and $\arg(1-t^2)$ has its principal value at $t=0$.

Equation (7.73) can be written in the alternative form

$$Q_\nu^\mu(z) = 2^{-\nu-1}e^{i\mu\pi}\frac{\Gamma(\mu+\nu+1)}{\Gamma(\nu+1)}(z^2-1)^{(1/2)\mu}$$

$$\times\int_0^1(1-t^2)^\nu\{(z+t)^{-\mu-\nu-1}+(z-t)^{-\mu-\nu-1}\}\,dt \qquad (\text{Re }\nu>-1). \tag{7.74}$$

Put $t=\cos\theta$. Then (7.74) becomes

$$Q_\nu^\mu(z) = 2^{-\nu-1}e^{i\mu\pi}\frac{\Gamma(\mu+\nu+1)}{\Gamma(\nu+1)}(z^2-1)^{(1/2)\mu}$$

$$\times\int_0^{(1/2)\pi}\{(z+\cos\theta)^{-\mu-\nu-1}+(z-\cos\theta)^{-\mu-\nu-1}\}\sin^{2\nu+1}\theta\,d\theta$$

$$(\text{Re }\nu>-1). \tag{7.75}$$

In (7.71) to (7.75), z is not a real number between $+1$ and $-\infty$.

On writing $z=\mu/x$, and letting $\mu\to\infty$, we find from (7.74), if Re $\nu>-1$ (see Poole, [*190*, 1934]),

$$\lim_{\mu\to\infty}\left[Q_\nu^\mu\left(\frac{\mu}{x}\right)\right]e^{-i\mu\pi}/\Gamma(\mu) = \frac{2^{-\nu}x^{\nu+1}}{\Gamma(\nu+1)}\int_0^1(1-t^2)^\nu\cosh xt\,dt$$

$$= (\tfrac{1}{2}\pi x)^{1/2}I_{\nu+(1/2)}(x), \tag{7.76}$$

where I is the modified Bessel function of the first kind (see §3.2).

7.6 The Nonhomogeneous Legendre Function $R_\nu^\mu(z)$

Consider the function $R_\nu^\mu(z)$ defined by

$$R_\nu^\mu(z) = 2^{-\nu-1}e^{-i\nu\pi}\Gamma(-\nu)\Gamma(\mu+\nu+1)(z^2-1)^{(1/2)\mu}u_5, \tag{7.77}$$

where

$$u_5 = -\frac{1}{2\pi i}\left[\int_0^{(1+)} (t^2-1)^\nu (t-z)^{-\mu-\nu-1}\,dt + \int_0^{(-1+)} (t^2-1)^\nu (t-z)^{-\mu-\nu-1}\,dt\right]$$
$$= -u_1 - u_2, \tag{7.78}$$

in which $\arg(t+1) = -2\pi$, $\arg(t-1) = \pi$, and $\arg(t-z) = \theta - \pi$ at the start of the contours, and z is not a real number $+1$ and $-\infty$ (the point z is taken to be outside the contours). From (7.71) and (7.77),

$$\frac{R_\nu^\mu(z)}{Q_\nu^\mu(z)} = \frac{u_5}{u_4}$$

and

$$Q_\nu^\mu(z) - R_\nu^\mu(z) = 2^{-\nu} e^{-i\nu\pi}\Gamma(-\nu)\Gamma(\mu+\nu+1)(z^2-1)^{(1/2)\mu} u_1, \tag{7.79}$$

where u_1 is given by (7.67).

$R_\nu^\mu(z)$ can be expressed in terms of the nonhomogeneous hypergeometric function $B(a, b; c; z)$, defined in Chapter 6. From §6.3, putting $a = \mu + \nu + 1$, $b = \nu + 1$, and $c = 2\nu + 2$, we see that

$$B(\mu+\nu+1, \nu+1; 2\nu+2; \zeta) = i(2\pi)^{-1} e^{-i\mu\pi}[\Gamma(-\nu)]^2 \Gamma(2\nu+2) v,$$

where

$$v = \frac{2^{-2\nu-1}}{\pi} e^{i\pi(\mu-\nu)}(\sin \nu\pi)\left\{\int_0^{(1+)} (1-s^2)^\nu [1 - \tfrac{1}{2}(1+s)\zeta]^{-\mu-\nu-1}\,ds + \int_0^{(-1+)} (1-s^2)^\nu [1 - \tfrac{1}{2}(1+s)\zeta]^{-\mu-\nu-1}\,ds\right\}, \tag{7.80}$$

where the arguments of $1 - s^2$ and $1 - \frac{1}{2}(1+s)\zeta$ both have their principal values at the start of the contours and ζ^{-1} is not a real number between 0 and 1. Putting $\zeta = 2(1+z)^{-1}$, we find, from (7.78) and (7.80), that

$$v = \frac{2^{-2\nu-1}}{\pi} e^{-i\pi\nu}(\sin \nu\pi)(1+z)^{\mu+\nu+1}(2\pi i u_5), \tag{7.81}$$

allowing for the difference in the arguments of s and t.

From (7.77) to (7.81), with $\zeta = 2(1+z)^{-1}$, we find, after some reduction,

$$R_\nu^\mu(z) = e^{i\mu\pi} 2^{-\nu-1}\pi^{1/2}\Gamma(1+\nu+\mu)[\Gamma(\nu+\tfrac{3}{2})]^{-1}(z+1)^{-(1/2)\mu-\nu-1}(z-1)^{(1/2)\mu} \times B\left(1+\nu+\mu, 1+\nu; 2+2\nu; \frac{2}{1+z}\right). \tag{7.82}$$

As shown in (6.47),

$$B(a, b; c; \zeta) = -(1-\zeta)^{-a} B\left(a, c-b; c; \frac{\zeta}{\zeta-1}\right). \tag{7.83}$$

From (7.82) and (7.83),

$$R_\nu^\mu(z) = -e^{i\mu\pi} 2^{-\nu-1} \pi^{1/2} \Gamma(1+\nu+\mu)[\Gamma(\nu+\tfrac{3}{2})]^{-1}$$

$$\times (z+1)^{(1/2)\mu} (z-1)^{-(1/2)\mu-\nu-1} B\left(1+\nu+\mu, 1+\nu; 2+2\nu; \frac{2}{1-z}\right). \tag{7.84}$$

As in §7.5, to make $R_\nu^\mu(z)$ one-valued, we consider the z plane with a cut along the real axis from $z=1$ to $-\infty$.

For Re $\nu > -1$, the contours of integration in (7.78) may be replaced by portions of the real axis. We find that

$$R_\nu^\mu(z) = -2^{-\nu-1} e^{-i\nu\pi} \frac{\Gamma(\mu+\nu+1)}{\Gamma(\nu+1)} (z^2-1)^{(1/2)\mu}$$

$$\times \left[\int_0^1 (1-t^2)^\nu (t-z)^{-\mu-\nu-1}\, dt - \int_{-1}^0 (1-t^2)^\nu (t-z)^{-\mu-\nu-1}\, dt\right]$$

$$= 2^{-\nu-1} e^{i\mu\pi} \frac{\Gamma(\mu+\nu+1)}{\Gamma(\nu+1)} (z^2-1)^{(1/2)\mu}$$

$$\times \left[\int_0^1 (1-t^2)^\nu (z-t)^{-\mu-\nu-1}\, dt - \int_{-1}^0 (1-t^2)^\nu (z-t)^{-\mu-\nu-1}\, dt\right], \tag{7.85}$$

where $\arg(z-t) = \theta$ and $\arg(1-t^2)$ has its principal value at $t=0$.

Equation (7.85) can be written in the alternative form

$$R_\nu^\mu(z) = 2^{-\nu-1} e^{i\mu\pi} \frac{\Gamma(\mu+\nu+1)}{\Gamma(\nu+1)} (z^2-1)^{(1/2)\mu}$$

$$\times \int_0^1 (1-t^2)^\nu \{(z-t)^{-\mu-\nu-1} - (z+t)^{-\mu-\nu-1}\}\, dt \qquad (\text{Re}\, \nu > -1). \tag{7.86}$$

Put $t = \cos\theta$. Then (7.86) becomes

$$R_\nu^\mu(z) = 2^{-\nu-1} e^{i\mu\pi} \frac{\Gamma(\mu+\nu+1)}{\Gamma(\nu+1)} (z^2-1)^{(1/2)\mu}$$

$$\times \int_0^{(1/2)\pi} \{(z-\cos\theta)^{-\mu-\nu-1} - (z+\cos\theta)^{-\mu-\nu-1}\} \sin^{2\nu+1}\theta\, d\theta \qquad (\text{Re}\, \nu > -1). \tag{7.87}$$

In (7.85) to (7.87), z is not a real number between $+1$ and $-\infty$.

From (7.74) and (7.86), if $\operatorname{Re} \nu > -1$,

$$Q_\nu^\mu(z) + R_\nu^\mu(z) = 2^{-\nu} e^{i\mu\pi} \frac{\Gamma(\mu+\nu+1)}{\Gamma(\nu+1)} (z^2-1)^{(1/2)\mu} \times \int_0^1 (1-t^2)^\nu (z-t)^{-\mu-\nu-1}\, dt \quad (7.88)$$

and

$$Q_\nu^\mu(z) - R_\nu^\mu(z) = 2^{-\nu} e^{i\mu\pi} \frac{\Gamma(\mu+\nu+1)}{\Gamma(\nu+1)} (z^2-1)^{(1/2)\mu} \times \int_0^1 (1-t^2)^\nu (z+t)^{-\mu-\nu-1}\, dt. \quad (7.89)$$

On writing $z = \mu/x$, and letting $\mu \to \infty$, we find from (7.86), if $\operatorname{Re} \nu > -1$,

$$\lim_{\mu\to\infty} \left[R_\nu^\mu\left(\frac{\mu}{x}\right) \right] e^{-i\mu\pi}/\Gamma(\mu) = \frac{2^{-\nu} x^{\nu+1}}{\Gamma(\nu+1)} \int_0^1 (1-t^2)^\nu \sinh xt\, dt = (\tfrac{1}{2}\pi x)^{1/2} L_{\nu+(1/2)}(x), \quad (7.90)$$

from (3.101), where L is the modified Struve function (see §3.14).

7.7 Expression for $R_\nu^\mu(-z)$ in Terms of $R_\nu^\mu(z)$

Putting $-z$ in place of z in (7.82), we find

$$R_\nu^\mu(-z) = e^{i\mu\pi} 2^{-\nu-1} \pi^{1/2} \Gamma(1+\nu+\mu) [\Gamma(\nu+\tfrac{3}{2})]^{-1} (-z+1)^{-(1/2)\mu-\nu-1} \times (-z-1)^{(1/2)\mu} B\left(1+\mu+\nu, 1+\nu; 2+2\nu; \frac{2}{1-z}\right). \quad (7.91)$$

Now in (7.84) and (7.97), the arguments of z, $-z$, $z+1$, $z-1$, $-z+1$, and $-z-1$ are all to be taken to lie between π and $-\pi$.

Thus

$$-z-1 = e^{-i\pi\varepsilon}(z+1)$$

and (7.92)

$$-z+1 = e^{-i\pi\varepsilon}(z-1),$$

where $\varepsilon = \operatorname{sgn}(\operatorname{Im} z) = 1, -1$, according as $\operatorname{Im} z > 0$, <0.

From (7.84), (7.91), and (7.92),

$$R_\nu^\mu(-z) = e^{i\nu\pi\varepsilon} R_\nu^\mu(z), \quad (7.93)$$

where $|\arg z| < \pi$, $\arg z \neq 0$.

7.8 Differential Equation Satisfied by $R_\nu^\mu(z)$

As in Hobson [*183*, 1931], it can be shown that

$$\left\{(1-z^2)\frac{\partial^2}{\partial z^2} - 2(\mu+1)z\frac{\partial}{\partial z} + (\nu-\mu)(\nu+\mu+1)\right\}(t^2-1)^\nu(t-z)^{-\mu-\nu-1}$$

$$= (\nu+\mu+1)\frac{\partial}{\partial t}[(t^2-1)^{\nu+1}(t-z)^{-\mu-\nu-2}]. \quad (7.94)$$

From (7.77), (7.78), and (7.94), after some reduction, we find that $(z^2-1)^{-(1/2)\mu}R_\nu^\mu(z)$ satisfies the nonhomogeneous linear differential equation

$$(1-z^2)\frac{d^2u}{dz^2} - 2(\mu+1)z\frac{du}{dz} + (\nu-\mu)(\nu+\mu+1)u$$

$$= -e^{i\pi\mu}\frac{2^{-\nu}\Gamma(\mu+\nu+2)}{\Gamma(\nu+1)}z^{-\mu-\nu-2}. \quad (7.95)$$

Finally, making the substitution $y = (z^2-1)^{(1/2)\mu}u$, we see that $R_\nu^\mu(z)$ satisfies the nonhomogeneous Legendre equation

$$(1-z^2)\frac{d^2y}{dz^2} - 2z\frac{dy}{dz} + [\nu(\nu+1) - \mu^2(1-z^2)^{-1}]y$$

$$= -e^{i\pi\mu}\frac{2^{-\nu}\Gamma(\mu+\nu+2)}{\Gamma(\nu+1)}z^{-\mu-\nu-2}(z^2-1)^{(1/2)\mu}. \quad (7.96)$$

Alternatively, putting $\zeta = z^2$, (7.95) becomes

$$\zeta(1-\zeta)\frac{d^2u}{d\zeta^2} + [\tfrac{1}{2} - (\mu+\tfrac{3}{2})\zeta]\frac{du}{d\zeta} + \tfrac{1}{4}(\nu-\mu)(\nu+1+\mu)u$$

$$= -e^{i\pi\mu}\frac{2^{-\nu-2}\Gamma(\mu+\nu+2)}{\Gamma(\nu+1)}\zeta^{-(1/2)\mu-(1/2)\nu-1}. \quad (7.97)$$

As shown in §6.16, a particular integral of (7.97) is

$$u = -e^{i\pi\mu}\frac{2^{-\nu-2}\Gamma(\mu+\nu+2)}{\Gamma(\nu+1)}F_{-(1/2)\mu-(1/2)\nu}(\tfrac{1}{2}\mu - \tfrac{1}{2}\nu, \tfrac{1}{2} + \tfrac{1}{2}\mu + \tfrac{1}{2}\nu; \tfrac{1}{2}; \zeta),$$

where $F_\sigma(a, b; c; z)$ is the nonhomogeneous hypergeometric function defined in §6.16. Thus a particular integral of (7.96) is

$$y = -e^{i\pi\mu}\frac{2^{-\nu-2}\Gamma(\mu+\nu+2)}{\Gamma(\nu+1)}(z^2-1)^{(1/2)\mu}$$

$$\times F_{-(1/2)\mu-(1/2)\nu}(\tfrac{1}{2}\mu - \tfrac{1}{2}\nu, \tfrac{1}{2} + \tfrac{1}{2}\mu + \tfrac{1}{2}\nu; \tfrac{1}{2}; z^2). \quad (7.98)$$

Now the general solution of (7.96) is

$$C_1 P_\nu^\mu(z) + C_2 Q_\nu^\mu(z) + R_\nu^\mu(z),$$

where C_1 and C_2 are arbitrary constants.

On comparing the power series for these two solutions in descending powers of z (the series converge for sufficiently large $|z|$), using (7.64), (7.65), and (7.82), we find

$$\begin{aligned} R_\nu^\mu(z) &= -e^{i\pi\mu}\frac{2^{-\nu-2}\Gamma(\mu+\nu+2)}{\Gamma(\nu+1)}(z^2-1)^{(1/2)\mu} \\ &\quad \times F_{-(1/2)\mu-(1/2)\nu}(\tfrac{1}{2}\mu-\tfrac{1}{2}\nu, \tfrac{1}{2}+\tfrac{1}{2}\mu+\tfrac{1}{2}\nu; \tfrac{1}{2}; z^2) \\ &= e^{i\pi\mu}\frac{2^{-\nu-1}\Gamma(\mu+\nu+2)}{\Gamma(\nu+2)} z^{-\mu-\nu-2}(z^2-1)^{(1/2)\mu} \\ &\quad \times {}_3F_2\left(1, \frac{\mu+\nu}{2}+1, \frac{\mu+\nu+3}{2}; \nu+2, \tfrac{3}{2}; \frac{1}{z^2}\right). \end{aligned} \tag{7.99}$$

From (7.99) we see that, as $|z| \to \infty$,

$$R_\nu^\mu(z) \sim e^{i\pi\mu}\frac{2^{-\nu-1}\Gamma(\mu+\nu+2)}{\Gamma(\nu+2)} z^{-\nu-2}. \tag{7.100}$$

The relation for the nonhomogeneous hypergeometric functions which corresponds to (7.99) is

$$\begin{aligned} B\left(1+\nu+\mu, 1+\nu; 2+2\nu; \frac{2}{1+z}\right) &= -\frac{(\mu+\nu+1)\Gamma(\nu+\frac{3}{2})}{2\pi^{1/2}\Gamma(\nu+1)}(z+1)^{\mu+\nu+1} \\ &\quad \times F_{-(1/2)\mu-(1/2)\nu}(\tfrac{1}{2}\mu-\tfrac{1}{2}\nu, \tfrac{1}{2}+\tfrac{1}{2}\mu+\tfrac{1}{2}\nu; \tfrac{1}{2}; z^2). \end{aligned} \tag{7.101}$$

Equation (7.101) can be written in the equivalent forms

$$\begin{aligned} B\left(a, b; 2b; \frac{2}{1+z}\right) &= -\frac{a\Gamma(b+\frac{1}{2})}{2\pi^{1/2}\Gamma(b)}(z+1)^a F_\sigma(1-b-\sigma, \tfrac{1}{2}-\sigma; \tfrac{1}{2}; z^2), \\ &= \frac{a\Gamma(b+\frac{1}{2})}{2\pi^{1/2}\Gamma(b)}\left(\frac{z+1}{z}\right)^a f_{1/2}\left(\tfrac{1}{2}a, \tfrac{1}{2}+\tfrac{1}{2}a; b+\tfrac{1}{2}; \frac{1}{z^2}\right), \end{aligned} \tag{7.102}$$

where $\sigma = \frac{1}{2}(1-a)$, and the nonhomogeneous hypergeometric function f is defined in §6.16. On replacing $2/(1+z)$ by z, (7.102) becomes

$$B(a, b; 2b; z) = C(1-\tfrac{1}{2}z)^{-a} f_{1/2}\left\{\tfrac{1}{2}a, \tfrac{1}{2}+\tfrac{1}{2}a; b+\tfrac{1}{2}; \left(\frac{z}{2-z}\right)^2\right\}, \tag{7.103}$$

where $C = a\Gamma(b+\frac{1}{2})/2\pi^{1/2}\Gamma(b)$. The corresponding equation for the hypergeometric function is that corresponding to the quadratic transformation (see Erdélyi [*111*, 1953a])

$$F(a, b; 2b; z) = (1-\tfrac{1}{2}z)^{-a}F\left\{\tfrac{1}{2}a, \tfrac{1}{2}+\tfrac{1}{2}a; b+\tfrac{1}{2}; \left(\frac{z}{2-z}\right)^2\right\}. \quad (7.104)$$

Differentiating (7.78) with respect to z, and using (7.77), we obtain

$$\frac{d}{dz}[(z^2-1)^{-(1/2)\mu}R_\nu^\mu(z)] = (z^2-1)^{-(1/2)(\mu+1)}R_\nu^{\mu+1}(z);$$

that is, (7.105)

$$\frac{d}{dz}R_\nu^\mu(z) = (z^2-1)^{-1/2}R_\nu^{\mu+1}(z) + \frac{\mu z}{z^2-1}R_\nu^\mu(z).$$

By repeated application of (7.105) we see that

$$R_\nu^m(z) = (z^2-1)^{(1/2)m}\frac{d^m}{dz^m}R_\nu^0(z), \quad (7.106)$$

where m is any positive integer.

By replacing μ by $-\mu$ and ν by $-\nu-1$ in (7.96), we obtain three other nonhomogeneous Legendre equations, of the form

$$(1-z^2)\frac{d^2y}{dz^2} - 2z\frac{dy}{dz} + [\nu(\nu+1) - \mu^2(1-z^2)^{-1}]y = f(z), \quad (7.107)$$

the solutions of which can be expressed in terms of the R functions. Thus we find the following particular integrals of (7.107):

$$y = R_\nu^{-\mu}(z) \quad \text{if} \quad f(z) = -e^{-i\pi\mu}\frac{2^{-\nu}\Gamma(\nu-\mu+2)}{\Gamma(\nu+1)}z^{\mu-\nu-2}(z^2-1)^{-(1/2)\mu}, \quad (7.108)$$

$$y = R_{-\nu-1}^{\mu}(z) \quad \text{if} \quad f(z) = -e^{i\pi\mu}\frac{2^{\nu+1}\Gamma(\mu-\nu+1)}{\Gamma(-\nu)}z^{-\mu+\nu-1}(z^2-1)^{(1/2)\mu}, \quad (7.109)$$

and

$$y = R_{-\nu-1}^{-\mu}(z) \quad \text{if} \quad f(z) = -e^{-i\pi\mu}\frac{2^{\nu+1}\Gamma(1-\mu-\nu)}{\Gamma(-\nu)}z^{\mu+\nu-1}(z^2-1)^{-(1/2)\mu}. \quad (7.110)$$

7.9 Relations Between Contiguous Functions

The four functions $R_{\nu\pm1}^{\mu\pm1}(z)$ are said to be contiguous to $R_\nu^\mu(z)$. We shall now derive various relations between these functions.

From (7.105),

$$(z^2-1)\frac{d^2}{dz^2}R_\nu^\mu(z) = R_\nu^{\mu+2}(z) + 2\mu z(z^2-1)^{-1/2}R_\nu^{\mu+1}(z) - \mu[1+(1-\mu)z^2] \times (z^2-1)^{-1}R_\nu^\mu(z). \quad (7.111)$$

From (7.96), (7.106), and (7.111),

$$R_\nu^{\mu+2}(z) + 2(\mu+1)z(z^2-1)^{-1/2}R_\nu^{\mu+1}(z) - (\nu-\mu)(\nu+\mu+1)R_\nu^\mu(z) = e^{i\pi\mu}\frac{2^{-\nu}\Gamma(\mu+\nu+2)}{\Gamma(\nu+1)}z^{-\mu-\nu-2}(z^2-1)^{(1/2)\mu};$$

that is, replacing μ by $\mu-1$,

$$R_\nu^{\mu+1}(z) + 2\mu z(z^2-1)^{-1/2}R_\nu^\mu(z) - (\nu+\mu)(\nu+1-\mu)R_\nu^{\mu-1}(z) = -e^{i\pi\mu}\frac{2^{-\nu}\Gamma(\mu+\nu+1)}{\Gamma(\nu+1)}z^{-\mu-\nu-1}(z^2-1)^{(1/2)\mu-(1/2)}. \quad (7.112)$$

Consider the identity

$$\begin{aligned}\frac{d}{dt}&[t(t^2-1)^\nu(t-z)^{-\mu-\nu}]\\ &= (t^2-1)^\nu(t-z)^{-\mu-\nu} + 2\nu t^2(t^2-1)^{\nu-1}(t-z)^{-\mu-\nu}\\ &\quad - (\mu+\nu)t(t^2-1)^\nu(t-z)^{-\mu-\nu-1}\\ &= (\nu-\mu+1)(t^2-1)^\nu(t-z)^{-\mu-\nu} + 2\nu(t^2-1)^{\nu-1}(t-z)^{-\mu-\nu}\\ &\quad - (\mu+\nu)z(t^2-1)^\nu(t-z)^{-\mu-\nu-1}. \qquad (7.113)\end{aligned}$$

Now

$$\int_0^{(-1+)}\frac{d}{dt}[t(t^2-1)^\nu(t-z)^{-\mu-\nu}]\,dt = 0.$$

On performing the same integration on the right side of (7.113), and using (7.67) and (7.79) and the recurrence formulas for $Q_\nu^\mu(z)$, we find

$$R_{\nu-1}^\mu(z) - zR_\nu^\mu(z) + (\nu-\mu+1)(z^2-1)^{1/2}R_\nu^{\mu-1}(z) = 0. \quad (7.114)$$

Consider next the identity

$$\begin{aligned}\frac{d}{dt}[(t^2-1)^{\nu+1}(t-z)^{-\mu-\nu-1}] &= 2(\nu+1)t(t^2-1)^{\nu}(t-z)^{-\mu-\nu-1} \\ &\quad -(\mu+\nu+1)(t^2-1)^{\nu+1}(t-z)^{-\mu-\nu-2} \\ &= 2(\nu+1)(t^2-1)^{\nu}(t-z)^{-\mu-\nu}+2(\nu+1)z(t^2-1)^{\nu}(t-z)^{-\mu-\nu-1} \\ &\quad -(\mu+\nu+1)(t^2-1)^{\nu+1}(t-z)^{-\mu-\nu-2}. \end{aligned} \tag{7.115}$$

Now

$$\int_0^{(-1+)} \frac{d}{dt}[(t^2-1)^{\nu+1}(t-z)^{-\mu-\nu-1}]\,dt = -2i(\sin\nu\pi)(ze^{-i\pi})^{-\mu-\nu-1},$$

the arguments of $t+1$, $t-1$, and $t-z$ being as in (7.70). On performing the same integration on the right side of (7.115), and using (7.67) and (7.79) and the recurrence formulas for $Q_\nu^\mu(z)$, we find

$$zR_\nu^\mu(z)-R_{\nu+1}^\mu(z)+(\mu+\nu)(z^2-1)^{1/2}R_\nu^{\mu-1}(z)=e^{i\pi\mu}\frac{2^{-\nu-1}\Gamma(\mu+\nu+1)}{\Gamma(\nu+2)} \times z^{-\mu-\nu-1}(z^2-1)^{(1/2)\mu}. \tag{7.116}$$

From (7.114) and (7.116),

$$(\mu+\nu)R_{\nu-1}^\mu(z)-(2\nu+1)zR_\nu^\mu(z)+(\nu+1-\mu)R_{\nu+1}^\mu(z) = e^{i\pi\mu}\frac{2^{-\nu-1}(\mu-\nu-1)\Gamma(\mu+\nu+1)}{\Gamma(\nu+2)}z^{-\mu-\nu-1}(z^2-1)^{(1/2)\mu}. \tag{7.117}$$

From (7.112) and (7.114),

$$(\mu+\nu)R_{\nu-1}^\mu(z)+(\mu-\nu)zR_\nu^\mu(z)+(z^2-1)^{1/2}R_\nu^{\mu+1}(z) = -e^{i\pi\mu}\frac{2^{-\nu}\Gamma(\mu+\nu+1)}{\Gamma(\nu+1)}z^{-\mu-\nu-1}(z^2-1)^{(1/2)\mu}. \tag{7.118}$$

From (7.117) and (7.118),

$$(\nu+1-\mu)R_{\nu+1}^\mu(z)-(\nu+\mu+1)zR_\nu^\mu(z)-(z^2-1)^{1/2}R_\nu^{\mu+1}(z) = e^{i\pi\mu}\frac{2^{-\nu-1}\Gamma(\mu+\nu+2)}{\Gamma(\nu+2)}z^{-\mu-\nu-1}(z^2-1)^{(1/2)\mu}. \tag{7.119}$$

From (7.105), (7.118), and (7.119),

$$(z^2-1)\frac{d}{dz}R_\nu^\mu(z)$$

$$= \nu z R_\nu^\mu(z) - (\mu+\nu)R_{\nu-1}^\mu(z) - e^{i\pi\mu}\frac{2^{-\nu}\Gamma(\mu+\nu+1)}{\Gamma(\nu+1)}$$

$$\times z^{-\mu-\nu-1}(z^2-1)^{(1/2)\mu}$$

$$= (\nu+1-\mu)R_{\nu+1}^\mu(z) - (\nu+1)zR_\nu^\mu(z) - e^{i\pi\mu}\frac{2^{-\nu-1}\Gamma(\mu+\nu+2)}{\Gamma(\nu+2)}$$

$$\times z^{-\mu-\nu-1}(z^2-1)^{(1/2)\mu}. \tag{7.120}$$

7.10 Power Series for $R_\nu^\mu(z)$

A power series for $R_\nu^\mu(z)$ in descending powers of $1+z$ can be obtained from (7.82) on expanding the B function (see §6.8); such an expansion is valid for $|1+z|>2$. Similarly, from (7.84), we can obtain an expansion in terms of descending powers of $1-z$, valid for $|1-z|>2$.

A power series for $R_\nu^\mu(z)$ in descending powers of z can be obtained from (7.99) on expanding the F_σ function (see §6.16); this expansion is valid for $|z|>1$.

From (7.99), together with the equation for the analytic continuation of the F_σ function [(6.212)], we find, for $|z|<1$,

$$R_\nu^\mu(z) = -e^{i\pi\mu}\frac{2^{-\nu-2}\Gamma(\mu+\nu+2)}{\Gamma(\nu+1)}$$

$$\times (z^2-1)^{(1/2)\mu} f_{-(1/2)\mu-(1/2)\nu}(\tfrac{1}{2}\mu-\tfrac{1}{2}\nu, \tfrac{1}{2}+\tfrac{1}{2}\mu+\tfrac{1}{2}\nu; \tfrac{1}{2}; z^2)$$

$$- e^{(1/2)i\pi(\mu+\nu)\varepsilon}2^{-\nu-1}\Gamma(\mu+\nu+1)(z^2-1)^{(1/2)\mu}$$

$$\times [AF(\tfrac{1}{2}\mu-\tfrac{1}{2}\nu, \tfrac{1}{2}+\tfrac{1}{2}\mu+\tfrac{1}{2}\nu; \tfrac{1}{2}; z^2)$$

$$+ Be^{-(1/2)i\pi\varepsilon}zF(\tfrac{1}{2}+\tfrac{1}{2}\mu-\tfrac{1}{2}\nu, 1+\tfrac{1}{2}\mu+\tfrac{1}{2}\nu; \tfrac{3}{2}; z^2)], \tag{7.121}$$

where

$$A = \frac{\Gamma(-\frac{1}{2}\mu-\frac{1}{2}\nu)}{\Gamma(1-\frac{1}{2}\mu+\frac{1}{2}\nu)}\cos\frac{\mu+\nu}{2}\pi,$$

$$B = \frac{2\Gamma(\frac{1}{2}-\frac{1}{2}\mu-\frac{1}{2}\nu)}{\Gamma(\frac{1}{2}-\frac{1}{2}\mu+\frac{1}{2}\nu)}\sin\frac{\mu+\nu}{2}\pi,$$

and $\varepsilon = \operatorname{sgn}(\operatorname{Im} z) = 1, -1$, according as $\operatorname{Im} z >, <0$. From (7.121) we can obtain a power-series expansion for $R_\nu^\mu(z)$ in terms of ascending powers of z, using the expansion of the f_σ function given in §6.16; this expansion is valid for $|z| < 1$. Equation (7.121) becomes nugatory if $\mu + \nu + 2$ is a positive integer. In that case, the particular integral has a logarithmic singularity at the origin (see §7.12). We see, from (7.121), that $R_\nu^\mu(z)$ is, in general, discontinuous across the real axis ($|z| < 1$).

7.11 Nonhomogeneous Legendre Function $R_\nu^\mu(x)$

In many physical applications of Legendre functions, interest is confined to the real values $z = x$, where $-1 < x < 1$. Now, as shown in §7.10, $R_\nu^\mu(z)$ is discontinuous across this part of the real axis. We therefore introduce the function $R_\nu^\mu(x)$ defined by

$$R_\nu^\mu(x) = \tfrac{1}{2}e^{-i\mu\pi}[e^{-(1/2)i\mu\pi}R_\nu^\mu(x + i0) + e^{(1/2)i\mu\pi}R_\nu^\mu(x - i0)] \qquad (-1 < x < 1), \tag{7.122}$$

where

$$R_\nu^\mu(x \pm i0) = \lim_{y\to 0} R_\nu^\mu(x \pm iy) \qquad (y > 0).$$

In obtaining the limiting values of $R_\nu^\mu(x \pm iy)$, we must replace $z - 1$ by $(1 - x)e^{\pm i\pi}$. This is considered further in §7.12, for the important particular case in which μ and ν are both positive integers.

7.12 Particular Cases of $R_\nu^\mu(z)$ and $R_\nu^\mu(x)$

If μ and ν are both nonnegative integers, it is possible to express $R_\nu^\mu(z)$ and $R_\nu^\mu(x)$ in terms of elementary functions. From (7.86),

$$R_0^0(z) = \frac{1}{2}\log\frac{z^2}{z^2 - 1}, \tag{7.123}$$

$$R_1^0(z) = -\frac{1}{2z} + \frac{1}{2}z\log\frac{z^2}{z^2 - 1} = -\frac{1}{2z} + \frac{1}{2}P_1^0(z)\log\frac{z^2}{z^2 - 1}, \tag{7.124}$$

and

$$\begin{aligned} R_2^0(z) &= -\frac{3}{4} - \frac{1}{8z^2} + \frac{1}{4}(3z^2 - 1)\log\frac{z^2}{z^2 - 1} \\ &= -\frac{3}{4} - \frac{1}{8z^2} + \frac{1}{2}P_2^0(z)\log\frac{z^2}{z^2 - 1}. \end{aligned} \tag{7.125}$$

From (7.82), together with the results of §6.10, we see that

$$R_{-1/2}^0(z) = u[F(\tfrac{1}{2}\pi, u) - 2F(\tfrac{1}{4}\pi, u)], \tag{7.126}$$

where $u = [2/(1 + z)]^{1/2}$ and F is the elliptic integral of the first kind.

Using (7.117) we see that, if n is any nonnegative integer,

$$R_n^0(z) = \frac{1}{2} P_n^0(z) \log \frac{z^2}{z^2 - 1} - g_n(z), \tag{7.127}$$

where

$$g_0 = 0, \qquad g_1 = \frac{1}{2z},$$

and (7.128)

$$n g_n - (2n-1) z g_{n-1} + (n-1) g_{n-2} = 2^{-n} z^{-n} \qquad (n \geqslant 2).$$

We see that g_n is a polynomial of degree n in $1/z$ $(n \geqslant 1)$.

Using (7.122) we find, if $-1 < x < 1$,

$$R_0^0(x) = \frac{1}{2} \log \frac{x^2}{1 - x^2}, \tag{7.129}$$

$$R_1^0(x) = -\frac{1}{2x} + \frac{1}{2} x \log \frac{x^2}{1 - x^2} = -\frac{1}{2x} + \frac{1}{2} P_1^0(x) \log \frac{x^2}{1 - x^2}, \tag{7.130}$$

$$\begin{aligned} R_2^0(x) &= -\frac{3}{4} - \frac{1}{8x^2} + \frac{1}{4}(3x^2 - 1) \log \frac{x^2}{1 - x^2} \\ &= -\frac{3}{4} - \frac{1}{8x^2} + \frac{1}{2} P_2^0(x) \log \frac{x^2}{1 - x^2}, \end{aligned} \tag{7.131}$$

and

$$R_n^0(x) = \frac{1}{2} P_n^0(x) \log \frac{x^2}{1 - x^2} - g_n(x), \tag{7.132}$$

where $g_n(x)$ is given by (7.128), in which z is replaced by x. These formulas show the nature of the singularities of $R_n^0(x)$ at $x = 0$ and at $x = 1$ when n is a nonnegative integer.

If m and n are positive integers, $R_n^m(z)$ is obtained from $R_n^0(z)$ by using (7.106). The corresponding formula for $R_n^m(x)$ is

$$R_n^m(x) = (-1)^m (1 - x^2)^{(1/2)m} \frac{d^m}{dx^m} R_n^0(x) \qquad (-1 < x < 1). \tag{7.133}$$

$R_n^m(x)$ is a particular integral of the nonhomogeneous differential equation

$$\begin{aligned} &(1 - x^2) \frac{d^2 y}{dx^2} - 2x \frac{dy}{dx} + [n(n+1) - m^2(1 - x^2)^{-1}] y \\ &\qquad = -\frac{2^{-n}(m + n + 1)!}{n!} x^{-m-n-2} (1 - x^2)^{(1/2)m}, \end{aligned} \tag{7.134}$$

where m and n are positive integers and $-1 < x < 1$. We see that $R_n^m(x)$ and $R_n^m(z)$ are odd or even functions of x (or z) according as $m + n$ is an odd or even integer (where both m and n are nonnegative integers).

7.13 The Zeros of $R_\nu^\mu(z)$ and $R_\nu^\mu(x)$ Where μ and ν Are Real

From (7.105), using Rolle's theorem, we see that, for $z > 1$, between two consecutive zeros of $R_\nu^\mu(z)$ there lies at least one zero of $R_\nu^{\mu+1}(z)$. This is also true, from (7.133), for the range $-1 < x < 1$. The point $x = 0$ must be excluded from the range considered if $\mu + \nu + 2$ is a positive integer. The converse of these statements is not true.

Other results follow from those given in §6.12, for the B function. Thus, from (7.82), we find that, if $1 + \nu + \mu > 0$ and $\frac{3}{2} + \nu > 0$, $R_\nu^\mu(z)$ has no zero for $z > 1$ (in this case, it tends to zero as $z \to \infty$).

7.14 Indefinite Integrals Connected with $R_\nu^\mu(z)$

A number of indefinite integrals connected with $R_\nu^\mu(z)$ can be derived directly from the differential relations given in §§7.8 and 7.9. Other integrals can be obtained by solving the differential equation

$$(1 - z^2)\frac{d^2y}{dz^2} - 2z\frac{dy}{dz} + [\nu(\nu+1) - \mu^2(1 - z^2)^{-1}]y$$
$$= -e^{i\pi\mu}\frac{2^{-\nu}\Gamma(\mu+\nu+2)}{\Gamma(\nu+1)} z^{-\mu-\nu-2}(z^2 - 1)^{(1/2)\mu} \qquad (7.135)$$

by the method of variation of parameters (see §1.5). The Wronskian corresponding to the solutions $P_\nu^\mu(z)$ and $Q_\nu^\mu(z)$ is given by (7.66). We find that

$$R_\nu^\mu(z) = \frac{2^{-\nu}(\mu+\nu+1)\Gamma(1+\nu-\mu)}{\Gamma(1+\nu)}\left[P_\nu^\mu(z)\int z^{-\mu-\nu-2}(z^2 - 1)^{(1/2)\mu}Q_\nu^\mu(z)\,dz\right.$$
$$\left. - Q_\nu^\mu(z)\int z^{-\mu-\nu-2}(z^2 - 1)^{(1/2)\mu}P_\nu^\mu(z)\,dz\right]. \qquad (7.136)$$

Now $u = P_\nu^\mu(z)$ is a solution of the differential equation

$$(1 - z^2)\frac{d^2u}{dz^2} - 2z\frac{du}{dz} + [\nu(\nu+1) - \mu^2(1 - z^2)^{-1}]u = 0. \qquad (7.137)$$

On multiplying (7.135) by u and (7.137) by y and subtracting, we obtain

$$(1 - z^2)\left(u\frac{d^2y}{dz^2} - y\frac{d^2u}{dz^2}\right) - 2z\left(u\frac{dy}{dz} - y\frac{du}{dz}\right)$$
$$= -e^{i\pi\mu}\frac{2^{-\nu}\Gamma(\mu+\nu+2)}{\Gamma(\nu+1)} z^{-\mu-\nu-2}(z^2 - 1)^{(1/2)\mu}u\,;$$

that is,

$$\frac{d}{dz}\left[(1-z^2)\left(u\frac{dy}{dz}-y\frac{du}{dz}\right)\right] = -e^{i\pi\mu}\frac{2^{-\nu}\Gamma(\mu+\nu+2)}{\Gamma(\nu+1)} \times z^{-\mu-\nu-2}(z^2-1)^{(1/2)\mu}u. \quad (7.138)$$

On integrating (7.138) and putting $u = P_\nu^\mu(z)$, we see that

$$\int z^{-\mu-\nu-2}(z^2-1)^{(1/2)\mu}P_\nu^\mu(z)\,dz$$

$$= e^{-i\pi\mu}\frac{2^\nu\Gamma(\nu+1)}{\Gamma(\mu+\nu+2)}(z^2-1)\left\{P_\nu^\mu(z)\frac{d}{dz}[R_\nu^\mu(z)] - R_\nu^\mu(z)\frac{d}{dz}[P_\nu^\mu(z)]\right\}$$

$$= e^{-i\pi\mu}\frac{2^\nu\Gamma(\nu+1)}{\Gamma(\mu+\nu+2)}(z^2-1)^{1/2}\{P_\nu^\mu(z)R_\nu^{\mu+1}(z) - R_\nu^\mu(z)P_\nu^{\mu+1}(z)\}. \quad (7.139)$$

In (7.139) we can replace the P functions by the corresponding Q functions, the integral being indefinite. Other integrals can be found by using the differential equations (7.108) to (7.110).

7.15 Infinite Integrals Connected with $R_\nu^\mu(z)$

An integral relationship between $R_\nu^\mu(z)$ and the modified Struve function $L_\nu(z)$ (defined in §3.14) follows immediately from (7.99) and (3.119). We find

$$R_\nu^\mu(z) = e^{i\pi\mu}(\tfrac{1}{2}\pi)^{1/2}(z^2-1)^{(1/2)\mu}\int_0^\infty e^{-tz}L_{\nu+(1/2)}(t)t^{\mu-(1/2)}\,dt$$

$$[\operatorname{Re} z > 1,\ \operatorname{Re}(\mu+\nu) > -2]. \quad (7.140)$$

The corresponding integral for $Q_\nu^\mu(z)$ is (Erdélyi [*56*, 1953b])

$$Q_\nu^\mu(z) = e^{i\pi\mu}(\tfrac{1}{2}\pi)^{1/2}(z^2-1)^{(1/2)\mu}\int_0^\infty e^{-tz}I_{\nu+(1/2)}(t)t^{\mu-(1/2)}\,dt$$

$$[\operatorname{Re} z > 1,\ \operatorname{Re}(\mu+\nu) > -1], \quad (7.141)$$

where I is the modified Bessel function of the first kind (see §3.2).

The formula

$$\int_1^\infty (z^2-1)^{\lambda-1}(a^2z^2-1)^{-(1/2)\mu}R_\nu^\mu(az)\,dz = e^{i\pi\mu}2^{\mu-1}\pi^{-1/2}\Gamma\left(\frac{\mu+\nu+3}{2}\right)\Gamma(\lambda)$$

$$\times\,\Gamma\left(\frac{\mu+\nu+3}{2}-\lambda\right)a^{-\mu-\nu-2}\,{}_3F_2\left(1,\frac{\mu+\nu+3}{2},\frac{\mu+\nu+3}{2}-\lambda;\nu+2,\tfrac{3}{2};\frac{1}{a^2}\right)$$

$$[|\arg(a-1)| < \pi,\ \operatorname{Re}\lambda > 0,\ \operatorname{Re}(2\lambda-\mu-\nu) < 3] \quad (7.142)$$

may be proved by expanding the integrand in descending powers of z and integrating term by term, using the formula

$$\int_1^\infty (u^2-1)^{x-1}u^{1-2x-2y}\,du = \frac{\Gamma(x)\Gamma(y)}{2\Gamma(x+y)}.$$

7.16 The Nonhomogeneous Legendre Functions $s^\mu_{\nu,\sigma}(z)$ and $S^\mu_{\nu,\sigma}(z)$

We consider next the solutions of the nonhomogeneous Legendre equation

$$(1-z^2)\frac{d^2y}{dz^2} - 2z\frac{dy}{dz} + [\nu(\nu+1) - \mu^2(1-z^2)^{-1}]y = z^{2\sigma-2}(z^2-1)^{(1/2)\mu}, \tag{7.143}$$

where μ, ν, and σ are constants. As stated above, the associated homogeneous equation has three regular singularities (at $z=-1$, 1, and ∞). We shall derive the properties of certain particular integrals of (7.143) in a similar manner to that given in §6.16 for the functions $f_\sigma(a, b; c; z)$ and $F_\sigma(a, b; c; z)$.

On making the substitution $y=(z^2-1)^{(1/2)\mu}u$, (7.143) becomes

$$(1-z^2)\frac{d^2u}{dz^2} - 2(\mu+1)z\frac{du}{dz} + (\nu-\mu)(\nu+1+\mu)u = z^{2\sigma-2}. \tag{7.144}$$

Finally, putting $\zeta = z^2$, (7.144) becomes

$$\zeta(1-\zeta)\frac{d^2u}{d\zeta^2} + [\tfrac{1}{2} - (\mu+\tfrac{3}{2})\zeta]\frac{du}{d\zeta} + \tfrac{1}{4}(\nu-\mu)(\nu+1+\mu)u = \tfrac{1}{4}\zeta^{\sigma-1}. \tag{7.145}$$

Comparing (7.145) with (6.184), we see that a particular integral of (7.145) is $\tfrac{1}{4}f_\sigma(\tfrac{1}{2}\mu-\tfrac{1}{2}\nu, \tfrac{1}{2}+\tfrac{1}{2}\mu+\tfrac{1}{2}\nu; \tfrac{1}{2}; \zeta)$, where the f_σ function is defined in §6.16.

Thus a particular integral of (7.143) is

$$\begin{aligned} s^\mu_{\nu,\sigma}(z) &= \tfrac{1}{4}(z^2-1)^{(1/2)\mu} f_\sigma(\tfrac{1}{2}\mu-\tfrac{1}{2}\nu, \tfrac{1}{2}+\tfrac{1}{2}\mu+\tfrac{1}{2}\nu; \tfrac{1}{2}; z^2) \\ &= \frac{z^{2\sigma}(z^2-1)^{(1/2)\mu}}{2\sigma(2\sigma-1)}\,{}_3F_2(1, \sigma+\tfrac{1}{2}\mu-\tfrac{1}{2}\nu, \sigma+\tfrac{1}{2}+\tfrac{1}{2}\mu+\tfrac{1}{2}\nu; \\ &\qquad \sigma+1, \sigma+\tfrac{1}{2}; z^2). \end{aligned} \tag{7.146}$$

From (7.146) we see that $(z^2-1)^{-(1/2)\mu}s^\mu_{\nu,\sigma}(z)$ can be expanded in a series of ascending powers of z which converges when $|z|<1$. The complete primitive of (7.143) is

$$y = C_1P^\mu_\nu(z) + C_2Q^\mu_\nu(z) + s^\mu_{\nu,\sigma}(z), \tag{7.147}$$

where C_1 and C_2 are arbitrary constants.

As shown in §6.16, the series solution (7.146) is not valid if $2\sigma - 1$ is zero or a negative integer. For these values of σ, the particular solution of (7.143) will, in general, contain logarithmic terms.

Using the results of §6.16, we find

$$s^{\mu}_{\nu,\sigma}(z) = s^{\mu}_{-\nu-1,\sigma}(z). \tag{7.148}$$

If $\sigma + \frac{1}{2}\mu - \frac{1}{2}\nu$ or $\sigma + \frac{1}{2} + \frac{1}{2}\mu + \frac{1}{2}\nu$ is zero or a negative integer, the series (7.146) terminates. In particular,

$$s^{\mu}_{\nu,(1/2)\nu-(1/2)\mu}(z) = \frac{z^{\nu-\mu}(z^2-1)^{(1/2)\mu}}{(\nu-\mu)(\nu-\mu-1)} \tag{7.149}$$

and

$$s^{\mu}_{\nu,-(1/2)-(1/2)\mu-(1/2)\nu}(z) = \frac{z^{-1-\mu-\nu}(z^2-1)^{(1/2)\mu}}{(\mu+\nu+1)(\mu+\nu+2)}. \tag{7.150}$$

Another particular integral of (7.145) is $\frac{1}{4}F_\sigma(\frac{1}{2}\mu - \frac{1}{2}\nu, \frac{1}{2} + \frac{1}{2}\mu + \frac{1}{2}\nu; \frac{1}{2}; \zeta)$, where the function F_σ is defined in §6.16. Thus a second particular integral of (7.143) is

$$\begin{aligned} S^{\mu}_{\nu,\sigma}(z) &= \tfrac{1}{4}(z^2-1)^{(1/2)\mu}F_\sigma(\tfrac{1}{2}\mu - \tfrac{1}{2}\nu, \tfrac{1}{2} + \tfrac{1}{2}\mu + \tfrac{1}{2}\nu; \tfrac{1}{2}; z^2) \\ &= -\frac{z^{2\sigma-2}(z^2-1)^{(1/2)\mu}}{(2\sigma+\mu+\nu-1)(2\sigma+\mu-\nu-2)}\, {}_3F_2\Big(1, 1-\sigma, \tfrac{3}{2}-\sigma; \\ &\qquad 2-\sigma-\tfrac{1}{2}\mu+\tfrac{1}{2}\nu, \tfrac{3}{2}-\sigma-\tfrac{1}{2}\mu-\tfrac{1}{2}\nu; \frac{1}{z^2}\Big). \end{aligned} \tag{7.151}$$

From (7.151), we see that $(z^2-1)^{-(1/2)\mu}S^{\mu}_{\nu,\sigma}(z)$ can be expressed as a series of descending powers of z which converges when $|z| > 1$.

Using the results of §6.16, we find

$$S^{\mu}_{\nu,\sigma}(z) = S^{\mu}_{-\nu-1,\sigma}(z), \tag{7.152}$$

$$S^{\mu}_{\nu,1}(z) = -\frac{(z^2-1)^{(1/2)\mu}}{(\mu+\nu+1)(\mu-\nu)}, \tag{7.153}$$

and

$$S^{\mu}_{\nu,3/2}(z) = -\frac{z(z^2-1)^{(1/2)\mu}}{(\mu+\nu+2)(\mu-\nu+1)}. \tag{7.154}$$

Also, from (7.99),

$$S^{\mu}_{\nu,-(1/2)\mu-(1/2)\nu}(z) = -e^{-i\pi\mu}\frac{2^\nu\Gamma(\nu+1)}{\Gamma(\mu+\nu+2)}R^{\mu}_{\nu}(z). \tag{7.155}$$

From (7.146) and (7.151),

$$S^{\mu}_{0,\sigma}(z) = -s^{\mu}_{0,1-\sigma-(1/2)\mu}\left(\frac{1}{z}\right) \tag{7.156}$$

and, conversely,

$$s^{\mu}_{0,\sigma}(z) = -S^{\mu}_{0,1-\sigma-(1/2)\mu}\left(\frac{1}{z}\right). \tag{7.157}$$

Using the results of §6.17, we find

$$s^{\mu}_{\nu,\sigma}(z) = S^{\mu}_{\nu,\sigma}(z) + A_1 e^{-i\pi[\sigma+(1/2)\mu-(1/2)\nu]\varepsilon} y_4 + B_1 e^{-i\pi[\sigma+(1/2)+(1/2)\mu+(1/2)\nu]\varepsilon} y_3 \tag{7.158}$$

where y_3 and y_4 are given by (7.60) and (7.61),

$$A_1 = \frac{2^{\mu-\nu-2\sigma}\Gamma(\nu+\frac{1}{2})\Gamma(2\sigma-1)\Gamma(1-\sigma-\frac{1}{2}\mu+\frac{1}{2}\nu)}{\Gamma(1-\mu+\nu)\Gamma(\frac{1}{2}+\sigma+\frac{1}{2}\mu+\frac{1}{2}\nu)},$$

$$B_1 = \frac{2^{1+\mu+\nu-2\sigma}\Gamma(-\nu-\frac{1}{2})\Gamma(2\sigma-1)\Gamma(\frac{1}{2}-\sigma-\frac{1}{2}\mu-\frac{1}{2}\nu)}{\Gamma(-\mu-\nu)\Gamma(\sigma+\frac{1}{2}\mu-\frac{1}{2}\nu)},$$

and $\varepsilon = \operatorname{sgn}(\operatorname{Im} z) = 1, -1$, according as $\operatorname{Im} z >, <0$.

On writing $z = \mu/x$, and letting $\mu \to \infty$, we find, from (7.151),

$$\lim_{\mu\to\infty}\left[\mu^{2-2\sigma} S^{\mu}_{\nu,\sigma-(1/2)\mu}\left(\frac{\mu}{x}\right)\right] = e^{i\pi[\sigma+(1/4)]} x^{1/2} s_{(1/2)-2\sigma,\nu+(1/2)}(e^{(1/2)i\pi}x) \tag{7.159}$$

and, from (7.146),

$$\lim_{\mu\to\infty}\left[\mu^{2-2\sigma} s^{\mu}_{\nu,\sigma-(1/2)\mu}\left(\frac{\mu}{x}\right)\right] = e^{i\pi[\sigma+(1/4)]} x^{1/2} S_{(1/2)-2\sigma,\nu+(1/2)}(^{(1/2)i\pi}\, x), \tag{7.160}$$

where the s and S functions on the right sides of (7.159) and (7.160) are the Lommel functions (see §§3.16 and 3.17).

7.17 Recurrence Formulas and Relations Between Contiguous Functions

Using the results of §6.18, we find, from (7.146),

$$(2\sigma+\mu-\nu)(2\sigma+1+\mu+\nu)s^{\mu}_{\nu,\sigma+1}(z) = 2\sigma(2\sigma-1)s^{\mu}_{\nu,\sigma}(z) - z^{2\sigma}(z^2-1)^{(1/2)\mu} \tag{7.161}$$

and

$$\begin{aligned}\frac{d}{dz}[(z^2-1)^{-(1/2)\mu}s^{\mu}_{\nu,\sigma}(z)] &= \tfrac{1}{2}z(\sigma-1)f_{\sigma-1}(1+\tfrac{1}{2}\mu-\tfrac{1}{2}\nu, \tfrac{3}{2}+\tfrac{1}{2}\mu+\tfrac{1}{2}\nu; \tfrac{3}{2}; z^2)\\ &= \tfrac{1}{2}(\sigma-1)f_{\sigma-(1/2)}(\tfrac{1}{2}+\tfrac{1}{2}\mu+\tfrac{1}{2}\nu, 1+\tfrac{1}{2}\mu+\tfrac{1}{2}\nu; \tfrac{1}{2}; z^2)\\ &= 2(\sigma-1)(z^2-1)^{-(1/2)(\mu+1)}s^{\mu+1}_{\nu,\sigma-1/2}(z);\end{aligned} \tag{7.162}$$

that is,

$$\frac{d}{dz} s^{\mu}_{\nu,\sigma}(z) = 2(\sigma - 1)(z^2 - 1)^{-1/2} s^{\mu+1}_{\nu,\sigma-(1/2)}(z) + \frac{\mu z}{z^2 - 1} s^{\mu}_{\nu,\sigma}(z). \quad (7.163)$$

By repeated application of (7.162) we see that

$$s^{m}_{\nu,\sigma-(1/2)m}(z) = \frac{\Gamma(2\sigma - m - 1)}{\Gamma(2\sigma - 1)} (z^2 - 1)^{(1/2)m} \frac{d^m}{dz^m} s^{0}_{\nu,\sigma}(z) \quad (7.164)$$

where m is any positive integer.

Differentiating (7.162) we obtain

$$\frac{d^2}{dz^2} s^{\mu}_{\nu,\sigma}(z) = 2(\sigma - 1)(2\sigma - 3)(z^2 - 1)^{-1} s^{\mu+2}_{\nu,\sigma-1}(z) + 4\mu(\sigma - 1)z(z^2 - 1)^{-3/2}$$
$$\times s^{\mu+1}_{\nu,\sigma-(1/2)}(z) + \mu(\mu z^2 - 1 - z^2)(z^2 - 1)^{-2} s^{\mu}_{\nu,\sigma}(z). \quad (7.165)$$

From (7.143), (7.163), and (7.165), we see that

$$-2(\sigma - 1)(2\sigma - 3) s^{\mu+2}_{\nu,\sigma-1}(z) - 4(\mu + 1)(\sigma - 1)z(z^2 - 1)^{-1/2} s^{\mu+1}_{\nu,\sigma-(1/2)}(z)$$
$$+ (\nu - \mu)(\nu + \mu + 1) s^{\mu}_{\nu,\sigma}(z) = z^{2\sigma-2}(z^2 - 1)^{(1/2)\mu}. \quad (7.166)$$

From (7.161) and (7.166),

$$-(2\sigma + \mu - \nu)(2\sigma + 1 + \mu + \nu) s^{\mu+2}_{\nu,\sigma} - 4(\mu + 1)(\sigma - 1)z(z^2 - 1)^{-1/2} s^{\mu+1}_{\nu,\sigma-(1/2)}(z)$$
$$+ (\nu - \mu)(\nu + \mu + 1) s^{\mu}_{\nu,\sigma}(z) = z^{2\sigma}(z^2 - 1)^{(1/2)\mu}. \quad (7.167)$$

Using the relations for contiguous f functions given in §6.18, we find

$$z(\sigma - 1) s^{\mu+1}_{\nu,\sigma-(1/2)}(z)$$
$$= (\sigma + \tfrac{1}{2}\mu - \tfrac{1}{2}\nu) s^{\mu+1}_{\nu-1,\sigma}(z) - \tfrac{1}{2}(\mu - \nu)(z^2 - 1)^{1/2} s^{\mu}_{\nu,\sigma}(z)$$
$$= (\sigma + \tfrac{1}{2} + \tfrac{1}{2}\mu + \tfrac{1}{2}\nu) s^{\mu+1}_{\nu+1,\sigma}(z) - \tfrac{1}{2}(1 + \mu + \nu)(z^2 - 1)^{1/2} s^{\mu}_{\nu,\sigma}(z)$$
$$= \frac{(\mu - \nu - 1)(\mu - \nu - 2)}{2(2\sigma + \mu - \nu - 2)} s^{\mu-1}_{\nu+1,\sigma}(z) - \tfrac{1}{2}[\mu - \nu - 1 + (\mu + \nu + 1)z^2]$$
$$\times (z^2 - 1)^{-(1/2)} s^{\mu}_{\nu,\sigma}(z) - \tfrac{1}{2} z^{2\sigma}(z^2 - 1)^{(1/2)(\mu-1)}/(2\sigma + \mu - \nu - 2)$$
$$= \frac{(\mu + \nu)(\mu + \nu - 1)}{2(2\sigma + \mu + \nu - 1)} s^{\mu-1}_{\nu-1,\sigma}(z) - \tfrac{1}{2}[\mu + \nu + (\mu - \nu)z^2](z^2 - 1)^{-(1/2)} s^{\mu}_{\nu,\sigma}(z)$$
$$- \tfrac{1}{2} z^{2\sigma}(z^2 - 1)^{(1/2)(\mu-1)}/(2\sigma + \mu + \nu - 1)$$
$$= \frac{(1 - \mu + \nu)(\mu + \nu)}{2(2\sigma - 1)} z s^{\mu-1}_{\nu,\sigma+1/2}(z) - \mu z^2(z^2 - 1)^{-(1/2)} s^{\mu}_{\nu,\sigma}(z)$$
$$- \tfrac{1}{2} z^{2\sigma}(z^2 - 1)^{(1/2)(\mu-1)}/(2\sigma - 1). \quad (7.168)$$

Using (7.151) we find that (7.161) to (7.168) hold if the function s is replaced throughout by S.

7.18 Nonhomogeneous Legendre Function $s^{\mu}_{\nu,\sigma}(x)$

When interest is confined to the real values $z = x$, where $-1 < x < 1$, it is convenient to introduce the function $s^{\mu}_{\nu,\sigma}(x)$ defined by

$$s^{\mu}_{\nu,\sigma}(x) = \tfrac{1}{4}(1 - x^2)^{(1/2)\mu} f_{\sigma}(\tfrac{1}{2}\mu - \tfrac{1}{2}\nu, \tfrac{1}{2} + \tfrac{1}{2}\mu + \tfrac{1}{2}\nu; \tfrac{1}{2}; x^2)$$
$$= \frac{x^{2\sigma}(1 - x^2)^{(1/2)\mu}}{2\sigma(2\sigma - 1)}\, {}_3F_2(1, \sigma + \tfrac{1}{2}\mu - \tfrac{1}{2}\nu, \sigma + \tfrac{1}{2} + \tfrac{1}{2}\mu + \tfrac{1}{2}\nu;$$
$$\sigma + 1, \sigma + \tfrac{1}{2}; x^2). \quad (7.169)$$

$s^{\mu}_{\nu,\sigma}(x)$ is a particular integral of the nonhomogeneous differential equation

$$(1 - x^2)\frac{d^2y}{dx^2} - 2x\frac{dy}{dx} + [\nu(\nu + 1) - \mu^2(1 - x^2)^{-1}]y = x^{2\sigma - 2}(1 - x^2)^{(1/2)\mu}. \quad (7.170)$$

7.19 Integrals Connected with $s^{\mu}_{\nu,\sigma}(z)$ and $S^{\mu}_{\nu,\sigma}(z)$

A number of indefinite integrals connected with $s^{\mu}_{\nu,\sigma}(z)$ and $S^{\mu}_{\nu,\sigma}(z)$ can be obtained from the differential relations given in §7.17. Other integrals can be obtained by solving the differential equation (7.143) by the method of variation of parameters. We find that

$$s^{\mu}_{\nu,\sigma}(z) = -e^{-i\pi\mu}\frac{\Gamma(1 + \nu - \mu)}{\Gamma(1 + \mu + \nu)}\Big[P^{\mu}_{\nu}(z)\int z^{2\sigma-2}(z^2 - 1)^{(1/2)\mu}Q^{\mu}_{\nu}(z)\,dz$$
$$- Q^{\mu}_{\nu}(z)\int z^{2\sigma-2}(z^2 - 1)^{(1/2)\mu}P^{\mu}_{\nu}(z)\,dz\Big]. \quad (7.171)$$

In a manner similar to that of §7.14, we can show that

$$\int z^{2\sigma-2}(z^2 - 1)^{(1/2)\mu}P^{\mu}_{\nu}(z)\,dz$$
$$= (z^2 - 1)\left\{s^{\mu}_{\nu,\sigma}(z)\frac{d}{dz}P^{\mu}_{\nu}(z) - P^{\mu}_{\nu}(z)\frac{d}{dz}s^{\mu}_{\nu,\sigma}(z)\right\}$$
$$= (z^2 - 1)^{1/2}[s^{\mu}_{\nu,\sigma}(z)P^{\mu+1}_{\nu}(z) - 2(\sigma - 1)P^{\mu}_{\nu}(z)s^{\mu+1}_{\nu,\sigma-(1/2)}(z)]. \quad (7.172)$$

In (7.172) we can substitute S for s on the right side, the integral on the left side being indefinite. Alternatively, from §7.18, we find, if $-1 < x - 1$, and $\sigma > \tfrac{1}{2}$,

$$\int x^{2\sigma-2}(1-x^2)^{(1/2)\mu}P^\mu_\nu(x)\,dx$$
$$= (1-x^2)^{1/2}[s^\mu_{\nu,\sigma}(x)P^{\mu+1}_\nu(x) - 2(\sigma-1)P^\mu_\nu(x)s^{\mu+1}_{\nu,\sigma-(1/2)}(x)]. \qquad (7.173)$$

If $\sigma > \frac{1}{2}$ and $\operatorname{Re}\mu < 0$, we find, on taking the limit as $x \to 1$,

$$\int_0^1 x^{2\sigma-2}(1-x^2)^{(1/2)\mu}P^\mu_\nu(x)\,dx = \frac{2^{\mu+1}}{\sigma(2\sigma-1)\Gamma(-\mu)}$$
$$\times\ {}_3F_2(1, \sigma+\tfrac{1}{2}\mu-\tfrac{1}{2}\nu, \sigma+\tfrac{1}{2}+\tfrac{1}{2}\mu+\tfrac{1}{2}\nu; \sigma+1, \sigma+\tfrac{1}{2}; 1). \qquad (7.174)$$

Now, as shown by Thomae [1879],

$${}_3F_2(a,b,c;e,f;1) = \frac{\Gamma(e)\Gamma(s)}{\Gamma(e-a)\Gamma(s+a)}\,{}_3F_2(a, f-b, f-c; f, s+a; 1), \qquad (7.175)$$

where $s = e+f-a-b-c$. From (7.174) and (7.175), if $\sigma > \frac{1}{2}$,

$$\int_0^1 x^{2\sigma-2}(1-x^2)^{(1/2)\mu}P^\mu_\nu(x)\,dx = \frac{2^{\mu}}{(2\sigma-1)\Gamma(1-\mu)}$$
$$\times\ {}_3F_2(1, \tfrac{1}{2}-\tfrac{1}{2}\mu+\tfrac{1}{2}\nu, -\tfrac{1}{2}\mu-\tfrac{1}{2}\nu; \sigma+\tfrac{1}{2}, 1-\mu; 1), \qquad (7.176)$$

in agreement with Barnes [*183*, 1908b].

7.20 The Nonhomogeneous Legendre Function $t^{\mu,\tau}_{\nu,\sigma}(z)$

As shown in §6.22, the solution of a number of nonhomogeneous Legendre equations can be expressed in terms of the nonhomogeneous hypergeometric functions. We shall here confine our attention to the equation

$$(1-z^2)\frac{d^2y}{dz^2} - 2z\frac{dy}{dz} + [\nu(\nu+1) - \mu^2(1-z^2)^{-1}]y$$
$$= z^{2\sigma-2}(z^2-1)^{(1/2)\mu+\tau-1}, \qquad (7.177)$$

where μ, ν, σ, and τ are constants. This equation is an obvious generalization of (7.143), and occurs in the solution of Poisson's equation in terms of spherical polar coordinates. We consider the z plane with a cut from $+1$ to $-\infty$. Thus

$$z-1 = (1-z)e^{i\pi\varepsilon}$$

and

$$z^2-1 = (1-z^2)e^{i\pi\varepsilon},$$

where $\varepsilon = \operatorname{sgn}(\operatorname{Im} z) = 1, -1$, according as $\operatorname{Im} z >, <0$.

On expanding $(1 - z^2)^{\tau-1}$ as a power series in ascending powers of z, we see, as in §1.12, that a particular integral of (7.177) is $t_{\nu,\sigma}^{\mu,\tau}(z)$, where

$$\begin{aligned} t_{\nu,\sigma}^{\mu,\tau}(z) &= e^{i\pi\varepsilon(\tau-1)} \sum_{n=0}^{\infty} \frac{\Gamma(n+1-\tau)}{\Gamma(1-\tau)\cdot n!}\, s_{\nu,\sigma+n}^{\mu}(z) \\ &= e^{i\pi\varepsilon(\tau-1)} \sum_{n=0}^{\infty} \frac{1}{4}\frac{\Gamma(n+1-\tau)}{(1-\tau)\cdot n!}(z^2-1)^{(1/2)\mu} \\ &\qquad \times f_{\sigma+n}(\tfrac{1}{2}\mu - \tfrac{1}{2}\nu, \tfrac{1}{2} + \tfrac{1}{2}\mu + \tfrac{1}{2}\nu; \tfrac{1}{2}; z^2) \\ &= \tfrac{1}{4}e^{i\pi\varepsilon(\tau-1)}(z^2-1)^{(1/2)\mu} C_{1,\sigma}^{(\tau)}(\tfrac{1}{2}\mu - \tfrac{1}{2}\nu, \tfrac{1}{2} + \tfrac{1}{2}\mu + \tfrac{1}{2}\nu; \tfrac{1}{2}; z^2), \end{aligned} \tag{7.178}$$

where $|z| < 1$ and the nonhomogeneous hypergeometric function C is defined in §6.20.

Using the results given in chapter 6, we find that (7.178) can be written in the alternative form

$$\begin{aligned} t_{\nu,\sigma}^{\mu,\tau}(z) &= e^{i\pi\varepsilon(\tau-1)} z^{2\sigma}(z^2-1)^{(1/2)\mu} \\ &\quad \times \sum_{n=0}^{\infty} 2^{2n-1} \frac{\Gamma(\sigma + \frac{1}{2}\mu - \frac{1}{2}\nu + n)\Gamma(\sigma + \frac{1}{2} + \frac{1}{2}\mu + \frac{1}{2}\nu + n)}{\Gamma(\sigma + \frac{1}{2}\mu - \frac{1}{2}\nu)\Gamma(\sigma + \frac{1}{2} + \frac{1}{2}\mu + \frac{1}{2}\nu)} \frac{\Gamma(2\sigma - 1)}{\Gamma(2\sigma + 2n)} \\ &\quad \times {}_3F_{2,(n+1)}[1-\tau, \sigma, \sigma - \tfrac{1}{2}; \sigma + \tfrac{1}{2}\mu - \tfrac{1}{2}\nu, \sigma + \tfrac{1}{2} + \tfrac{1}{2}\mu + \tfrac{1}{2}\nu; 1] z^{2n}, \end{aligned} \tag{7.179}$$

where ${}_3F_{2,(n+1)}$ stands for the first $n+1$ terms of the generalized hypergeometric series with the given parameters.

Using the results of §6.20, we find

$$t_{\nu,\sigma}^{\mu,\tau}(z) = t_{-\nu-1,\sigma}^{\mu,\tau}(z) \tag{7.180}$$

and

$$t_{\nu,\sigma}^{\mu,1}(z) = s_{\nu,\sigma}^{\mu}(z). \tag{7.181}$$

7.21 Recurrence Formulas and Relations Between Contiguous Functions

Using the results of §6.21, we find, from (7.178),

$$t_{\nu,\sigma}^{\mu,\tau}(z) = t_{\nu,\sigma+1}^{\mu,\tau-1}(z) - t_{\nu,\sigma}^{\mu,\tau-1}(z). \tag{7.182}$$

From (7.182) we see that any function $t_{\nu,\sigma}^{\mu,\tau}(z)$ can be expressed in terms of $n+1$ functions of the form $t_{\nu,\sigma+m}^{\mu,\tau-n}(z)$ ($m = 0$ to n). Alternatively, we see from (7.182) that any function $t_{\nu,\sigma}^{\mu,\tau}(z)$ can be expressed in terms of $n+1$ functions of the form $t_{\nu,\sigma-n}^{\mu,\tau+m}(z)$ ($m = 0$ to n).

It is easily verified that $y = z^{2\sigma}(z^2-1)^{(1/2)\mu+\tau}$ is a particular solution of the equation

$$(1-z^2)\frac{d^2y}{dz^2}-2z\frac{dy}{dz}+[\nu(\nu+1)-\mu^2(1-z^2)^{-1}]y=z^{2\sigma-2}(z^2-1)^{(1/2)\mu+\tau-1}$$
$$\times[-2\sigma(2\sigma-1)+\{4\sigma(2\sigma+\mu+2\tau)+2\tau+(\mu-\nu)(\mu+\nu+1)\}z^2$$
$$-\{2\sigma(2\sigma+2\mu+4\tau+1)+(\mu+2\tau-\nu)(\mu+2\tau+\nu+1)\}z^4]. \quad (7.183)$$

Now the general solution of (7.183) can be written in the form

$$-2\sigma(2\sigma-1)t^{\mu,\tau}_{\nu,\sigma}(z)+\{4\sigma(2\sigma+\mu+2\tau)+2\tau+(\mu-\nu)(\mu+\nu+1)\}t^{\mu,\tau}_{\nu,\sigma+1}(z)$$
$$-\{2\sigma(2\sigma+2\mu+4\tau+1)+(\mu+2\tau-\nu)(\mu+2\tau+\nu+1)\}t^{\mu,\tau}_{\nu,\sigma+2}(z)$$
$$+C_1P^\mu_\nu(z)+C_2Q^\mu_\nu(z),$$

where C_1 and C_2 are arbitrary constants. On comparing the power series for these two solutions in ascending powers of z we find that

$$-2\sigma(2\sigma-1)t^{\mu,\tau}_{\nu,\sigma}(z)+\{4\sigma(2\sigma+\mu+2\tau)+2\tau+(\mu-\nu)(\mu+\nu+1)\}t^{\mu,\tau}_{\nu,\sigma+1}(z)$$
$$-\{2\sigma(2\sigma+2\mu+4\tau+1)+(\mu+2\tau-\nu)(\mu+2\tau+\nu+1)\}t^{\mu,\tau}_{\nu,\sigma+2}(z)$$
$$=z^{2\sigma}(z^2-1)^{(1/2)\mu+\tau}. \quad (7.184)$$

On differentiating (7.178), and using (7.162), we find that

$$\frac{d}{dz}[(z^2-1)^{-(1/2)\mu}t^{\mu,\tau}_{\nu\,\sigma}(z)]$$
$$=2e^{i\pi\varepsilon(\tau-1)}(z^2-1)^{-(1/2)(\mu+1)}\sum_{n=0}^{\infty}(\sigma+n-1)\frac{\Gamma(n+1-\tau)}{\Gamma(1-\tau)\cdot n!}s^{\mu+1}_{\nu,\sigma+n-(1/2)}(z)$$
$$=2e^{i\pi\varepsilon(\tau-1)}(z^2-1)^{-(1/2)(\mu+1)}\Bigg[(\sigma-1)\sum_{n=0}^{\infty}\frac{\Gamma(n+1-\tau)}{\Gamma(1-\tau)\cdot n!}s^{\mu+1}_{\nu,\sigma+n-(1/2)}(z)$$
$$+(1-\tau)\sum_{n=1}^{\infty}\frac{\Gamma(n+1-\tau)}{\Gamma(2-\tau)(n-1)!}s^{\mu+1}_{\nu,\sigma+n-(1/2)}(z)\Bigg];$$

that is,

$$\frac{d}{dz}[(z^2-1)^{-(1/2)\mu}t^{\mu,\tau}_{\nu,\sigma}(z)]=2(z^2-1)^{-(1/2)(\mu+1)}[(\sigma-1)t^{\mu+1,\tau}_{\nu,\sigma-(1/2)}(z)$$
$$+(\tau-1)t^{\mu+1,\tau-1}_{\nu,\sigma+(1/2)}(z)]. \quad (7.185)$$

Using (7.168), we find

$$\tfrac{1}{2}z(z^2-1)^{(1/2)(\mu+1)}\frac{d}{dz}[(z^2-1)^{-(1/2)\mu}t^{\mu,\tau}_{\nu,\sigma}(z)]$$
$$=(\sigma+\tfrac{1}{2}\mu-\tfrac{1}{2}\nu)t^{\mu+1,\tau}_{\nu-1,\sigma}(z)+(\tau-1)t^{\mu+1,\tau-1}_{\nu-1,\sigma+1}(z)$$
$$-\tfrac{1}{2}(\mu-\nu)(z^2-1)^{1/2}t^{\mu,\tau}_{\nu,\sigma}(z)$$
$$=(\sigma+\tfrac{1}{2}+\tfrac{1}{2}\mu+\tfrac{1}{2}\nu)t^{\mu+1,\tau}_{\nu+1,\sigma}(z)+(\tau-1)t^{\mu+1,\tau-1}_{\nu+1,\sigma+1}(z)$$
$$-\tfrac{1}{2}(1+\mu+\nu)(z^2-1)^{1/2}t^{\mu,\tau}_{\nu,\sigma}(z). \quad (7.186)$$

7.22 Nonhomogeneous Legendre Function $t^{\mu,\tau}_{\nu,\sigma}(x)$

When interest is confined to the real values $z = x$, where $-1 < x < 1$, it is convenient to introduce the function $t^{\mu,\tau}_{\nu,\sigma}(x)$, defined by

$$t^{\mu,\tau}_{\nu,\sigma}(x) = \tfrac{1}{4}(1 - x^2)^{(1/2)\mu} C^{(\tau)}_{1,\sigma}(\tfrac{1}{2}\mu - \tfrac{1}{2}\nu, \tfrac{1}{2} + \tfrac{1}{2}\mu + \tfrac{1}{2}\nu; \tfrac{1}{2}; x^2). \qquad (7.187)$$

$t^{\mu,\tau}_{\nu,\sigma}(x)$ is a particular integral of the nonhomogeneous differential equation

$$(1 - x^2)\frac{d^2y}{dx^2} - 2x\frac{dy}{dx} + [\nu(\nu + 1) - \mu^2(1 - x^2)^{-1}]y$$
$$= x^{2\sigma-2}(1 - x^2)^{(1/2)\mu+\tau-1}. \qquad (7.188)$$

7.23 Related Differential Equations

We shall now briefly consider certain second-order differential equations, the solutions of which can be expressed in terms of $t^{\mu,\tau}_{\nu,\sigma}(z)$.

In (7.177), put $u = (z^2 - 1)^{-\lambda}y$. Then

$$(1 - z^2)\frac{d^2u}{dz^2} - 2(2\lambda + 1)z\frac{du}{dz}$$
$$+ [(\nu - 2\lambda)(\nu + 1 + 2\lambda) + (4\lambda^2 - \mu^2)(1 - z^2)^{-1}]u$$
$$= z^{2\sigma-2}(z^2 - 1)^{(1/2)\mu+\tau-1-\lambda}. \qquad (7.189)$$

Finally, in (7.189), put

$$x = \zeta^\alpha u = \zeta^\alpha(z^2 - 1)^{-\lambda}y, \qquad z = \beta\zeta^\gamma, \qquad (7.190)$$

where α, β, and γ are constants. Equation (7.189) is then transformed into

$$(1 - \beta^2\zeta^{2\gamma})\zeta^2\frac{d^2x}{d\zeta^2} + [(1 - 2\alpha - \gamma)\zeta - \beta^2(1 - 2\alpha + \gamma + 4\lambda\gamma)\zeta^{1+2\gamma}]\frac{dx}{d\zeta}$$
$$+ [\alpha(\alpha + \gamma) + \{\gamma^2(\nu - 2\lambda)(\nu + 1 + 2\lambda) + \alpha\gamma(4\lambda + 1) - \alpha^2\}\beta^2\zeta^{2\gamma}$$
$$+ (4\lambda^2 - \mu^2)\beta^2\gamma^2\zeta^{2\gamma}(1 - \beta^2\zeta^{2\gamma})^{-1}]x$$
$$= \beta^{2\sigma}\gamma^2\zeta^{\alpha+2\sigma\gamma}(\beta^2\zeta^{2\gamma} - 1)^{(1/2)\mu+\tau-1-\lambda}. \qquad (7.191)$$

A particular integral of (7.191) is

$$x = \zeta^\alpha(\beta^2\zeta^{2\gamma} - 1)^{-\lambda}t^{\mu,\tau}_{\nu,\sigma}(\beta\zeta^\gamma).$$

The complementary function is

$$\zeta^\alpha(\beta^2\zeta^{2\gamma} - 1)^{-\lambda}[C_1P^\mu_\nu(\beta\zeta^\gamma) + C_2Q^\mu_\nu(\beta\zeta^\gamma)].$$

Some special cases of this transformation are of interest. In (7.191) put

$\gamma = 1$. Then (7.191) becomes

$$(1-\beta^2\zeta^2)\frac{d^2x}{d\zeta^2} - 2\left[\beta^2(1-\alpha+2\lambda)\zeta + \frac{\alpha}{\zeta}\right]\frac{dx}{d\zeta} + \left[\frac{\alpha(\alpha+1)}{\zeta^2}\right.$$

$$\left. + \{(\nu-2\lambda)(\nu+1+2\lambda) + \alpha(4\lambda+1) - \alpha^2\}\beta^2 + (4\lambda^2-\mu^2)\beta^2(1-\beta^2\zeta^2)^{-1}\right]x$$

$$= \beta^{2\sigma}\zeta^{\alpha+2\sigma-2}(\beta^2\zeta^2-1)^{(1/2)\mu+\tau-1-\lambda}, \quad (7.192)$$

with a particular integral $x = \zeta^{\alpha}(\beta^2\zeta^2-1)^{-\lambda}t_{\nu,\sigma}^{\mu,\tau}(\beta\zeta)$.

In (7.192) put $\alpha = 0$. Then (7.192) becomes

$$(1-\beta^2\zeta^2)\frac{d^2x}{d\zeta^2} - 2\beta^2(2\lambda+1)\zeta\frac{dx}{d\zeta} + [(\nu-2\lambda)(\nu+1+2\lambda)$$

$$+ (4\lambda^2-\mu^2)(1-\beta^2\zeta^2)^{-1}]\beta^2 x = \beta^{2\sigma}\zeta^{2\sigma-2}(\beta^2\zeta^2-1)^{(1/2)\mu+\tau-1-\lambda}, \quad (7.193)$$

with a particular integral $x = (\beta^2\zeta^2-1)^{-\lambda}t_{\nu,\sigma}^{\mu,\tau}(\beta\zeta)$.

In (7.193) put $\lambda = \frac{1}{2}\mu$. Then (7.193) becomes

$$(1-\beta^2\zeta^2)\frac{d^2x}{d\zeta^2} - 2\beta^2(\mu+1)\zeta\frac{dx}{d\zeta} + [(\nu-\mu)(\nu+1+\mu)]\beta^2 x$$

$$= \beta^{2\sigma}\zeta^{2\sigma-2}(\beta^2\zeta^2-1)^{\tau-1}, \quad (7.194)$$

with a particular integral $x = (\beta^2\zeta^2-1)^{-(1/2)\mu}t_{\nu,\sigma}^{\mu,\tau}(\beta\zeta)$.

In (7.191) put $\gamma = \frac{1}{2}$. Then (7.191) becomes

$$(1-\beta^2\zeta)\zeta\frac{d^2x}{d\zeta^2} + [\tfrac{1}{2} - 2\alpha - \beta^2(\tfrac{3}{2} - 2\alpha + 2\lambda)\zeta]\frac{dx}{d\zeta}$$

$$+ [\{\tfrac{1}{4}(\nu-2\lambda)(\nu+1+2\lambda) + \tfrac{1}{2}\alpha(4\lambda+1) - \alpha^2\}\beta^2 + \alpha(\alpha+\tfrac{1}{2})\zeta^{-1}$$

$$+ (\lambda^2 - \tfrac{1}{4}\mu^2)\beta^2(1-\beta^2\zeta)^{-1}]x = \tfrac{1}{4}\beta^{2\sigma}\zeta^{\alpha+\sigma-1}(\beta^2\zeta-1)^{(1/2)\mu+\tau-1-\lambda}, \quad (7.195)$$

with a particular integral $x = \zeta^{\alpha}(\beta^2\zeta-1)^{-\lambda}t_{\nu,\sigma}^{\mu,\tau}(\beta\zeta^{1/2})$.

In (7.191) put $\gamma = -\frac{1}{2}$. Then (7.191) becomes

$$\zeta(\zeta-\beta^2)\frac{d^2x}{d\zeta^2} + [(\tfrac{3}{2}-2\alpha)\zeta - \beta^2(\tfrac{1}{2} - 2\alpha - 2\lambda)]\frac{dx}{d\zeta}$$

$$+ [\alpha(\alpha-\tfrac{1}{2}) + \{\tfrac{1}{4}(\nu-2\lambda)(\nu+1+2\lambda) - \tfrac{1}{2}\alpha(4\lambda+1) - \alpha^2\}\beta^2\zeta^{-1}$$

$$+ (\lambda^2 - \tfrac{1}{4}\mu^2)\beta^2(\zeta-\beta^2)^{-1}]x = \tfrac{1}{4}\beta^{2\sigma}\zeta^{\alpha-\sigma}(\beta^2\zeta^{-1}-1)^{(1/2)\mu+\tau-1-\lambda}, \quad (7.196)$$

with a particular integral $x = \zeta^{\alpha}(\beta^2\zeta^{-1}-1)^{-\lambda}t_{\nu,\sigma}^{\mu,\tau}(\beta\zeta^{-1/2})$.

In (7.191) put $\gamma = -1$. Then (7.191) becomes

$$(\zeta^2 - \beta^2)\frac{d^2x}{d\zeta^2} + 2\left[(1-\alpha)\zeta + \frac{\beta^2(\alpha + 2\lambda)}{\zeta}\right]\frac{dx}{d\zeta}$$

$$+\left[\alpha(\alpha - 1) + \{(\nu - 2\lambda)(\nu + 1 + 2\lambda) - \alpha(4\lambda + 1) - \alpha^2\}\frac{\beta^2}{\zeta^2}\right.$$

$$\left.+\frac{(4\lambda^2 - \mu^2)\beta^2}{\zeta^2 - \beta^2}\right]x = \beta^{2\sigma}\zeta^{\alpha - 2\sigma}(\beta^2\zeta^{-2} - 1)^{(1/2)\mu + \tau - 1 - \lambda}, \qquad (7.197)$$

with a particular integral $x = \zeta^{\alpha}(\beta^2\zeta^{-2} - 1)^{-\lambda}t_{\nu,\sigma}^{\mu,\tau}(\beta\zeta^{-1})$.

PROBLEMS

1. Prove that

$$p_w\begin{pmatrix}0 & \infty & 1\\ \alpha & \beta & \gamma\\ \alpha' & \beta' & \gamma'\end{pmatrix}[w^{-r}(1-w)^{-s}y]$$

$$= w^{-r}(1-w)^{-s}p_w\begin{pmatrix}0 & \infty & 1\\ \alpha + r & \beta - r - s & \gamma + s\\ \alpha' + r & \beta' - r - s & \gamma' + s\end{pmatrix}y.$$

Hence show that

$$w^r(1-w)^sP\begin{Bmatrix}0 & \infty & 1 & \\ \alpha & \beta & \gamma & w\\ \alpha' & \beta' & \gamma' & \end{Bmatrix} = P\begin{Bmatrix}0 & \infty & 1 & \\ \alpha + r & \beta - r - s & \gamma + s & w\\ \alpha' + r & \beta' - r - s & \gamma' + s & \end{Bmatrix}.$$

2. Show that the solution of the differential equation

$$p_w\begin{pmatrix}0 & \infty & 1\\ \alpha & \beta & \gamma\\ \alpha' & \beta' & \gamma'\end{pmatrix}u = w^{\alpha - 1}(1 - \tfrac{1}{2}w)^{-\alpha-\beta-\gamma-1}(1-w)^{\gamma - 1}$$

can always be expressed in terms of that of the nonhomogeneous hypergeometric equation satisfied by $B(a, b; c; w)$, where $a = \alpha + \beta + \gamma$, $b = \alpha + \beta' + \gamma$, $c = 1 + \alpha - \alpha'$, and $\alpha + \alpha' + \beta + \beta' + \gamma + \gamma' = 1$.

3. Starting from (7.99), show that

$$\frac{d}{dz}R_\nu^\mu(z) = (z^2 - 1)^{-(1/2)}R_\nu^{\mu+1}(z) + \frac{\mu z}{z^2 - 1}R_\nu^\mu(z).$$

4. Starting from (7.99), show that

$$R^{\mu}_{\nu-1}(z) - zR^{\mu}_{\nu}(z) + (\nu - \mu + 1)(z^2 - 1)^{1/2}R^{\mu-1}_{\nu}(z) = 0$$

and

$$zR^{\mu}_{\nu}(z) - R^{\mu}_{\nu+1}(z) + (\mu + \nu)(z^2 - 1)^{1/2}R^{\mu-1}_{\nu}(z)$$
$$= e^{i\pi\mu}\frac{2^{-\nu-1}\Gamma(\mu+\nu+1)}{\Gamma(\nu+2)}z^{-\mu-\nu-1}(z^2-1)^{(1/2)\mu}.$$

5. Prove that

$$R^{\mu}_{\nu-1}(z) - R^{\mu}_{\nu+1}(z) + (2\nu + 1)(z^2 - 1)^{1/2}R^{\mu-1}_{\nu}(z)$$
$$= e^{i\pi\mu}\frac{2^{-\nu-1}\Gamma(\mu+\nu+1)}{\Gamma(\nu+2)}z^{-\mu-\nu-1}(z^2-1)^{(1/2)\mu}$$

and

$$(\nu - \mu)(\nu - \mu + 1)R^{\mu}_{\nu+1}(z) - (\nu + \mu)(\nu + \mu + 1)R^{\mu}_{\nu-1}(z)$$
$$-(2\nu+1)(z^2-1)^{1/2}R^{\mu+1}_{\nu}(z) = e^{i\pi\mu}\frac{2^{-\nu-1}(3\nu-\mu+2)\Gamma(\mu+\nu+2)}{\Gamma(\nu+2)}$$
$$\times z^{-\mu-\nu-1}(z^2-1)^{(1/2)\mu}.$$

6. Show that $\log[x^2/(1-x^2)]$ is a particular solution of the differential equation

$$(1-x^2)\frac{d^2y}{dx^2} - 2x\frac{dy}{dx} = -\frac{2}{x^2}.$$

Hence show that $R^0_0(x) = \frac{1}{2}\log[x^2/(1-x^2)]$.

7. Show that, if n is a positive integer,

$$nR^0_n(x) - (2n-1)xR^0_{n-1}(x) + (n-1)R^0_{n-2}(x) = -(2x)^{-n} \qquad (n \geqslant 2)$$

and

$$(1-x^2)\frac{d}{dx}R^0_{n-1}(x) = nxR^0_{n-1}(x) - nR^0_n(x) + (2x)^{-n} \qquad (n \geqslant 1).$$

8. Show that, if n is a positive integer,

$$\frac{d}{dx}R^0_{n+1}(x) - \frac{d}{dx}R^0_{n-1}(x) = (2n+1)R^0_n(x) + 2^{-n-1}x^{-n-2}.$$

9. Show that, if n is a nonnegative integer,

$$\lim_{x\to 1-}\left(\frac{R^0_n(x)}{Q^0_n(x)}\right) = 1.$$

10. Show that

$$\lim_{x\to 0}\left[\frac{R_0^0(x)}{\log x}\right] = 1$$

and

$$\lim_{x\to 0}\,[(2x)^n R_n^0(x)] = -\frac{1}{n},$$

where n is a positive integer.

11. Express $(z^2-1)^{-(1/2)\mu} s^{\mu}_{\nu,\sigma}(z)$ as a series of ascending powers of z. Hence prove that

$$s^{\mu}_{\nu,\sigma}(z) = s^{\mu}_{-\nu-1,\sigma}(z),$$

and

$$(2\sigma+\mu-\nu)(2\sigma+1+\mu+\nu)s^{\mu}_{\nu,\sigma+1}(z)$$
$$= 2\sigma(2\sigma-1)s^{\mu}_{\nu,\sigma}(z) - z^{2\sigma}(z^2-1)^{(1/2)\mu}.$$

12. Express $(z^2-1)^{-(1/2)\mu} S^{\mu}_{\nu,\sigma}(z)$ as a series of descending powers of z. Hence prove that

$$S^{\mu}_{\nu,\sigma}(z) = S^{\mu}_{-\nu-1,\sigma}(z)$$

and

$$(2\sigma+\mu-\nu)(2\sigma+1+\mu+\nu)S^{\mu}_{\nu,\sigma+1}(z)$$
$$= 2\sigma(2\sigma-1)S^{\mu}_{\nu,\sigma}(z) - z^{2\sigma}(z^2-1)^{(1/2)\mu}.$$

13. Use the substitution $u = y^{1-k}$ to show that the solution of the nonlinear differential equation

$$y\frac{d^2y}{dz^2} = k\left(\frac{dy}{dz}\right)^2 - \frac{1}{z^2-1}\left[2zy\frac{dy}{dz} - \frac{\{\nu(\nu+1)+\mu^2(z^2-1)^{-1}\}}{1-k}y^2 + \frac{z^{2\sigma-2}(z^2-1)^{(1/2)\mu}}{1-k}y^{1+k}\right]$$

is

$$y = [C_1 P^{\mu}_{\nu}(z) + C_2 Q^{\mu}_{\nu}(z) + S^{\mu}_{\nu,\sigma}(z)]^{1/(1-k)},$$

where C_1 and C_2 are arbitrary constants.

CHAPTER 8

Nonhomogeneous Generalized Hypergeometric Functions

8.1 Introduction

In Chapter 6 we considered the properties of the solutions of certain nonhomogeneous linear differential equations which have as their associated homogeneous equation the hypergeometric equation

$$z(1-z)\frac{d^2y}{dz^2} + [c-(a+b+1)z]\frac{dy}{dz} - aby = 0;$$

that is, (8.1)

$$[\delta(\delta+c-1) - z(\delta+a)(\delta+b)]y = 0,$$

where $\delta \equiv z(d/dz)$ and a, b, and c are constants.

We now consider certain generalizations of these functions, which satisfy nonhomogeneous linear differential equations of order higher than two. We consider first the nonhomogeneous generalized hypergeometric function

$${}_pB_q\left[\begin{matrix}\alpha_1, \ldots, \alpha_p; z \\ \beta_1, \ldots, \beta_q\end{matrix}\right],$$

defined in §8.3. For conciseness, we shall often write this function in the form ${}_pB_q[\alpha_r; \beta_t; z]$. The function ${}_pB_q[\alpha_r; \beta_t; z]$ bears the same relation to the nonhomogeneous hypergeometric function $B(a, b; c; z)$ (defined in Chapter 6) as the generalized hypergeometric function ${}_pF_q[\alpha_r; \beta_t; z]$ does to $F(a, b; c; z)$. As shown in §8.5, ${}_pB_q[\alpha_r; \beta_t; z]$ is a particular integral of the nonhomogeneous equation

$$[\delta(\delta+\beta_1-1)\cdots(\delta+\beta_q-1) - z(\delta+\alpha_1)\cdots(\delta+\alpha_p)]y$$
$$= \frac{2^{1-\beta_q}\Gamma(\beta_q)}{\Gamma(\alpha_p)\Gamma(\beta_q-\alpha_p)}\alpha_1\cdots\alpha_{p-1}z\;{}_{p-1}F_{q-1}\left[\begin{matrix}\alpha_1+1, \ldots, \alpha_{p-1}+1; \tfrac{1}{2}z \\ \beta_1, \ldots, \beta_{q-1}\end{matrix}\right]. \quad (8.2)$$

In §8.2, we summarize various properties of the ${}_pF_q$ function, and in the following sections we discuss in detail the properties of the ${}_pB_q$ function.

In §§8.10 to 8.12, we discuss the properties of the nonhomogeneous generalized hypergeometric functions

$$ {}_pf_{q,\sigma}\left[\begin{matrix}\alpha_1, \ldots, \alpha_p; z\\ \beta_1, \ldots, \beta_q\end{matrix}\right] \quad \text{and} \quad {}_pF_{q,\sigma}\left[\begin{matrix}\alpha_1, \ldots, \alpha_p; z\\ \beta_1, \ldots, \beta_q\end{matrix}\right], $$

which satisfy the equation

$$ [\delta(\delta+\beta_1-1)\cdots(\delta+\beta_q-1) - z(\delta+\alpha_1)\cdots(\delta+\alpha_p)]y = z^\sigma. \tag{8.3} $$

In Chapter 9 we consider other generalizations of the hypergeometric functions, which lead to the nonhomogeneous Lamé and Mathieu functions.

8.2 Some Properties of Generalized Hypergeometric Functions

The theory of generalized hypergeometric functions is fully set out in Erdélyi [1953a], Bailey [1935], and Appell and Kampé de Feriet [1926]. We shall here briefly summarize various properties of these functions.

The function ${}_pF_q[\alpha_r; \beta_t; z]$ is defined by

$$ {}_pF_q[\alpha_r;\beta_t;z] = {}_pF_q\left[\begin{matrix}\alpha_1, \ldots, \alpha_p; z\\ \beta_1, \ldots, \beta_q\end{matrix}\right] = \sum_{n=0}^{\infty} \frac{(\alpha_1)_n \cdots (\alpha_p)_n\, z^n}{(\beta_1)_n \cdots (\beta_q)_n\, n!} \tag{8.4} $$

where

$$ (\alpha_v)_n = \frac{\Gamma(\alpha_v + n)}{\Gamma(\alpha_v)} \qquad (n = 1, 2, 3, \ldots) $$

and (8.5)

$$ (\beta_v)_n = \frac{\Gamma(\beta_v + n)}{\Gamma(\beta_v)} \qquad (n = 1, 2, 3, \ldots). $$

${}_pF_q[\alpha_r; \beta_t; z]$ satisfies the equation

$$ [\delta(\delta+\beta_1-1)\cdots(\delta+\beta_q-1) - z(\delta+\alpha_1)\cdots(\delta+\alpha_p)]y = 0, \tag{8.6} $$

where $\delta \equiv z\,d/dz$. Equation (8.6) is a linear differential equation of order (max $p, q+1$). If $p \leqslant q$, (8.6) is of the form

$$ z^q D^{q+1} y + \sum_{n=1}^{q} z^{n-1}(a_n z - b_n) D^n y + a_0 y = 0, \tag{8.7} $$

where $D \equiv d/dz$, and has a regular singular point at $z = 0$ and an irregular singular point at infinity. If $p = q + 1$, (8.6) is of the form

$$ z^q(1-z) D^{q+1} y + \sum_{n=1}^{q} z^{n-1}(A_n z - B_n) D^n y + A_0 y = 0. \tag{8.8} $$

This is a differential equation of Fuchsian type (see §1.11) with regular singularities at $z = 0$, 1, and at infinity.

We see, from (8.4), that ${}_pF_q[\alpha_r; \beta_t; z]$ converges for all z if $p \leqslant q$, converges for $|z| < 1$ if $p = q + 1$, and diverges for all nonzero z if $p > q + 1$. Other solutions of (8.6) are

$$y = z^{1-\beta_1} {}_pF_q\left[\begin{matrix} 1 + \alpha_1 - \beta_1, 1 + \alpha_2 - \beta_1, 1 + \alpha_3 - \beta_1, \ldots, 1 + \alpha_p - \beta_1; z \\ 2 - \beta_1, 1 + \beta_2 - \beta_1, \ldots, 1 + \beta_q - \beta_1 \end{matrix}\right] \tag{8.9}$$

and $q - 1$ similar expressions. These solutions are independent if no two of the numbers, 1, $\beta_1, \beta_2, \ldots \beta_{q-1}$ differ by an integer. When any β_ν is zero or a negative integer, ${}_pF_q[\alpha_r; \beta_t; z]$ is infinite. Equation (8.6) then has a solution containing logarithmic terms.

The solutions of (8.6) can also be expressed in the form

$$y = z^{-\alpha_1} {}_{q+1}F_{p-1}\left[\begin{matrix} \alpha_1, 1 + \alpha_1 - \beta_1, \ldots, 1 + \alpha_1 - \beta_q; (-1)^{p-q-1}z^{-1} \\ 1 + \alpha_1 - \alpha_2, \ldots, 1 + \alpha_1 - \alpha_p \end{matrix}\right] \tag{8.10}$$

and $p - 1$ similar expressions. If $p \geqslant q + 2$, the series (8.10) converges for all z; if $p = q + 1$, it converges for $|z| > 1$. As shown by Smith [1938], if $p = q + 1$ and no two of the α_r or β_t are equal or differ by an integer, the solutions given by (8.4) and (8.9) can be expressed linearly in terms of those given by (8.10), and vice versa.

8.3 Nonhomogeneous Generalized Hypergeometric Functions

${}_pB_q[\alpha_r; \beta_t; z]$

The function ${}_pB_q[\alpha_r; \beta_t; z]$ is defined by

$${}_pB_q[\alpha_r; \beta_t; z] = {}_pB_q\left[\begin{matrix} \alpha_1, \ldots, \alpha_p; z \\ \beta_1, \ldots, \beta_q \end{matrix}\right] = \sum_{n=0}^{\infty} \frac{(\alpha_1)_n \cdots (\alpha_p)_n}{(\beta_1)_n \cdots (\beta_q)_n} \times \Omega(\alpha_p + n, \beta_q + n; 0) \frac{z^n}{n!}, \tag{8.11}$$

where $(\alpha_\nu)_n$ and $(\beta_\nu)_n$ are given by (8.5) and Ω is the generalized modified Struve function defined in §4.3.

Now, as shown in §4.8,

$$\lim_{n \to \infty} \Omega(\alpha_p + n, \beta_q + n; 0) = 1 \qquad (\text{Re } \beta_q > \text{Re } \alpha_p).$$

Thus, if Re $\beta_q >$ Re α_p, the series (8.11) converges for all z if $p \leqslant q$, converges for $|z| < 1$ if $p = q + 1$, and diverges for all nonzero z if $p > q + 1$. We shall confine our attention to the case $2 \leqslant p \leqslant q + 1$.

From (8.5) and (8.11) we see that

$$ {}_pB_q\left[\begin{matrix}\alpha_1, \ldots, \alpha_p; 0\\ \beta_1, \ldots, \beta_q\end{matrix}\right] = \Omega(\alpha_p, \beta_q; 0) \tag{8.12}$$

where Ω is the generalized modified Struve function defined in §4.3. We note that the value of ${}_pB_q$ for $z = 0$ depends only on the parameters α_p and β_q. The properties of $\Omega(a, c; 0)$ were discussed in §4.8. In particular, it was shown that, if $\operatorname{Re} a > 0$,

$$\Omega(a, 2a; 0) = 0. \tag{8.13}$$

Using (8.4) and (8.12), together with the results of (4.107), we find

$$ {}_pB_q\left[\begin{matrix}\alpha_1, \ldots, \alpha_p; z\\ \beta_1, \ldots, \beta_q\end{matrix}\right] - \Omega(\alpha_p, \beta_q; 0)\, {}_pF_q\left[\begin{matrix}\alpha_1, \ldots, \alpha_p; z\\ \beta_1, \ldots, \beta_q\end{matrix}\right]$$

$$= \sum_{n=1}^{\infty} \frac{(\alpha_1)_n \cdots (\alpha_p)_n}{(\beta_1)_n \cdots (\beta_q)_n} [\Omega(\alpha_p + n, \beta_q + n; 0) - \Omega(\alpha_p, \beta_q; 0)] \frac{z^n}{n!}$$

$$= \frac{2^{1-\beta_q}\Gamma(\beta_q)}{\Gamma(\alpha_p + 1)\Gamma(\beta_q - \alpha_p)} \sum_{n=1}^{\infty} \frac{(\alpha_1)_n \cdots (\alpha_p)_n}{(\beta_1)_n \cdots (\beta_q)_n} F_{(n)}(1, \beta_q; \alpha_p + 1; \tfrac{1}{2}) \frac{z^n}{n!}, \tag{8.14}$$

where $F_{(n)}$ stands for the first n terms of the hypergeometric series with the given parameters.

As in §6.8, we find, if $\operatorname{Re} \beta_q > \operatorname{Re} \alpha_p > 0$,

$$ {}_pF_q[\alpha_r; \beta_t; z] + {}_pB_q[\alpha_r; \beta_t; z] = 2\frac{\Gamma(\beta_q)}{\Gamma(\alpha_p)\Gamma(\beta_q - \alpha_p)}$$

$$\times \sum_{n=0}^{\infty} \frac{(\alpha_1)_n \cdots (\alpha_{p-1})_n}{(\beta_1)_n \cdots (\beta_{q-1})_n} B_{1/2}(\beta_q - \alpha_p, \alpha_p + n) \frac{z^n}{n!} \tag{8.15}$$

and

$$ {}_pF_q[\alpha_r; \beta_t; z] - {}_pB_q[\alpha_r; \beta_t; z] = 2\frac{\Gamma(\beta_q)}{\Gamma(\alpha_p)\Gamma(\beta_q - \alpha_p)}$$

$$\times \sum_{n=0}^{\infty} \frac{(\alpha_1)_n \cdots (\alpha_{p-1})_n}{(\beta_1)_n \cdots (\beta_{q-1})_n} B_{1/2}(\alpha_p + n, \beta_q - \alpha_p) \frac{z^n}{n!}, \tag{8.16}$$

where $B_{1/2}$ is the incomplete beta function (see §4.8). Now for all real values of x and y, $B_{1/2}(x, y)$ is positive. Thus, if $p \leqslant q + 1$ and $0 \leqslant z < 1$, and all α_r and β_t are positive,

$$|{}_pF_q[\alpha_r; \beta_t; z]| \geqslant |{}_pB_q[\alpha_r; \beta_t; z]| \qquad (\beta_q > \alpha_p). \tag{8.17}$$

8.4 Relations for Contiguous Functions

There are $2p + 2q$ functions which are contiguous to ${}_pB_q[\alpha_r; \beta_t; z]$. We shall now show that there are simple relations between $p + q$ of these functions and ${}_pB_q$ and its derivative. The corresponding relations for ${}_pF_q[\alpha_r; \beta_t; z]$ are given by Rainville [1945]. The method we shall use is precisely the same as that used by Rainville. For conciseness, in this section we shall use the notation

$$B = {}_pB_q\left[\begin{matrix}\alpha_1, \ldots, \alpha_p; z\\ \beta_1, \ldots, \beta_q\end{matrix}\right] = \sum_{n=0}^{\infty} c_n \frac{z^n}{n!}, \tag{8.18}$$

$$B[\alpha_1+] = {}_pB_q\left[\begin{matrix}\alpha_1 + 1, \alpha_2, \ldots, \alpha_p; z\\ \beta_1, \beta_2, \ldots, \beta_q\end{matrix}\right] = \sum_{n=0}^{\infty} \frac{\alpha_1 + n}{\alpha_1} c_n \frac{z^n}{n!}, \tag{8.19}$$

$$B[\beta_1-] = {}_pB_q\left[\begin{matrix}\alpha_1, \alpha_2, \ldots, \alpha_p; z\\ \beta_1 - 1, \beta_2, \ldots, \beta_q\end{matrix}\right] = \sum_{n=0}^{\infty} \frac{\beta_1 + n - 1}{\beta_1 - 1} c_n \frac{z^n}{n!}. \tag{8.20}$$

Let $\delta \equiv z\, d/dz$. Then, from (8.18),

$$(\delta + \alpha_1)B = \sum_{n=0}^{\infty} (\alpha_1 + n)c_n \frac{z^n}{n!} = \alpha_1 B[\alpha_1+],$$

and similarly,

$$(\delta + \alpha_m)B = \alpha_m B[\alpha_m+] \qquad (m = 1 \text{ to } p - 1), \tag{8.21}$$

and

$$(\delta + \alpha_p)B = \sum_{n=0}^{\infty} (\alpha_p + n) \frac{(\alpha_1)_n \cdots (\alpha_p)_n}{(\beta_1)_n \cdots (\beta_q)_n} \Omega(\alpha_p + n, \beta_q + n; 0) \frac{z^n}{n!}. \tag{8.22}$$

Now, from §4.8, if $c \neq 0$,

$$\Omega(a + 1, c; 0) - \Omega(a, c; 0) = \frac{2^{2-c}\Gamma(c)}{\Gamma(a + 1)\Gamma(c - a)}. \tag{8.23}$$

From (8.22) and (8.23), we find

$$(\delta + \alpha_p)B = \alpha_p B[\alpha_p+] - \frac{2^{2-\beta_q}\Gamma(\beta_q)}{\Gamma(\alpha_p)\Gamma(\beta_q - \alpha_p)} {}_{p-1}F_{q-1}\left[\begin{matrix}\alpha_1, \ldots, \alpha_{p-1}; \tfrac{1}{2}z\\ \beta_1, \ldots, \beta_{q-1}\end{matrix}\right]. \tag{8.24}$$

Similarly, we find

$$(\delta + \beta_m - 1)B = (\beta_m - 1)B[\beta_m -], \qquad (m = 1 \text{ to } q - 1) \tag{8.25}$$

and

$$(\delta + \beta_q - 1)B = \sum_{n=0}^{\infty} (\beta_q + n - 1) \frac{(\alpha_1)_n \cdots (\alpha_p)_n}{(\beta_1)_n \cdots (\beta_q)_n} \Omega(\alpha_p + n, \beta_q + n; 0) \frac{z^n}{n!}. \tag{8.26}$$

Now, from §4.8, if $c \neq 0, 1$,

$$\Omega(a, c-1; 0) - \Omega(a, c; 0) = \frac{2^{2-c}\Gamma(c-1)}{\Gamma(a)\Gamma(c-a)}. \tag{8.27}$$

From (8.26) and (8.27), we find

$$(\delta + \beta_q - 1)B = (\beta_q - 1)B[\beta_q -] - \frac{2^{2-\beta_q}\Gamma(\beta_q)}{\Gamma(\alpha_p)\Gamma(\beta_q - \alpha_p)} \times {}_{p-1}F_{q-1}\left[\begin{matrix}\alpha_1, \ldots, \alpha_{p-1}; \frac{1}{2}z \\ \beta_1, \ldots, \beta_{q-1}\end{matrix}\right]. \tag{8.28}$$

From the $p + q$ equations (8.21), (8.24), (8.25), and (8.28), we can obtain $p + q - 1$ independent linear relations between ${}_pB_q$ and pairs of contiguous functions.

8.5 Differential Equation Satisfied by ${}_pB_q[\alpha_r; \beta_t; z]$

From (8.11),

$$\begin{aligned}\frac{d}{dz}\, {}_pB_q[\alpha_r; \beta_t; z] &= \sum_{n=0}^{\infty} n \frac{(\alpha_1)_n \cdots (\alpha_p)_n}{(\beta_1)_n \cdots (\beta_q)_n} \Omega(\alpha_p + n, \beta_q + n; 0) \frac{z^{n-1}}{n!} \\ &= \frac{\alpha_1 \cdots \alpha_p}{\beta_1 \cdots \beta_q} \sum_{n=1}^{\infty} \frac{(\alpha_1 + 1)_{n-1} \cdots (\alpha_p + 1)_{n-1}}{(\beta_1 + 1)_{n-1} \cdots (\beta_q + 1)_{n-1}} \\ &\quad \times \Omega(\alpha_p + n, \beta_q + n; 0) \frac{z^{n-1}}{(n-1)!};\end{aligned}$$

that is,

$$\frac{d}{dz}\, {}_pB_q\left[\begin{matrix}\alpha_1, \alpha_2, \ldots, \alpha_p; z \\ \beta_1, \beta_2, \ldots, \beta_q\end{matrix}\right] = \frac{\alpha_1 \cdots \alpha_p}{\beta_1 \cdots \beta_q}\, {}_pB_q\left[\begin{matrix}\alpha_1 + 1, \alpha_2 + 1, \ldots, \alpha_p + 1; z \\ \beta_1 + 1, \beta_2 + 1, \ldots, \beta_q + 1\end{matrix}\right]. \tag{8.29}$$

Similarly,

$$\frac{d^n}{dz^n}\, {}_pB_q\left[\begin{matrix}\alpha_1, \alpha_2, \ldots, \alpha_p; z \\ \beta_1, \beta_2, \ldots, \beta_q\end{matrix}\right] = \frac{(\alpha_1)_n \cdots (\alpha_p)_n}{(\beta_1)_n \cdots (\beta_q)_n}\, {}_pB_q\left[\begin{matrix}\alpha_1 + n, \alpha_2 + n, \ldots, \alpha_p + n; z \\ \beta_1 + n, \beta_2 + n, \ldots, \beta_q + n\end{matrix}\right]. \tag{8.30}$$

From (8.29),

$$\delta B = \frac{\alpha_1 \cdots \alpha_p}{\beta_1 \cdots \beta_q} z \, {}_pB_q\left[\begin{matrix} \alpha_1 + 1, \alpha_2 + 1, \ldots, \alpha_p + 1; z \\ \beta_1 + 1, \beta_2 + 1, \ldots, \beta_q + 1 \end{matrix}\right]. \tag{8.31}$$

Now, from (8.25), (8.28), and (8.31),

$$\begin{aligned}
&\delta(\delta + \beta_1 - 1) \cdots (\delta + \beta_q - 1) {}_pB_q\left[\begin{matrix} \alpha_1, \alpha_2, \ldots, \alpha_p; z \\ \beta_1, \beta_2, \ldots, \beta_q \end{matrix}\right] \\
&\qquad - \alpha_1 \cdots \alpha_p z \, {}_pB_q\left[\begin{matrix} \alpha_1 + 1, \alpha_2 + 1, \ldots, \alpha_p + 1; z \\ \beta_1, \beta_2, \ldots, \beta_q \end{matrix}\right] \\
&= -\frac{2^{2-\beta_q}\Gamma(\beta_q)}{\Gamma(\alpha_p)\Gamma(\beta_q - \alpha_p)} \\
&\qquad \times \delta(\delta + \beta_1 - 1) \cdots (\delta + \beta_{q-1} - 1) \, {}_{p-1}F_{q-1}\left[\begin{matrix} \alpha_1, \ldots, \alpha_{p-1}; \tfrac{1}{2}z \\ \beta_1, \ldots, \beta_{q-1} \end{matrix}\right] \\
&= -\frac{2^{1-\beta_q}\Gamma(\beta_q)}{\Gamma(\alpha_p)\Gamma(\beta_q - \alpha_p)} \\
&\qquad \times \alpha_1 \cdots \alpha_{p-1} z \, {}_{p-1}F_{q-1}\left[\begin{matrix} \alpha_1 + 1, \alpha_2 + 1, \ldots, \alpha_{p-1} + 1; \tfrac{1}{2}z \\ \beta_1, \beta_2, \ldots, \beta_{q-1} \end{matrix}\right].
\end{aligned} \tag{8.32}$$

Similarly, from (8.21) and (8.24),

$$\begin{aligned}
&z(\delta + \alpha_1) \cdots (\delta + \alpha_p) {}_pB_q\left[\begin{matrix} \alpha_1, \alpha_2, \ldots, \alpha_p; z \\ \beta_1, \beta_2, \ldots, \beta_q \end{matrix}\right] \\
&\qquad - \alpha_1 \cdots \alpha_p z \, {}_pB_q\left[\begin{matrix} \alpha_1 + 1, \alpha_2 + 1, \ldots, \alpha_p + 1; z \\ \beta_1, \beta_2, \ldots, \beta_q \end{matrix}\right] \\
&= -\frac{2^{2-\beta_q}\Gamma(\beta_q)}{\Gamma(\alpha_p)\Gamma(\beta_q - \alpha_p)} \\
&\qquad \times z(\delta + \alpha_1) \cdots (\delta + \alpha_{p-1}) \, {}_{p-1}F_{q-1}\left[\begin{matrix} \alpha_1, \ldots, \alpha_{p-1}; \tfrac{1}{2}z \\ \beta_1, \ldots, \beta_{q-1} \end{matrix}\right] \\
&= -\frac{2^{2-\beta_q}\Gamma(\beta_q)}{\Gamma(\alpha_p)\Gamma(\beta_q - \alpha_p)} \\
&\qquad \times \alpha_1 \cdots \alpha_{p-1} z \, {}_{p-1}F_{q-1}\left[\begin{matrix} \alpha_1 + 1, \alpha_2 + 1, \ldots, \alpha_{p-1} + 1; \tfrac{1}{2}z \\ \beta_1, \beta_2, \ldots, \beta_{q-1} \end{matrix}\right].
\end{aligned} \tag{8.33}$$

From (8.32) and (8.33), we see that ${}_pB_q[\alpha_r;\,\beta_t;\,z]$ satisfies the nonhomogeneous differential equation

$$[\delta(\delta+\beta_1-1)\cdots(\delta+\beta_q-1)-z(\delta+\alpha_1)\cdots(\delta+\alpha_p)]y$$
$$=\frac{2^{1-\beta_q}\Gamma(\beta_q)}{\Gamma(\alpha_p)\Gamma(\beta_q-\alpha_p)}\alpha_1\cdots\alpha_{p-1}z\,{}_{p-1}F_{q-1}\left[\begin{matrix}\alpha_1+1,\ldots,\alpha_{p-1}+1;\,\frac{1}{2}z\\ \beta_1,\ldots,\beta_{q-1}\end{matrix}\right]. \tag{8.34}$$

Equation (8.34) is a linear differential equation of order (max $p,q+1$). The associated homogeneous equation is the generalized hypergeometric equation (8.6), the solutions of which are given in §8.2.

By repeated application of (8.21) we find, using the method given in §6.6,

$$\frac{d^n}{dz^n}\left(z^{\alpha_1+n-1}\,{}_pB_q\left[\begin{matrix}\alpha_1,\ldots,\alpha_p;\,z\\ \beta_1,\ldots,\beta_q\end{matrix}\right]\right)$$
$$=(\alpha_1)_n z^{\alpha_1-1}\,{}_pB_q\left[\begin{matrix}\alpha_1+n,\,\alpha_2,\ldots,\alpha_p;\,z\\ \beta_1,\beta_2,\ldots,\beta_q\end{matrix}\right]\qquad(p\neq 1). \tag{8.35}$$

In (8.35) we may replace α_1 by α_m ($m=1$ to $p-1$).

8.6 Degenerate Cases of ${}_pB_q[\alpha_r;\,\beta_t;\,z]$

When any α_m is zero or a negative integer, and no β_t is zero or a negative integer, the power series (8.11) terminates and ${}_pB_q$ is a polynomial in z. In particular, if any α_m is zero,

$${}_pB_q[\alpha_r;\,\beta_t;\,z]=\Omega(\alpha_p,\beta_q;0). \tag{8.36}$$

Consider next the values of ${}_pB_q[\alpha_r;\,\beta_t;\,z]$ when either α_p or $\beta_q-\alpha_p$ (but not both) is zero or a negative integer. In these cases (8.34) reduces to the generalized hypergeometric equation (8.6).

Now, as shown in §4.8, when a is zero or a negative integer,

$$\Omega(a,c;0)=-1, \tag{8.37}$$

and, when $c-a$ is zero or a negative integer,

$$\Omega(a,c;0)=1. \tag{8.38}$$

Thus, from (8.4) and (8.11), when α_p is zero or a negative integer,

$${}_pB_q[\alpha_r;\,\beta_t;\,z]=-{}_pF_q[\alpha_r;\,\beta_t;\,z], \tag{8.39}$$

and, when $\beta_q-\alpha_p$ is zero or a negative integer,

$${}_pB_q[\alpha_r;\,\beta_t;\,z]={}_pF_q[\alpha_r;\,\beta_t;\,z]. \tag{8.40}$$

Equations (8.37) to (8.40) are not valid when β_q is zero or a negative integer.

8.7 The Zeros of ${}_pB_q[\alpha_r; \beta_t; z]$ Where All α_r, β_t Are Real

From (8.29), using Rolle's theorem, we see that, if no β_t is zero or a negative integer, between two consecutive zeros of ${}_pB_q[\alpha_r; \beta_t; z]$ there lies at least one zero of ${}_pB_q[\alpha_r + 1; \beta_t + 1; z]$. Similarly, from (8.35), if no β_t is zero or a negative integer, between two consecutive zeros (both positive or both negative) of ${}_pB_q[\alpha_r; \beta_t; z]$, there lies at least one zero of each of

$$ {}_pB_q\left[\begin{matrix}\alpha_1, \ldots, \alpha_{m-1}, \alpha_m + 1, \alpha_{m+1}, \ldots, \alpha_p; z\\ \beta_1, \beta_2, \ldots, \beta_q\end{matrix}\right] \qquad (m = 1 \text{ to } p-1). $$

The converse of these statements is not true.

Considering the coefficients of the terms in the power series (8.11), we see, as in §6.12, that, if all α_r and β_t are positive, and $2\alpha_p > \beta_q > \alpha_p$, all the coefficients are positive; in this case, ${}_pB_q[\alpha_r; \beta_t; z] > 0$ for $0 \leqslant z < 1$ $(p \leqslant q + 1)$. If all α_r and β_t are positive and $\beta_q > 2\alpha_p$, the coefficients of the lower powers of z in (8.11) are negative, and those of all subsequent powers of z are positive. As in §6.12, we see that in that case ${}_pB_q[\alpha_r; \beta_t; z]$ cannot have more than one zero in the range $0 < z < 1$.

8.8 Definite Integrals Connected with ${}_pB_q[\alpha_r; \beta_t; z]$

A number of integral representations of generalized hypergeometric functions ${}_pF_q$ are given by Erdélyi [1937]. We shall now obtain similar formulas for ${}_pB_q$.

The formula

$$ {}_pB_q\left[\begin{matrix}\alpha_1, \ldots, \alpha_p; z\\ \beta_1, \ldots, \beta_q\end{matrix}\right] = \int_0^1 \cdots \int_0^1 \phi \, {}_pB_q\left[\begin{matrix}a_1, \ldots, a_m, \alpha_{m+1}, \ldots, \alpha_p; t_1 \cdots t_m z\\ \beta_1, \ldots, \beta_q\end{matrix}\right] dt_1 \cdots dt_m $$

$$ (\operatorname{Re} a_1 > \operatorname{Re} \alpha_1 > 0, \ldots, \operatorname{Re} a_m > \operatorname{Re} \alpha_m > 0,\ q + 1 \geqslant p > m), \qquad (8.41) $$

where

$$ \phi = \prod_{i=1}^{m} \frac{\Gamma(a_i)}{\Gamma(\alpha_i)\Gamma(a_i - \alpha_i)} t_i^{\alpha_i - 1}(1 - t_i)^{a_i - \alpha_i - 1}, \qquad (8.42) $$

can be proved by expanding ${}_pB_q$ as a power series in z and integrating term by term (if $p = q + 1$, $|z|$ must be less than 1). In particular, if $a_r = \beta_r$ $(r = 1$ to m, $m < q)$, (8.41) becomes

$$ {}_pB_q\left[\begin{matrix}\alpha_1, \ldots, \alpha_p; z\\ \beta_1, \ldots, \beta_q\end{matrix}\right] = \int_0^1 \cdots \int_0^1 \phi \, {}_{p-m}B_{q-m}\left[\begin{matrix}\alpha_{m+1}, \ldots, \alpha_p; t_1 \cdots t_m z\\ \beta_{m+1}, \ldots, \beta_q\end{matrix}\right] dt_1 \cdots dt_m. \qquad (8.43) $$

Precisely similar formulas can be obtained with the B functions replaced by F functions in (8.42) and (8.43) (see Erdélyi [1937]).

Now, from §6.3, if $\operatorname{Re} c > \operatorname{Re} b > 0$,

$$
\begin{aligned}
{}_2B_1(a, b; c; z) &= B(a, b; c; z) \\
&= 2^{1-c}\frac{\Gamma(c)}{\Gamma(b)\Gamma(c-b)}\int_0^1 (1-s^2)^{(1/2)c-1}\left\{\left(\frac{1+s}{1-s}\right)^{b-(1/2)c}\right. \\
&\quad \times [1-\tfrac{1}{2}(1+s)z]^{-a} - \left.\left(\frac{1-s}{1+s}\right)^{b-(1/2)c}[1-\tfrac{1}{2}(1-s)z]^{-a}\right\} ds.
\end{aligned}
\tag{8.44}
$$

From (8.43) and (8.44),

$$
\begin{aligned}
{}_{q+1}B_q[\alpha_r; \beta_t; z] &= 2^{1-\beta_q}\frac{\Gamma(\beta_q)}{\Gamma(\alpha_{q+1})\Gamma(\beta_q-\alpha_{q+1})}\int_0^1 \cdots \int_0^1 \psi(1-s^2)^{(1/2)\beta_q-1} \\
&\times \left\{\left(\frac{1+s}{1-s}\right)^{\alpha_{q+1}-(1/2)\beta_q}[1-\tfrac{1}{2}(1+s)t_1\cdots t_m z]^{-\alpha_q} - \left(\frac{1-s}{1+s}\right)^{\alpha_{q+1}-(1/2)\beta_q}\right. \\
&\times \left.[1-\tfrac{1}{2}(1-s)t_1\cdots t_m z]^{-\alpha_q}\right\} dt_1\cdots dt_m\, ds
\end{aligned}
$$

$$
\begin{aligned}
&(|z|<1,\ \operatorname{Re}\beta_1 > \operatorname{Re}\alpha_1 > 0, \ldots, \operatorname{Re}\beta_{q-1} > \operatorname{Re}\alpha_{q-1} > 0, \\
&\quad \operatorname{Re}\beta_q > \operatorname{Re}\alpha_{q+1} > 0),
\end{aligned}
\tag{8.45}
$$

where

$$
\psi = \prod_{i=1}^{q-1}\frac{\Gamma(\beta_i)}{\Gamma(\alpha_i)\Gamma(\beta_i-\alpha_i)}\, t_i^{\alpha_i-1}(1-t_i)^{\beta_i-\alpha_i-1}. \tag{8.46}
$$

Using the results of §6.3, we find, in a similar way,

$$
\begin{aligned}
{}_{q+1}F_q[\alpha_r; \beta_t; z] + {}_{q+1}B_q[\alpha_r; \beta_t; z] &= 2^{2-\beta_q}\frac{\Gamma(\beta_q)}{\Gamma(\alpha_{q+1})\Gamma(\beta_q-\alpha_{q+1})} \\
\times \int_0^1 \cdots \int_0^1 \psi(1+s)^{\alpha_{q+1}-1}&(1-s)^{\beta_q-\alpha_{q+1}-1}[1-\tfrac{1}{2}(1+s)t_1\cdots t_m z]^{-\alpha_q} \\
\times\, dt_1\cdots dt_m\, ds \qquad &(|z|<1,\ \operatorname{Re}\beta_1 > \operatorname{Re}\alpha_1 > 0, \ldots, \\
&\operatorname{Re}\beta_{q-1} > \operatorname{Re}\alpha_{q-1} > 0, \qquad \operatorname{Re}\beta_q > \operatorname{Re}\alpha_{q+1})
\end{aligned}
\tag{8.47}
$$

and

$$ {}_{q+1}F_q[\alpha_r; \beta_t; z] - {}_{q+1}B_q[\alpha_r; \beta_t; z] = 2^{2-\beta_q} \frac{\Gamma(\beta_q)}{\Gamma(\alpha_{q+1})\Gamma(\beta_q - \alpha_{q+1})} $$

$$ \times \int_0^1 \cdots \int_0^1 \psi(1-s)^{\alpha_{q+1}-1}(1+s)^{\beta_q-\alpha_{q+1}-1}[1 - \tfrac{1}{2}(1-s)t_1 \cdots t_m z]^{-\alpha_q} $$

$$ \times dt_1 \cdots dt_m \, ds \qquad (|z| < 1, \operatorname{Re}\beta_1 > \operatorname{Re}\alpha_1 > 0, \ldots, $$

$$ \operatorname{Re}\beta_{q-1} > \operatorname{Re}\alpha_{q-1} > 0, \operatorname{Re}\alpha_{q+1} > 0). \qquad (8.48) $$

Similarly, from §4.3, if $\operatorname{Re} c > \operatorname{Re} a > 0$,

$$ {}_1B_1(a, c; z) = \Omega(a, c; z) $$

$$ = 2^{2-c} \frac{\Gamma(c)}{\Gamma(a)\Gamma(c-a)} e^{(1/2)z} \int_0^1 (1-u^2)^{(1/2)c-1} $$

$$ \times \sinh\left[\tfrac{1}{2}zu + (a - \tfrac{1}{2}c)\log\frac{1+u}{1-u}\right]du. \qquad (8.49) $$

From (8.43) and (8.49),

$$ {}_qB_q[\alpha_r; \beta_t; z] = 2^{2-\beta_q} \frac{\Gamma(\beta_q)}{\Gamma(\alpha_q)\Gamma(\beta_q - \alpha_q)} \int_0^1 \cdots \int_0^1 \psi e^{(1/2)t_1 \ldots t_m z}(1-u^2)^{(1/2)\beta_q - 1} $$

$$ \times \sinh\left[\tfrac{1}{2}t_1 \cdots t_m u + (\alpha_q - \tfrac{1}{2}\beta_q)\log\frac{1+u}{1-u}\right]dt_1 \cdots dt_m \, \mathrm{du} $$

$$ (\operatorname{Re}\beta_1 > \operatorname{Re}\alpha_1 > 0, \ldots, \operatorname{Re}\beta_q > \operatorname{Re}\alpha_q > 0), \qquad (8.50) $$

where ψ is given by (8.46). Using the results of §4.3, we find, in a similar way,

$$ {}_qF_q[\alpha_r; \beta_t; z] + {}_qB_q[\alpha_r; \beta_t; z] = 2^{2-\beta_q} \frac{\Gamma(\beta_q)}{\Gamma(\alpha_q)\Gamma(\beta_q - \alpha_q)} \int_0^1 \cdots \int_0^1 \psi $$

$$ \times e^{(1/2)t_1 \ldots t_m z(1+u)}(1+u)^{\alpha_q - 1}(1-u)^{\beta_q - \alpha_q - 1} du $$

$$ (\operatorname{Re}\beta_1 > \operatorname{Re}\alpha_1 > 0, \ldots, \operatorname{Re}\beta_{q-1} > \operatorname{Re}\alpha_{q-1} > 0, \operatorname{Re}\beta_q > \operatorname{Re}\alpha_q) \qquad (8.51) $$

and

$$ {}_qF_q[\alpha_r; \beta_t; z] - {}_qB_q[\alpha_r; \beta_t; z] = 2^{2-\beta_q} \frac{\Gamma(\beta_q)}{\Gamma(\alpha_q)\Gamma(\beta_q - \alpha_q)} \int_0^1 \cdots \int_0^1 \psi $$

$$ \times e^{(1/2)t_1 \ldots t_m z(1-u)}(1+u)^{\beta_q - \alpha_q - 1}(1-u)^{\alpha_q - 1} du $$

$$ (\operatorname{Re}\beta_1 > \operatorname{Re}\alpha_1 > 0, \ldots, \operatorname{Re}\beta_{q-1} > \operatorname{Re}\alpha_{q-1} > 0, \operatorname{Re}\alpha_q > 0). \qquad (8.52) $$

The formula

$$
{}_pB_q\left[\begin{matrix}\alpha_1, \ldots, \alpha_p; z\\ \beta_1, \ldots, \beta_q\end{matrix}\right]
= \int_0^1 \cdots \int_0^1 \bar{\phi}\, {}_pB_q\left[\begin{matrix}\alpha_1, \ldots, \alpha_p; u_1 \cdots u_n z\\ b_1, \ldots, b_n, \beta_{n+1}, \ldots, \beta_q\end{matrix}\right] du_1 \cdots du_n,
$$

$$
(\operatorname{Re} \beta_1 > \operatorname{Re} b_1 > 0, \ldots, \operatorname{Re} \beta_n > \operatorname{Re} b_n > 0, q > n, q + 1 \geqslant p), \tag{8.53}
$$

where

$$
\bar{\phi} = \prod_{i=1}^{n} \frac{\Gamma(\beta_i)}{\Gamma(b_i)\Gamma(\beta_i - b_i)}\, u_i^{b_i - 1}(1 - u_i)^{\beta_i - b_i - 1}, \tag{8.54}
$$

can be proved by expanding ${}_pB_q$ as a power series in z and integrating term by term (if $p = q + 1$, $|z|$ must be less than 1).

Combining (8.41) and (8.53), we obtain

$$
{}_pB_q\left[\begin{matrix}\alpha_1, \ldots, \alpha_p; z\\ \beta_1, \ldots, \beta_q\end{matrix}\right]
= \int_0^1 \cdots \int_0^1 \phi\bar{\phi}\, {}_pB_q\left[\begin{matrix}a_1, \ldots, a_m, \alpha_{m+1}, \ldots, \alpha_p; t_1 \cdots t_m u_1 \cdots u_n z\\ b_1, \ldots, b_n, \beta_{n+1}, \ldots, \beta_q\end{matrix}\right]
$$

$$
\times\, dt_1 \cdots dt_m\, du_1 \cdots du_n, \qquad (\operatorname{Re} a_1 > \operatorname{Re} \alpha_1 > 0, \ldots,
$$

$$
\operatorname{Re} a_m > \operatorname{Re} \alpha_m > 0, q + 1 \geqslant p > m, \operatorname{Re} \beta_1 > \operatorname{Re} b_1 > 0, \ldots,
$$

$$
\operatorname{Re} \beta_n > \operatorname{Re} b_n > 0, q > n), \tag{8.55}
$$

where ϕ and $\bar{\phi}$ are given by (8.42) and (8.54).

8.9 Infinite Integrals Connected with ${}_pB_q[\alpha_r; \beta_t; z]$

The formulas

$$
\int_0^\infty e^{-az}\, {}_pB_q\left[\begin{matrix}\alpha_1, \ldots, \alpha_p; bz\\ \beta_1, \ldots, \beta_q\end{matrix}\right] z^{\mu - 1}\, dz
= \Gamma(\mu) a^{-\mu}\, {}_{p+1}B_q\left[\begin{matrix}\mu, \alpha_1, \ldots, \alpha_p; b/a\\ \beta_1, \ldots, \beta_q\end{matrix}\right] \qquad (\operatorname{Re} \mu > 0) \tag{8.56}
$$

and

$$
\int_0^\infty e^{-az}\, {}_pB_q\left[\begin{matrix}\alpha_1, \ldots, \alpha_p; bz\\ \beta_1, \ldots, \beta_q\end{matrix}\right] z^{\beta_m - 1}\, dz
= \Gamma(\beta_m) a^{-\beta_m}\, {}_pB_{q-1}\left[\begin{matrix}\alpha_1, \ldots, \alpha_p; b/a\\ \beta_1, \ldots, \beta_{m-1}, \beta_{m+1}, \ldots, \beta_q\end{matrix}\right]
$$

$$
(\operatorname{Re} \beta_m > 0, m \neq q), \tag{8.57}
$$

where $\operatorname{Re} a > 0$ if $p < q$ and $\operatorname{Re} a > \operatorname{Re} b$ if $p = q$, can be proved by expanding ${}_pB_q$ as a power series in z and integrating term by term.

Similarly, by using Gauss's multiplication formula for the gamma function (Whittaker and Watson [*240*, 1935]), we can show that, if k is a positive integer,

$$\int_0^\infty e^{-az}\,{}_pB_q\left[\begin{matrix}\alpha_1,\ldots,\alpha_p;\,(bz)^k\\ \beta_1,\ldots,\beta_q\end{matrix}\right]z^{\mu-1}\,dz$$

$$= \Gamma(\mu)a^{-\mu}\,{}_{p+k}B_q\left[\begin{matrix}\frac{\mu}{k},\frac{\mu+1}{k},\ldots,\frac{\mu+k-1}{k},\alpha_1,\ldots,\alpha_p;\left(\frac{kb}{a}\right)^k\\ \beta_1,\ldots,\beta_q\end{matrix}\right], \tag{8.58}$$

where $\operatorname{Re} a \geqslant 0$ if $p + k < q + 1$, $\operatorname{Re} a > |\operatorname{Re}(kb)|$ if $p + k = q + 1$.

8.10 The Nonhomogeneous Generalized Hypergeometric Functions ${}_pf_{q,\sigma}[\alpha_r; \beta_t; z]$ and ${}_pF_{q,\sigma}[\alpha_r; \beta_t; z]$

We consider next the solution of the nonhomogeneous generalized hypergeometric equation

$$[\delta(\delta+\beta_1-1)\cdots(\delta+\beta_q-1) - z(\delta+\alpha_1)\cdots(\delta+\alpha_p)]y = z^\sigma, \tag{8.59}$$

where $\alpha_1,\ldots,\alpha_p$, $\beta_1,\ldots,\beta_q$, and σ are constants and the operator $\delta \equiv z\,d/dz$. As stated above, if $p \leqslant q$, the associated homogeneous equation (8.6) has a regular singular point at $z = 0$ and an irregular singular point at infinity; if $p = q + 1$, (8.6) has regular singularities at $z = 0$, 1, and at infinity.

Using the properties of the operator δ, given in §2.7, we find, by the method of Frobenius (§1.12), that a particular integral of (8.59) is

$${}_pf_{q,\sigma}[\alpha_r;\beta_t;z]$$

$$= {}_pf_{q,\sigma}\left[\begin{matrix}\alpha_1,\ldots,\alpha_p;\,z\\ \beta_1,\ldots,\beta_q\end{matrix}\right]$$

$$= \frac{z^\sigma}{\sigma(\sigma+\beta_1-1)\cdots(\sigma+\beta_q-1)}\,{}_{p+1}F_{q+1}\left[\begin{matrix}1,\sigma+\alpha_1,\ldots,\sigma+\alpha_p;\,z\\ \sigma+1,\sigma+\beta_1,\ldots,\sigma+\beta_q\end{matrix}\right]. \tag{8.60}$$

From §8.2, we see that, if $p \leqslant q$, the series (8.60) converges for all z; if $p = q + 1$, it converges for $|z| < 1$. The series (8.60) is not valid if σ or any $\sigma + \beta_m - 1$ ($m = 1$ to q) is zero or a negative integer. As shown in §1.12, for these values of σ, the particular integral of (8.59) will, in general, contain logarithmic terms.

From (8.60),

$$
{}_pf_{q,\sigma+1-\beta_m}\begin{bmatrix}\alpha_1,\ldots,\alpha_p;\, z\\ \beta_1,\ldots,\beta_q\end{bmatrix}
= z^{1-\beta_m}\,{}_pf_{q,\sigma}\begin{bmatrix}1+\alpha_1-\beta_m,\ldots,1+\alpha_p-\beta_m;\, z\\ 1+\beta_1-\beta_m,\ldots,1+\beta_{m-1}-\beta_m,\\ 2-\beta_m,1+\beta_{m+1}-\beta_m,\ldots,1+\beta_q-\beta_m\end{bmatrix}
$$

$$(m = 1 \text{ to } q). \quad (8.61)$$

We see also that ${}_pf_{q,\sigma}[\alpha_r;\beta_t;z]$ is unchanged if the order of the α_r or of the β_t terms is changed. If any $\sigma+\alpha_r$ $(r = 1$ to $p)$ is zero or a negative integer, the series (8.60) terminates. In particular,

$$
{}_pf_{q,-\alpha_m}[\alpha_r;\beta_t;z] = -\frac{z^{-\alpha_m}}{\alpha_m(\beta_1-\alpha_m-1)\cdots(\beta_q-\alpha_m-1)} \qquad (m = 1 \text{ to } p). \quad (8.62)
$$

Consider now the solution of (8.59) expressed as a series of descending powers of z (see §1.13). Such a particular integral is

$$
\begin{aligned}
{}_pF_{q,\sigma}[\alpha_r;\beta_t;z]
&= {}_pF_{q,\sigma}\begin{bmatrix}\alpha_1,\ldots,\alpha_p;\, z\\ \beta_1,\ldots,\beta_q\end{bmatrix}\\
&= -\frac{z^{\sigma-1}}{(\sigma+\alpha_1-1)\cdots(\sigma+\alpha_p-1)}\\
&\quad\times {}_{q+2}F_p\begin{bmatrix}1,1-\sigma,2-\sigma-\beta_1,\ldots,2-\sigma-\beta_q;\,(-1)^{p-q-1}z^{-1}\\ 2-\sigma-\alpha_1,\ldots,2-\sigma-\alpha_p\end{bmatrix}.
\end{aligned} \quad (8.63)
$$

If $p \geqslant q+2$, the series (8.63) converges for all z; if $p = q+1$, it converges for $|z| > 1$.

If σ or $\sigma+\beta_m-1$ $(m = 1$ to $q)$ is a positive integer, the series (8.63) terminates after a finite number of terms. In this case, the series (8.63) can be expressed in terms of a truncated form of the series (8.4) or (8.9).

From (8.63),

$$
{}_pF_{q,\sigma+1-\beta_m}\begin{bmatrix}\alpha_1,\ldots,\alpha_p;\, z\\ \beta_1,\ldots,\beta_q\end{bmatrix}
= z^{1-\beta_m}\,{}_pF_{q,\sigma}\begin{bmatrix}1+\alpha_1-\beta_m,\ldots,1+\alpha_p-\beta_m;\, z\\ 1+\beta_1-\beta_m,\ldots,1+\beta_{m-1}-\beta_m,\\ 2-\beta_m,1+\beta_{m+1}-\beta_m,\ldots,1+\beta_q-\beta_m\end{bmatrix}
$$

$$(m = 1 \text{ to } q). \quad (8.64)$$

We see also that ${}_pF_{q,\sigma}[\alpha_r; \beta_t; z]$ is unchanged if the order of the α_r or of the β_t is changed. Also, from (8.63),

$$ {}_pF_{q,1}[\alpha_r; \beta_t; z] = -(\alpha_1\alpha_2 \cdots \alpha_p)^{-1} \tag{8.65}$$

and

$$ {}_pF_{q,2-\beta_m}[\alpha_r; \beta_t; z] = -\frac{z^{1-\beta_m}}{(1+\alpha_1-\beta_m)\cdots(1+\alpha_p-\beta_m)} \qquad (m = 1 \text{ to } q). \tag{8.66}$$

More generally, from (8.60) and (8.63),

$$ {}_pF_{q,\sigma}[\alpha_r; \beta_t; z] = e^{i\pi\theta}z^{-\alpha_m}\,{}_{q+1}f_{p-1,1-\sigma-\alpha_m} \left[\begin{matrix} \alpha_m, 1+\alpha_m-\beta_1, \ldots, 1+\alpha_m-\beta_q; e^{i\pi(p-q-1)}z^{-1} \\ 1+\alpha_m-\alpha_1, \ldots, 1+\alpha_m-\alpha_{m-1}, 1+\alpha_m-\alpha_{m+1}, \ldots, 1+\alpha_m-\alpha_p \end{matrix}\right] $$

$$(m = 1 \text{ to } p), \quad (8.67)$$

and conversely,

$$ {}_pf_{q,\sigma}[\alpha_r; \beta_t; z] = e^{i\pi\theta}z^{-\alpha_m}\,{}_{q+1}F_{p-1,1-\sigma+\alpha_m} \left[\begin{matrix} \alpha_m, 1+\alpha_m-\beta_1, \ldots, 1+\alpha_m-\beta_q; e^{i\pi(p-q-1)}z^{-1} \\ 1+\alpha_m-\alpha_1, \ldots, 1+\alpha_m-\alpha_{m-1}, 1+\alpha_m-\alpha_{m+1}, \ldots, 1+\alpha_m-\alpha_p \end{matrix}\right] $$

$$(m = 1 \text{ to } p), \quad (8.68)$$

where $\theta = q + (p-q-1)(\sigma+\alpha_m)$.

8.11 Recurrence Formulas and Relations for Contiguous Functions

From (8.60) we see that

$$ (\sigma+\alpha_1)\cdots(\sigma+\alpha_p)\,{}_pf_{q,\sigma+1}[\alpha_r; \beta_t; z] = \sigma(\sigma+\beta_1-1)\cdots(\sigma+\beta_q-1)\,{}_pf_{q,\sigma}[\alpha_r; \beta_t; z] - z^{\sigma}. \tag{8.69}$$

On differentiating (8.60) we find that

$$ \frac{d}{dz}\,{}_pf_{q,\sigma}[\alpha_r; \beta_t; z] = (\sigma-1)\,{}_pf_{q,\sigma-1}\left[\begin{matrix} \alpha_1+1, \ldots, \alpha_p+1; z \\ \beta_1+1, \ldots, \beta_q+1 \end{matrix}\right]. \tag{8.70}$$

Simple relations can be obtained between $p+q$ of the functions which are contiguous to ${}_pf_{q,\sigma}[\alpha_r; \beta_t; z]$. As in §8.4, it is convenient to use a concise notation; in this section we shall use the notation

$$f = {}_pf_{q,\sigma}\left[\begin{matrix}\alpha_1, \ldots, \alpha_p; z\\ \beta_1, \ldots, \beta_q\end{matrix}\right],$$

$$f[\alpha_1+] = {}_pf_{q,\sigma}\left[\begin{matrix}\alpha_1 + 1, \alpha_2, \ldots, \alpha_p; z\\ \beta_1, \ldots, \beta_q\end{matrix}\right],$$

$$f[\beta_1-] = {}_pf_{q,\sigma}\left[\begin{matrix}\alpha_1, \ldots, \alpha_p; z\\ \beta_1 - 1, \beta_2, \ldots, \beta_q\end{matrix}\right],$$

and similarly for the other parameters α_r and β_t.
Let $\delta \equiv z d/dz$. Then, from (8.60),

$$(\delta + \alpha_m)f = (\sigma + \alpha_m)f[\alpha_m+] \qquad (m = 1 \textit{ to } p) \tag{8.71}$$

and

$$(\delta + \beta_m - 1)f = (\sigma + \beta_m - 2)f[\beta_m-] \qquad (m = 1 \text{ to } q). \tag{8.72}$$

From the $p + q$ equations (8.71) and (8.72), we can obtain $p + q - 1$ independent linear relations between ${}_pf_{q,\sigma}$ and pairs of contiguous functions. Using (8.63), we find that (8.69) to (8.72) hold true if the function f_σ is replaced by F_σ.

8.12 Integrals Connected with ${}_pf_{q,\sigma}[\alpha_r; \beta_t; z]$

The formulas

$$\int_0^1 (1 - z)^{\nu-1}\, {}_pf_{q,\sigma}[\alpha_r; \beta_t; az]dz$$

$$= \frac{\Gamma(\sigma)\Gamma(\nu)}{\Gamma(\sigma + \nu)} a^{-\nu}\, {}_pf_{q,\sigma+\nu}\left[\begin{matrix}\alpha_1 - \nu, \ldots, \alpha_p - \nu; a\\ \beta_1 - \nu, \ldots, \beta_q - \nu\end{matrix}\right]$$

$$[\text{Re}\, \nu > 0,\ \text{Re}\, \sigma > 0,\ \text{Re}(\sigma + \beta_m) > 1 \quad (m = 1 \text{ to } q)] \tag{8.73}$$

and

$$\int_0^1 z^{\beta_m - 1}(1 - z)^{\nu-1}\, {}_pf_{q,\sigma}[\alpha_r; \beta_t; az]dz$$

$$= \frac{\Gamma(\sigma + \beta_m - 1)\Gamma(\nu)}{\Gamma(\sigma + \beta_m + \nu - 1)}\, {}_pf_{q,\sigma}\left[\begin{matrix}\alpha_1, \ldots, \alpha_p; a\\ \beta_1, \ldots, \beta_{m-1}, \beta_m + \nu, \beta_{m+1}, \ldots, \beta_q\end{matrix}\right]$$

$$(m = 1 \text{ to } q) \quad [\text{Re}\, \nu > 0,\ \text{Re}\, \sigma > 0,\ \text{Re}(\sigma + \beta_t) > 1 \quad (t = 1 \text{ to } q)] \tag{8.74}$$

may be proved by expanding ${}_pf_{q,\sigma}$ as a power series in z and integrating term by term. If $p = q + 1$, we have the additional restriction $|a| < 1$ in (8.73) and (8.74).

Similarly, if Re $\nu > 0$ and Re $\beta_m > 1$ ($m = 1$ to q),

$$\int_0^1 (1-z)^{\nu-1}\,{}_pF_q[\alpha_r;\beta_t;az]dz$$
$$= \prod_{m=1}^{q}(\beta_m - 1)a^{-\nu}\,{}_pf_{q,\nu}\begin{bmatrix}\alpha_1-\nu,\ldots,\alpha_p-\nu;a\\ \beta_1-\nu,\ldots,\beta_q-\nu\end{bmatrix}$$

(if $p = q+1$, $|a|$ must be less than 1). (8.75)

The formula

$$\int_0^s z^{\varrho-1}(s-z)^{\nu-1}\,{}_pf_{q,\sigma}[\alpha_r;\beta_t;az]dz = \frac{\Gamma(\rho+\sigma)\Gamma(\nu)}{\Gamma(\rho+\nu+\sigma-1)}s^{\sigma+\nu-1}$$
$$\times\ {}_{p+1}f_{q+1,\sigma}\begin{bmatrix}\rho,\alpha_1,\ldots,\alpha_p;as\\ \rho+\nu,\beta_1,\ldots,\beta_q\end{bmatrix}$$

[Re $\sigma > 0$, Re $\nu > 0$, Re $\rho > 0$, Re$(\sigma + \beta_m) > 1$ ($m = 1$ to q)] (8.76)

can be proved by expanding ${}_pf_{q,\sigma}$ as a power series in z and integrating term by term. If $p = q + 1$, we have the additional restriction $|as| < 1$.

Similarly we find (for $p \leqslant q$)

$$\int_0^\infty e^{-bz}z^{\varrho-1}\,{}_pf_{q,\sigma}[\alpha_r;\beta_t;az]dz$$
$$= \Gamma(\rho+\sigma)b^{-\rho}\,{}_{p+1}f_{q,\sigma}\begin{bmatrix}\rho,\alpha_1,\ldots,\alpha_p;a/b\\ \beta_1,\ldots,\beta_q\end{bmatrix},$$

[Re $\sigma > 0$, Re $\rho > 0$, Re$(\sigma + \beta_m) > 1$ ($m = 1$ to q)]. (8.77)

In particular, if $\rho = 1$,

$$\int_0^\infty e^{-bz}\,{}_pf_{q,\sigma}[\alpha_r;\beta_t;az]dz$$
$$= \frac{\Gamma(\sigma)a^\sigma}{(\sigma+\beta_1-1)\cdots(\sigma+\beta_q-1)b^{\sigma+1}}\,{}_{p+1}F_q\begin{bmatrix}1,\sigma+\alpha_1,\ldots,\sigma+\alpha_p;a/b\\ \sigma+\beta_1,\ldots,\sigma+\beta_q\end{bmatrix},$$

[Re $\sigma > 0$. Re$(\sigma + \beta_m) > 1$ ($m = 1$ to q)]. (8.78)

If $p = q$, we have the additional restriction $|a/b| < 1$ in (8.77) and (8.78).

PROBLEMS

1. Show that

$${}_2B_1(\alpha_1,\alpha_2;\beta;z) = B(\alpha_1,\alpha_2;\beta;z)$$

and

$${}_1B_1(\alpha;\beta;z) = \Omega(\alpha,\beta;z).$$

2. Prove that, if $\beta_q = \alpha_p + 1$,

$$ {}_pB_q\begin{bmatrix} \alpha_1, \ldots, \alpha_p; 0 \\ \beta_1, \ldots, \beta_q \end{bmatrix} = 1 - 2^{1-\alpha_p} \qquad (\alpha_p > 0). $$

3. Prove that, if Re $\beta_q \to \infty$ while α_p is constant (Re $\alpha_p > 0$ and $2 \leqslant p \leqslant q + 1$),

$$ {}_pB_q[\alpha_r; \beta_t; z] \to -1 \qquad \text{if } |z| < 1. $$

4. Prove that, if Re $p > 0$ and Re $(\alpha + \nu + \frac{1}{2}) > 0$,

$$ \int_0^\infty e^{-pt} t^{\alpha+\nu-(1/2)} \, {}_1B_2(\tfrac{1}{2} + \nu; \tfrac{1}{2} + \nu + \alpha, 1 + 2\nu; 2t)\, dt $$
$$ = 2^\nu \Gamma(\nu + 1)\Gamma(\alpha + \nu + \tfrac{1}{2}) p^{-\alpha-(1/2)} e^{1/p} L_\nu(1/p). $$

5. Show that

$$ {}_2f_{1,\sigma}(\alpha_1, \alpha_2; \beta; z) = f_\sigma(\alpha_1, \alpha_2; \beta; z), $$
$$ {}_2F_{1,\sigma}(\alpha_1, \alpha_2; \beta; z) = F_\sigma(\alpha_1, \alpha_2; \beta; z), $$
$$ {}_1f_{1,\sigma}(\alpha; \beta; z) = \theta_\sigma(\alpha, \beta; z), $$

and

$$ {}_1F_{1,\sigma}(\alpha; \beta; z) = \Theta_\sigma(\alpha, \beta; z). $$

6. Verify that $y = z^\sigma$ is a particular solution of the differential equation

$$ \delta(\delta + \beta_1 - 1) \cdots (\delta + \beta_q - 1) - z(\delta + \alpha_1) \cdots (\delta + \alpha_p) $$
$$ = \sigma(\sigma + \beta_1 - 1) \cdots (\sigma + \beta_q - 1) z^\sigma - (\sigma + \alpha_1) \cdots (\sigma + \alpha_p) z^{\sigma+1}. $$

Hence show that

$$ (\sigma + \alpha_1) \cdots (\sigma + \alpha_p) \, {}_pf_{q,\sigma+1}[\alpha_r; \beta_t; z] $$
$$ = \sigma(\sigma + \beta_1 - 1) \cdots (\sigma + \beta_q - 1) \, {}_pf_{q,\sigma}[\alpha_r; \beta_t; z] - z^\sigma. $$

7. Prove that, if Re $\lambda > 0$, Re $\alpha > 0$, and Re $p > 0$,

$$ \int_0^\infty e^{-pt} t^{\alpha+1} \, {}_2f_{1,\alpha}(\tfrac{1}{2} - \alpha - \mu + \nu, \tfrac{1}{2} - \alpha - \mu - \nu; \tfrac{3}{2}; -\lambda^2 t^2) dt $$
$$ = 4\Gamma(2\alpha) \lambda^{2\mu-1} p^{1-2\alpha-2\mu} S_{2\mu,2\nu}(p/\lambda). $$

8. Prove that

$$ {}_pB_q\begin{bmatrix} \alpha_1, \ldots, \alpha_p; z \\ \beta_1, \ldots, \beta_q \end{bmatrix} = \Omega(\alpha_p, \beta_q; 0) \, {}_pF_q\begin{bmatrix} \alpha_1, \ldots, \alpha_p; z \\ \beta_1, \ldots, \beta_q \end{bmatrix} $$
$$ + \alpha_1 \cdots \alpha_{p-1} \frac{2^{1-\beta_q}\Gamma(\beta_q)}{\Gamma(\alpha_p)\Gamma(\beta_q - \alpha_p)} \sum_{n=0}^\infty \frac{(\alpha_1 + 1)_n \cdots (\alpha_{p-1} + 1)_n 2^{-n}}{(\beta_1)_n \cdots (\beta_{q-1})_n \cdot n!} $$
$$ \times \, {}_pf_{q,n+1}\begin{bmatrix} \alpha_1, \ldots, \alpha_p; z \\ \beta_1, \ldots, \beta_q \end{bmatrix}. $$

CHAPTER 9

Nonhomogeneous Heun, Lamé, and Mathieu Functions

9.1 Introduction

In Chapter 8 we considered certain generalized hypergeometric functions which satisfied nonhomogeneous linear differential equations of order higher than two. As shown in Chapter 6, the hypergeometric equation

$$z(1-z)\frac{d^2y}{dz^2}+[c-(a+b+1)z]\frac{dy}{dz}-aby=0 \tag{9.1}$$

is an equation of the second order with three regular singularities (at $z=0$, 1, and ∞). We now consider second-order equations with four regular singularities. Any such equation can be reduced to Heun's equation

$$\frac{d^2y}{dz^2}+\left(\frac{\gamma}{z}+\frac{\varepsilon}{z-1}+\frac{\delta}{z-a}\right)\frac{dy}{dz}+\frac{\alpha\beta z+b}{z(z-1)(z-a)}y=0, \tag{9.2}$$

where

$$\alpha+\beta-\gamma-\delta-\varepsilon+1=0. \tag{9.3}$$

Equation (9.2) can be written in the alternative form

$$\begin{aligned} &z(z-1)(z-a)\frac{d^2y}{dz^2}\\ &\quad+[(\alpha+\beta+1)z^2-\{a(\alpha+\beta-\delta+1)+\gamma+\delta\}z+a\gamma]\frac{dy}{dz}\\ &\quad+(\alpha\beta z+b)y=0. \end{aligned} \tag{9.4}$$

In §9.2 we summarize various properties of (9.2) and, in §§9.3 to 9.5 we discuss in detail the properties of the nonhomogeneous Heun functions $f_\sigma(a,b;\alpha,\beta,\gamma,\delta;z)$ and $F_\sigma(a,b;\alpha,\beta,\gamma,\delta;z)$, which are particular integrals of

$$\frac{d^2y}{dz^2}+\left(\frac{\gamma}{z}+\frac{\varepsilon}{z-1}+\frac{\delta}{z-a}\right)\frac{dy}{dz}+\frac{\alpha\beta z+b}{z(z-1)(z-a)}y=\frac{z^{\sigma-2}}{(z-1)(z-a)}, \tag{9.5}$$

where α, β, γ, δ, and ε satisfy (9.3). As shown in §9.3, the relations between these functions and the nonhomogeneous hypergeometric functions $f_\sigma(a, b; c; z)$ and $F_\sigma(a, b; c; z)$ (defined in §6.16) are similar to the relations between Heun's F function and the hypergeometric function.

For certain values of the parameters, (9.5) reduces to the nonhomogeneous Lamé equation

$$\frac{d^2y}{dz^2} + \frac{1}{2}\left(\frac{1}{z} + \frac{1}{z-1} + \frac{1}{z-k^{-2}}\right)\frac{dy}{dz} + \frac{hk^{-2} - \nu(\nu+1)z}{4z(z-1)(z-k^{-2})}\,y = \frac{z^{\sigma-2}}{(z-1)(z-k^{-2})}, \tag{9.6}$$

that is, writing $z = (\text{sn } x)^2$,

$$\frac{d^2y}{dx^2} + \{h - \nu(\nu+1)[k \text{ sn } x]^2\}y = 4k^2[\text{sn } x]^{2\sigma-2}. \tag{9.7}$$

The properties of solutions of (9.6) and (9.7) are considered in §§9.6 and 9.7.

As shown in §9.8, a degenerate form of (9.6) is the nonhomogeneous Mathieu equation

$$4z(1-z)\frac{d^2u}{dz^2} + 2(1-2z)\frac{du}{dz} + (h + 4\theta z)u = z^{\sigma-1}; \tag{9.8}$$

that is, writing $z = \sin^2 x$ and $h = p^2$,

$$\frac{d^2u}{dx^2} + (p^2 + 4\theta \sin^2 x)u = [\sin x]^{2\sigma-2}. \tag{9.9}$$

Properties of solutions of this equation are considered in §§ 9.10 to 9.12.

As will be shown in Chapter 11, these equations occur in the solution of Poisson's equation in terms of elliptic coordinates.

9.2 Some Properties of Heun Functions

The properties of the solutions of Heun's equation (9.4) are given in Heun [1889a and b] and Snow [1952] (see also Erdélyi [1955], Whittaker and Watson [1935], and Ince [1926]). We shall here briefly summarize various properties of these functions, basing our notation on that used by Snow.

If γ is not an integer and $a \neq 0$, two independent solutions of (9.4) are

$$y_1 = F(a, b; \alpha, \beta, \gamma, \delta; z) = \sum_{n=0}^{\infty} c_n z^n \tag{9.10}$$

and

$$y_2 = z^{1-\gamma}F(a, b_2; 1+\alpha-\gamma, 1+\beta-\gamma, 2-\gamma, \delta; z), \tag{9.11}$$

where

$$b_2 = b - (1-\gamma)(\delta + a\varepsilon)$$

and the coefficients c_n are given by

$$c_0 = 1, \qquad c_1 = -\frac{b}{\gamma a},$$

$$\begin{aligned}(n+2)(n+1+\gamma)ac_{n+2} \\ = \{(n+1)^2(a+1) + (n+1)[(\alpha+\beta-\delta)a + \gamma + \delta - 1] - b\}c_{n+1} \\ -(n+\alpha)(n+\beta)c_n \qquad (n \geqslant 0).\end{aligned} \tag{9.12}$$

As shown by Heun, the series for $F(a, b; \alpha, \beta, \gamma, \delta; z)$ is convergent if both $|z| < a$ and $|z| < 1$. If $|a| > 1$, the series converges for $|z| = 1$ if $\mathrm{Re}(\gamma + \delta - \alpha - \beta) > 0$. We see that c_n is a polynomial of degree n in b. The n values of b which make c_n vanish are said to be *characteristic values*. If, in addition, α (or β) is equal to $1-n$, the series (9.10) will terminate after n terms and the F function will then be a polynomial in z of degree $n-1$.

When $\delta = 0$ and $b = -\alpha\beta a$, we see, on removing the factor $z - a$, that (9.4) reduces to the hypergeometric equation

$$z(1-z)\frac{d^2y}{dz^2} + [\gamma - (\alpha+\beta+1)z]\frac{dy}{dz} - \alpha\beta y = 0. \tag{9.13}$$

On putting $\delta = 0$ and $b = -\alpha\beta a$ in (9.10), we see from (9.10) and (9.12) that

$$F(a, -\alpha\beta a; \alpha, \beta, \gamma, 0; z) = F(\alpha, \beta; \gamma; z), \tag{9.14}$$

where the F function on the right side of (9.14) is the hypergeometric function.

When $a = 0$ and $b = 0$, (9.4) reduces to the hypergeometric equation

$$z(1-z)\frac{d^2y}{dz^2} + [\gamma + \delta - (\alpha+\beta+1)z]\frac{dy}{dz} - \alpha\beta y = 0. \tag{9.15}$$

On putting $b = -\alpha\beta\gamma a/(\gamma+\delta)$ in (9.10) and letting $a \to 0$, we see from (9.10) and (9.12) that, if $\gamma + \delta$ is not zero or a negative integer,

$$\lim_{a\to 0} F\left[a, -\frac{\alpha\beta\gamma a}{\gamma+\delta}; \alpha, \beta, \gamma, \delta; z\right] = F(\alpha, \beta; \gamma+\delta; z). \tag{9.16}$$

Again, when $b = av$ and $a \to \infty$, (9.2) reduces to

$$\frac{d^2y}{dz^2} + \left(\frac{\gamma}{z} + \frac{\varepsilon}{z-1}\right)\frac{dy}{dz} - \frac{v}{z(z-1)}y = 0. \tag{9.17}$$

Equation (9.17) can be written in the alternative form

$$z(1-z)\frac{d^2y}{dz^2}+[\gamma-(2\mu+1)z]\frac{dy}{dz}+\nu y=0\,, \tag{9.18}$$

where

$$\mu=\tfrac{1}{2}(\alpha+\beta-\delta)\,. \tag{9.19}$$

On putting $b=a\nu$ in (9.10) and letting $a\to\infty$, we see from (9.10) and (9.12) that, if γ is not zero or a negative integer,

$$\lim_{a\to\infty}F(a,a\nu;\alpha,\beta,\gamma,\delta;z)=F(\mu+\sqrt{\mu^2+\nu},\mu-\sqrt{\mu^2+\nu};\gamma;z), \tag{9.20}$$

where μ is given by (9.19).

There are 192 functions of the type

$$z^p(z-1)^q(z-a)^r F(a',b';\alpha',\beta',\gamma',\delta';z'),$$

which are solutions of Heun's equation (9.4), where p, q, r, α', β', γ' and δ' are *linear functions* of α, β, γ, and δ and where z' is one of the variables

$$z,\ 1-z,\ \frac{1}{z},\ \frac{1}{1-z},\ \frac{z}{z-1},\ \frac{z-1}{z},$$

$$\frac{z}{a},\ \frac{a-z}{a},\ \frac{a}{z},\ \frac{a}{a-z},\ \frac{z}{z-a},\ \frac{z-a}{z},$$

$$\frac{z-a}{1-a},\ \frac{1-z}{1-a},\ \frac{1-a}{z-a},\ \frac{1-a}{1-z},\ \frac{z-a}{z-1},\ \frac{z-1}{z-a},$$

$$\frac{z-a}{a(z-1)},\ \frac{(a-1)z}{a(z-1)},\ \frac{a(z-1)}{z-a},\ \frac{a(z-1)}{(a-1)z},\ \frac{z-a}{(1-a)z},\ \frac{(1-a)z}{z-a}.$$

In fact, only 96 of these series are distinct. Thus we find

$$F(a,b;\alpha,\beta,\gamma,\delta;z)=F\left(\frac{1}{a},\frac{b}{a};\alpha,\beta,\gamma,\varepsilon;\frac{z}{a}\right). \tag{9.21}$$

The Wronskian of y_1 and y_2 is

$$W(y_1,y_2)=y_1Dy_2-y_2Dy_1=(1-\gamma)z^{-\gamma}(1-z)^{-\varepsilon}\left(1-\frac{z}{a}\right)^{-\delta}, \tag{9.22}$$

where $D\equiv d/dz$. When $\gamma=1$, $y_1=y_2$, and the solutions given by (9.10) and (9.11) are identical.

When $\gamma-1$ is a negative integer, y_1 is infinite. Similarly, when $\gamma-1$ is a positive integer, y_2 is infinite. Thus, when γ is an integer, one solution of (9.4) is given by y_1 or y_2, and the second solution will contain logarithmic terms.

9.3 The Nonhomogeneous Heun Functions $f_\sigma(a, b; \alpha, \beta, \gamma, \delta; z)$ and $F_\sigma(a, b; \alpha, \beta, \gamma, \delta; z)$

We consider now the solutions of the nonhomogeneous Heun equation

$$\frac{d^2y}{dz^2} + \left(\frac{\gamma}{z} + \frac{\varepsilon}{z-1} + \frac{\delta}{z-a}\right)\frac{dy}{dz} + \frac{\alpha\beta z + b}{z(z-1)(z-a)}\,y = \frac{z^{\sigma-2}}{(z-1)(z-a)}, \tag{9.23}$$

where a, b, α, β, γ, δ, ε, and σ are constants ($a \neq 0$) and

$$\alpha + \beta - \gamma - \delta - \varepsilon + 1 = 0. \tag{9.24}$$

Equation (9.23) can be written in the alternative form

$$\begin{aligned} &z(z-1)(z-a)\frac{d^2y}{dz^2} \\ &\quad + [(\alpha+\beta+1)z^2 - \{a(\alpha+\beta-\delta+1)+\gamma+\delta\}z + a\gamma]\frac{dy}{dz} \\ &\quad + (\alpha\beta z + b)y = z^{\sigma-1}. \end{aligned} \tag{9.25}$$

The associated homogeneous equation is Heun's equation (9.4), which has regular singularities at $z = 0$, 1, a, and at infinity. We shall analyze the properties of certain particular integrals of (9.25) in a manner similar to that given in §6.16, for the functions $f_\sigma(a, b; c; z)$ and $F_\sigma(a, b; c; z)$.

Using the method of Frobenius (§1.12), we see that a particular integral of (9.25) is

$$f_\sigma(a, b; \alpha, \beta, \gamma, \delta; z) = \frac{z^\sigma}{a\sigma(\sigma+\gamma-1)}\sum_{n=0}^{\infty} f_n z^n \tag{9.26}$$

where

$$f_0 = 1, \qquad f_1 = \frac{\sigma^2(a+1) + \sigma[(\alpha+\beta-\delta)a+\gamma+\delta-1] - b}{a(\sigma+1)(\sigma+\gamma)},$$

$$\begin{aligned} &(\sigma+n+2)(\sigma+n+1+\gamma)af_{n+2} \\ &\quad = \{(\sigma+n+1)^2(a+1) + (\sigma+n+1)[(\alpha+\beta-\delta)a+\gamma+\delta-1)] - b\}f_{n+1} \\ &\qquad - (\sigma+n+\alpha)(\sigma+n+\beta)f_n \qquad (n \geqslant 0). \end{aligned} \tag{9.27}$$

Now as $n \to \infty$,

$$a\frac{f_{n+2}}{f_n} \to \left[(a+1)\frac{f_{n+1}}{f_n} - 1\right].$$

Thus

$$\frac{f_{n+2} - f_{n+1}}{f_{n+1} - f_n} \to \frac{1}{a} \qquad \text{and} \qquad \frac{a^2 f_{n+2} - af_{n+1}}{af_{n+1} - f_n} \to a.$$

By repeated application of these formulas we find that, if $|a| > 1$, $f_{n+1}/f_n \to 1$, and, if $|a| < 1$, $f_{n+1}/f_n \to 1/a$.

Thus the series (9.26) converges inside a circle with center at the origin the radius of which equals the distance from the origin to the nearer of the two singular points $z = a$ and $z = 1$. As in the case of Heun's F function, it can be shown that, if $|a| > 1$, the series converges for $|z| = 1$ if $\text{Re}(\gamma + \delta - \alpha - \beta) > 0$. The complete primitive of (9.25) is thus

$$y = C_1 F(a, b; \alpha, \beta, \gamma, \delta; z) + C_2 z^{1-\gamma} F(a, b_2; 1 + \alpha - \gamma, 1 + \beta - \gamma, 2 - \gamma, \delta; z) + f_\sigma(a, b; \alpha, \beta, \gamma, \delta; z), \quad (9.28)$$

where

$$b_2 = b - (1 - \gamma)(\delta + a\varepsilon). \quad (9.29)$$

The series solution (9.26) is not valid if σ or $\sigma + \gamma - 1$ is zero or a negative integer (since in these cases all the coefficients after a certain value of n become infinite). As shown in §1.12, for these values of σ the particular solution of (9.25) will, in general, contain logarithmic terms.

If $\sigma = m$, a positive integer, and *in addition* $c_{m-1} = 0$ in (9.12), (9.26) can be written

$$f_m(a, b; \alpha, \beta, \gamma, \delta; z) = \frac{1}{am(m + \gamma - 1)c_m} \sum_{n=m}^{\infty} c_n z^n, \quad (9.30)$$

where c_n is given by (9.12).

If $\sigma + \alpha$ (or $\sigma + \beta$) is equal to m (where m is zero or a negative integer), the series (9.26) will terminate after $m + 1$ terms if $f_{m+1} = 0$. Now, from (9.27), f_{m+1} is a polynomial of degree $m + 1$ in b. There are thus $m + 1$ polynomial solutions of (9.25) of degree m in z, corresponding to these $m + 1$ values of b.

From (9.26) and (9.27),

$$f_{\sigma+1-\gamma}(a, b; \alpha, \beta, \gamma, \delta; z) = z^{1-\gamma} f_\sigma(a, b_2; 1 + \alpha - \gamma, 1 + \beta - \gamma, 2 - \gamma, \delta; z), \quad (9.31)$$

where b_2 is given by (9.29).

Similarly, we find

$$f_\sigma(a, b; \alpha, \beta, \gamma, \delta; z) = a^{\sigma-2} f_\sigma\left(\frac{1}{a}, \frac{b}{a}; \alpha, \beta, \gamma, \varepsilon; \frac{z}{a}\right), \quad (9.32)$$

where ε is given by (9.24). We also see that

$$f_\sigma(a, b; \alpha, \beta, \gamma, \delta; z) = f_\sigma(a, b; \beta, \alpha, \gamma, \delta; z). \quad (9.33)$$

On putting $b = av$ in (9.26) and letting $a \to \infty$, we see from (9.26) and (9.27) that, if neither σ nor $\sigma + \gamma - 1$ is zero or a negative integer,

$$\lim_{a\to\infty} [af_\sigma(a, av; \alpha, \beta, \gamma, \delta; z)] = f_\sigma(\mu + \sqrt{\mu^2 + v}, \mu - \sqrt{\mu^2 + v}; \gamma; z), \quad (9.34)$$

where

$$\mu = \tfrac{1}{2}(\alpha + \beta - \delta) \quad (9.35)$$

and the f_σ function on the right side of (9.34) is the nonhomogeneous hypergeometric function defined in §6.16. If $\delta = 0$ and $v = -\alpha\beta$, (9.34) becomes

$$\lim_{a\to\infty} [af_\sigma(a, -a\alpha\beta; \alpha, \beta, \gamma, 0; z)] = f_\sigma(\alpha, \beta; \gamma; z). \quad (9.36)$$

Consider now the solution of (9.25) expressed as a series of decreasing powers of z (see §1.13). Such a particular integral is

$$F_\sigma(a, b; \alpha, \beta, \gamma, \delta; z) = \frac{z^{\sigma-2}}{(2-\sigma-\alpha)(2-\sigma-\beta)} \sum_{n=0}^{\infty} F_n \left(\frac{1}{z}\right)^n, \quad (9.37)$$

where

$$F_0 = 1,\ F_1 = \frac{(2-\sigma)^2(a+1) - (2-\sigma)[(\alpha+\beta-\delta)a + \gamma + \delta - 1] - b}{(3-\sigma-\alpha)(3-\sigma-\beta)},$$

$$\begin{aligned}(n+2-\sigma-\alpha)(n+2-\sigma-\beta)F_n &= \{(n+1-\sigma)^2(a+1)\\ &\quad - (n+1-\sigma)[(\alpha+\beta-\delta)a + \gamma + \delta - 1] - b\}F_{n-1}\\ &\quad - (n-\sigma)(n+1-\sigma-\gamma)aF_{n-2} \qquad (n \geqslant 2).\end{aligned} \quad (9.38)$$

Now, as $n \to \infty$, we find that, if $|a| > 1$, $F_{n+1}/F_n \to a$ and, if $|a| < 1$, $F_{n+1}/F_n \to 1$. Thus the series converges for $|z| > \max(1, |a|)$. The series solution (9.37) is not valid if $\sigma + \alpha - 1$ or $\sigma + \beta - 1$ is a positive integer. If σ or $\sigma + \gamma - 1$ is equal to m, where m is a positive integer ($\geqslant 2$), the series (9.37) will terminate after $m - 1$ terms if $F_{m-1} = 0$.

If $\sigma = m$ (where m is a positive integer $\geqslant 2$) and $F_{m-1} = 0$, (9.37) can be written in the form

$$F_m(a, b; \alpha, \beta, \gamma, \delta; z) = \frac{1}{(2-m-\alpha)(2-m-\beta)} \sum_{n=0}^{m-2} F_{m-2-n} z^n. \quad (9.39)$$

In this case, on comparing (9.12) and (9.38) we find

$$F_{m-2-n} = c_n F_{m-2} \qquad (n = 0 \text{ to } m-2)$$

and

$$c_{m-1} = 0.$$

Thus (9.39) becomes

$$F_m(a, b; \alpha, \beta, \gamma, \delta; z) = \frac{1}{(2-m-\alpha)(2-m-\beta)c_{m-2}} \sum_{n=0}^{m-2} c_n z^n$$

$$= -\frac{1}{am(m+\gamma-1)c_m} \sum_{n=0}^{m-2} c_n z^n, \tag{9.40}$$

where c_n is given by (9.12). From (9.30) and (9.40), we see that, if $\sigma = m$, a positive integer ($\geqslant 2$) and, in addition, $c_{m-1} = 0$,

$$f_m(a, b; \alpha, \beta, \gamma, \delta; z) - F_m(a, b; \alpha, \beta, \gamma, \delta; z) = \frac{1}{am(m+\gamma-1)c_m}$$

$$\times F(a, b; \alpha, \beta, \gamma, \delta; z) \qquad [|z| < \min(1, |a|)]. \tag{9.41}$$

From (9.37) and (9.38),

$$F_{\sigma+1-\gamma}(a, b; \alpha, \beta, \gamma, \delta; z) = z^{1-\gamma} F_\sigma(a, b_2; 1+\alpha-\gamma, 1+\beta-\gamma, 2-\gamma, \delta; z), \tag{9.42}$$

where b_2 is given by (9.29).
Similarly, we find

$$F_\sigma(a, b; \alpha, \beta, \gamma, \delta; z) = a^{\sigma-2} F_\sigma\left(\frac{1}{a}, \frac{b}{a}; \alpha, \beta, \gamma, \varepsilon; \frac{z}{a}\right), \tag{9.43}$$

where ε is given by (9.24). We also see that

$$F_\sigma(a, b; \alpha, \beta, \gamma, \delta; z) = F_\sigma(a, b; \beta, \alpha, \gamma, \delta; z). \tag{9.44}$$

On putting $a = 0$ and $b = 0$, we see from (9.37) and (9.38) that, if neither $\sigma + \alpha - 1$ nor $\sigma + \beta - 1$ is a positive integer,

$$F_\sigma(0, 0; \alpha, \beta, \gamma, \delta; z) = -F_{\sigma-1}(\alpha, \beta; \gamma + \delta; z), \tag{9.45}$$

where the $F_{\sigma-1}$ function on the right side of (9.45) is the nonhomogeneous hypergeometric function defined in §6.16.

From (9.26), (9.27), (9.37), and (9.38),

$$F_\sigma(a, b; \alpha, \beta, \gamma, \delta; z) = \frac{1}{a} z^{-\alpha} f_{2-\sigma-\alpha}\left(\frac{1}{a}, b_3; \alpha, \alpha+1-\gamma, \alpha+1-\beta, \delta; \frac{1}{z}\right)$$

$$= \frac{1}{a} z^{-\beta} f_{2-\sigma+\beta}\left(\frac{1}{a}, b_3'; \beta, \beta+1-\gamma, \beta+1-\alpha, \delta; \frac{1}{z}\right), \tag{9.46}$$

and, conversely,

$$f_\sigma(a, b; \alpha, \beta, \gamma, \delta; z) = \frac{1}{a} z^{-\alpha} F_{2-\sigma-\alpha}\left(\frac{1}{a}, b_3; \alpha, \alpha + 1 - \gamma, \alpha + 1 - \beta, \delta; \frac{1}{z}\right)$$
$$= \frac{1}{a} z^{-\beta} F_{2-\sigma-\beta}\left(\frac{1}{a}, b_3'; \beta, \beta + 1 - \gamma, \beta + 1 - \alpha, \delta; \frac{1}{z}\right), \tag{9.47}$$

where

$$b_3 = \alpha(\beta - \delta) + \frac{b - \alpha(\varepsilon - \beta)}{a}, \quad b_3' = \beta(\alpha - \delta) + \frac{b - \beta(\varepsilon - \alpha)}{a}. \tag{9.48}$$

If $\gamma = \delta = \varepsilon = \frac{1}{2}$, $f_\sigma(a, b; \alpha, \beta, \gamma, \delta; z)$ and $F_\sigma(a, b; \alpha, \beta, \gamma, \delta; z)$ are particular integrals of the nonhomogeneous Lamé equation (see §9.6).

9.4 Recurrence Formulas and Differential Relations

It is easily verified that $y = z^\sigma$ is a particular solution of the equation

$$z(z-1)(z-a)\frac{d^2y}{dz^2} + [(\alpha+\beta+1)z^2 - \{a(\alpha+\beta+1)+\gamma+\delta\}z + a\gamma]\frac{dy}{dz}$$
$$+ (a\alpha\beta + b)y = (\sigma+\alpha)(\sigma+\beta)z^{\sigma+1} - \{\sigma^2(a+1) + \sigma$$
$$\times [(\alpha+\beta-\delta) + \gamma + \delta - 1] - b\}z^\sigma$$
$$+ a\sigma(\sigma+\gamma-1)z^{\sigma-1}. \tag{9.49}$$

Now the general solution of (9.49) can be written in the form

$$(\sigma+\alpha)(\sigma+\beta)f_{\sigma+2}(a, b; \alpha, \beta, \gamma, \delta; z)$$
$$- \{\sigma^2(a+1) + \sigma[(\alpha+\beta-\delta)a + \gamma + \delta - 1] - b\}$$
$$\times f_{\sigma+1}(a, b; \alpha, \beta, \gamma, \delta; z) + a\sigma(\sigma+\gamma-1)f_\sigma(a, b; \alpha, \beta, \gamma, \delta; z)$$
$$+ C_1 F(a, b; \alpha, \beta, \gamma, \delta; z)$$
$$+ C_2 z^{1-\gamma} F(a, b_2; 1+\alpha-\gamma, 1+\beta-\gamma, 2-\gamma, \delta; z),$$

where C_1 and C_2 are arbitrary constants.

On comparing the power series for these two solutions we find that

$$(\sigma+\alpha)(\sigma+\beta)f_{\sigma+2}(a, b; \alpha, \beta, \gamma, \delta; z)$$
$$- \{\sigma^2(a+1) + \sigma[(\alpha+\beta-\delta)a + \gamma + \delta - 1] - b\}$$
$$\times f_{\sigma+1}(a, b; \alpha, \beta, \gamma, \delta; z) + a\sigma(\sigma+\gamma-1)f_\sigma(a, b; \alpha, \beta, \gamma, \delta; z) = z^\sigma. \tag{9.50}$$

The derivative of f_σ cannot be expressed as a function of $f_{\sigma-1}$ unless certain parameters are zero. Then

$$\frac{d}{dz}f_\sigma(a, b; 0, \beta, \gamma, \delta; z) = (\sigma - 1)f_{\sigma-1}(a, b_4; 2, \beta + 1, \gamma + 1, \delta + 1; z), \quad (9.51)$$

$$\frac{d}{dz}f_\sigma(a, b; \alpha, 0, \gamma, \delta; z) = (\sigma - 1)f_{\sigma-1}(a, b_4; \alpha + 1, 2, \gamma + 1, \delta + 1; z), \quad (9.52)$$

and

$$\frac{d}{dz}f_\sigma(a, 0; \alpha, \beta, 0, \delta; z) = (\sigma - 2)f_{\sigma-1}(a, 0; \alpha + 1, \beta + 1, 0, \delta + 1; z), \quad (9.53)$$

where

$$b_4 = b - a(\beta - \delta + 1) - \gamma - \delta. \quad (9.54)$$

More generally, (9.25) can be put in the form

$$[a\theta(\theta + \gamma - 1) - z\{a\theta(\theta + \alpha + \beta - \delta) + \theta(\theta + \gamma + \delta - 1) - b\} + z^2(\theta + \alpha)(\theta + \beta)]y = z^\sigma, \quad (9.55)$$

where $\theta \equiv zd/dz$.

Operating on both sides of (9.55) with the operator $(\theta + \alpha)$, we find that, if

$$b = -\alpha[a(\beta - \delta) + \gamma + \delta - \alpha - 1] = -\alpha[a(\beta - \delta) + \beta - \varepsilon], \quad (9.56)$$

$$\left[a\theta(\theta + \gamma - 1) - z\left\{a\theta(\theta + \alpha + \beta - \delta + 1) + \theta(\theta + \gamma + \delta) - b\left(1 + \frac{1}{\alpha}\right)\right\} + z^2(\theta + \alpha + 2)(\theta + \beta)\right]y' = (\sigma + \alpha)z^\sigma, \quad (9.57)$$

where

$$y' = (\theta + \alpha)y. \quad (9.58)$$

On comparing (9.55) and (9.57), we see that a particular integral of (9.57) is

$$(\sigma + \alpha)f_\sigma\left[a, b\left(1 + \frac{1}{\alpha}\right); \alpha + 2, \beta, \gamma, \delta + 1; z\right].$$

On expanding this function and y' as power series in ascending powers of z

we find that, if

$$b = -\alpha[a(\beta - \delta) + \gamma + \delta - \alpha - 1],$$

$$(\theta + \alpha)f_\sigma(a, b; \alpha, \beta, \gamma, \delta; z) = (\sigma + \alpha)f_\sigma\left[a, b\left(1 + \frac{1}{\alpha}\right); \alpha + 2, \beta, \gamma, \delta + 1; z\right], \tag{9.59}$$

where $\theta \equiv z d/dz$. The corresponding result for the Heun function F is

$$(\theta + \alpha)F(a, b; \alpha, \beta, \gamma, \delta; z) = \alpha F\left[a, b\left(1 + \frac{1}{\alpha}\right); \alpha + 2, \beta, \gamma, \delta + 1; z\right], \tag{9.60}$$

where b is given by (9.56).

Similarly, we find

$$(\theta + \beta)f_\sigma(a, b'; \alpha, \beta, \gamma, \delta; z) = (\sigma + \beta)f_\sigma\left[a, b'\left(1 + \frac{1}{\beta}\right); \alpha, \beta + 2, \gamma, \delta + 1; z\right] \tag{9.61}$$

where

$$b' = -\beta[a(\alpha - \delta) + \gamma + \delta - \beta - 1] = -\beta[a(\alpha - \delta) + \alpha - \varepsilon]. \tag{9.62}$$

Again, on dividing (9.55) throughout by z^2 and then operating on both sides with the operator $(\theta + \gamma - 1)$ we find that, if

$$b = -(\gamma - 1)[a(\alpha + \beta - \gamma - \delta + 1) + \delta] = -(\gamma - 1)(a\varepsilon + \delta), \tag{9.63}$$

$$\left[a\theta(\theta + \gamma - 3) - z\left\{a\theta(\theta + \alpha + \beta - \delta - 1) + \theta(\theta + \gamma + \delta - 2) - b\left(\frac{\gamma - 2}{\gamma - 1}\right)\right\} + z^2(\theta + \alpha)(\theta + \beta)\right]y'' = (\sigma + \gamma - 3)z^\sigma, \tag{9.64}$$

where

$$y'' = (\theta + \gamma - 1)y. \tag{9.65}$$

On comparing (9.55) and (9.64), we see that a particular integral of (9.64) is

$$(\sigma + \gamma - 3)f_\sigma\left[a, b\left(\frac{\gamma - 2}{\gamma - 1}\right); \alpha, \beta, \gamma - 2, \delta + 1; z\right].$$

On expanding this function and y'' as a power series in ascending powers of z we find that, if

$$b = -(\gamma - 1)[a(\alpha + \beta - \gamma - \delta + 1) + \delta],$$

$$(\theta + \gamma - 1)f_\sigma(a, b; \alpha, \beta, \gamma, \delta; z)$$
$$= (\sigma + \gamma - 3)f_\sigma\left[a, b\left(\frac{\gamma - 2}{\gamma - 1}\right); \alpha, \beta, \gamma - 2, \delta + 1; z\right], \tag{9.66}$$

where $\theta \equiv z d/dz$. The corresponding result for the Heun function F is

$$(\theta + \gamma - 1)F(a, b; \alpha, \beta, \gamma, \delta; z)$$
$$= (\gamma - 1)F\left[a, b\left(\frac{\gamma - 2}{\gamma - 1}\right); \alpha, \beta, \gamma - 2, \delta + 1; z\right], \tag{9.67}$$

where b is given by (9.63).

Using (9.37) we find that the formulas in this section hold true if the f_σ functions are replaced throughout by the F_σ functions with the same parameters.

9.5 Integrals Connected with $f_\sigma(a, b; \alpha, \beta, \gamma, \delta; z)$ and $F_\sigma(a, b; \alpha, \beta, \gamma, \delta; z)$

A number of indefinite integrals connected with the f_σ and F_σ functions can be obtained from the differential relations given in §9.4. Other integrals can be obtained by solving the differential equation

$$z(z-1)(z-a)\frac{d^2y}{dz^2} + [(\alpha + \beta + 1)z^2 - \{a(\alpha + \beta - \delta + 1) + \gamma + \delta\}z + a\gamma]$$
$$\times \frac{dy}{dz} + (\alpha\beta z + b)y = z^{\sigma - 1} \tag{9.68}$$

by the method of variation of parameters (see §1.5). The Wronskian corresponding to the solutions $F(a, b; \alpha, \beta, \gamma, \delta; z)$ and $z^{1-\gamma}F(a, b_2; 1 + \alpha - \gamma, 1 + \beta - \gamma, 2 - \gamma, \delta; z)$ is given by (9.22). We find that

$$f_\sigma(a, b; \alpha, \beta, \gamma, \delta; z) = \frac{1}{a(\gamma - 1)}\left[F(a, b; \alpha, \beta, \gamma, \delta; z)\int z^{\sigma-1}(1-z)^{\varepsilon-1}\right.$$
$$\times \left(1 - \frac{z}{a}\right)^{\delta - 1} F(a, b_2; 1 + \alpha - \gamma, 1 + \beta - \gamma, 2 - \gamma, \delta; z)\,dz$$
$$- z^{1-\gamma}F(a, b_2; 1 + \alpha - \gamma, 1 + \beta - \gamma, 2 - \gamma, \delta; z)\int z^{\sigma+\gamma-2}(1-z)^{\varepsilon-1}$$
$$\left.\times \left(1 - \frac{z}{a}\right)^{\delta - 1} F(a, b; \alpha, \beta, \gamma, \delta; z)\,dz\right]. \tag{9.69}$$

Now $x = F(a, b; \alpha, \beta, \gamma, \delta; z)$ is a solution of the differential equation

$$z(z-1)(z-a)\frac{d^2x}{dz^2} + [(\alpha + \beta + 1)z^2 - \{a(\alpha + \beta - \delta + 1) + \gamma + \delta\}z + a\gamma]$$
$$\times \frac{dx}{dz} + (\alpha\beta z + b)x = 0. \tag{9.70}$$

On multiplying (9.68) by $xz^{\gamma-1}(1-z)^{\varepsilon-1}[1-(z/a)]^{\delta-1}$ and (9.70) by $yz^{\gamma-1}(1-z)^{\varepsilon-1}[1-(z/a)]^{\delta-1}$ and subtracting, we obtain

$$az^{\gamma}(1-z)^{\varepsilon}\left(1-\frac{z}{a}\right)^{\delta}\left[x\frac{d^2y}{dz^2}-y\frac{d^2x}{dz^2}\right]$$

$$+[(\alpha+\beta+1)z^2-\{a(\alpha+\beta-\delta+1)+\gamma+\delta\}z+a\gamma]$$

$$\times z^{\gamma-1}(1-z)^{\varepsilon-1}\left(1-\frac{z}{a}\right)^{\delta-1}\left(x\frac{dy}{dz}-y\frac{dx}{dz}\right)$$

$$=z^{\sigma+\gamma-2}(1-z)^{\varepsilon-1}\left(1-\frac{z}{a}\right)^{\delta-1}x;$$

that is,

$$\frac{d}{dz}\left[az^{\gamma}(1-z)^{\varepsilon}\left(1-\frac{z}{a}\right)^{\delta}\left(x\frac{dy}{dz}-y\frac{dx}{dz}\right)\right]$$

$$=z^{\sigma+\gamma-2}(1-z)^{\varepsilon-1}\left(1-\frac{z}{a}\right)^{\delta-1}x. \tag{9.71}$$

On integrating (9.71) and putting $x = F(a, b; \alpha, \beta. \gamma, \delta; z)$, we see that

$$\int z^{\sigma+\gamma-2}(1-z)^{\varepsilon-1}\left(1-\frac{z}{a}\right)^{\delta-1}F(a, b; \alpha, \beta, \gamma, \delta; z)dz$$

$$=az^{\gamma}(1-z)^{\varepsilon}\left(1-\frac{z}{a}\right)^{\delta}\left[F(z)\frac{d}{dz}f_{\sigma}(z)-f_{\sigma}(z)\frac{d}{dz}F(z)\right], \tag{9.72}$$

where $F(z) \equiv F(a, b; \alpha, \beta, \gamma, \delta; z)$ and $f_{\sigma}(z) \equiv f_{\sigma}(a, b; \alpha, \beta, \gamma, \delta; z)$.

In (9.72) we can substitute F_{σ} for f_{σ} on the right side, the integral on the left side being indefinite.

9.6 The Nonhomogeneous Lamé Equations

In (9.23), put $\alpha = -\frac{1}{2}\nu$, $\beta = \frac{1}{2}(\nu+1)$, $\gamma = \delta = \varepsilon = \frac{1}{2}$, $a = 1/k^2$, and $b = \frac{1}{4}h/k^2$. Equation (9.23) then reduces to the nonhomogeneous equation

$$\frac{d^2y}{dz^2}+\frac{1}{2}\left(\frac{1}{z}+\frac{1}{z-1}+\frac{1}{z-k^{-2}}\right)\frac{dy}{dz}$$

$$+\frac{hk^{-2}-\nu(\nu+1)z}{4z(z-1)(z-k^{-2})}y=\frac{z^{\sigma-2}}{(z-1)(z-k^{-2})}, \tag{9.73}$$

where h, k, ν, and σ are constants. Equation (9.73) can be written in the alternative form

$$4z(1-z)(1-k^2z)\frac{d^2y}{dz^2}+2[3k^2z^2-2(1+k^2)z+1]\frac{dy}{dz}$$
$$+[h-\nu(\nu+1)k^2z]y=4k^2z^{\sigma-1}. \tag{9.74}$$

Let $z=s^2$. Then (9.74) becomes

$$(1-s^2)(1-k^2s^2)\frac{d^2y}{ds^2}-s(1+k^2-2k^2s^2)\frac{dy}{ds}$$
$$+[h-\nu(\nu+1)k^2s^2]y=4k^2s^{2\sigma-2}, \tag{9.75}$$

with particular integrals $f_\sigma[k^{-2}, \frac{1}{4}hk^{-2}; -\frac{1}{2}\nu, \frac{1}{2}(\nu+1), \frac{1}{2}, \frac{1}{2}; s^2]$ and $F_\sigma[k^{-2}, \frac{1}{4}hk^{-2}; -\frac{1}{2}\nu, \frac{1}{2}(\nu+1), \frac{1}{2}, \frac{1}{2}; s^2]$.

Equation (9.75) can be generalized by putting $t=ps$, $q=p/k$. Then (9.75) becomes

$$(t^2-p^2)(t^2-q^2)\frac{d^2y}{dt^2}+t(2t^2-p^2-q^2)\frac{dy}{dt}$$
$$+[hq^2-\nu(\nu+1)t^2]y=4p^{3-\sigma}t^{\sigma-1}, \tag{9.76}$$

with the particular integrals $f_\sigma[-q^2/p^2, \frac{1}{4}hq^2/p^2; -\frac{1}{2}\nu, \frac{1}{2}(\nu+1), \frac{1}{2}, \frac{1}{2}; (t/p)^2]$ and $F_\sigma[-q^2/p^2, \frac{1}{4}hq^2/p^2; -\frac{1}{2}\nu, \frac{1}{2}\nu(\nu+1), \frac{1}{2}, \frac{1}{2}; (t/p)^2]$.

Equations (9.73) to (9.76) are various algebraic forms of the nonhomogeneous Lamé equation. A trigonometric form of this equation can be obtained by putting $s=\cos\zeta$. Equation (9.75) then becomes

$$(1-k^2\cos^2\zeta)\frac{d^2y}{d\zeta^2}+k^2\cos\zeta\sin\zeta\frac{dy}{d\zeta}$$
$$+[h-\nu(\nu+1)k^2\cos^2\zeta]y=4k^2[\cos\zeta]^{2\sigma-2}, \tag{9.77}$$

with a particular integral $f_\sigma[k^{-2}, \frac{1}{4}hk^{-2}; -\frac{1}{2}\nu, \frac{1}{2}(\nu+1), \frac{1}{2}, \frac{1}{2}; \cos^2\zeta]$.

On putting $s=\operatorname{sn} x$, where $\operatorname{sn} x$ is the Jacobian elliptic function (of modulus k) (Erdélyi [*340*, 1953b]), we find that (9.75) becomes

$$\frac{d^2y}{dx^2}+\{h-\nu(\nu+1)k^2[\operatorname{sn} x]^2\}y=4k^2[\operatorname{sn} x]^{2\sigma-2}, \tag{9.78}$$

which is the Jacobian form of the nonhomogeneous Lamé equation, with particular integrals $f_\sigma[k^{-2}, \frac{1}{4}hk^{-2}; -\frac{1}{2}\nu, \frac{1}{2}(\nu+1), \frac{1}{2}, \frac{1}{2}; (\operatorname{sn} x)^2]$ and $F_\sigma[k^{-2}, \frac{1}{4}hk^{-2}; -\frac{1}{2}\nu, \frac{1}{2}\nu(\nu+1), \frac{1}{2}, \frac{1}{2}; (\operatorname{sn} x)^2]$.

The properties of the functions f_σ and F_σ were considered in §§9.3 to 9.5. In particular we note that, with $a=1/k^2$, if $|k|<1$, the f_σ function converges for $|s|\leqslant 1$. Just as these functions can (for certain values of the parameters) be reduced to nonhomogeneous hypergeometric functions, so the solutions of (9.73) to (9.78) can (in certain cases) be reduced to nonhomogeneous Legendre functions.

Thus in (9.75) put $y = k^2 u$ and $h = (\mu + \frac{1}{2})^2$, and let $k \to 0$. Then (9.75) becomes

$$(1 - s^2)\frac{d^2u}{ds^2} - s\frac{du}{ds} + (\mu + \tfrac{1}{2})^2 u = 4s^{2\sigma - 2}, \tag{9.79}$$

with a particular integral $u = 4(s^2 - 1)^{1/4} s_{\mu,\sigma}^{-1/2}(s)$. From (9.35) and (7.146), we see that

$$\begin{aligned} &\lim_{k \to 0} \{k^{-2} f_\sigma[k^{-2}, \tfrac{1}{4}(\mu + \tfrac{1}{2})^2 k^{-2}; -\tfrac{1}{2}\nu, \tfrac{1}{2}(\nu + 1), \tfrac{1}{2}, \tfrac{1}{2}; s^2]\} \\ &\qquad = f_\sigma[\tfrac{1}{2}\mu + \tfrac{1}{4}, -\tfrac{1}{2}\mu - \tfrac{1}{4}; \tfrac{1}{2}; s^2] \\ &\qquad = 4(s^2 - 1)^{1/4} s_{\mu,\sigma}^{-1/2}(s), \end{aligned} \tag{9.80}$$

where the s function is the nonhomogeneous Legendre function defined in §7.16.

9.7 Nonhomogeneous Lamé Polynomials

Consider now (9.78), with $|k| < 1$. The elliptic function s ($=\text{sn}\, x$) lies between ± 1 for all real values of x. Now the particular integral of (9.78) which involves F_σ is represented by a series which is divergent if $|s| < 1$, unless the series terminates. As shown in §9.3, if $\sigma = m$, where m is a positive integer ($\geqslant 2$), the function F_σ can (for certain values of the parameters) be expressed as a polynomial of degree $m - 2$. We shall now investigate the corresponding polynomial solutions of (9.78) in powers of sn x. For conciseness we write

$$s = \text{sn}\, x, \tag{9.81}$$

the modulus of the elliptic function being k, and its period $4K$.

THE NONHOMOGENEOUS LAMÉ FUNCTION $L_{\nu,m}^h(s)$

When $\sigma = m$, the nonhomogeneous Lamé function $L_{\nu,m}^h(s)$ is a particular integral of (9.78), where

$$\begin{aligned} L_{\nu,m}^h(s) &= F_m[k^{-2}, \tfrac{1}{4}hk^{-2}; -\tfrac{1}{2}\nu, \tfrac{1}{2}(\nu + 1), \tfrac{1}{2}, \tfrac{1}{2}; s^2] \\ &= \frac{s^{2m-4}}{(m - \frac{1}{2}\nu - 2)(m + \frac{1}{2}\nu - \frac{3}{2})} \sum_{n=0}^{m-2} F_n \left(\frac{1}{s}\right)^{2n}, \end{aligned} \tag{9.82}$$

where m is a positive integer ($\geqslant 2$) and the parameters h and k are so related that $F_{m-1} = 0$.

As shown in §9.3, (9.82) can be put in the equivalent form

$$L^h_{\nu,m}(s) = \frac{1}{(m - \frac{1}{2}\nu - 2)(m + \frac{1}{2}\nu - \frac{3}{2})c_{m-2}} \sum_{n=0}^{m-2} c_n s^{2n}, \tag{9.83}$$

where the c_n are given by

$$c_0 = 1, \qquad c_1 = -\tfrac{1}{2}h,$$

$$(n+2)(n+\tfrac{3}{2})c_{n+2} = \{(n+1)^2(1+k^2) - \tfrac{1}{4}h\}c_{n+1} - (n - \tfrac{1}{2}\nu)(n + \tfrac{1}{2}\nu + \tfrac{1}{2})k^2 c_n \qquad (n \geqslant 0) \tag{9.84}$$

and

$$c_{m-1} = 0. \tag{9.85}$$

The series solution (9.83) is not valid if either $\frac{1}{2}\nu$ or $-\frac{1}{2}(1+\nu)$ is zero or a positive integer less than $m - 1$ (since in these cases certain coefficients become infinite).

The corresponding solution of the associated homogeneous Lamé equation

$$(1 - s^2)(1 - k^2s^2)\frac{d^2y}{ds^2} - s(1 + k^2 - 2k^2s^2)\frac{dy}{ds} + [h - \nu(\nu+1)k^2s^2]y = 0$$

or

$$\frac{d^2y}{dx^2} + \{h - \nu(\nu+1)k^2[\operatorname{sn} x]^2\}y = 0, \tag{9.86}$$

where $s = \operatorname{sn} x$, is (Ince [1939])

$$y = \sum_{n=0}^{\infty} c_n s^{2n}, \tag{9.87}$$

where $c_0, c_1, \ldots$ are given by (9.84).

For the function $L^h_{\nu,m}(s)$, the relation between h and k is determined from (9.85). As shown by Ince, this relation can be put in the form of a continued fraction,

$$h = \frac{\frac{1}{2}\nu(\nu+1)k^2}{1 + k^2 - \frac{1}{4}h} + \frac{3(\nu-2)(\nu+3)k^2/4}{4(1+k^2) - \frac{1}{4}h} + \frac{15(\nu-4)(\nu+5)k^2/8}{9(1+k^2) - \frac{1}{4}h} + \cdots, \tag{9.88}$$

where the right-hand member terminates at the $(m-2)$th continued fraction (since c_{m-1} is zero). We note that ν is not restricted to integer values.

We see, from (9.83), that $L^h_{\nu,m}(s)$ can be expanded as a series of even powers of s; thus $L^h_{\nu,m}(s)$, considered as a function of x, has the real period $2K$. From the properties of the sn function, we see that, if m is a positive integer $\geqslant 2$, the values of $L^h_{\nu,m}(\operatorname{sn} x)$ are equal at x and $2K - x$; the derivative of $L^h_{\nu,m}(\operatorname{sn} x)$ with respect to x vanishes at $x = 0, K, 2K, 3K, \ldots$.

Equation (9.88) can be reduced to a polynomial of degree $m - 1$ in h, the roots of which correspond to certain special (or characteristic) values of h (these values differ from those for the homogeneous Lamé functions). There will thus be $m - 1$ nonhomogeneous Lamé polynomials of the form $L^h_{\nu,m}(s)$, where m is a positive integer ($\geqslant 2$). In particular, if $\sigma = m = 2$, $c_1 = 0$. Thus $h = 0$ and

$$L^h_{\nu,2}(s) = -\frac{1}{\frac{1}{2}\nu(\frac{1}{2} + \frac{1}{2}\nu)}. \tag{9.89}$$

If $\sigma = m = 3$, $c_2 = 0$. The characteristic values of h are the roots of

$$h^2 - 4(1 + k^2)h + 2\nu(\nu + 1)k^2 = 0 \tag{9.90}$$

and

$$L^h_{\nu,3}(s) = -\frac{1}{(1 - \frac{1}{2}\nu)(\frac{3}{2} + \frac{1}{2}\nu)}\frac{2}{h}(1 - \tfrac{1}{2}hs^2), \tag{9.91}$$

where h is one of the roots of (9.90).

THE NONHOMOGENEOUS LAMÉ FUNCTION $L^h_{\nu,m+(1/2)}(s)$

Consider now the solution of (9.78) when $\sigma = m + \frac{1}{2}$, where m is a positive integer ($\geqslant 2$). The nonhomogeneous Lamé function $L^h_{\nu,m+(1/2)}(s)$ is a particular integral of (9.78), where

$$L^h_{\nu,m+(1/2)}(s) = F_{m+(1/2)}[k^{-2}, \tfrac{1}{4}hk^{-2}; -\tfrac{1}{2}\nu, \tfrac{1}{2}(\nu + 1), \tfrac{1}{2}, \tfrac{1}{2}; s^2], \tag{9.92}$$

where h and k are so related that the expression on the right side of (9.92) is a polynomial in s.

Using (9.42), we see that (9.92) can be put in the form

$$\begin{aligned} L^h_{\nu,m+(1/2)}(s) &= sF_m[k^{-2}, \tfrac{1}{4}(h - k^2 - 1)k^{-2}; \tfrac{1}{2}(1 - \nu), \tfrac{1}{2}\nu + 1, \tfrac{3}{2}, \tfrac{1}{2}; s^2] \\ &= \frac{s^{2m-3}}{(m - \frac{1}{2}\nu - \frac{3}{2})(m + \frac{1}{2}\nu - 1)} \sum_{n=0}^{m-2} F_n \left(\frac{1}{s}\right)^{2n}, \end{aligned} \tag{9.93}$$

where m is a positive integer ($\geqslant 2$) and the parameters h and k are so related that $F_{m-1} = 0$. As shown in §9.3, (9.93) can be put in the equivalent form

$$L^h_{\nu,m+(1/2)}(s) = \frac{1}{(m - \frac{1}{2}\nu - \frac{3}{2})(m + \frac{1}{2}\nu - 1)d_{m-2}} \sum_{n=0}^{m-2} d_n s^{2n+1}, \tag{9.94}$$

where the d_n are given by

$$d_0 = 1, \qquad d_1 = -\tfrac{1}{6}(h - k^2 - 1),$$

$$(n+2)(n+\tfrac{5}{2})d_{n+2} = \{(n+\tfrac{3}{2})^2(1+k^2) - \tfrac{1}{4}h\}d_{n+1} \\ - (n - \tfrac{1}{2}\nu + \tfrac{1}{2})(n + \tfrac{1}{2}\nu + 1)k^2 d_n \qquad (n \geqslant 0) \tag{9.95}$$

and

$$d_{m-1} = 0. \tag{9.96}$$

The series solution (9.93) is not valid if either $\frac{1}{2}(\nu - 1)$ or $-(\frac{1}{2}\nu + 1)$ is zero or a positive integer less than $m - 1$ (since in these cases certain coefficients become infinite).

The corresponding solution of the associated homogeneous Lamé equation (9.86) is (Ince [1939])

$$y = \sum_{n=0}^{\infty} d_n s^{2n+1}, \tag{9.97}$$

where $d_0, d_1, \ldots$ are given by (9.95).

For the function $L^h_{\nu,m+(1/2)}(s)$, the relation between h and k is determined from (9.96). As shown by Ince, this relation can be put in the form of a continued fraction,

$$h = k^2 + 1 + \frac{3(\nu-1)(\nu+2)k^2/2}{(9/4)(1+k^2) - \frac{1}{4}h} \\ + \frac{5(\nu-3)(\nu+4)k^2/4}{(25/4)(1+k^2) - \frac{1}{4}h +} \; \frac{21(\nu-5)(\nu+6)k^2/8}{(49/4)(1+k^2) - \frac{1}{4}h +} \cdots, \tag{9.98}$$

where the right-hand member terminates at the $(m-2)$th continued fraction (since d_{m-1} is zero). We note here, too, that ν is not restricted to integer values.

We see from (9.94) that $L^h_{\nu,m+(1/2)}(s)$ can be expressed as a series of odd powers of s; thus $L^h_{\nu,m+(1/2)}(s)$, considered as a function of x, has the real period $4K$. From the properties of the sn function, we see that, if m is a positive integer ($\geqslant 2$), the values of $L^h_{\nu,m+(1/2)}(\text{sn}\,x)$ are equal at x and $2K - x$, and are equal (but of opposite sign) to those at $x + 2K$ and $4K - x$. $L^h_{\nu,m+(1/2)}(\text{sn}\,x)$ vanishes at $x = 0, 2K, 4K, \ldots$; its derivative (with respect to x) vanishes at $x = K, 3K, 5K, \ldots$.

Equation (9.98) can be reduced to a polynomial of degree $m - 1$ in h, the roots of which correspond to certain special (or characteristic) values of h. We see that there will be $m - 1$ nonhomogeneous Lamé polynomials of the form $L^h_{\nu,m+(1/2)}(s)$, where m is a positive integer ($\geqslant 2$). In particular, if

$\sigma = m + \frac{1}{2} = \frac{5}{2}$, $d_1 = 0$. Thus $h = k^2 + 1$ and

$$L^h_{\nu,5/2}(s) = \frac{1}{(\frac{1}{2} - \frac{1}{2}\nu)(1 + \frac{1}{2}\nu)}\, s\,. \tag{9.99}$$

If $\sigma = m + \frac{1}{2} = \frac{7}{2}$, $d_2 = 0$. The characteristic values of h are the roots of

$$h^2 - 10(1 + k^2)h + 9(1 + k^2)^2 - 6(1 - \nu)(2 + \nu)k^2 = 0 \tag{9.100}$$

and

$$L^h_{\nu,7/2}(s) = -\frac{6}{(\frac{3}{2} - \frac{1}{2}\nu)(2 + \frac{1}{2}\nu)(h - k^2 - 1)}\,[s - \tfrac{1}{6}(h - k^2 - 1)s^3]\,, \tag{9.101}$$

where h is one of the roots of (9.100).

9.8 The Nonhomogeneous Mathieu Equations

We consider, finally, the degenerate case of the nonhomogeneous Lamé equations when $\nu \to \infty$ and $k \to 0$ in such a manner that

$$\nu(\nu + 1)k^2 \to -4\theta\,, \tag{9.102}$$

where θ is a finite quantity.

On putting $y = 4k^2 u$, and using (9.102), (9.74) becomes

$$4z(1 - z)\frac{d^2u}{dz^2} + 2(1 - 2z)\frac{du}{dz} + (h + 4\theta z)u = z^{\sigma - 1}. \tag{9.103}$$

Let $z = s^2$. Then (9.103) becomes, with $h = p^2$,

$$(1 - s^2)\frac{d^2u}{ds^2} - s\frac{du}{ds} + (p^2 + 4\theta s^2)u = s^{2\sigma - 2}. \tag{9.104}$$

On putting $s = \sin x$, (9.104) becomes

$$\frac{d^2u}{dx^2} + (p^2 + 4\theta \sin^2 x)u = [\sin x]^{2\sigma - 2}, \tag{9.105}$$

or

$$\frac{d^2u}{dx^2} + (a - 2\theta \cos 2x)u = [\sin x]^{2\sigma - 2}, \tag{9.106}$$

where

$$a = p^2 + 2\theta\,. \tag{9.107}$$

Equations (9.105) and (9.106) are nonhomogeneous Mathieu equations, for which (9.103) and (9.104) are the algebraic forms. All these equations are degenerate forms of the nonhomogeneous Heun equation (see §9.3).

9.9 Solution of the Algebraic Mathieu Equation

In view of our subsequent analysis, we shall find it convenient to develop the theory of Mathieu functions in a manner rather different from that usually given. The merit of this approach is that it emphasizes the connection between nonhomogeneous Heun functions, Lamé functions, and Mathieu functions.

The solution of the homogeneous algebraic Mathieu equation corresponding to (9.103) was given by Lindemann [1883]. We shall find it more convenient to discuss the solution of Mathieu's equation in the forms

$$(1-s^2)\frac{d^2y}{ds^2} - s\frac{dy}{ds} + (p^2 + 4\theta s^2)y = 0, \tag{9.108}$$

and, putting $s = \sin x$,

$$\frac{d^2y}{dx^2} + (p^2 + 4\theta \sin^2 x)y = 0. \tag{9.109}$$

Equation (9.108) has regular singularities at $s = \pm 1$ and an irregular singular point at infinity. We shall briefly summarize various properties of the solutions of (9.108). The results follow immediately from §9.2.

Two independent solutions of (9.108) are

$$y_1 = Mc_p(\theta; s) = \sum_{n=0}^{\infty} a_n s^{2n} \tag{9.110}$$

and

$$y_2 = Ms_p(\theta; s) = p\sum_{n=0}^{\infty} b_n s^{2n+1}, \tag{9.111}$$

where the coefficients a_n are given by

$$a_0 = 1, \qquad a_1 = -\tfrac{1}{2}p^2,$$
$$(n+2)(n+\tfrac{3}{2})a_{n+2} = \{(n+1)^2 + \tfrac{1}{4}p^2\}a_{n+1} - \theta a_n \qquad (n \geqslant 0), \tag{9.112}$$

and the coefficients b_n by

$$b_0 = 1, \qquad b_1 = (1-p^2)/6,$$
$$(n+2)(n+\tfrac{5}{2})b_{n+2} = \{(n+\tfrac{3}{2})^2 - \tfrac{1}{4}p^2\}b_{n+1} - \theta b_n \qquad (n \geqslant 0). \tag{9.113}$$

As $n \to \infty$, a_{n+2}/a_{n+1} and b_{n+2}/b_{n+1} both tend to $1 - (3/2n) + 0(1/n^2)$. Thus the series (9.112) and (9.113) converge if $|s| \leqslant 1$. However, $(d/dx)Mc_p(\theta; s)$

and $(d/dx)Ms_p(\theta; s)$ are both indeterminate at $x = \pm\frac{1}{2}\pi$. Considered as functions of x (where $s = \sin x$), both $Mc_p(\theta; s)$ and $Ms_p(\theta; s)$ are periodic functions; however, these functions will, in general, have a discontinuous slope at points $x = \pm\frac{1}{2}\pi, \pm 3\pi/2, \pm 5\pi/2, \ldots$.

We see that

$$\begin{aligned} Mc_p(\theta; 0) &= 1, \\ \left[\frac{d}{ds} Mc_p(\theta; s)\right]_{s=0} &= 0, \\ Ms_p(\theta; 0) &= 0, \\ \left[\frac{d}{ds} Ms_p(\theta; s)\right]_{s=0} &= p. \end{aligned} \tag{9.114}$$

If $\theta = 0$, two independent solutions of (9.109) are $\sin px$ and $\cos px$. On expanding these solutions as power series in s ($=\sin x$) and comparing them with (9.110) and (9.111), we find that, if $-\frac{1}{2}\pi \leqslant x \leqslant \frac{1}{2}\pi$,

$$Mc_p(0; s) = \cos px$$

and

$$Ms_p(0; s) = \sin px, \tag{9.115}$$

where $s = \sin x$.

Equations (9.115) hold, *for this restricted range of* x, for all values of p. If p is an even integer, the series (9.112) for $Mc_p(0; s)$ terminates and is valid for all values of s (and x). Similarly, if p is an odd integer, the series (9.113) for $Ms_p(0; s)$ terminates and is valid for all values of s (and x). Then, from (9.115), if n is a positive integer,

$$Mc_{2n}(0; s) = \cos 2nx$$

and

$$Ms_{2n+1}(0; s) = \sin(2n+1)x, \tag{9.116}$$

for all values of x.

As is shown in standard texts on Mathieu functions—e.g., Ince [1926], Whittaker and Watson [1935], Poole [1936], and McLachlan [1947]—solutions of the Mathieu equation, which are integral functions of x with period 2π, exist if $\theta \neq 0$, provided that p has certain characteristic values.

9.10 The Nonhomogeneous Mathieu Functions

We consider now the solutions of the nonhomogeneous Mathieu equation

$$(1 - s^2)\frac{d^2y}{ds^2} - s\frac{dy}{ds} + (p^2 + 4\theta s^2)y = s^{2\sigma-2}, \tag{9.117}$$

or, putting $s = \sin x$,

$$\frac{d^2y}{dx^2} + (p^2 + 4\theta \sin^2 x)y = [\sin x]^{2\sigma - 2}, \tag{9.118}$$

where p, θ, and σ are constants. We shall analyze the properties of certain particular integrals of (9.117) in a manner similar to that given in §9.3 for the Heun functions.

Using the method of Frobenius (§1.12), we see that a particular integral of (9.117) is

$$M_{p,\sigma}(\theta; s) = \frac{s^{2\sigma}}{2\sigma(2\sigma - 1)} \sum_{n=0}^{\infty} A_n s^{2n}, \tag{9.119}$$

where

$$A_0 = 1, \qquad A_1 = \frac{\sigma^2 - \frac{1}{4}p^2}{(\sigma + 1)(\sigma + \frac{1}{2})},$$

$$(\sigma + n + 2)(\sigma + n + \tfrac{3}{2})A_{n+2} = \{(\sigma + n + 1)^2 - \tfrac{1}{4}p^2\}A_{n+1} - \theta A_n \qquad (n \geqslant 0). \tag{9.120}$$

As $n \to \infty$, $A_{n+1}/A_n \to 1$. Thus the series (9.119) converges if $|s| < 1$. It can be shown that the series converges for $|s| \leqslant 1$. The complete primitive of (9.117) is thus

$$y = C_1 Mc_p(\theta; s) + C_2 Ms_p(\theta; s) + M_{p,\sigma}(\theta; s). \tag{9.121}$$

The series solution (9.119) is not valid if $2\sigma - 2$ is a negative integer (since in this case all the coefficients after a certain value of n become infinite). As shown in (§1.12), for these values of σ, the particular solution of (9.117) will, in general, contain logarithmic terms.

If $\sigma = m$, a positive integer ($\geqslant 2$), and *in addition* $a_{m-1} = 0$ in (9.110), (9.119) can be written

$$M_{p,m}(\theta; s) = \frac{1}{2m(2m - 1)a_m} \sum_{n=m}^{\infty} a_n s^{2n}, \tag{9.122}$$

where a_n is given by (9.112).

Similarly, if $\sigma = m + \frac{1}{2}$, where m is a positive integer, and *in addition* $b_{m-1} = 0$ in (9.111), (9.119) can be written

$$M_{p,m+(1/2)}(\theta; s) = \frac{1}{2m(2m + 1)b_m} \sum_{n=m}^{\infty} b_m s^{2n+1}, \tag{9.123}$$

where b_n is given by (9.113).

Comparing (9.119) with (9.26), we see that the nonhomogeneous Mathieu function $M_{p,\sigma}(\theta; s)$ and the nonhomogeneous Heun function f_σ are related by the equation

$$\lim_{\substack{\nu\to\infty\\k\to 0}} \frac{1}{4k^2} f_\sigma\left[k^{-2}, \frac{1}{4}\left(\frac{p}{k}\right)^2; -\tfrac{1}{2}\nu, \tfrac{1}{2}(\nu+1), \tfrac{1}{2}, \tfrac{1}{2}; s^2\right] = M_{p,\sigma}(\theta; s), \tag{9.124}$$

where $\nu(\nu+1)k^2 \to -4\theta$. The recurrence formula (9.50) becomes

$$4\theta M_{p,\sigma+2}(\theta; s) + (p^2 - 4\sigma^2)M_{p,\sigma+1}(\theta; s) + 2\sigma(2\sigma-1)M_{p,\sigma}(\theta; s) = s^{2\sigma}. \tag{9.125}$$

Consider now the solution of (9.117) expressed as a series of descending powers of s (see §1.13). If $\theta \neq 0$, such a particular integral is

$$y = \frac{s^{2\sigma-4}}{4\theta} \sum_{n=0}^{\infty} B_n \left(\frac{1}{s}\right)^{2n}, \tag{9.126}$$

where

$$B_0 = 1, \qquad B_1 = \frac{(\sigma-2)^2 - \frac{1}{4}p^2}{\theta},$$

$$\theta B_n = \{(\sigma - n - 1)^2 - \tfrac{1}{4}p^2\} B_{n-1} - (\sigma - n)(\sigma - n - \tfrac{1}{2})B_{n-2} \qquad (n \geqslant 2). \tag{9.127}$$

In general, this series does not terminate and is divergent. However, if $\sigma = m$ or $m + \frac{1}{2}$ (where m is a positive integer $\geqslant 2$) and B_{m-1} vanishes, the series (9.126) terminates after $m - 1$ terms, and is a solution of (9.117), valid for all values of s (and x).

9.11 The Nonhomogeneous Mathieu Functions $N_{p,m}(\theta; s)$ and $N_{p,m+(1/2)}(\theta; s)$

When $\sigma = m$ and $\theta \neq 0$, the nonhomogeneous Mathieu function $N_{p,m}(\theta; s)$ is a particular integral of (9.117), where

$$N_{p,m}(\theta; s) = \frac{s^{2m-4}}{4\theta} \sum_{n=0}^{m-2} B_n \left(\frac{1}{s}\right)^{2n}, \tag{9.128}$$

where m is a positive integer ($\geqslant 2$), B_n is given by (9.127), and the parameters p and θ are so related that $B_{m-1} = 0$. For such values of σ, (9.128) can be put in the equivalent form

$$N_{p,m}(\theta; s) = \frac{1}{4\theta a_{m-2}} \sum_{n=0}^{m-2} a_n s^{2n}, \tag{9.129}$$

where the a_n are given by (9.112) and

$$a_{m-1} = 0. \tag{9.130}$$

In this case, from (9.112),

$$4\theta a_{m-2} = -2m(2m-1)a_m,$$

and thus, from (9.122) and (9.129), if m is a positive integer ($\geqslant 2$), and in addition $a_{m-1} = 0$,

$$M_{p,m}(\theta; s) - N_{p,m}(\theta; s) = \frac{1}{2m(2m-1)a_m} Mc_p(\theta; s) \qquad (|s| < 1). \qquad (9.131)$$

For the function $N_{p,m}(\theta; s)$, the relation between p and θ is determined from (9.130). As shown in §9.7, this relation can be put in the form of a continued fraction,

$$p^2 = \frac{-2\theta}{1 - \frac{1}{4}p^2 -} \frac{3\theta}{4 - \frac{1}{4}p^2 -} \frac{15\theta/2}{9 - \frac{1}{4}p^2 -} \cdots, \qquad (9.132)$$

where the right-hand member terminates at the $(m-2)$th continued fraction (since $a_{m-1} = 0$).

We see from (9.129) that, if $\theta \neq 0$, $N_{p,m}(\theta; s)$ can be expressed as a terminating series of even powers of s ($= \sin x$); thus $N_{p,m}(\theta; s)$, considered as a function of x, has a period of π. We see too that *if m is a positive integer* $\geqslant 2$, the values of $N_{p,m}(\theta; \sin x)$ are equal at x and $\pi - x$; the derivative of $N_{p,m}(\theta; \sin x)$ with respect to x vanishes at $x = 0, \frac{1}{2}\pi, \pi, 3\pi/2, \ldots$. Equation (9.132) can be reduced to a polynomial of degree $m-1$ in p^2, the roots of which correspond to certain special (or characteristic) values of p^2 (these values differ from the characteristic values for the homogeneous Mathieu functions). There will thus be $m-1$ nonhomogeneous Mathieu polynomials of the form $N_{p,m}(\theta; s)$, where m is a positive integer ($\geqslant 2$). In particular, if $\sigma = m = 2$, $a_1 = 0$. Thus $p = 0$ and

$$N_{p,2}(\theta; s) = \frac{1}{4\theta}. \qquad (9.133)$$

If $\sigma = m = 3$, $a_2 = 0$. The characteristic values of p are the roots of

$$p^4 - 4p^2 - 8\theta = 0 \qquad (9.134)$$

and

$$N_{p,3}(\theta; s) = -\frac{1}{2\theta p^2}(1 - \tfrac{1}{2}p^2 s^2), \qquad (9.135)$$

where p is one of the roots of (9.134).

Consider now the solution of (9.117) when $\sigma = m + \frac{1}{2}$, where m is a positive integer ($\geqslant 2$) and $\theta \neq 0$. The nonhomogeneous Mathieu function

$N_{p,m+(1/2)}(\theta; s)$ is a particular integral of (9.117), where

$$N_{p,m+(1/2)}(\theta; s) = \frac{s^{2m-3}}{4\theta} \sum_{n=0}^{m-2} B_n \left(\frac{1}{s}\right)^{2n}, \tag{9.136}$$

where m is a positive integer ($\geqslant 2$), B_n is given by (9.127), and the parameters p and θ are so related that $B_{m-1} = 0$.

For such values of σ, (9.136) can be put in the equivalent form

$$N_{p,m+(1/2)}(\theta; s) = \frac{1}{4\theta b_{m-2}} \sum_{n=0}^{m-2} b_n s^{2n+1}, \tag{9.137}$$

where the b_n are given by (9.113) and

$$b_{m-1} = 0. \tag{9.138}$$

In this case, from (9.113),

$$4\theta b_{m-2} = -2m(2m+1)b_m,$$

and thus, from (9.123) and (9.136), if m is a positive integer ($\geqslant 2$), and in addition $b_{m-1} = 0$,

$$M_{p,m+(1/2)}(\theta; s) - N_{p,m+(1/2)}(\theta; s) = \frac{1}{2m(2m+1)pb_m} Ms_p(\theta; s) \qquad (|s| < 1). \tag{9.139}$$

For the function $N_{p,m+(1/2)}(\theta; s)$, the relation between p and θ is determined from (9.138). As shown in §9.7, this relation can be put in the form of a continued fraction,

$$p^2 = 1 - \frac{6\theta}{\frac{9}{4} - \frac{1}{4}p^2 -} \frac{5\theta}{\frac{25}{4} - \frac{1}{4}p^2 -} \frac{21\theta/2}{\frac{49}{4} - \frac{1}{4}p^2 -} \cdots, \tag{9.140}$$

where the right-hand member terminates at the $(m-2)$th continued fraction (since $b_{m-1} = 0$).

We see from (9.137) that, if $\theta \neq 0$, $N_{p,m+(1/2)}(\theta; s)$ can be expressed as a terminating series of odd powers of s ($= \sin x$); thus $N_{p,m+(1/2)}(\theta; s)$, considered as a function of x, has a period of 2π. We see too that *if m is a positive integer $\geqslant 2$*, the values of $N_{p,m+(1/2)}(\theta; \sin x)$ are equal at x and $\pi - x$ and are equal to (but of opposite sign from) those at $x + \pi$ and $2\pi - x$. $N_{p,m+(1/2)}(\theta; \sin x)$ vanishes at $x = 0, \pi, 2\pi, \ldots$; its derivative (with respect to x) vanishes at $x = \pi/2, 3\pi/2, 5\pi/2, \ldots$. Equation (9.140) can be reduced to a polynomial of degree $m - 1$ in p^2, the roots of which correspond to certain special (or characteristic) values of p^2. We see that there will be $m - 1$ nonhomogeneous Mathieu polynomials of the form $N_{p,m+(1/2)}(\theta; s)$, where m is a positive integer ($\geqslant 2$). In particular, if $\sigma = m + \frac{1}{2} = \frac{5}{2}$, $b_1 = 0$. Thus $p^2 = 1$ and

$$N_{p,5/2}(\theta; s) = \frac{s}{4\theta}. \tag{9.141}$$

If $\sigma = m + \frac{1}{2} = \frac{7}{2}$, $b_2 = 0$. The characteristic values of p are the roots of

$$p^4 - 10p^2 + 9 - 24\theta = 0 \tag{9.142}$$

and

$$N_{p,7/2}(\theta; s) = \frac{3}{2\theta(1 - p^2)} \left[s + \frac{1 - p^2}{6} s^3 \right], \tag{9.143}$$

where p is one of the roots of (9.142).

Comparing (9.83) and (9.129), we find that the nonhomogeneous Lamé and Mathieu functions are related by the equation

$$\lim_{\substack{\nu \to \infty \\ k \to 0}} \frac{1}{4k^2} L^h_{\nu,m}(\text{sn}\, x) = N_{p,m}(\theta; \sin x), \tag{9.144}$$

where $\nu(\nu + 1)k^2 \to -4\theta$ and $h = p^2$. Similarly, from (9.94) and (9.137),

$$\lim_{\substack{\nu \to \infty \\ k \to 0}} \frac{1}{4k^2} L^h_{\nu,m+(1/2)}(\text{sn}\, x) = N_{p,m+(1/2)}(\theta; \sin x). \tag{9.145}$$

The corresponding characteristic values of p^2 can be deduced from those of h by the same limiting process.

The functions $N_{p,m}(\theta; s)$ and $N_{p,m+(1/2)}(\theta; s)$ are periodic nonhomogeneous Mathieu functions. If the nonhomogeneous equation (9.118) had a particular integral of the form $e^{\mu x}P(x)$, where $P(x)$ is a periodic function with period $n\pi$, this would imply that $e^{\mu(x+n\pi)}P(x)$ was also a particular integral of (9.118). But, from §1.2, the difference between two particular integrals of a nonhomogeneous linear differential equation is always a solution of the associated homogeneous equation, and this is not the case here. Thus equation (9.118) has no solution of the form $e^{\mu x}P(x)$.

9.12 Degenerate Case of the Nonhomogeneous Mathieu Equation

If $\theta = 0$, the solution (9.126) becomes nugatory. Equation (9.117) is then

$$(1 - s^2)\frac{d^2y}{ds^2} - s\frac{dy}{ds} + p^2 y = s^{2\sigma - 2}. \tag{9.146}$$

As shown in Chapter 7, this equation has the particular integrals

$$y = (s^2 - 1)^{1/4} s_{p-(1/2),\sigma}^{-(1/2)}(s) \tag{9.147}$$

and

$$y = (s^2 - 1)^{1/4} S_{p-(1/2),\sigma}^{-(1/2)}(s), \tag{9.148}$$

where the s and S functions are the nonhomogeneous Legendre functions defined in §7.16. On comparing the particular integral given by (9.147) (expressed as a power series in ascending powers of s) with the series for $M_{p,\sigma}(0; s)$, given by (9.119), we find that

$$\begin{aligned} M_{p,\sigma}(0; s) &= (s^2 - 1)^{1/4} s_{p-(1/2),\sigma}^{-(1/2)}(s) \\ &= \frac{s^{2\sigma}}{2\sigma(2\sigma - 1)}\, {}_3F_2(1, \sigma + \tfrac{1}{2}p, \sigma - \tfrac{1}{2}p; \sigma + 1, \sigma + \tfrac{1}{2}; s^2) \end{aligned}$$

$$(|s| < 1). \tag{9.149}$$

As shown in §7.16, the particular integral given by (9.148) can be expressed as a series of descending powers of s which converges when $|s| > 1$. If $2\sigma - 1$ is a positive integer, the series terminates and is thus valid for all values of s (provided that $\sigma - \frac{1}{2}p$ is not a positive integer, where p is taken to be positive). If, in this case, $\sigma - \frac{1}{2}p$ is a positive integer, one or more of the coefficients in the power series become infinite. Thus the solution of (9.118), with $\theta = 0$, in the form

$$\frac{d^2y}{dx^2} + p^2 y = [\sin x]^{m-2}, \tag{9.150}$$

where m is a positive integer ($\geqslant 2$), can be expressed as a terminating power series in $\sin x$ (and thus has a period 2π or, if only even powers are involved, π) provided that $m - p$ is not an even positive integer (where p is taken to be positive). This result can, of course, be found by elementary means (see Problem 6, Chapter 2).

9.13 Related Differential Equations

We shall now briefly consider two classes of second-order differential equations, the solutions of which can be expressed in terms of the nonhomogeneous Heun functions f_σ and F_σ defined in §9.3 (or, in certain cases, in terms of nonhomogeneous Lamé or Mathieu functions).

In (9.23) put

$$u = z^{\bar{\alpha}_0}(z - 1)^{\bar{\alpha}_1}(z - a)^{\bar{\alpha}_2} y$$

and let

$$
\begin{aligned}
\alpha &= \bar{\alpha}_0 + \bar{\alpha}_1 + \bar{\alpha}_2 + \bar{\alpha}_3 \,, \\
\beta &= \bar{\alpha}_0 + \bar{\alpha}_1 + \bar{\alpha}_2 + \bar{\beta}_3 \,, \\
\gamma &= 1 + \bar{\alpha}_0 - \bar{\beta}_0 \,, \\
\varepsilon &= 1 + \bar{\alpha}_1 - \bar{\beta}_1 \,, \\
\delta &= 1 + \bar{\alpha}_2 - \bar{\beta}_2 \,.
\end{aligned} \tag{9.151}
$$

From (9.24) and (9.151), we see that

$$
\sum_{r=0}^{3} (\bar{\alpha}_r + \bar{\beta}_r) = 2 \,. \tag{9.152}
$$

Equation (9.23) then becomes

$$
\begin{aligned}
&\frac{d^2u}{dz^2} + \left\{\frac{1 - \bar{\alpha}_0 - \bar{\beta}_0}{z} + \frac{1 - \bar{\alpha}_1 - \bar{\beta}_1}{z - 1} + \frac{1 - \bar{\alpha}_2 - \bar{\beta}_2}{z - a}\right\} \frac{du}{dz} \\
&\quad + \left\{\bar{\alpha}_3\bar{\beta}_3 z + \bar{b} + \bar{\alpha}_0\bar{\beta}_0 \frac{a}{z} + \bar{\alpha}_1\bar{\beta}_1 \frac{1 - a}{z - 1} + \bar{\alpha}_2\bar{\beta}_2 \frac{a(a - 1)}{z - a}\right\} \\
&\quad \times \frac{u}{z(z - 1)(z - a)} = z^{\bar{\alpha}_0 + \sigma - 2}(1 - z)^{\bar{\alpha}_1 - 1}(z - a)^{\bar{\alpha}_2 - 1},
\end{aligned} \tag{9.153}
$$

where

$$
\begin{aligned}
b = \bar{b} &+ \bar{\alpha}_0[\bar{\beta}_0(a + 1) + \bar{\beta}_1 a + \bar{\beta}_2 - a - 1] \\
&+ \bar{\alpha}_1[(\bar{\beta}_0 - 1)a + \bar{\beta}_1(a - 1)] + \bar{\alpha}_2[\bar{\beta}_0 - 1 - \bar{\beta}_2(a - 1)] \,.
\end{aligned} \tag{9.154}
$$

Equation (9.153) has the particular integral

$$
u = z^{\bar{\alpha}_0}(z - 1)^{\bar{\alpha}_1}(z - a)^{\bar{\alpha}_2} f_\sigma(a, b; \alpha, \beta, \gamma, \delta; z),
$$

where b is given by (159.4), α, β, γ, and δ by (9.151), and $\bar{\alpha}_0$, $\bar{\beta}_0$, . . . satisfy (9.152). The complementary function is

$$
\begin{aligned}
&C_1 z^{\bar{\alpha}_0}(z - 1)^{\bar{\alpha}_1}(z - a)^{\bar{\alpha}_2} F(a, b; \alpha, \beta, \gamma, \delta; z) \\
&\quad + C_2 z^{\bar{\beta}_0}(z - 1)^{\bar{\alpha}_1}(z - a)^{\bar{\alpha}_2} F(a, b_2; 1 + \alpha - \gamma, 1 + \beta - \gamma, 2 - \gamma; z),
\end{aligned}
$$

where

$$
b_2 = b - (1 - \gamma)(\delta + a\varepsilon) \,.
$$

We see that (9.153) has regular singularities at $z = 0$, 1, and at infinity.

Making the substitution

$$z = \frac{w - w_0}{w - w_3}\,\frac{w_1 - w_3}{w_1 - w_0};$$

that is, (9.155)

$$w = \frac{w_3(w_0 - w_1)z - w_0(w_3 - w_1)}{(w_0 - w_1)z - (w_3 - w_1)},$$

where w_0, w_1, and w_3 are constants, (9.153) becomes

$$\begin{aligned}
&\frac{d^2u}{dw^2} + \left\{\frac{1 - \bar{\alpha}_0 - \bar{\beta}_0}{w - w_0} + \frac{1 - \bar{\alpha}_1 - \bar{\beta}_1}{w - w_1} + \frac{1 - \bar{\alpha}_2 - \bar{\beta}_2}{w - w_2} + \frac{1 - \bar{\alpha}_3 - \bar{\beta}_3}{w - w_3}\right\}\frac{du}{dw} \\
&\quad + \left\{B + \frac{\bar{\alpha}_0\bar{\beta}_0(w_0 - w_1)(w_0 - w_2)(w_0 - w_3)}{w - w_0}\right. \\
&\qquad + \frac{\bar{\alpha}_1\bar{\beta}_1(w_1 - w_0)(w_1 - w_2)(w_1 - w_3)}{w - w_1} \\
&\qquad + \frac{\bar{\alpha}_2\bar{\beta}_2(w_2 - w_0)(w_2 - w_1)(w_2 - w_3)}{w - w_2} \\
&\qquad \left. + \frac{\bar{\alpha}_3\bar{\beta}_3(w_3 - w_0)(w_3 - w_1)(w_3 - w_2)}{w - w_3}\right\} \\
&\quad \times \frac{u}{(w - w_0)(w - w_1)(w - w_2)(w - w_3)} \\
&\qquad = \frac{(w_3 - w_0)^{\bar{\alpha}_1 + \bar{\alpha}_2}(w_3 - w_1)^{\bar{\alpha}_0 + \bar{\alpha}_2 + \sigma - 1}}{(w_0 - w_1)^{\bar{\alpha}_0 + \bar{\alpha}_1 + \bar{\alpha}_2 + \sigma - 2}(w_3 - w_2)^{\bar{\alpha}_2 - 1}} \\
&\qquad\quad \times \frac{(w - w_0)^{\bar{\alpha}_0 + \sigma - 2}(w - w_1)^{\bar{\alpha}_1 - 1}(w - w_2)^{\bar{\alpha}_2 - 1}}{(w - w_3)^{\bar{\alpha}_0 + \bar{\alpha}_1 + \bar{\alpha}_2 + \sigma}},
\end{aligned} \tag{9.156}$$

where

$$w_2 = \frac{w_3(w_0 - w_1)a - w_0(w_3 - w_1)}{(w_0 - w_1)a - (w_3 - w_1)},$$

that is, (9.157)

$$a = \frac{w_2 - w_0}{w_2 - w_3}\,\frac{w_1 - w_3}{w_1 - w_0},$$

and

$$\begin{aligned}
B = {}& \bar{b}(w_3 - w_2)(w_0 - w_1) + \bar{\alpha}_0\bar{\beta}_0(w_0 - w_1)(w_0 - w_2) + \bar{\alpha}_1\bar{\beta}_1(w_1 - w_0) \\
& \times (w_1 - w_2) + \bar{\alpha}_2\bar{\beta}_2(w_2 - w_0)(w_2 - w_1) + \bar{\alpha}_3\bar{\beta}_3(w_3 - w_1)(w_3 - w_2).
\end{aligned} \tag{9.158}$$

Equation (9.156) has a particular integral

$$u = \frac{(w_3 - w_0)^{\bar{\alpha}_1+\bar{\alpha}_2}(w_3 - w_1)^{\bar{\alpha}_0+\bar{\alpha}_2}}{(w_0 - w_1)^{\bar{\alpha}_0+\bar{\alpha}_1+\bar{\alpha}_2}(w_3 - w_2)^{\bar{\alpha}_2}} \frac{(w - w_0)^{\bar{\alpha}_0}(w - w_1)^{\bar{\alpha}_1}(w - w_2)^{\bar{\alpha}_2}}{(w - w_3)^{\bar{\alpha}_0+\bar{\alpha}_1+\bar{\alpha}_2}} \times f_\sigma(a, b; \alpha, \beta, \gamma, \delta; z), \tag{9.159}$$

where z is given by (9.155), a by (9.157), b by (9.154), α, β, γ, and δ by (9.151), and $\bar{\alpha}_0$, $\bar{\beta}_0$, . . . satisfy (9.152). Thus the equation

$$\begin{aligned}\frac{d^2u}{dw^2} &+ \left\{\frac{1 - \bar{\alpha}_0 - \bar{\beta}_0}{w - w_0} + \frac{1 - \bar{\alpha}_1 - \bar{\beta}_1}{w - w_1} + \frac{1 - \bar{\alpha}_2 - \bar{\beta}_2}{w - w_2} + \frac{1 - \bar{\alpha}_3 - \bar{\beta}_3}{w - w_3}\right\} \frac{du}{dw} \\ &+ \left\{B + \frac{\bar{\alpha}_0\bar{\beta}_0(w_0 - w_1)(w_0 - w_2)(w_0 - w_3)}{w - w_0}\right. \\ &\qquad + \frac{\bar{\alpha}_1\bar{\beta}_1(w_1 - w_0)(w_1 - w_2)(w_1 - w_3)}{w - w_1} \\ &\qquad + \frac{\bar{\alpha}_2\bar{\beta}_2(w_2 - w_0)(w_2 - w_1)(w_2 - w_3)}{w - w_2} \\ &\qquad \left. + \frac{\bar{\alpha}_3\bar{\beta}_3(w_3 - w_0)(w_3 - w_1)(w_3 - w_2)}{w - w_3}\right\} \\ &\qquad \times \frac{u}{(w - w_0)(w - w_1)(w - w_2)(w - w_3)} \\ &= \frac{(w - w_0)^{\bar{\alpha}_0+\sigma-2}(w - w_1)^{\bar{\alpha}_1-1}(w - w_2)^{\bar{\alpha}_2-1}}{(w - w_3)^{\bar{\alpha}_0+\bar{\alpha}_1+\bar{\alpha}_2+\sigma}}\end{aligned} \tag{9.160}$$

has a particular integral

$$u = \frac{(w_0 - w_1)^{\sigma-2}}{(w_3 - w_1)^{\sigma-1}(w_3 - w_2)} \frac{(w - w_0)^{\bar{\alpha}_0}(w - w_1)^{\bar{\alpha}_1}(w - w_2)^{\bar{\alpha}_2}}{(w - w_3)^{\bar{\alpha}_0+\bar{\alpha}_1+\bar{\alpha}_2}} \times f_\sigma(a, b; \alpha, \beta, \gamma, \delta; z),$$

where z is given by (9.155), a by (9.157), b by (9.154), α, β, γ, and δ by (9.151), and $\bar{\alpha}_0$, $\bar{\beta}_0$, . . . satisfy (9.152).

Letting $w_3 \to \infty$, from (9.155),

$$z = \frac{w - w_0}{w_1 - w_0},$$

that is, (9.161)

$$w = (w_1 - w_0)z + w_0,$$

we see, from (9.153) that the equation

$$\frac{d^2u}{dw^2} + \left\{\frac{1-\bar{\alpha}_0-\bar{\beta}_0}{w-w_0} + \frac{1-\bar{\alpha}_1-\bar{\beta}_1}{w-w_1} + \frac{1-\bar{\alpha}_2-\bar{\beta}_2}{w-w_2}\right\}\frac{du}{dw}$$

$$+ \left\{\bar{\alpha}_3\bar{\beta}_3(w-w_0) + \bar{b}(w_1-w_0) + \bar{\alpha}_0\bar{\beta}_0\frac{(w_0-w_1)(w_0-w_2)}{w-w_0}\right.$$

$$\left. + \bar{\alpha}_1\bar{\beta}_1\frac{(w_1-w_0)(w_1-w_2)}{w-w_1} + \bar{\alpha}_2\bar{\beta}_2\frac{(w_2-w_0)(w_2-w_1)}{(w-w_2)}\right\}$$

$$\times \frac{u}{(w-w_0)(w-w_1)(w-w_2)}$$

$$= \frac{(w-w_0)^{\bar{\alpha}_0+\sigma-2}(w-w_1)^{\bar{\alpha}_1-1}(w-w_2)^{\bar{\alpha}_2-1}}{(w_1-w_0)^{\sigma-2}}, \tag{9.162}$$

where

$$w_2 = (w_1-w_0)a + w_0,$$

that is, (9.163)

$$a = \frac{w_2-w_0}{w_1-w_0},$$

has a particular integral

$$u = (w-w_0)^{\bar{\alpha}_0}(w-w_1)^{\bar{\alpha}_1}(w-w_2)^{\bar{\alpha}_2}f_\sigma(a, b; \alpha, \beta, \gamma, \delta; z),$$

where z is given by (9.161), α, β, γ, and δ by (9.151), and $\bar{\alpha}_0$, $\bar{\beta}_0$, . . . satisfy (9.152).

In particular, if $\bar{\alpha}_0 = \bar{\alpha}_1 = \bar{\alpha}_2 = 0$, $\bar{\alpha}_3 = -\frac{1}{2}v$, $\bar{\beta}_0 = \bar{\beta}_1 = \bar{\beta}_2 = \frac{1}{2}$, $\bar{\beta}_3 = \frac{1}{2}(v+1)$, $w_0 = e_3$, $w_1 = e_2$, and $w_2 = e_1$, we see from (9.162) that the equation

$$\frac{d^2u}{dw^2} + \frac{1}{2}\left\{\frac{1}{w-e_1} + \frac{1}{w-e_2} + \frac{1}{w-e_3}\right\}\frac{du}{dw}$$

$$+ \frac{H - v(v+1)w}{4(w-e_1)(w-e_2)(w-e_3)}u$$

$$= \frac{1}{(e_2-e_3)^{\sigma-2}}\frac{(w-e_3)^{\sigma-2}}{(w-e_1)(w-e_2)}, \tag{9.164}$$

where

$$H = 4b(e_2-e_3) + v(v+1)e_3, \tag{9.165}$$

has a particular integral $u = f_\sigma[a, b; -\frac{1}{2}v, \frac{1}{2}(v+1), \frac{1}{2}, \frac{1}{2}; z]$, where z is given by (9.161) and a by (9.163).

On putting $w = \mathscr{P}(x)$, where $\mathscr{P}(x)$ is Weierstrasse's elliptic function

(Erdélyi [*328*, 1953b]) which satisfies the equation

$$\left[\frac{d}{dx}\mathscr{P}(x)\right] = 2\{[\mathscr{P}(x) - e_1][\mathscr{P}(x) - e_2][\mathscr{P}(x) - e_3]\}^{1/2},$$

(9.164) becomes

$$\frac{d^2u}{dx^2} + [H - \nu(\nu+1)\mathscr{P}(x)]u = \frac{4}{(e_2 - e_3)^{\sigma-2}}(\mathscr{P}(x) - e_3)^{\sigma-1}, \quad (9.166)$$

with a particular integral

$$u = f_\sigma\left[\frac{e_1 - e_3}{e_2 - e_3}, b; -\tfrac{1}{2}\nu, \tfrac{1}{2}(\nu+1), \tfrac{1}{2}, \tfrac{1}{2}; \frac{\mathscr{P}(x) - e_3}{e_2 - e_3}\right],$$

where b is given by (9.165). Equation (9.166) is the Weierstrassian form of the nonhomogeneous Lamé equation (9.78); (9.164) is the corresponding algebraic form.

In (9.164), put $H = he_1$, and let $e_1 \to \infty$ and $\nu \to \infty$ in such a manner that $\nu(\nu+1)/e_1 \to -4\theta$. Then, if $u = 4(e_2 - e_3)v/e_1$, (9.164) becomes, on letting $e_1 \to \infty$,

$$\frac{d^2v}{dw^2} + \frac{1}{2}\left\{\frac{1}{w - e_2} + \frac{1}{w - e_3}\right\}\frac{dv}{dw} - \frac{h + 4\theta w}{4(w - e_2)(w - e_3)}v = -\frac{1}{4(e_2 - e_3)^{\sigma-1}}\frac{(w - e_3)^{\sigma-2}}{w - e_2},$$

or (9.167)

$$4(w - e_2)(w - e_3)\frac{d^2v}{dw^2} + 2(2w - e_2 - e_3)\frac{dv}{dw} - (h + 4\theta w)v = -\left(\frac{w - e_3}{e_2 - e_3}\right)^{\sigma-1}.$$

Equation (9.167) has a particular integral

$$v = \lim_{\substack{e_1\to\infty \\ \nu\to\infty}}\left\{\frac{e_1}{4(e_2 - e_3)} \times f_\sigma\left[\frac{e_1 - e_3}{e_2 - e_3}, \frac{he_1 - \nu(\nu+1)e_3}{4(e_2 - e_3)}; -\tfrac{1}{2}\nu, \tfrac{1}{2}\nu(\nu+1), \tfrac{1}{2}, \tfrac{1}{2}; \frac{w - e_3}{e_2 - e_3}\right]\right\};$$

that is, using (9.124), with $h = p^2$,

$$v = M_{p,\sigma}\left[\theta(e_2 - e_3); \left(\frac{w - e_3}{e_2 - e_3}\right)^{1/2}\right],$$

where $M_{p,\sigma}$ is the nonhomogeneous Mathieu function defined in §9.10.

In (9.167), put $e_3 = 0$, $e_2 = K$, where K is a constant. Then (9.167) becomes

$$4w(K-w)\frac{d^2v}{dw^2} + 2(K-2w)\frac{dv}{dw} + (p^2+4\theta w)v = \left(\frac{w}{K}\right)^{\sigma-1}, \tag{9.168}$$

with a particular integral $v = M_{p,\sigma}[K\theta; (w/K)^{1/2}]$. In (9.168) put $w = s^2$. Then (9. 168) becomes

$$(K - s^2)\frac{d^2v}{ds^2} - s\frac{dv}{ds} + (p^2 + 4\theta s^2)v = K^{1-\sigma}s^{2\sigma-2}, \tag{9.169}$$

with a particular integral $v = M_{p,\sigma}[K\theta; s/K^{1/2}]$.

On putting $s = a \sin x$, where $a^2 = K$, (9.169) becomes

$$\frac{d^2v}{dx^2} + (p^2 + 4a^2\theta \sin^2 x)v = [\sin x]^{2\sigma-2}, \tag{9.170}$$

with a particular integral $v = M_{p,\sigma}(a^2\theta; \sin x)$.

In (9.169), put $s = b \sinh x$, where $b^2 = e^{i\pi}K$. Equation (9.169) then becomes

$$\frac{d^2v}{dx^2} - (p^2 + 4b^2\,\theta \sinh^2 x)v = e^{i\pi\sigma}[\sinh x]^{2\sigma-2}, \tag{9.171}$$

with a particular integral $v = M_{p,\sigma}(-b^2\theta; e^{(1/2)i\pi} \sinh x)$. Equation (9.171) is the nonhomogeneous modified Mathieu equation.

PROBLEMS

1. Show that $z^{\gamma-1}f_{\sigma+1-\gamma}(a, b; \alpha, \beta, \gamma, \delta; z)$ satisfies the differential equation

$$z(z-1)(z-a)\frac{d^2y}{dz^2}$$
$$+ [(3+\alpha+\beta-2\gamma)z^2 - \{a(3+\alpha+\beta-2\gamma-\delta)+2-\gamma+\delta\}z + a(2-\gamma)]$$
$$\times \frac{dy}{dz} + [(1+\alpha-\gamma)(1+\beta-\gamma)z + b_2]y = z^{\sigma-1},$$

where $\alpha + \beta - \gamma - \delta - \varepsilon + 1 = 0$ and $b_2 = b - (1-\gamma)(\delta + a\varepsilon)$. Hence prove that

$$f_{\sigma+1-\gamma}(a, b; \alpha, \beta, \gamma, \delta; z) = z^{1-\gamma}f_\sigma(a, b_2; 1+\alpha-\gamma, 1+\beta-\gamma, 2-\gamma, \delta; z).$$

2. Use the power-series expansion to show that

$$\lim_{a \to \infty} [af_\sigma(a, -a\alpha\beta; \alpha, \beta, \gamma, 0; z)] = f_\sigma(\alpha, \beta; \gamma; z).$$

3. Use the power-series expansion to show that

$$\frac{d}{dz} f_\sigma(a, b; 0, \beta, \gamma, \delta; z) = (\sigma - 1) f_{\sigma-1}(a, b_4; 2, \beta + 1, \gamma + 1, \delta + 1; z),$$

where $b_4 = b - a(\beta - \delta + 1) - \gamma - \delta$.

4. Use the power-series expansion to show that

$$(\theta + \gamma - 1) F_\sigma(a, b; \alpha, \beta, \gamma, \delta; z)$$

$$= (\sigma + \gamma - 3) F_\sigma\left[a, b\left(\frac{\gamma - 2}{\gamma - 1}\right); \alpha, \beta, \gamma - 2, \delta + 1; z\right]$$

where $\theta \equiv z d/dz$.

5. Obtain the series expansion for the nonhomogeneous Lamé function $L^h_{\nu,m}(s)$ in powers of s ($=\operatorname{sn} z$) directly from the differential equation

$$\frac{d^2 y}{dx^2} + \{h - \nu(\nu + 1) k^2 s^2\} y = 4k^2 s^{2m-2}.$$

6. Derive the recurrence formula for the nonhomogeneous Mathieu function directly from the power-series expansion.

CHAPTER 10

Nonhomogeneous Linear Partial Differential Equations

10.1 Introduction

In the previous chapters we discussed the properties of the solutions of various nonhomogeneous *ordinary* differential equations which are linear and involve only one independent variable. We now consider nonhomogeneous *partial* differential equations which are linear and involve two or more independent variables (and the partial derivatives with respect to these independent variables). Equations of this kind frequently occur in the analysis of physical systems (e.g., Poisson's equation, Lorenz's equation, and the nonhomogeneous equation of heat conduction). In this chapter we discuss methods of obtaining solutions of this class of partial differential equation. Our aim in this chapter is to keep the discussion as general as possible.

In §10.2, we consider the general nonhomogeneous linear partial differential equation, and in §§10.3 and 10.4 we consider the important case in which the coefficients are constants. Returning to the general case in §10.6, we show that, by the method of separation of variables, the problem of solving certain partial differential equations can be reduced to that of solving a number of ordinary differential equations. The chapter concludes with a discussion of integral transforms and the use of Green's functions.

All the methods given in this chapter will be applied in Chapter 11 to the partial differential equations of mathematical physics.

10.2 The General Nonhomogeneous Linear Partial Differential Equation

The general nonhomogeneous linear partial differential equation can be written in the form

$$\Phi\left(\frac{\partial}{\partial x_1}, \frac{\partial}{\partial x_2}, \ldots, \frac{\partial}{\partial x_n}\right) z = f(x_1, \ldots, x_n), \tag{10.1}$$

where Φ is a rational integral algebraic function which is linear with respect to the dependent variable z and all its partial derivatives, and f is any function of the independent variables $x_1, x_2, \ldots, x_n$. Such an equation can occur when we consider the potential in a Newtonian field (e.g., within a field of attracting matter), or the motion of a stretched string under the influence of external forces. The associated homogeneous equation is

$$\Phi\left(\frac{\partial}{\partial x_1}, \frac{\partial}{\partial x_2}, \ldots, \frac{\partial}{\partial x_n}\right) z = 0. \tag{10.2}$$

In the case of a stretched string, this would correspond to the equation of motion under no external forces.

Let $F(x_1, x_2, \ldots, x_n)$ be any particular integral of (10.1); then

$$\Phi\left(\frac{\partial}{\partial x_1}, \frac{\partial}{\partial x_2}, \ldots, \frac{\partial}{\partial x_n}\right) F = f. \tag{10.3}$$

In (10.1) put $z = Z + F$, and subtract (10.3). We see that

$$\Phi\left(\frac{\partial}{\partial x_1}, \frac{\partial}{\partial x_2}, \ldots, \frac{\partial}{\partial x_n}\right) Z = 0. \tag{10.4}$$

Then Z satisfies the homogeneous equation (10.2). Thus the general integral of (10.1) will be obtained by adding any particular integral of (10.1) to the most general integral of (10.2); as in the theory of ordinary differential equations, the general integral of the associated homogeneous equation (10.2) is called the *complementary function*.

As in the case of ordinary differential equations (Chapter 1), if Z_r ($r = 1$ to m) are m independent solutions of (10.2), then

$$z = C_1 Z_1 + C_2 Z_2 + \cdots + C_m Z_m, \tag{10.5}$$

where $C_1, C_2, \ldots, C_m$ are arbitrary *constants*, is also a solution of (10.2). This does not, however, always lead to a term of the general integral, since, as shown in textbooks on partial differential equations, e.g., Forsyth [1929], Kamke [1930], Piaggio [1937], Duff [1956], and Sneddon [1957], the general integral usually contains a number of arbitrary *functions* (which in any physical system would be determined by the nature of the boundary conditions of the system). The determination of a solution satisfying the boundary conditions is sometimes a difficult problem; indeed, the boundary conditions usually influence the choice of the method of solving the equation if more than one method is available. The general integral (or *complete integral*) of (10.2) is the most general relation possible between z and $x_1, x_2, \ldots, x_n$ such that when substituted in the differential equation, the latter becomes an identity.

We note that for a complete solution of a nonhomogeneous linear partial differential equation we require to know only *one* particular integral, together with the complementary function, which is the complete integral of the associated homogeneous equation. As in Chapter 1, it should be noted that if a particular integral $F_1(x_1, x_2, \ldots, x_n)$ is known for the equation

$$\Phi\left(\frac{\partial}{\partial x_1}, \frac{\partial}{\partial x_2}, \ldots, \frac{\partial}{\partial x_n}\right) z = f_1,$$

and another particular integral $F_2(x_1, x_2, \ldots, x_n)$ is known for the equation

$$\Phi\left(\frac{\partial}{\partial x_1}, \frac{\partial}{\partial x_2}, \ldots, \frac{\partial}{\partial x_n}\right) z = f_2,$$

then, since the equations are linear, $K_1F_1 + K_2F_2$ is a particular integral of

$$\Phi\left(\frac{\partial}{\partial x_1}, \frac{\partial}{\partial x_2}, \ldots, \frac{\partial}{\partial x_n}\right) z = K_1 f_1 + K_2 f_2,$$

where K_1 and K_2 are constants.

The methods of solving both homogeneous and nonhomogeneous linear partial differential equations of the first and second orders are fully set out in the standard textbooks mentioned above. As stated in §10.1, we shall first discuss the solution of linear equations with constant coefficients; most of the differential equations of mathematical physics come into this category (when referred to certain coordinate systems).

10.3 Equations with Constant Coefficients

We now consider the important particular case of nonhomogeneous linear partial differential equations in n independent variables $x_1, \ldots, x_n$, the equations having constant coefficients. Such an equation can be written

$$\sum_{r_1}\sum_{r_2}\cdots\sum_{r_n} A_{r_1r_2\cdots r_n} D_1^{r_1} D_2^{r_2} \cdots D_n^{r_n}\, z = f(x_1, x_2, \ldots, x_n), \tag{10.6}$$

where $D_m \equiv \partial/\partial x_m$ ($m = 1$ to n) and the coefficients A are constants. For conciseness, this equation will sometimes be written

$$\psi(D_1, D_2, \ldots, D_n)z = f. \tag{10.7}$$

Such equations occur in the theory of forced vibrations of continuous mechanical systems (e.g., the transverse vibrations of a bar) which undergo only small displacements from their equilibrium position. Equations of this type (e.g., Poisson's equation) occur in electric field theory; in this case, the function f represents a certain charge distribution.

THE SOLUTION OF THE ASSOCIATED HOMOGENEOUS EQUATION

In general, the linear operator ψ cannot be resolved into simple linear factors. In that case, it is not always possible to find the general integral of the associated homogeneous equation

$$\psi(D_1, D_2, \ldots, D_n)z = 0 \tag{10.8}$$

in terms of arbitrary functions. However, solutions of (10.8) can always be found which contain arbitrary constants. Thus

$$z = Ce^{h_1x_1 + h_2x_2 + \cdots + h_nx_n}, \tag{10.9}$$

where $C, h_1 \ldots, h_n$ are constants, will be a solution of (10.8) if $h_1, \ldots, h_n$ satisfy the equation

$$\psi(h_1, h_2, \ldots, h_n) = 0. \tag{10.10}$$

Thus

$$z = \sum_r C_r \exp(h_1x_1 + h_2x_2 + \cdots + h_nx_n), \tag{10.11}$$

where $C_r, h_1, \ldots, h_n$ are constants, will also be a solution of (10.8) provided that $h_1, \ldots, h_n$ satisfy (10.10). We see that C_r and $h_1, \ldots, h_{n-1}$ may be regarded as arbitrary constants, h_n being determined in terms of $h_1, \ldots, h_{n-1}$ from (10.10).

By considering the limit of two solutions h_r and $h_r + \delta h_r$, we find that

$$z = \frac{\partial}{\partial h_r} \exp(h_1x_1 + h_2x_2 + \cdots + h_nx_n) \qquad (r = 1 \quad \text{to} \quad n-1)$$

is also a solution of (10.8), where h_n is given by (10.10). Similarly, we find

$$z = \frac{\partial^a}{\partial h_1^a}\frac{\partial^b}{\partial h_2^b}\cdots\frac{\partial^\lambda}{\partial h_{n-1}^\lambda} \exp(h_1x_1 + h_2x_2 + \cdots + h_nx_n) \tag{10.12}$$

is a solution of (10.8), where $a, b, \ldots, \lambda$ are any positive integers.

If the operator ψ has a linear factor of the form

$$\alpha_1D_1 + \alpha_2D_2 + \cdots + \alpha_nD_n + \alpha_{n+1},$$

where all the α_r are constants and $\alpha_n \neq 0$, (10.10) will be satisfied by

$$\alpha_1h_1 + \alpha_2h_2 + \cdots + \alpha_nh_n + \alpha_{n+1} = 0,$$

and the integral (10.11) will contain a number of terms of the form

$$\exp\left(-\frac{\alpha_{n+1}}{\alpha_n}x_n\right)C\exp\left[h_1\left(x_1 - \frac{\alpha_1}{\alpha_n}x_n\right) + h_2\left(x_2 - \frac{\alpha_2}{\alpha_n}x_n\right)\right.$$
$$\left. + \cdots + h_{n-1}\left(x_{n-1} - \frac{\alpha_{n-1}}{\alpha_n}x_n\right)\right].$$

Since C and $h_1, \ldots, h_{n-1}$ are completely arbitrary, these terms may be replaced by

$$\exp\left(-\frac{\alpha_{n+1}}{\alpha_n}x_n\right)\phi\left(x_1-\frac{\alpha_1}{\alpha_n}x_n, x_2-\frac{\alpha_2}{\alpha_n}x_n, \ldots, x_{n-1}-\frac{\alpha_{n-1}}{\alpha_n}x_n\right),$$

where ϕ is an arbitrary function.

Similarly, if the operator ψ has a linear factor of the form

$$\alpha_1 D_1 + \alpha_2 D_2 + \cdots + \alpha_{n-1}D_{n-1} + \alpha_{n+1},$$

where all the α_r are constants and $\alpha_{n-1} \neq 0$, (10.10) will be satisfied by

$$\alpha_1 h_1 + \alpha_2 h_2 + \cdots + \alpha_{n-1}h_{n-1} + \alpha_{n+1} = 0,$$

and the integral (10.11) will contain a number of terms of the form

$$\exp\left(-\frac{\alpha_{n+1}}{\alpha_{n-1}}x_{n-1}\right)$$
$$\times C\exp\left[h_1\left(x_1-\frac{\alpha_1}{\alpha_{n-1}}x_{n-1}\right)+\cdots+h_{n-2}\left(x_{n-2}-\frac{\alpha_{n-2}}{\alpha_{n-1}}x_{n-1}\right)\right].$$

Since, in this case, C and $h_1, \ldots, h_{n-2}$ are completely arbitrary, these terms may be replaced by

$$\exp\left(-\frac{\alpha_{n+1}}{\alpha_{n-1}}x_{n-1}\right)$$
$$\times\phi\left(x_1-\frac{\alpha_1}{\alpha_{n-1}}x_{n-1}, x_2-\frac{\alpha_2}{\alpha_{n-1}}x_{n-1}, \ldots, x_{n-2}-\frac{\alpha_{n-2}}{\alpha_{n-1}}x_{n-1}\right),$$

where ϕ is an arbitrary function.

If all the α_r are zero ($r = 1$ to n) except one, say, α_p, we find that the integral (10.11) will have a term of the form

$$\exp\left(-\frac{\alpha_{n+1}}{\alpha_p}x_p\right)\phi(x_1, x_2, \ldots, x_{p-1}, x_{p+1}, \ldots, x_n).$$

This method can also be used when, although $\psi(D_1, D_2, \ldots, D_n)$ has no factors, factors can be found on putting one or more $D_r = 0$. The integral thus obtained will, of course, involve only those independent variables for which the corresponding derivatives have not been suppressed.

More generally, if all the factors of $\psi(D_1, D_2, \ldots, D_n)$ are known (and are distinct), the general integral of the associated homogeneous linear equation is

$$z = \sum_r \exp\left(-\frac{\alpha_{n+1,r}}{\alpha_{n,r}}x_n\right)\phi_r\left(x_1 - \frac{\alpha_{1,r}}{\alpha_{n,r}}x_n, \ldots, x_{n-1} - \frac{\alpha_{n-1,r}}{\alpha_{n,r}}x_n\right), \quad (10.13)$$

where

$$\psi(D_1, D_2, \ldots, D_n) = \prod_r (\alpha_{1,r}D_1 + \alpha_{2,r}D_2 + \cdots + \alpha_{n,r}D_n + \alpha_{n+1,r})$$

and the ϕ_r are arbitrary functions. The case of repeated factors is dealt with in the standard textbooks.

THE PARTICULAR INTEGRAL

Consider now the determination of the particular integral of the non-homogeneous equation (10.6), or (10.7). Equation (10.7) can be written in the alternative form

$$z = [\psi(D_1, D_2, \ldots, D_n)]^{-1}f. \quad (10.14)$$

As in Chapter 2, a particular integral of (10.14) can often be found, if f is some simple function of the independent variables, by making use of the properties of the operator ψ and its inverse ψ^{-1}. We see that

$$\psi^{-1} \cdot \psi = 1.$$

Case a. Let

$$f = e^{a_1x_1+a_2x_2+\cdots+a_nx_n},$$

where $a_1, a_2, \ldots, a_n$ are constants. Then

$$D_p^r(e^{a_1x_1+a_2x_2+\cdots+a_nx_n}) = a_p^r e^{a_1x_1+a_2x_2+\cdots+a_nx_n}$$

and thus

$$\psi(D_1, D_2, \ldots, D_n)e^{a_1x_1+a_2x_2+\cdots+a_nx_n} = \psi(a_1, a_2, \ldots, a_n)e^{a_1x_2+a_2x_2+\cdots+a_nx_n}. \quad (10.15)$$

More generally, from Leibnitz's theorem,

$$\begin{aligned} D_p^r(e^{a_1x_1+a_2x_2+\cdots+a_nx_n}V) &= \sum_{s=0}^{r} \frac{r!}{s!(r-s)!}(D_p^s e^{a_1x_1+a_2x_2+\cdots+a_nx_n})(D_p^{r-s}V) \\ &= e^{a_1x_1+a_2x_2+\cdots+a_nx_n} \sum_{s=0}^{r} \frac{r!}{s!(r-s)!} a_p^s D_p^{r-s}V \\ &= e^{a_1x_1+a_2x_2+\cdots+a_nx_n}(D_p + a_p)^r V, \end{aligned}$$

and thus

$$F(D_1, D_2, \ldots, D_n)(e^{a_1x_1+a_2x_2+\cdots+a_nx_n}V)$$
$$= e^{a_1x_1+a_2x_2+\cdots+a_nx_n}F(D_1 + a_1, D_2 + a_2, \ldots, D_n + a_n)V, \quad (10.16)$$

where F is any polynomial in $D_1, D_2, \ldots, D_n$ and V is a function of $x_1, x_2, \ldots, x_n$. Operating upon both sides of (10.15) by ψ^{-1}, we see that

$$[\psi(D_1, D_2, \cdots, D_n)]^{-1}\psi(a_1, a_2, \ldots, a_n)e^{a_1x_1+a_2x_2+\cdots+a_nx_n}$$
$$= e^{a_1x_1+a_2x_2+\cdots+a_nx_n};$$

that is,

$$[\psi(D_1, D_2, \ldots, D_n)]^{-1}e^{a_1x_1+a_2x_2+\cdots+a_nx_n}$$
$$= [\psi(a_1, a_2, \ldots, a_n)]^{-1}e^{a_1x_1+a_2x_2+\cdots+a_nx_n}.$$

Thus, if $f = e^{a_1x_1+a_2x_2+\cdots+a_nx_n}$, a particular integral of (10.6) is

$$\frac{e^{a_1x_1+a_2x_2+\cdots+a_nx_n}}{\psi(a_1, a_2, \ldots, a_n)},$$

if $\psi(a_1, a_2, \ldots, a_n) \neq 0$.

More generally, it can be shown that (10.16) holds when F is any rational function of $D_1, D_2, \ldots, D_n$. Thus if $f = e^{a_1x_1+a_2x_2+\cdots+a_nx_n}V(x_1, x_2, \ldots, x_n)$, the particular integral is

$$z = [\psi(D_1, D_2, \ldots, D_n)]^{-1}[e^{a_1x_1+a_2x_2+\cdots+a_nx_n}V(x_1, x_2, \ldots, x_n)]$$
$$= e^{a_1x_1+a_2x_2+\cdots+a_nx_n}[\psi(D_1 + a_1, D_2 + a_2, \ldots, D_n + a_n)]^{-1}$$
$$\times V(x_1, x_2, \ldots, x_n). \quad (10.17)$$

If $\psi(a_1, a_2, \ldots, a_n) = 0$, we let

$$z = ue^{a_2x_2+\cdots+a_nx_n},$$

where u is a function of $x_1, x_2, \ldots, x_n$. Equation (10.7) then becomes, on using (10.16),

$$\psi(D_1, D_2 + a_2, \ldots, D_n + a_n)u = e^{a_1x_1}. \quad (10.18)$$

Now, if (10.18) has a particular integral which is a function of x_1 alone, this particular integral will satisfy the ordinary differential equation

$$\psi(D, a_2, a_3, \ldots, a_n)u = e^{a_1x_1}, \quad (10.19)$$

where $D \equiv d/dx_1$. Since $\psi(a_1, a_2, \ldots, a_n) = 0$, $(D - a_1)$ must be a factor of ψ, considered as a polynomial in D. Suppose that $\psi(D, a_2, \ldots, a_n) = (D - a_1)^p\phi(D)$, where $\phi(a_1) \neq 0$. Using the results of §2.2, we see that a particular integral of (10.19) is

$$u = \frac{x_1^p e^{a_1 x_1}}{\phi(a_1) \cdot p!}.$$

Thus, if $f = e^{a_1x_1 + a_2x_2 + \cdots + a_nx_n}$ and a_1 is a repeated root of order p of $\psi(D_1, a_2, \ldots, a_n) = 0$ (considered as a polynomial in D_1), a particular integral of (10.7) is

$$z = \frac{x_1^p e^{a_1x_1 + a_2x_2 + \cdots + a_nx_n}}{[\phi(a_1) \cdot p!]}. \tag{10.20}$$

Similarly we find that, in this case, another particular integral is

$$z = \frac{x_2^q e^{a_1x_1 + a_2x_2 + \cdots + a_nx_n}}{[\bar{\phi}(a_2) \cdot q!]},$$

where

$$\psi(a_1, D_2, a_3, \ldots, a_n) = (D_2 - a_2)^q \bar{\phi}(D_2),$$

and similarly for $x_3, x_4, \ldots, x_n$. It is easily shown that the difference between any two of these particular integrals is an integral of the associated homogeneous equation, of the form (10.12).

Case b. If

$$f = P\cos(a_1x_1 + a_2x_2 + \cdots + a_nx_n) + Q\sin(a_1x_1 + a_2x_2 + \cdots + a_nx_n),$$

where P, Q, and all the a_r are constants, we can write

$$f = \tfrac{1}{2}P\{e^{i(a_1x_1 + a_2x_2 + \cdots + a_nx_n)} + e^{-i(a_1x_1 + a_2x_2 + \cdots + a_nx_n)}\}$$
$$- \tfrac{1}{2}iQ\{e^{i(a_1x_1 + a_2x_2 + \cdots + a_nx_n)} - e^{-i(a_1x_1 + a_2x_2 + \cdots + a_nx_n)}\}$$

and use the above method. Now we can write

$$\psi(D_1, D_2, \ldots, D_n) = \psi_0(D_1, D_2, \ldots, D_n) + \sum_{r=1}^{n} \psi_r(D_1, D_2, \ldots, D_n)D_r,$$

where $\psi_0, \psi_1, \ldots, \psi_n$ contain only derivatives of even order (e.g., D_1^2, D_1D_2, D_2^2, $D_1^3D_2, \ldots$). We find that

$$\psi(ia_1, ia_2, \ldots, ia_n) = \psi_0(ia_1, ia_2, \ldots, ia_n) + i\sum_{r=1}^{n} a_r\psi_r(ia_1, ia_2, \ldots, ia_n),$$

the functions $\psi_0, \psi_1, \ldots, \psi_n$ on the right side of this equation being real.

Applying the results of case *a*, we find, after some simplification, that a particular integral of

$$\psi(D_1, D_2, \ldots, D_n)z = P\cos(a_1x_1 + \cdots + a_nx_n) + Q\sin)a_1x_1 + \cdots + a_nx_n)$$

is

$$z = \Big\{\psi_0(ia_1, ia_2, \ldots, ia_n)[P\cos(a_1x_1 + \cdots + a_nx_n) + Q\sin(a_1x_1 + \cdots + a_nx_n)] + \left[\sum_{r=1}^{n} a_r\psi_r(ia_1, ia_2, \ldots, ia_n)\right] \times \left[P\sin(a_1x_1 + \cdots + a_nx_n) - Q\cos(a_1x_1 + \cdots + a_nx_n)\right]\Big\} \times \left\{\psi_0^2(ia_1, ia_2, \ldots, ia_n) + \left[\sum_{r=1}^{n} a_r\psi_r^2(ia_1, ia_2, \ldots, ia_n)\right]^2\right\}^{-1}.$$

Case c. Let

$$f = x_1^{p_1}x_2^{p_2}\cdots x_n^{p_n},$$

where $p_1, p_2, \ldots, p_n$ are positive integers. We write

$$\psi(D_1, D_2, \ldots, D_n) = a_0[1 - \Psi(D_1, D_2, \ldots, D_n)],$$

where a_0 is a constant ($\neq 0$) and Ψ is a rational integral algebraic function which vanishes when $D_1 = D_2 = \cdots = D_n = 0$. Expanding $1 - \Psi$ by the binomial theorem, we obtain

$$\psi^{-1}f = \frac{(1 + \Psi + \Psi^2 + \cdots + \Psi^n + \cdots)f}{a_0}.$$

If f is of the given form, the series on the right side of the last equation will terminate after a certain value of n; thus no convergence test is needed. Thus, if $f = x_1^{p_1}x_2^{p_2}\cdots x_n^{p_n}$, a particular integral of (10.7) is

$$z = \frac{(1 + \Psi + \Psi^2 + \cdots + \Psi^q)x_1^{p_1}x_2^{p_2}\cdots x_n^{p_n}}{a_0},$$

where $\Psi = 1 - \psi/a_0$, and q is such that the lowest derivative in Ψ^q is of order $p_1 + p_2 + \cdots + p_n$.

If $a_0 = 0$, we can write

$$\psi(D_1, D_2, \ldots, D_n) = c_0D_r^c\left[1 - \frac{\Psi(D_1, D_2, \ldots, D_n)}{D_r^c}\right],$$

where c_0 is a constant ($\neq 0$) and Ψ is a rational integral algebraic function which vanishes when $D_1 = D_2 = \cdots = D_n = 0$. By a precisely similar analysis to that given above, we find that a particular integral of (10.7) is

$$z = \left(1 + \frac{\Psi}{D_r^c} + \frac{\Psi^2}{D_r^{2c}} + \cdots + \frac{\Psi^q}{D_r^{qc}}\right)\frac{D_r^{-c}x_1^{p_1}x_2^{p_2}\cdots x_n^{p_n}}{c_0};$$

that is,

$$z = \sum_{s=0}^{q} \Psi^s x_1^{p_1} x_2^{p_2} \cdots x_{r-1}^{p_{r-1}} x_r^{p_r + c(1+s)} x_{r+1}^{p_{r+1}} \cdots x_n^{p_n} \frac{p_r!}{(p_r + c[1+s])!\, c_0},$$

where $\Psi = 1 - D_r^{-c}\psi/c_0$ and q is such that the lowest derivative in Ψ^q is of order $p_1 + p_2 + \cdots + p_n + c(1+q)$.

The general solution will be obtained by adding the particular integral of (10.7) to the general solution of (10.8). The required solution in any physical problem will, of course, depend on the boundary conditions (including, possibly, the behavior of the solution at infinity).

10.4 Equations Which Are Homogeneous with Respect to the Derivatives

We consider now the important particular case in which there are only two independent variables (x_1, x_2) and ψ is homogeneous with respect to the derivatives D_1 and D_2; in this case, from (10.6), $r_1 + r_2 = n$, a constant; i.e., only differential coefficients of the nth order occur in (10.6). $\psi(D_1, D_2)$ can then be factorized in the form

$$\psi(D_1, D_2) = A_0(D_1 - \lambda_1 D_2)(D_1 - \lambda_2 D_2) \cdots (D_1 - \lambda_n D_2), \quad (10.21)$$

where A_0 is a constant.

Consider the solution of

$$z = [\psi(D_1, D_2)]^{-1} f(x_1, x_2), \quad (10.22)$$

where ψ is homogeneous with respect to D_1 and D_2. The expression for $[\psi(D_1, D_2)]^{-1}$ can be resolved into partial fractions in a manner precisely similar to that given in Chapter 2. We find that, if (10.21) has no repeated factors, a particular integral is

$$y = \frac{1}{D_2^{n-1}} \sum_{r=1}^{n} \frac{\alpha_r}{D_1 - \lambda_r D_2} f(x_1, x_2), \quad (10.23)$$

where

$$\alpha_r = 1 \Big/ \left[A_0 \prod_{\substack{s=1 \\ s \neq r}}^{n} (\lambda_r - \lambda_s) \right].$$

If (10.21) has a repeated root λ_p (of order q), the corresponding partial-fraction expansion will contain q terms $\beta_m(D_1 - \lambda_p D_2)^{-m} f$ ($m = 1$ to q), where β_m is a constant.

If f has any of the forms given in §10.3, the particular integral can be found by the methods given there. More generally, the particular solution given by (10.23) can be expressed in terms of multiple integrals.

Let

$$F(x_1, x_2) = \int^{x_1} f(\xi, x_2 + \lambda x_1 - \lambda\xi)\, d\xi .$$

Then

$$(D_1 - \lambda D_2)F(x_1, x_2) = f(x_1, x_2)$$

and thus

$$(D_1 - \lambda D_2)^{-1} f(x_1, x_2) = F(x_1, x_2) = \int^{x_1} f(\xi, x_2 + \lambda x_1 - \lambda\xi)\, d\xi . \tag{10.24}$$

From (10.23) and (10.24), we see that a particular integral of (10.22) is

$$z = \sum_{r=1}^{n} \alpha_r \iint \cdots \iint^{x_1} f(\xi, x_2 + \lambda_r x_1 - \lambda_r \xi)\, d\xi\, dx_2^{n-1} . \tag{10.25}$$

If $f(x_1, x_2) = g(a_1 x_1 + a_2 x_2)$, an alternative integral solution can be found. Equation (10.23) can then be put in the form

$$y = \frac{1}{D_2^n} \sum_{r=1}^{n} \frac{\alpha_r D_2}{D_1 - \lambda_r D_2} g(a_1 x_1 + a_2 x_2) = \frac{1}{D_2^n} \sum_{r=1}^{n} \frac{\alpha_r a_2}{a_1 - \lambda_r a_2} g(a_1 x_1 + a_2 x_2)$$

$$= \frac{1}{\psi(a_1, a_2)} \frac{1}{D^n} [a_2^n g(a_1 x_1 + a_2 x_2)] .$$

Thus, if $f(x_1, x_2) = g(a_1 x_1 + a_2 x_2)$, a particular integral of (10.22) is

$$z = \frac{1}{\psi(a_1, a_2)} \iint \cdots \int g(x)\, dx^n , \tag{10.26}$$

where $x = a_1 x_1 + a_2 x_2$.

10.5 Equations Reducible to Linear Equations with Constant Coefficients

Consider next the linear equation

$$\sum_{r_1} \sum_{r_2} \cdots \sum_{r_n} A_{r_1 r_2 \cdots r_n} x_1^{r_1} x_2^{r_2} \cdots x_n^{r_n} D_1^{r_1} D_2^{r_2} \cdots D_n^{r_n} z = f(x_1, x_2, \ldots, x_n) , \tag{10.27}$$

where the coefficients A are constants. As shown in textbooks on differential equations (see §10.2), on putting $x_r = \exp(u_r)$, (10.27) reduces to a linear differential equation with constant coefficients. As in Chapter 2, this is most readily seen by using the symbolic operator $\delta_r \equiv \partial/\partial u_r = x_r \partial/\partial x_r = x_r D_r$. Then, as in §2.7,

$$x_r^p \frac{\partial^p z}{\partial x_r^p} = \delta_r(\delta_r - 1) \cdots (\delta_r - p + 1)z,$$

$$x_r^p x_s^q \frac{\partial^{p+q} z}{\partial x_r^p \partial x_s^q} = \delta_r(\delta_r - 1) \cdots (\delta_r - p + 1)\delta_s(\delta_s - 1) \cdots (\delta_s - q + 1)z,$$

and thus (10.27) reduces to

$$\sum_{r_1} \sum_{r_2} \cdots \sum_{r_n} A_{r_1 r_2 \cdots r_n} \prod_{s=1}^{n} [\delta_s(\delta_s - 1) \cdots (\delta_s - r_s + 1)]z$$
$$= f(x_1, x_2, \ldots, x_n) = F(u_1, u_2, \ldots, u_n)$$

which is a linear differential equation in the independent variables $u_1, u_2, \ldots, u_n$ with constant coefficients.

Equations such as (10.27) can be solved directly by making use of the properties of the operator δ_r. For conciseness, we shall write (10.27) in the form

$$\Omega(\delta_1, \delta_2, \ldots, \delta_n)z = f. \tag{10.28}$$

Now

$$\delta_r(x_1^{h_1} x_2^{h_2} \cdots x_n^{h_n}) = h_r x_1^{h_1} x_2^{h_2} \cdots x_n^{h_n}. \tag{10.29}$$

Thus

$$z = C x_1^{h_1} x_2^{h_2} \cdots x_n^{h_n}, \tag{10.30}$$

where $C, h_1, \ldots, h_n$ are constants, will be a solution of the associated homogeneous equation

$$\Omega(\delta_1, \delta_2, \ldots, \delta_n)z = 0, \tag{10.31}$$

if $h_1, h_2, \ldots, h_n$ satisfy the equation

$$\Omega(h_1, h_2, \ldots, h_n) = 0. \tag{10.32}$$

We see that

$$z = \sum_r C_r x_1^{h_1} x_2^{h_2} \cdots x_n^{h_n}, \tag{10.33}$$

where $C_r, h_1, \ldots, h_n$ are constants, will also be a solution of (10.31), provided that $h_1, h_2, \ldots. h_n$ satisfy (10.32). As in §10.3, $C_r, h_1, \ldots, h_{n-1}$ may be regarded as arbitrary constants, h_n being determined in terms of $h_1, \ldots, h_{n-1}$ from (10.32).

If the operator Ω has a linear factor of the form

$$\alpha_1\delta_1 + \alpha_2\delta_2 + \cdots + \alpha_n\delta_n + \alpha_{n+1},$$

where all the α_r are constants, $\alpha_n \neq 0$, we find, by a similar analysis to that in §10.3, that the integral (10.33) will contain a number of terms of the form

$$x_n^{-\alpha_{n+1}/\alpha_n} C(x_1 x_n^{-\alpha_1/\alpha_n})^{h_1} (x_2 x_n^{-\alpha_2/\alpha_n})^{h_2} \cdots (x_{n-1} x_n^{-\alpha_{n-1}/\alpha_n})^{h_{n-1}}.$$

Since C and $h_1, \ldots, h_{n-1}$ are arbitrary constants, these terms may be replaced by

$$x_n^{-\alpha_{n+1}/\alpha_n} \phi\left(\frac{x_1^{\alpha_n}}{x_n^{\alpha_1}}, \frac{x_2^{\alpha_n}}{x_n^{\alpha_2}}, \ldots, \frac{x_{n-1}^{\alpha_n}}{x_n^{\alpha_{n-1}}}\right),$$

where ϕ is an arbitrary function.

The particular integral of (10.28) is

$$z = [\Omega(\delta_1, \delta_2, \ldots, \delta_n)]^{-1} f. \tag{10.34}$$

As in Chapter 2, a particular solution of (10.34) can often be found, if f is some simple function of the independent variables, by making use of the properties of the operator Ω and its inverse Ω^{-1}.

Let

$$f = x_1^{a_1} x_2^{a_2} \cdots x_n^{a_n},$$

where $a_1, a_2, \ldots, a_n$ are constants. Then, from (10.29),

$$\Omega(\delta_1, \delta_2, \ldots, \delta_n) x_1^{a_1} x_2^{a_2} \cdots x_n^{a_n} = \Omega(a_1, a_2, \ldots, a_n) x_1^{a_1} x_2^{a_2} \cdots x_n^{a_n}. \tag{10.35}$$

More generally, using (10.16), we find

$$F(\delta_1, \delta_2, \ldots, \delta_n)[x_1^{a_1} x_2^{a_2} \cdots x_n^{a_n} V] = x_1^{a_1} x_2^{a_2} \cdots x_n^{a_n} F(\delta_1 + a_1, \ldots, \delta_n + a_n) V, \tag{10.36}$$

where F is any polynomial in $\delta_1, \delta_2, \ldots, \delta_n$ and V is a function of $x_1, x_2, \ldots, x_n$. Operating upon both sides of (10.35) by Ω^{-1}, we see that

$$[\Omega(\delta_1, \delta_2, \ldots, \delta_n)]^{-1} \Omega(a_1, a_2, \ldots, a_n) x_1^{a_1} x_2^{a_2} \ldots x_n^{a_n} = x_1^{a_1} x_2^{a_2} \ldots x_n^{a_n};$$

that is,

$$[\Omega(\delta_1, \delta_2, \ldots, \delta_n)]^{-1} x_1^{a_1} x_2^{a_2} \ldots x_n^{a_n} = [\Omega(a_1, a_2, \ldots, a_n)]^{-1} x_1^{a_1} x_2^{a_2} \ldots x_n^{a_n}.$$

Thus, if $f = x_1^{a_1} x_2^{a_2} \cdots x_n^{a_n}$, a particular integral of (10.28) is

$$\frac{x_1^{a_1} x_2^{a_2} \ldots x_n^{a_n}}{\Omega(a_1, a_2, \ldots, a_n)},$$

if $\Omega(a_1, a_2 \ldots, a_n) \neq 0$.

More generally, it can be shown that (10.36) holds when F is any rational function of $\delta_1, \delta_2, \ldots, \delta_n$; thus, if $f = x_1^{a_1}x_2^{a_2} \cdots x_n^{a_n}V$, the particular integral of (10.28) is

$$\begin{aligned} z &= [\Omega(\delta_1, \delta_2, \ldots, \delta_n)]^{-1}[x_1^{a_1}x_2^{a_2} \cdots x_n^{a_n}V] \\ &= x_1^{a_1}x_2^{a_2} \cdots x_n^{a_n}[\Omega(\delta_1 + a_1, \delta_2 + a_2, \ldots, \delta_n + a_n)]^{-1}V. \end{aligned}$$

If $f = x_1^{a_1}x_2^{a_2} \cdots x_n^{a_n}$ and $\Omega(a_1, a_2, \ldots, a_n) = 0$, it can be shown, in a manner similar to that given in §10.3, that a particular integral of (10.28) is

$$\frac{(\log x_1)^p x_1^{a_1}x_2^{a_2} \cdots x_n^{a_n}}{\phi(a_1) \cdot p!},$$

where $\Omega(\delta, a_2, a_3, \ldots, a_n) = (\delta - a_1)^p\phi(\delta)$ and $\phi(a_1) \neq 0$.

10.6 Separation of Variables

Let us return now to the solution of the general nonhomogeneous linear partial differential equation. In the rest of this chapter we shall discuss general methods of solving such an equation. The first of these methods is the very important method of separation of variables.

We shall first consider the associated homogeneous equation (10.2). If, on putting

$$z = X_1(x_1)X_2(x_2) \cdots X_n(x_n), \tag{10.37}$$

it is possible to write (10.2) in the form

$$X_2 \cdots X_nF_1(D_1)X_1 + X_1X_3 \cdots X_nF_2(D_2)X_2 + \cdots + X_1X_2 \cdots X_{n-1}F_n(D_n)X_n = 0$$

where $F_r(D_r)$ ($r = 1$ to n) is a linear differential operator, then, on dividing throughout by $X_1X_2 \cdots X_n$, we obtain

$$\frac{1}{X_1}F_1(D_1)X_1 + \frac{1}{X_2}F_2(D_2)X_2 + \cdots + \frac{1}{X_n}F_n(D_n)X_n = 0. \tag{10.38}$$

We see that (10.38) is an expression involving the sum of n terms, each of which is a function of only *one* of the independent variables. Equation (10.38) is an identity, and can therefore only hold if each of these terms is itself a constant. We thus have n equations

$$\frac{1}{X_r}F_r(D_r)X_r = \mu_r \qquad (r = 1 \text{ to } n), \tag{10.39}$$

where μ_r ($r = 1$ to n) are arbitrary constants, subject only to the condition

$$\sum_{r=1}^{n} \mu_r = 0. \tag{10.40}$$

Equation (10.39) can be put in the form

$$F_r(D_r)X_r - \mu_r X_r = 0 \qquad (r = 1 \quad \text{to} \quad n), \tag{10.41}$$

where D_r can now be taken to be d/dx_r. We thus see that the problem of solving the linear partial differential equation (10.2) can in this way be reduced to that of solving n ordinary linear differential equations. The arbitrary constants μ_r are known as the constants of separation.

Consider now the nonhomogeneous linear partial differential equation

$$\Phi(D_1, D_2, \ldots, D_n)z = f(x_1, \ldots, x_n). \tag{10.42}$$

If, on assuming a solution of the form

$$z = \overline{X}_1(x_1)\overline{X}_2(x_2) \cdots \overline{X}_n(x_n), \tag{10.43}$$

it is possible to write (10.42) in the form

$$\overline{X}_2 \cdots \overline{X}_n F_1(D_1)\overline{X}_1 + \overline{X}_1\overline{X}_3 \cdots \overline{X}_n F_2(D_2)\overline{X}_2 + \cdots + \overline{X}_1\overline{X}_2 \cdots \overline{X}_{n-1}F_n(D_n)\overline{X}_n = f(x_1, \ldots, x_n),$$

that is,

$$\frac{1}{\overline{X}_1} F_1(D_1)\overline{X}_1 + \frac{1}{\overline{X}_2} F_2(D_2)\overline{X}_2 + \cdots + \frac{1}{\overline{X}_n} F_n(D_n)\overline{X}_n = \frac{f(x_1, \ldots, x_n)}{\overline{X}_1\overline{X}_2 \cdots \overline{X}_n}, \tag{10.44}$$

we see as above that the left side of (10.44) is the sum of n terms, each of which is a function of only one of the independent variables.

Suppose now that

$$\frac{f(x_1, \ldots, x_n)}{\overline{X}_1\overline{X}_2 \cdots \overline{X}_n} = \frac{g(x_s)}{\overline{X}_s(x_s)}. \tag{10.45}$$

We find, in a manner similar to that given above, that

$$\frac{1}{\overline{X}_r} F_r(D_r)\overline{X}_r = \mu_r \qquad (r = 1 \quad \text{to} \quad n, r \neq s) \tag{10.46}$$

and

$$\frac{1}{\overline{X}_s} [F_s(D_s)\overline{X}_s - g(x_s)] = \mu_s, \tag{10.47}$$

where μ_r $(r = 1$ to $n)$ are arbitrary constants, subject only to the condition

$$\sum_{r=1}^{n} \mu_r = 0. \tag{10.48}$$

From (10.39) and (10.46), we see that the functions X_r and $\overline{X}_r$ satisfy the same ordinary differential equation (if $r \neq s$). Thus, if X_r is taken to refer to *any* solution of this equation, (10.39) and (10.46) become identical. Equations (10.46) and (10.47) can then be put in the form

$$F_r(D_r)X_r - \mu_r X_r = 0 \qquad (r = 1 \quad \text{to} \quad n, r \neq s) \tag{10.49}$$

and

$$F_s(D_s)\overline{X}_s - \mu_s \overline{X}_s = g(x_s). \tag{10.50}$$

We see that, if f is given by (10.45), the problem of solving the nonhomogeneous partial differential equation (10.42) can be reduced to that of solving n ordinary linear differential equations, of which one is nonhomogeneous, of the form (10.50), and $n - 1$ are homogeneous, of the form (10.49). The particular solution of (10.42) derived in this way is of the form

$$z = X_1(x_1)X_2(x_2) \cdots X_{s-1}(x_{s-1})\overline{X}_s(x_s)X_{s+1}(x_{s+1}) \cdots X_n(x_n), \tag{10.51}$$

where

$$\frac{f(x_1, \ldots, x_n)}{X_1X_2 \cdots X_{s-1}X_{s+1} \cdots X_n} = g(x_s). \tag{10.52}$$

In (10.51), X_1, X_2, . . . , X_n refer to *any* of the solutions of the corresponding equations (10.49) and $\overline{X}_s$ refers to *any* solution of (10.50). The arbitrary constants $\mu_1, \ldots, \mu_n$ in (10.49) and (10.50) (called *separation constants*) are still at our disposal, subject only to the condition (10.48). We can find particular integrals of the form (10.51) whenever f is given by (10.52). This enables us to find particular integrals of a large number of nonhomogeneous partial differential equations which have the same associated homogeneous equation.

The associated homogeneous equation corresponding to (10.50) is that one of the set of equations (10.41) for which $r = s$. We thus see that the solutions of the form (10.37) and (10.51) differ only in the functions X_s and $\overline{X}_s$, which are both functions of x_s.

The resulting ordinary linear differential equations can be solved by the methods given in Chapters 1 and 2. As shown in Chapter 11, for the partial differential equations of mathematical physics, it often happens that the resulting ordinary differential equations are of the types discussed in Chapters 3 to 9, for which the solutions are already known. It is for this reason that the method of separation of variables is so important. To facilitate the application of this method, it is necessary to choose independent variables that fit in with the boundary conditions (e.g., selecting rectangular, cylindrical, spherical, and ellipsoidal coordinates as the particular problem may warrant). In any physical problem, it may be possible to discard immediately certain solutions of the form (10.37) and (10.51) which have undesirable singularities at given points in the field (or whose behavior at infinity is not physically possible). This will be discussed further in Chapter 11.

This method can be extended immediately (as shown in §10.2) to f functions of the form

$$\frac{f(x_1, x_2, \ldots, x_n)}{\overline{X}_1\overline{X}_2 \cdots \overline{X}_n} = \sum_{r=1}^{n} \frac{g_r(x_r)}{\overline{X}_r(x_r)}; \tag{10.53}$$

the right side of (10.53) is an expression involving the sum of n terms, each of which is a function of only one of the independent variables.

In certain cases, on making the substitution (10.37), we find that (10.2) becomes

$$\frac{R_1}{X_1} F_1(D_1)X_1 + \frac{R_2}{X_2} F_2(D_2)X_2 + \cdots + \frac{R_n}{X_n} F_n(D_n)X_n = 0, \tag{10.54}$$

where the R functions involve one or more of the independent variables. It may still be possible to use the method of separation of variables.

Thus, if $R_n = R(x_1)$ and all the other R functions are unity, we can replace the first equation in (10.39) by

$$\frac{1}{X_1} F_1(D_1)X_1 + R\mu_n = \mu_1;$$

that is,

$$F_1(D_1)X_1 + (R\mu_n - \mu_1)X_1 = 0, \tag{10.55}$$

the other equations in the set (10.39) being unchanged. Equation (10.40) is now replaced by

$$\sum_{r=1}^{n-1} \mu_r = 0. \tag{10.56}$$

Similarly, if $R_{n-1} = R(x_1)$ and $R_n = R(x_1)S(x_{n-1})$, the first and the $(n-1)$th equations in (10.39) become

$$\frac{1}{X_1} F_1(D_1)X_1 + R\mu_{n-1} = \mu_1$$

and

$$\frac{1}{X_{n-1}} F_{n-1}(D_{n-1})X_{n-1} + S\mu_n = \mu_{n-1};$$

that is,

$$F_1(D_1)X_1 + (R\mu_{n-1} - \mu_1)X_1 = 0$$

and (10.57)

$$F_{n-1}(D_{n-1})X_{n-1} + (S\mu_n - \mu_{n-1})X_{n-1} = 0,$$

the other equations in the set (10.39) being unchanged. Equation (10.40) is now replaced by

$$\sum_{r=1}^{n-2} \mu_r = 0. \tag{10.58}$$

Again, if in (10.54), $R_1 = \lambda R_2 = [R(x_1) + \bar{R}(x_2)]^{-1}$, where λ is a constant, the other R functions being unity, we can replace the first two equations in (10.39) by

$$\frac{1}{X_1} F_1(D_1)X_1 = \mu_2 R(x_1) + \mu_1$$

and

$$\frac{1}{\lambda X_2} F_2(D_2)X_2 = \mu_2 \bar{R}(x_2) - \mu_1\,;$$

that is,

$$F_1(D_1)X_1 - (R\mu_2 + \mu_1)X_1 = 0$$

and (10.59)

$$F_2(D_2)X_2 - \lambda(\bar{R}\mu_2 - \mu_1)X_2 = 0,$$

the other equations in the set (10.39) being unchanged. Equation (10.40) is now replaced by

$$\sum_{r=2}^{n} \mu_r = 0. \tag{10.60}$$

The parallel case of the nonhomogeneous equation (10.42) can be treated in a precisely similar manner. The formula (10.45) may need to be modified in these cases, e.g., by the inclusion of one of the functions $R(x_1)$ or $R(x_1) + \bar{R}(x_2)$ (see §§11.5 and 11.10).

In all the cases we have considered so far in this section, we have been able to reduce the problem of solving the partial differential equations (10.2) or (10.42) to that of solving n ordinary differential equations. Examples of the use of this method occur in Chapter 11.

It may happen that, although no solution of the form (10.37) is possible, a partial separation is possible. Thus, if on putting

$$z = X_1(x_1)X_2(x_2)\cdots X_p(x_p)X(x_{p+1}, \ldots, x_n), \tag{10.61}$$

it is possible to write (10.2) in the form

$$\frac{1}{X_1} F_1(D_1)X_1 + \cdots + \frac{1}{X_p} F_p(D_p)X_p + \frac{1}{X} F(D_{p+1}, \ldots, D_n)X = 0, \tag{10.62}$$

then, by a precisely similar analysis to that given above, we derive the $p + 1$ equations

$$F_r(D_r)X_r - \mu_r X_r = 0 \qquad (r = 1 \quad \text{to} \quad p) \tag{10.63}$$

and

$$F(D_{p+1}, \ldots, D_n)X - \mu X = 0, \tag{10.64}$$

where μ_r ($r = 1$ to p) and μ are arbitrary constants, subject only to the condition

$$\mu + \sum_{r=1}^{p} \mu_r = 0. \tag{10.65}$$

In this case the solution of the linear partial differential equation (10.2) is reduced to the problem of solving p ordinary differential equations and one *partial* differential equation. It is sometimes possible to apply the same method to (10.64), after multiplying this equation by some function of $x_p, \ldots, x_n$.

For the nonhomogeneous equation (10.42), we may find a similar solution of the form

$$z = X_1(x_1)X_2(x_2) \cdots X_p(x_p)\bar{X}(x_{p+1}, \ldots, x_n), \tag{10.66}$$

where

$$F_r(D_r)X_r - \mu_r X_r = 0 \qquad (r = 1 \text{ to } p) \tag{10.67}$$

and

$$F(D_{p+1}, \ldots, D_n)\bar{X} - \mu\bar{X} = g(x_{p+1}, \ldots, x_n), \tag{10.68}$$

the f function in (10.42) being of the form

$$\frac{f(x_1, \ldots, x_n)}{X_1 X_2 \cdots X_p} = g(x_{p+1}, \ldots, x_n). \tag{10.69}$$

Here, too, we have p ordinary differential equations and one nonhomogeneous partial differential equation.

10.7 Integral Transforms

In Chapter 2 the Laplace transform was used to solve ordinary linear differential equations with particular initial conditions. A similar method can be used to find the solution of a certain class of partial differential equations (see Carslaw and Jaeger [1947]). More generally, the method can be used with Fourier, Mellin, and Hankel transforms, as well as with Laplace transforms. The method given here is based on that given by Sneddon [*126*, 1957].

Consider a linear partial differential equation of the form

$$\phi_1(D_1)z + \phi_2(D_2, \ldots, D_n)z = f(x_1, \ldots, x_n), \tag{10.70}$$

where ϕ_1 and ϕ_2 are linear differential operators. Let $\bar{z}$ be the integral transform of z with the kernel (or nucleus) $K(t, x_1)$. Then

$$\bar{z}(t, x_2, \ldots, x_n) = \int_\alpha^\beta z(x_1, x_2, \ldots, x_n)K(t, x_1)\, dx_1, \tag{10.71}$$

where α and β are constants (e.g., 0, ∞ or $-\infty$, ∞). Similarly, we define

$$\bar{f}(t, x_2, \ldots, x_n) = \int_\alpha^\beta f(x_1, x_2, \ldots, x_n)K(t, x_1)\, dx_1. \tag{10.72}$$

On multiplying (10.70) by $K(t, x_1)$ and integrating with respect to x_1, we find, using (10.71) and (10.72),

$$\int_\alpha^\beta K(t, x_1)\phi(D_1)z\, dx_1 + \phi_2(D_2, \ldots, D_n)\bar{z} = \bar{f}. \tag{10.73}$$

Let $\bar{\phi}_1(D_1)$ be the linear operator which is adjoint to $\phi_1(D_1)$. Then, from §1.9, if

$$\begin{aligned} \phi_1(D_1)z &= p_0 D^n z + p_1 D_1^{n-1}z + \cdots + p_n z, \\ \bar{\phi}_1(D_1)z &= (-1)^n D_1^n(p_0 z) + (-1)^{n-1}D_1^{n-1}(p_1 z) + \cdots + p_n z. \end{aligned} \tag{10.74}$$

Also, from (1.52), we have the Lagrange identity

$$K(t, x_1)\phi_1(D_1)z - z\bar{\phi}_1(D_1)K(t, x_1) = \frac{\partial}{\partial x_1} P(z, K), \tag{10.75}$$

where the bilinear concomitant $P(z, K)$ is given by

$$P(z, K) = q_0 D_1^{n-1}z + q_1 D_1^{n-1}z + \cdots + q_{n-1}z \tag{10.76}$$

and

$$\begin{aligned} q_0 &= p_0 K, \\ q_1 &= p_1 K - D_1(p_0 K), \\ q_2 &= p_2 K - D_1(p_1 K) + D_1^2(p_0 K), \\ &\vdots \\ q_{n-1} &= p_{n-1}K - D_1(p_{n-2}K) + D_1^2(p_{n-3}K) + \cdots + (-1)^{n-1}D_1^{n-1}(p_0 K). \end{aligned} \tag{10.77}$$

From (10.75),

$$\int_\alpha^\beta K(t, x_1)\phi_1(D_1)z\, dx_1 = g(t, x_2, \ldots, x_n) + \int_\alpha^\beta z\bar{\phi}_1(D_1)K(t, x_1)\, dx_1, \tag{10.78}$$

where

$$g(t, x_2, \ldots, x_n) = \Big[P(z, K)\Big]_{\alpha}^{\beta}. \tag{10.79}$$

If we can choose the kernel $K(t, x_1)$ so that

$$\bar{\phi}_1(D_1)K(t, x_1) = \lambda K(t, x_1), \tag{10.80}$$

where λ is a constant, we see from (10.78) that

$$\int_{\alpha}^{\beta} K(t, x_1)\phi_1(D_1)z\, dx_1 = g + \lambda \bar{z},$$

and hence, from (10.72),

$$[\phi_2(D_2, \ldots, D_n) + \lambda]\bar{z}(t, x_2, \ldots, x_n) = F(t, x_2, \ldots, x_n), \tag{10.81}$$

where

$$F = \bar{f} - g. \tag{10.82}$$

We see that the given partial differential equation in n variables has been modified to one in $n - 1$ variables, with a parameter t. By repeating this process, we can derive the complete solution of (10.70).

We see that this method involves the solution of ordinary differential equations such as (10.80) to find the required kernel K. These equations are often nonhomogeneous equations of the types discussed in Chapters 1 to 9. We see, too, that we have finally to apply an inverse transformation to find z, knowing $\bar{z}$.

This method is particularly appropriate if the original equation is of the second order and there are only two independent variables (see Problem 12). Applications of the use of integral transforms in solving partial differential equations are given in Carslaw and Jaeger [1947] and Sneddon [1951].

10.8 Green's Functions

In §1.14, the theory of Green's functions was developed for the solution of linear ordinary differential equations with assigned boundary conditions. As shown there, the Green's function (or influence function) of a given homogeneous linear ordinary differential equation

$$\Phi(D)y = 0$$

is also the solution of the nonhomogeneous equation

$$\Phi(D)y = -\delta(x - \xi),$$

where the function δ is Dirac's delta function, defined by the equation

$$\int_{-\infty}^{\infty} f(x)\delta(x-\xi)\,dx = f(\xi),$$

where f is any continuous function. Thus

$$\int_{-\infty}^{\infty} \delta(x-\xi)\,dx = 1,$$

and $\delta(x-\xi)$ vanishes if $x \neq \xi$.

The theory of Green's functions can be used to determine the solutions of linear partial differential equations with given boundary conditions. We have to use the δ function in the n-dimensional space $(x_1, \ldots, x_n)$, defined by the equation

$$\iint\cdots\int F(x_1, \ldots, x_n)\delta(x_1-\xi_1, \ldots, x_n-\xi_n)\,dx_1\cdots dx_n = F(\xi_1, \ldots, \xi_n), \tag{10.83}$$

where $F(x_1, \ldots, x_n)$ is any continuous function and the integral is taken over *any* finite region which completely surrounds the point $(\xi_1, \xi_2, \ldots, \xi_n)$. With this definition, it follows that the n-dimensional δ function is the product of n one-dimensional δ functions (see Friedman [*255*, 1956]). Thus

$$\delta(x_1-\xi_1, x_2-\xi_2, \ldots, x_n-\xi_n) = \delta(x_1-\xi_1)\delta(x_2-\xi_2)\cdots\delta(x_n-\xi_n). \tag{10.84}$$

Consider first the homogeneous partial differential equation

$$\phi(D_1, D_2, \ldots, D_n)u = 0 \tag{10.85}$$

in a simply connected region R bounded by a closed surface S, together with a certain boundary condition (to be specified later) at all points on S. The Green's function $G(x_1, \ldots, x_n; \xi_1, \ldots, \xi_n)$ (if such a function exists) for the operator ϕ is that function which is continuous and possesses continuous derivatives at all points in R (except at the point $\xi_1, \ldots, \xi_n$ which is within R) and is a solution of

$$\phi(D_1, \ldots, D_n)u = -\delta(x_1-\xi_1, \ldots, x_n-\xi_n) \tag{10.86}$$

together with the given boundary conditions. We see that $G(x_1, \ldots, x_n; \xi_1, \ldots, \xi_n)$ satisfies the associated homogeneous equation (10.85) at all points in R except the point $(\xi_1, \ldots, \xi_n)$. For conciseness we shall often write

$$G(x_r; \xi_r) \equiv G(x_1, \ldots, x_n; \xi_1, \ldots, \xi_n). \tag{10.87}$$

The Green's function will have a singularity at the point $x_r = \xi_r$ ($r = 1$ to n); this point is sometimes called a source point (see §11.4). The precise nature of the singularity will depend upon the operator ϕ. Thus, for Laplace's equation

$$\frac{\partial^2 u}{\partial x^2} + \frac{\partial^2 u}{\partial y^2} + \frac{\partial^2 u}{\partial z^2} = 0, \tag{10.88}$$

the Green's function is of the form (Courant and Hilbert [*364*, 1953])

$$G(x, y, z; \xi, \eta, \zeta) = \frac{1}{4\pi\rho'} + g(x, y, z; \xi, \eta, \zeta),$$

where

$$\rho' = [(x-\xi)^2 + (y-\eta)^2 + (z-\zeta)^2]^{1/2},$$

and $g(x, y, z; \xi, \eta, \zeta)$ and its derivatives are continuous in a given region for which the point (ξ, η, ζ) is an interior point.

ADJOINT OPERATORS

By analogy with (1.52), the adjoint operator $\bar{\phi}$ is defined by the property

$$v\phi(D_1, \ldots, D_n)u - u\bar{\phi}(D_1, \ldots, D_n)v = \sum_{r=1}^{n} \frac{\partial P_r(u, v)}{\partial x_r}, \tag{10.89}$$

where $P_1, \ldots, P_n$ can be expressed in terms of u and v and their partial derivatives. $P_1, \ldots, P_n$ will be linear in u and its partial derivatives (and also in v and its partial derivatives) (see Morse and Feshbach [*876*, 1953a]). Thus, if $\phi(D_1, \ldots, D_n)u$ denotes the operator

$$\phi(D_1, \ldots, D_n)u \equiv \sum_{r=1}^{n} \sum_{s=1}^{n} S_{rs} \frac{\partial^2 u}{\partial x_r \partial x_s} + \sum_{r=1}^{n} T_r \frac{\partial u}{\partial x_r} + Uu, \tag{10.90}$$

where S_{rs}, T_r, and U are functions of $x_1, \ldots, x_n$ (with $S_{rs} = S_{sr}$), the adjoint operator $\bar{\phi}(D_1, \ldots, D_n)v$ is given by

$$\bar{\phi}(D_1, \ldots, D_n)v = \sum_{r=1}^{n} \sum_{s=1}^{n} \frac{\partial^2}{\partial x_r \partial x_s}(S_{rs}v) - \sum_{r=1}^{n} \frac{\partial}{\partial x_r}(T_r v) + Uv \tag{10.91}$$

and

$$P_r(u, v) = \sum_{s=1}^{n} \left[vS_{rs} \frac{\partial u}{\partial x_s} - u \frac{\partial}{\partial x_s}(vS_{rs}) \right] + T_r uv + P'_r, \tag{10.92}$$

where P'_r ($r = 1$ to n) are arbitrary functions of $u, v, x_1, \ldots, x_n$, subject only to the condition that

$$\sum_{r=1}^{n} \frac{\partial P'_r}{\partial x_r} = 0. \tag{10.93}$$

On integrating (10.89) over a simply connected region R bounded by a surface S, and using the n-dimensional form of Green's theorem, we obtain

$$\int \cdots \int [v\phi(D_1, \ldots, D_n)u - u\bar{\phi}(D_1, \ldots, D_n)v] \, dx_1 \cdots dx_n$$
$$= \int \left[\sum_{r=1}^{n} l_r P_r(u, v) \right] dS, \quad (10.94)$$

where l_r ($r = 1$ to n) are the direction cosines of the outward pointing normal to the surface S, the integral on the right side of (10.94) being taken over the whole surface S. Equation (10.94) is the generalized form of Green's identity

$$\iint_R (v\Delta u - u\Delta v) \, dx \, dy = \int_C \left(v \frac{\partial u}{\partial n} - u \frac{\partial v}{\partial n} \right) ds, \quad (10.95)$$

where $\Delta \equiv (\partial^2/\partial x^2) + (\partial^2/\partial y^2)$ and dn is the element of the outward normal to a closed curve C which surrounds the simply connected region R. The boundary conditions satisfied by u and v are said to be *adjoint boundary conditions* if

$$\sum_{r=1}^{n} l_r P_r(u, v) = 0 \quad (10.96)$$

for all points on S.

By analogy with §1.9, if

$$\phi(D_1, \ldots, D_n)u \equiv (-1)^n \bar{\phi}(D_1, \ldots, D_n)u,$$

where n is the order of the differential operators, ϕ and $\bar{\phi}$ are said to be self-adjoint. We see that, if ϕ and $\bar{\phi}$ are given by (10.90) and (10.91), they will be self-adjoint if

$$\sum_{r=1}^{n} \frac{\partial S_{rs}}{\partial x_r} = T_s \qquad (s = 1 \text{ to } n). \quad (10.97)$$

THE GREEN'S FUNCTION $\bar{G}$

The Green's function $\bar{G}(x_1, \ldots, x_n; \xi_1, \ldots, \xi_n)$ for the adjoint operator $\bar{\phi}$ is that function which is continuous and possesses continuous derivatives at all points in R (except at the point $\xi_1, \ldots, \xi_n$ which is within R) and which is a solution of

$$\bar{\phi}(D_1, \ldots, D_n)v = -\delta(x_1 - \xi_1, \ldots, x_n - \xi_n) \quad (10.98)$$

together with the adjoint boundary conditions

$$\sum_{r=1}^{n} l_r P_r(G, \bar{G}) = 0 \quad (10.99)$$

at all points on the closed surface S which bounds the simply connected region R. As above, for conciseness, we shall write

$$\bar{G}(x_r; \bar{\xi}_r) \equiv \bar{G}(x_1, \ldots, x_n; \bar{\xi}_1, \ldots, \bar{\xi}_n). \qquad (10.100)$$

On multiplying (10.86) by $\bar{G}$ and (10.98) by G and subtracting, we obtain

$$\bar{G}(x_r; \bar{\xi}_r)\phi(D_1, \ldots, D_n)G(x_r; \xi_r) - G(x_r; \xi_r)\bar{\phi}(D_1, \ldots, D_n)\bar{G}(x_r; \bar{\xi}_r)$$
$$= G(x_r; \xi_r)\delta(x_1 - \bar{\xi}_1, \ldots, x_n - \bar{\xi}_n) - \bar{G}(x_r; \bar{\xi}_r)\delta(x_1 - \xi_1, \ldots, x_n - \xi_n). \qquad (10.101)$$

On integrating (10.101) over the simply connected region R bounded by a surface S, and using (10.83) and (10.94), we see that

$$G(\bar{\xi}_r; \xi_r) - \bar{G}(\xi_r; \bar{\xi}_r) = \iint \left[\sum_{r=1}^{n} l_r P_r(G, \bar{G}) \right] dS. \qquad (10.102)$$

Thus, from (10.99) and (10.102), we obtain

$$G(\bar{\xi}_r; \xi_r) = \bar{G}(\xi_r; \bar{\xi}_r),$$

or, since $\bar{\xi}_r$ can be arbitrarily chosen (within R), we obtain the *reciprocity condition*

$$G(x_r; \xi_r) = \bar{G}(\xi_r; x_r). \qquad (10.103)$$

If the given system is self-adjoint, we see that (as for ordinary differential operators) the Green's function is symmetrical; that is,

$$G(x_r; \xi_r) = G(\xi_r; x_r). \qquad (10.104)$$

THE NONHOMOGENEOUS EQUATION

Consider now the nonhomogeneous partial differential equation

$$\phi(D_1, \ldots, D_n)u = f(x_1, \ldots, x_n) \qquad (10.105)$$

with the boundary conditions

$$\sum_{r=1}^{n} l_r P_r(u, \bar{G}) = 0 \qquad (10.106)$$

at all points on the closed surface S which bounds the simply connected region R. The solution of (10.105) will be shown to be

$$u(x_1, \ldots, x_n) = -\int \cdots \int G(x_r; \xi_r) f(\xi_1, \ldots, \xi_n)\, d\xi_1 \ldots d\xi_n, \qquad (10.107)$$

where the integral is taken over the whole of the simply connected region R, the Green's function G satisfying (10.86) together with the prescribed boundary conditions. The point $(\xi_1, \ldots, \xi\ )$ is within R.

From (10.98) and (10.105), putting $\xi_r = \bar{\xi}_r$ and $v = \bar{G}(x_r; \xi_r)$, we find

$$v\phi(D_1, \ldots, D_n)u - u\bar{\phi}(D_1, \ldots, D_n)v = \bar{G}(x_r; \xi_r)f(x_1, \ldots, x_n) + u\delta(x_1 - \xi_1, \ldots, x_n - \xi_n). \quad (10.108)$$

On integrating over the whole of the region R, we find, from (10.83) and (10.94),

$$u(\xi_1, \ldots, \xi_n) = -\int \cdots \int \bar{G}(x_r; \xi_r)f(x_1, \ldots, x_n)\, dx_1 \ldots dx_n + \iint \left[\sum_{r=1}^{n} l_r P_r(u, \bar{G})\right] dS. \quad (10.109)$$

On using (10.106), we see that the surface integral vanishes. Thus, from (10.103) and (10.109),

$$u(\xi_1, \ldots, \xi_n) = -\int \cdots \int G(\xi_r; x_r)f(x_1, \ldots, x_n)\, dx_1 \cdots dx_n,$$

or, interchanging the roles of ξ and x,

$$u(x_1, \ldots, x_n) = -\int \cdots \int G(x_r; \xi_r)f(\xi_1, \ldots, \xi_n)\, d\xi_1 \cdots d\xi_n. \quad (10.110)$$

BOUNDARY CONDITIONS

From (10.99) and (10.106), we see that u and $G(x_r; \xi_r)$ satisfy the same boundary conditions on S. In many cases of interest, these conditions can be considerably simplified. Thus, for Laplace's equation (10.88), or Poisson's equation

$$\frac{\partial^2 u}{\partial x^2} + \frac{\partial^2 u}{\partial y^2} + \frac{\partial^2 u}{\partial z^2} = f(x, y, z), \quad (10.111)$$

the boundary conditions over a closed boundary can be simply expressed either by specifying the values of u on the boundary S (Dirichlet condition) or by specifying the gradient of u normal to the boundary (Neumann condition) (see Morse and Feshbach [*495*, 1953a]). In particular, if $f(x, y, z)$ vanishes outside a certain finite region R', we can take as our boundary condition $u = 0$ at some surface surrounding the region R'.

PROBLEMS

1. If Z_1 and Z_2 are two solutions of the nonhomogeneous linear equation

$$\phi(D_1, \ldots, D_n)z = f(x_1, \ldots, x_n),$$

then $Z_1 - Z_2$ is a solution of the associated homogeneous equation. Under what conditions can $Z_1 - Z_2$ be expressed as the sum of n independent arbitrary functions, where n is the order of the differential operator ϕ?

2. Show that $\phi_1(x - iy)$, $\phi_2(x - iz)$, $\phi_3(y - iz)$, where ϕ_1, ϕ_2, and ϕ_3 are arbitrary functions, are all solutions of Laplace's equation

$$\frac{\partial^2 u}{\partial x^2} + \frac{\partial^2 u}{\partial y^2} + \frac{\partial^2 u}{\partial z^2} = 0.$$

Verify that four particular integrals of the nonhomogeneous equation

$$\frac{\partial^2 u}{\partial x^2} + \frac{\partial^2 u}{\partial y^2} + \frac{\partial^2 u}{\partial z^2} = 1$$

are $u_1 = \frac{1}{2}x^2$, $u_2 = \frac{1}{2}y^2$, $u_3 = \frac{1}{2}z^2$, and $u_3 = \frac{1}{6}(x^2 + y^2 + z^2)$, and verify that the difference between any of these particular integrals is a solution of the associated homogeneous equation.

3. Find a solution of Poisson's equation

$$\frac{\partial^2 u}{\partial x^2} + \frac{\partial^2 u}{\partial y^2} = e^{-x}$$

which satisfies the following boundary conditions: $x = 0$, $u = 0$; $x = 1$, $u = u_0$, a constant.

4. Solve the following second-order equations:

(a) $\dfrac{\partial^2 z}{\partial x^2} + \dfrac{\partial^2 z}{\partial y^2} = e^x \cos by$, for the cases $b = 1$, $b \neq 1$.

(b) $\dfrac{\partial^2 z}{\partial x^2} - \dfrac{\partial^2 z}{\partial y^2} = \cos mx \cos ny$, for the cases $m = n$, $m \neq n$.

(c) $\dfrac{\partial^2 z}{\partial x^2} + a\dfrac{\partial z}{\partial y} - z = ae^{-x}$.

5. Solve the following equations which are homogeneous with respect to their derivatives, expressing the solution in terms of arbitrary functions and in terms of multiple integrals:

(a) $\dfrac{\partial^2 z}{\partial x^2} - 5\dfrac{\partial^2 z}{\partial x\,\partial y} + 6\dfrac{\partial^2 z}{\partial y^2} = x^2 y$.

(b) $\dfrac{\partial^4 z}{\partial x^4} - 2\dfrac{\partial^4 z}{\partial x^2\,\partial y^2} + \dfrac{\partial^4 z}{\partial y^4} = \sin(x + 2y)$.

(c) $\dfrac{\partial^2 z}{\partial x^2} - \dfrac{\partial^2 z}{\partial y^2} = x^2$.

6. Solve the following equations:

(a) $x^2 \dfrac{\partial^2 z}{\partial x^2} - y^2 \dfrac{\partial^2 z}{\partial y^2} = xy + x^2 y^2 .$

(b) $x^2 \dfrac{\partial^2 z}{\partial x^2} + 2xy \dfrac{\partial^2 z}{\partial x\,\partial y} + y^2 \dfrac{\partial^2 z}{\partial y^2} = \dfrac{x}{y}.$

(c) $x^2 \dfrac{\partial^2 z}{\partial x^2} - y \dfrac{\partial z}{\partial y} = \log x .$

7. In cylindrical coordinates, Poisson's equation is

$$\frac{\partial^2 V}{\partial \rho^2} + \frac{1}{\rho}\frac{\partial V}{\partial \rho} + \frac{1}{\rho^2}\frac{\partial^2 V}{\partial \phi^2} + \frac{\partial^2 V}{\partial z^2} = f(\rho, \phi, z).$$

Show that, if $f = f_1(\rho)F_2(\phi)F_3(z)$, there is a solution

$$V = F_1(\rho)F_2(\phi)F_3(z),$$

where F_1, F_2, and F_3 satisfy the ordinary differential equations

$$\frac{d^2 F_1}{d\rho^2} + \frac{1}{\rho}\frac{dF_1}{d\rho} + \left(a^2 - \frac{\nu^2}{\rho^2}\right)F_1 = f_1(\rho),$$

$$\frac{d^2 F_2}{d\phi^2} + \frac{\nu^2}{\rho^2} F_2 = 0, \qquad \text{and} \qquad \frac{d^2 F_3}{dz^2} - a^2 F_3 = 0,$$

where a and ν are constants. Hence show that, if $f_1 = \rho^{\nu-1}$, the solution for V can be expressed in terms of Struve functions.

8. Show that the equation

$$h^2\left(\frac{\partial^2 u}{\partial r^2} + \frac{2}{r}\frac{\partial u}{\partial r}\right) + 6c = \frac{\partial u}{\partial t}$$

has a particular solution $u = -cr^2/h^2$, where c and h are constants. Using the method of separation of variables, show that the associated homogeneous equation has solutions of the type $r^{-1}\exp(-\lambda^2 h^2 t)\cos \lambda r$, $r^{-1}\exp(-\lambda^2 h^2 t)\sin \lambda r$, where λ is any constant.

[If u is the temperature, this is the equation of heat conduction for a sphere in the interior of which heat is generated at a uniform rate (proportional to c). If the outside temperature of the sphere is suddenly raised to u_1 at $t = 0$ and maintained at that temperature for all positive t, the internal temperature at any point in the sphere is given by

$$u = u_1 + \frac{c}{h^2}(a^2 - r^2) + \frac{1}{r}\sum_{n=1}^{\infty} A_n \sin\frac{n\pi r}{a}\exp\left(\frac{-n^2\pi^2 h^2 t}{a^2}\right),$$

where a is the radius of the sphere. The constants A_n are found from the initial conditions governing the temperature distribution throughout the sphere (Bateman [*353*, 1932]).]

9. In parabolic cylinder coordinates, Poisson's equation is

$$\frac{1}{\xi^2+\eta^2}\left(\frac{\partial^2 V}{\partial \xi^2}+\frac{\partial^2 V}{\partial \eta^2}\right)+\frac{\partial^2 V}{\partial \zeta^2}=f(\xi,\eta,\zeta).$$

If $f=1$, show that there is a particular solution $(1/12)(\xi^4+\eta^4)$, and that, in this case, no solution can be found in which V is a function of ξ or η alone. If $f=f_1(\xi)F_2(\eta)F_3(\zeta)/(\xi^2+\eta^2)$, show that there is a solution of the form $V=F_1(\xi)F_2(\eta)F_3(\zeta)$, where F_1, F_2, and F_3 satisfy ordinary differential equations.

10. In spherical polar coordinates, Poisson's equation is

$$\frac{\partial^2 V}{\partial r^2}+\frac{2}{r}\frac{\partial V}{\partial r}+\frac{1}{r^2}\frac{\partial^2 V}{\partial \theta^2}+\frac{\cot\theta}{r^2}\frac{\partial V}{\partial \theta}+\frac{1}{r^2\sin^2\theta}\frac{\partial^2 V}{\partial \phi^2}=f(r,\theta,\phi).$$

If $f=1$, show that there is a particular solution $\frac{1}{6}r^2$, but that, in this case, no solution can be found in which V is a function of θ or ϕ only.

Show that, if $f=r^{\nu-2}\sin\mu\phi\, f_1(\theta)$, there is a solution $V=r^\nu \sin\mu\phi\, F(\theta)$ and find the differential equation satisfied by F. Show that, if $f_1=(\cos\theta)^{-\mu-\nu-2}(\sin\theta)^\mu$, where μ and ν are constants, V can be expressed in terms of the nonhomogeneous Legendre functions $R_\nu^\mu(\cos\theta)$ (see §7.6).

11. Use the method of separation of variables to solve the equation

$$c^2\frac{\partial^2 y}{\partial x^2}-\frac{\partial^2 y}{\partial t^2}=f(x)\cos pt.$$

Show that, if $f(x)=a$, a constant, and $y=0$ at $x=0$, l, then

$$y=-\frac{a}{k^2\sin kl}\{\sin kx+\sin k(l-x)-\sin kl\}\cos pt,$$

where $k=p/c$. Use the method of variation of parameters to show that, if there is a continuous distribution of applied force given by $f(x)\cos pt$, then $y=\phi(x)\cos pt$, where

$$\phi(x)=\frac{\sin k(l-x)}{k\sin kl}\int_0^x \sin k\xi\, f(\xi)\,d\xi+\frac{\sin kx}{k\sin kl}\int_x^l \sin k(l-\xi)f(\xi)\,d\xi.$$

[If y is the displacement, this is the equation for the forced vibrations of a weightless string. The solution $y=\phi(x)\cos pt$ gives a standing wave. We see that the solution required is composed of two waves, both of which have the same frequency as the applied force (Webster [*113*, 1947]).]

12. Use the finite Fourier sine transform to show that a solution of the equation

$$c^2 \frac{\partial^2 y}{\partial x^2} - \frac{\partial^2 y}{\partial t^2} = f(x, t),$$

with the boundary conditions $y = 0$ for $x = 0,\ l$ and $y = 0$ for $t < 0$, can be put in the form

$$\frac{d^2 \bar{y}(n)}{dt^2} + \frac{\pi^2 c^2 n^2}{l^2}\, \bar{y}(n) = -c^2 \bar{f},$$

where

$$\bar{f}(n, \tau) = \int_0^\pi f\left(\frac{lz}{\pi}, \tau\right) \sin nz\, dz \qquad \text{and} \qquad z = \frac{\pi x}{l}.$$

By applying the inverse transformation show that

$$y = -\frac{2cl}{\pi^2} \sum_{n=1}^{\infty} \frac{1}{n} \sin \frac{n\pi x}{l} \int_0^t \bar{f}(n, \tau) \sin \frac{n\pi c(t-\tau)}{l}\, d\tau$$

(Sneddon [*103*, 1951]).

[This is the equation of motion of a weightless string of length l subjected to a general applied force $f(x, t)$, the string being set in motion from rest in its equilibrium position.]

13. Use the method of separation of variables to solve the equation

$$\frac{\partial^4 y}{\partial x^4} + \frac{1}{k^2} \frac{\partial^2 y}{\partial t^2} = f(x) \cos pt.$$

Find the Green's function $K(x, \xi)$ for the case $p = 0$, with end conditions $y = 0$, $\partial y/\partial x = 0$ at $x = 0$ and at $x = l$. Show that, if $y = \phi(x) \cos pt$, ϕ satisfies the integral equation

$$\phi(\xi) - \frac{p^2}{k^2} \int_0^l K(x, \xi) \phi(x)\, dx = \int_0^l K(x, \xi) f(x)\, dx$$

(Webster [*142*, 1947]).

(If y is the displacement, this is the equation for the forced transverse vibrations of a beam. The conditions imposed on the Green's function correspond to the case of a beam of length l clamped at both ends.)

14. The two-dimensional wave equation for forced vibrations is

$$\frac{\partial^2 z}{\partial x^2} + \frac{\partial^2 z}{\partial y^2} - \frac{1}{c^2} \frac{\partial^2 z}{\partial t^2} = f(x, y, t).$$

The Green's function for this equation is (by analogy with Laplace's equation in three dimensions)

$$G(x, y, t; \xi, \eta, \tau) = \frac{c}{4\pi[c^2(t-\tau)^2 - R^2]^{1/2}} \qquad [R < c(t-\tau)]$$

$$= 0 \qquad [R > c(t-\tau)],$$

where $R^2 = (x-\xi)^2 + (y-\eta)^2$. Derive an expression for z in terms of a triple integral involving the Green's function.

(If z is the displacement, this is the equation for the forced vibration of a thin membrane.)

CHAPTER 11

Nonhomogeneous Partial Differential Equations of Mathematical Physics

11.1 Introduction

In Chapter 10 we discussed methods of solving nonhomogeneous linear partial differential equations. We shall now apply these methods to determine the solutions of three equations of common occurrence in mathematical physics—Poisson's equation,

$$\frac{\partial^2 V}{\partial x^2}+\frac{\partial^2 V}{\partial y^2}+\frac{\partial^2 V}{\partial z^2}=f(x, y, z), \tag{11.1}$$

Lorenz's equation (or the nonhomogeneous wave equation),

$$\frac{\partial^2 V}{\partial x^2}+\frac{\partial^2 V}{\partial y^2}+\frac{\partial^2 V}{\partial z^2}-\frac{1}{c^2}\frac{\partial^2 V}{\partial t^2}=f(x, y, z, t), \tag{11.2}$$

and the nonhomogeneous diffusion equation,

$$\frac{\partial^2 V}{\partial x^2}+\frac{\partial^2 V}{\partial y^2}+\frac{\partial^2 V}{\partial z^2}-\frac{1}{k}\frac{\partial V}{\partial t}=f(x, y, z, t), \tag{11.3}$$

where the functions on the right sides of (11.1), (11.2), and (11.3) are some known functions of the independent variables.

Poisson's equation (11.1) occurs in the theory of gravitational potential in regions occupied by attracting matter [Kellogg, 1929]. In that case V is the gravitational potential and, if (x, y, z) are the rectangular coordinates of any point, $f(x, y, z) = -4\pi\rho$, where ρ is the density of gravitating matter at that point. Poisson's equation also occurs in electrostatics (V is the electrostatic potential and ρ is the density of electric charge), in the theory of vortex motion and in that of the flow of viscous liquids, the rate of flow being small (f is then proportional to the vorticity). The associated homogeneous equation is Laplace's equation

$$\frac{\partial^2 V}{\partial x^2}+\frac{\partial^2 V}{\partial y^2}+\frac{\partial^2 V}{\partial z^2}=0. \tag{11.4}$$

For conciseness, we shall often write (11.4) in the form

$$\Delta V = 0, \tag{11.5}$$

where

$$\Delta \equiv \frac{\partial^2}{\partial x^2} + \frac{\partial^2}{\partial y^2} + \frac{\partial^2}{\partial z^2}. \tag{11.6}$$

Lorenz's equation (11.2) occurs in investigations of phenomena involving the propagation of small disturbances, the parameter c in (11.2) being the velocity of propagation of such disturbances (in the theory of sound, V can be taken to be the compression of the fluid). These disturbances may be due to the presence of variable sources of sound in the given field or to external periodic disturbing forces. [A simple instance of the latter case is that of the forced motion of a stretched string (see Problem 11, Chapter 10); V is then the displacement of the string.] A region where the function f is not zero is sometimes called a *source of sound.* Lorenz's equation can also occur in unsteady flow in hydrodynamics (e.g., forced waves), in which case $f(x, y, z, t)$ is due to the disturbing forces. Equation (11.2) also occurs in the theory of elasticity, when an elastic body is subjected to external forces (in this case, V is the dilatation of the body). The associated homogeneous equation is the wave equation,

$$\frac{\partial^2 V}{\partial x^2} + \frac{\partial^2 V}{\partial y^2} + \frac{\partial^2 V}{\partial z^2} - \frac{1}{c^2}\frac{\partial^2 V}{\partial t^2} = 0. \tag{11.7}$$

For conciseness, this is sometimes written

$$\Box V = 0, \tag{11.8}$$

where

$$\Box \equiv \frac{\partial^2}{\partial x^2} + \frac{\partial^2}{\partial y^2} + \frac{\partial^2}{\partial z^2} - \frac{1}{c^2}\frac{\partial^2}{\partial t^2}. \tag{11.9}$$

If $f = F(x, y, z)e^{\pm ikct}$, where k is a constant, we see that a solution of (11.2) is

$$V = U(x, y, z)e^{\pm ikct}, \tag{11.10}$$

where

$$(\Delta + k^2)U = F(x, y, z). \tag{11.11}$$

This form of Lorenz's equation is known as the *nonhomogeneous Helmholtz equation.*

The nonhomogeneous diffusion equation (11.3) occurs in the theory of heat conduction in solids in which heat is being generated. In that case, V is the temperature and k is the thermometric conductivity, the heat generated per unit time at a given internal point being given by $H = -Kf(x, y, z, t)$, where K is the thermal conductivity of the solid. The equation occurs also in the theory of oscillations of viscous fluids and in the theory of diffusing particles (e.g., neutrons), $f(x, y, z, t)$ being proportional to the rate of production of neutrons. The associated homogeneous equation is

$$\frac{\partial^2 V}{\partial x^2} + \frac{\partial^2 V}{\partial y^2} + \frac{\partial^2 V}{\partial z^2} - \frac{1}{k}\frac{\partial V}{\partial t} = 0. \tag{11.12}$$

If, in (11.3), $f(x, y, z, t) = g(x, y, z)e^{-k\lambda^2 t}$, where λ is a constant, we may put

$$V = \Phi(x, y, z)e^{-k\lambda^2 t}.$$

We see that (11.3) reduces to

$$(\Delta + \lambda^2)\Phi = g(x, y, z). \tag{11.13}$$

In all three cases we see that the nonhomogeneous equations (11.1), (11.2), and (11.3) can be reduced to an equation involving the Laplacian operator Δ given by (11.6). The equations given above have been referred to rectangular Cartesian coordinates (x, y, z). It is often advantageous to use another set of orthogonal coordinates (the choice of coordinate systems is often suggested by the boundary conditions in any particular problem). The transformation of the Laplacian operator in such a change of coordinates is considered in §11.2.

In §11.3 we summarize various properties of the solutions of Laplace's equation, and in the following sections we discuss in detail the solutions of Poisson's equation. The solutions of Lorenz's equation and those of the nonhomogeneous diffusion equation are discussed in like manner in §§11.10 and 11.15. It is shown that, in many cases, the solutions of all these nonhomogeneous partial differential equations can be simply expressed in terms of the nonhomogeneous functions defined in Chapters 3 to 9. Solutions involving Green's functions are given in §§11.4, 11.6, 11.8, 11.11, 11.14, and 11.16.

11.2 The Laplacian Operator Δ

The Laplacian operator is defined by the equation

$$\Delta \equiv \frac{\partial^2}{\partial x^2} + \frac{\partial^2}{\partial y^2} + \frac{\partial^2}{\partial z^2}, \tag{11.14}$$

where x, y, and z are rectangular Cartesian coordinates. When referred to another orthogonal curvilinear system (q_1, q_2, q_3), the operator becomes (see Bateman [1918], Sneddon [1957], and Moon and Spencer [1961])

$$\Delta V \equiv \frac{1}{h_1h_2h_3}\left\{\frac{\partial}{\partial q_1}\left(\frac{h_2h_3}{h_1}\frac{\partial V}{\partial q_1}\right)+\frac{\partial}{\partial q_2}\left(\frac{h_3h_1}{h_2}\frac{\partial V}{\partial q_2}\right)+\frac{\partial}{\partial q_3}\left(\frac{h_1h_2}{h_3}\frac{\partial V}{\partial q_3}\right)\right\}, \quad (11.15)$$

where the general element of length ds in the two systems is given by

$$\begin{aligned}(ds)^2 &= (dx)^2+(dy)^2+(dz)^2\\ &= h_1^2(dq_1)^2+h_2^2(dq_2)^2+h_3^2(dq_3)^2.\end{aligned} \quad (11.16)$$

Alternatively, we see that

$$h_r^2=\left(\frac{\partial x}{\partial q_r}\right)^2+\left(\frac{\partial y}{\partial q_r}\right)^2+\left(\frac{\partial z}{\partial q_r}\right)^2 \qquad (r=1,2,3). \quad (11.17)$$

Equation (11.15) is known as Lamé's formula. We shall now derive expressions for Δ in terms of some commonly used systems of orthogonal curvilinear coordinates.

CYLINDRICAL POLAR COORDINATES (ρ, ϕ, z)

$$\begin{gathered} x=\rho\cos\phi, \qquad y=\rho\sin\phi, \qquad z=z.\\ h_1=1, \qquad h_2=\rho, \qquad h_3=1.\\ \Delta V=\frac{\partial^2 V}{\partial\rho^2}+\frac{1}{\rho}\frac{\partial V}{\partial\rho}+\frac{1}{\rho^2}\frac{\partial^2 V}{\partial\phi^2}+\frac{\partial^2 V}{\partial z^2}.\end{gathered} \quad (11.18)$$

SPHERICAL POLAR COORDINATES (r, θ, ϕ)

$$\begin{gathered} x=r\sin\theta\cos\phi, \qquad y=r\sin\theta\sin\phi, \qquad z=r\cos\theta.\\ h_1=1, \qquad h_2=r, \qquad h_3=r\sin\theta.\\ \Delta V=\frac{\partial^2 V}{\partial r^2}+\frac{2}{r}\frac{\partial V}{\partial r}+\frac{1}{r^2}\frac{\partial^2 V}{\partial\theta^2}+\frac{\cot\theta}{r^2}\frac{\partial V}{\partial\theta}+\frac{1}{r^2\sin^2\theta}\frac{\partial^2 V}{\partial\phi^2}.\end{gathered} \quad (11.19)$$

COORDINATES OF CONFOCAL CONES (r, β, γ)

$$x=kr\,\mathrm{sn}\,\beta\,\mathrm{sn}\,\gamma, \qquad y=i(k/k')r\,\mathrm{cn}\,\beta\,\mathrm{cn}\,\gamma, \qquad z=(1/k')r\,\mathrm{dn}\,\beta\,\mathrm{dn}\,\gamma, \quad (11.20)$$

k being the modulus of the Jacobian elliptic functions and $k'^2=1-k^2$.

$$\begin{gathered} h_1^2=1, \qquad h_2^2=k^2r^2[(\mathrm{sn}\,\gamma)^2-(\mathrm{sn}\,\beta)^2],\ h_3^2=k^2r^2[(\mathrm{sn}\,\beta)^2-(\mathrm{sn}\,\gamma)^2].\\ \Delta V=\frac{\partial^2 V}{\partial r^2}+\frac{2}{r}\frac{\partial V}{\partial r}+\frac{1}{k^2r^2[(\mathrm{sn}\,\gamma)^2-(\mathrm{sn}\,\beta)^2]}\left(\frac{\partial^2 V}{\partial\beta^2}-\frac{\partial^2 V}{\partial\gamma^2}\right).\end{gathered} \quad (11.21)$$

PARABOLIC CYLINDER COORDINATES (ξ, η, ζ)

$$x = \xi\eta, \qquad y = \tfrac{1}{2}\xi^2 - \tfrac{1}{2}\eta^2, \qquad z = \zeta.$$

$$h_1 = h_2 = (\xi^2 + \eta^2)^{1/2}, \qquad h_3 = 1. \tag{11.22}$$

$$\Delta V = \frac{1}{\xi^2 + \eta^2}\left(\frac{\partial^2 V}{\partial \xi^2} + \frac{\partial^2 V}{\partial \eta^2}\right) + \frac{\partial^2 V}{\partial \zeta^2}.$$

COORDINATES OF THE PARABOLOID OF REVOLUTION (ξ, η, ϕ)

$$x = \xi\eta \cos\phi, \qquad y = \xi\eta \sin\phi, \qquad z = \tfrac{1}{2}\xi^2 - \tfrac{1}{2}\eta^2.$$

$$h_1 = h_2 = (\xi^2 + \eta^2)^{1/2}, \qquad h_3 = \xi\eta. \tag{11.23}$$

$$\Delta V = \frac{1}{\xi^2 + \eta^2}\left(\frac{\partial^2 V}{\partial \xi^2} + \frac{1}{\xi}\frac{\partial V}{\partial \xi} + \frac{\partial^2 V}{\partial \eta^2} + \frac{1}{\eta}\frac{\partial V}{\partial \eta}\right) + \frac{1}{\xi^2\eta^2}\frac{\partial^2 V}{\partial \phi^2}.$$

ELLIPTIC CYLINDER COORDINATES (u, v, w)

$$x = c\cosh u \cos v, \qquad y = c \sinh u \sin v, \qquad z = w.$$

$$h_1 = h_2 = c(\sinh^2 u + \sin^2 v)^{1/2}, \qquad h_3 = 1. \tag{11.24}$$

$$\Delta V = \frac{1}{c^2(\sinh^2 u + \sin^2 v)}\left(\frac{\partial^2 V}{\partial u^2} + \frac{\partial^2 V}{\partial v^2}\right) + \frac{\partial^2 V}{\partial w^2}.$$

ELLIPSOIDAL COORDINATES (α, β, γ)

In the notation of Erdélyi [*46*, 1955],

$$\begin{aligned} x &= k^2(a^2 - c^2)^{1/2}\,\mathrm{sn}\,\alpha\,\mathrm{sn}\,\beta\,\mathrm{sn}\,\gamma, \\ y &= -\frac{k^2}{k'}(a^2 - c^2)^{1/2}\,\mathrm{cn}\,\alpha\,\mathrm{cn}\,\beta\,\mathrm{cn}\,\gamma, \\ z &= \frac{i}{k'}(a^2 - c^2)^{1/2}\,\mathrm{dn}\,\alpha\,\mathrm{dn}\,\beta\,\mathrm{dn}\,\gamma, \end{aligned} \tag{11.25}$$

the modulus of the Jacobian elliptic functions being k, where

$$k^2 = \frac{a^2 - b^2}{a^2 - c^2}, \qquad k'^2 = \frac{b^2 - c^2}{a^2 - c^2} = 1 - k^2 \qquad (0 < k, k' < 1). \tag{11.26}$$

$$\begin{aligned} h_1^2 &= \frac{(a^2 - b^2)^2}{a^2 - c^2}[(\mathrm{sn}\,\alpha)^2 - (\mathrm{sn}\,\beta)^2][(\mathrm{sn}\,\alpha)^2 - (\mathrm{sn}\,\gamma)^2], \\ h_2^2 &= \frac{(a^2 - b^2)^2}{a^2 - c^2}[(\mathrm{sn}\,\beta)^2 - (\mathrm{sn}\,\gamma)^2][(\mathrm{sn}\,\beta)^2 - (\mathrm{sn}\,\alpha)^2], \\ h_3^2 &= \frac{(a^2 - b^2)^2}{a^2 - c^2}[(\mathrm{sn}\,\gamma)^2 - (\mathrm{sn}\,\alpha)^2][(\mathrm{sn}\,\gamma)^2 - (\mathrm{sn}\,\beta)^2], \end{aligned} \tag{11.27}$$

$$\Delta V = \frac{a^2 - c^2}{(a^2 - b^2)^2}\{[(\mathrm{sn}\,\alpha)^2 - (\mathrm{sn}\,\beta)^2][(\mathrm{sn}\,\beta)^2 - (\mathrm{sn}\,\gamma)^2][(\mathrm{sn}\,\gamma)^2 - (\mathrm{sn}\,\alpha)^2]\}^{-1}$$

$$\times\left\{[(\mathrm{sn}\,\gamma)^2 - (\mathrm{sn}\,\beta)^2]\frac{\partial^2 V}{\partial\alpha^2} + [(\mathrm{sn}\,\alpha)^2 - (\mathrm{sn}\,\gamma)^2]\frac{\partial^2 V}{\partial\beta^2}\right. \tag{11.28}$$

$$\left. + [(\mathrm{sn}\,\beta)^2 - (\mathrm{sn}\,\alpha)^2]\frac{\partial^2 V}{\partial\gamma^2}\right\}.$$

PROLATE SPHEROIDAL COORDINATES (u, v, ϕ)

$$x = c\sinh u\sin v\cos\phi, \qquad y = c\sinh u\sin v\sin\phi, \qquad z = c\cosh u\cos v.$$

$$h_1 = h_2 = c(\sinh^2 u + \sin^2 v)^{1/2}, \qquad h_3 = c\sinh u\sin v.$$

$$\Delta V = \frac{1}{c^2(\sinh^2 u + \sin^2 v)}\left(\frac{\partial^2 V}{\partial u^2} + \coth u\frac{\partial V}{\partial u} + \frac{\partial^2 V}{\partial v^2} + \cot v\frac{\partial V}{\partial v}\right) \tag{11.29}$$

$$+ \frac{1}{c^2\sinh^2 u\sin^2 v}\frac{\partial^2 V}{\partial\phi^2}.$$

OBLATE SPHEROIDAL COORDINATES (u, v, ϕ)

$$x = c\cosh u\sin v\cos\phi, \qquad y = c\cosh u\sin v\sin\phi, \qquad z = c\sinh u\cos v.$$

$$h_1 = h_2 = c(\cosh^2 u - \sin^2 v)^{1/2}, \qquad h_3 = c\cosh u\sin v.$$

$$\Delta V = \frac{1}{c^2(\cosh^2 u - \sin^2 v)}\left(\frac{\partial^2 V}{\partial u^2} + \tanh u\frac{\partial V}{\partial u} + \frac{\partial^2 V}{\partial v^2} + \cot v\frac{\partial V}{\partial v}\right) \tag{11.30}$$

$$+ \frac{1}{c^2\cosh^2 u\sin^2 v}\frac{\partial^2 V}{\partial\phi^2}.$$

11.3 Solutions of Laplace's Equation

The properties of solutions of Laplace's equation (11.4) are fully set out in Whittaker and Watson [1935], Webster [1947], Sneddon [1957], and Bland [1961]. We shall here briefly summarize various properties of these solutions.

Consider first the two-dimensional form of Laplace's equation

$$\frac{\partial^2 V}{\partial x^2} + \frac{\partial^2 V}{\partial y^2} = 0. \tag{11.31}$$

As shown in §10.3,

$$V = Ce^{ax \pm iay},$$

where a and C are constants, will be a solution of (11.31). The general integral of (11.31) can be put in the form

$$V = \phi_1(x + iy) + \phi_2(x - iy), \tag{11.32}$$

where ϕ_1 and ϕ_2 are arbitrary functions.

The corresponding solution for the three-dimensional form of Laplace's equation

$$\frac{\partial^2 V}{\partial x^2} + \frac{\partial^2 V}{\partial y^2} + \frac{\partial^2 V}{\partial z^2} = 0 \tag{11.33}$$

is

$$V = Ce^{lx+my+nz} \tag{11.34}$$

where l, m, n, and C are constants such that

$$l^2 + m^2 + n^2 = 0. \tag{11.35}$$

As shown by Whittaker, the general solution of Laplace's equation can be written

$$V = \int_{-\pi}^{\pi} f(z + ix \cos u + iy \sin u, u)\, du. \tag{11.36}$$

Consider next the solution of (11.33) by the method of separation of variables. If the solution is assumed to be of the form

$$V = X(x)Y(y)Z(z),$$

we see from §10.6, that X, Y, and Z satisfy the equations

$$\frac{d^2X}{dx^2} + aX = 0, \tag{11.37}$$

$$\frac{d^2Y}{dy^2} + bY = 0, \tag{11.38}$$

$$\frac{d^2Z}{dz^2} - (a + b)Z = 0, \tag{11.39}$$

where a and b are arbitrary constants of separation (which may be imaginary). The solutions of (11.37) to (11.39) can be found immediately, in the form (11.34), or in alternative forms such as

$$V = \begin{pmatrix}\sin\\ \cos\end{pmatrix}(\sqrt{a}\,x)\begin{pmatrix}\sin\\ \cos\end{pmatrix}(\sqrt{b}\,y)e^{\pm\sqrt{a+b}\,z}.$$

The method of separation of variables can be applied to find solutions of Laplace's equation referred to other sets of orthogonal curvilinear coordinates, using the results of §11.2. We give here examples of these results.

CYLINDRICAL POLAR COORDINATES (ρ, ϕ, z)

$V = R(\rho)\Phi(\phi)Z(z)$, where, from (11.18), and (10.55),

$$\frac{d^2R}{d\rho^2} + \frac{1}{\rho}\frac{dR}{d\rho} + \left(\frac{a}{\rho^2} + b\right)R = 0, \qquad (11.40)$$

$$\frac{d^2\Phi}{d\phi^2} - a\Phi = 0, \qquad (11.41)$$

$$\frac{d^2Z}{dz^2} - bZ = 0, \qquad (11.42)$$

where a and b are arbitrary constants of separation. We see, from Chapter 3, that the solutions of (11.40) can be expressed in terms of Bessel functions. Put $a = -\nu^2$ and $b = \beta^2$. Then there are particular solutions of Laplace's equation of the form

$$V = J_{\pm\nu}(\beta\rho)\binom{\sin}{\cos}\nu\phi e^{\pm\beta z}. \qquad (11.43)$$

SPHERICAL POLAR COORDINATES (r, θ, ϕ)

$V = R(r)\Theta(\theta)\Phi(\phi)$ where, from (11.19) and (10.57),

$$r^2\frac{d^2R}{dr^2} + 2r\frac{dR}{dr} - aR = 0, \qquad (11.44)$$

$$\frac{d^2\Theta}{d\theta^2} + \cot\theta\frac{d\Theta}{d\theta} + \left(a + \frac{b}{\sin^2\theta}\right)\Theta = 0, \qquad (11.45)$$

$$\frac{d^2\Phi}{d\phi^2} - b\Phi = 0, \qquad (11.46)$$

where a and b are arbitrary constants of separation. In (11.45), put $\zeta = \cos\theta$. Then (11.45) becomes

$$(1-\zeta^2)\frac{d^2\Theta}{d\zeta^2} - 2\zeta\frac{d\Theta}{d\zeta} + [a + b(1-\zeta^2)^{-1}]\Theta = 0. \qquad (11.47)$$

We see, from Chapter 7, that the solutions of (11.47) can be expressed in terms of Legendre functions. Put $a = \nu(\nu+1)$, $b = -\mu^2$, $\delta = rd/dr$. Then (11.44) becomes

$$(\delta - \nu)(\delta + \nu + 1)R = 0,$$

with solutions r^ν and $r^{-\nu-1}$. Thus there are particular solutions of Laplace's equation of the form

$$V = r^{\nu}\begin{pmatrix} P_\nu^\mu(\cos\theta) \\ Q_\nu^\mu(\cos\theta)\end{pmatrix}\begin{pmatrix}\sin \\ \cos\end{pmatrix}\mu\phi$$

and (11.48)

$$V = r^{-\nu-1}\begin{pmatrix} P_\nu^\mu(\cos\theta) \\ Q_\nu^\mu(\cos\theta)\end{pmatrix}\begin{pmatrix}\sin \\ \cos\end{pmatrix}\mu\phi .$$

More generally, as shown by Bateman [*198*, 1918], if $V = F(r, \theta, \phi)$ is a solution of Laplace's equation, then another solution is

$$V = \frac{1}{r} F\left(\frac{1}{r}, \theta, \phi\right). \tag{11.49}$$

This can be stated in an alternative form (Bateman [*199*, 1918]). If $F(x, y, z)$ is a solution of Laplace's equation,

$$V = \frac{1}{r} F\left(\frac{x}{r^2}, \frac{y}{r^2}, \frac{z}{r^2}\right) \tag{11.50}$$

is also a solution.

COORDINATES OF CONFOCAL CONES (r, β, γ)

$V = R(r)B(\beta)C(\gamma)$, where, from (11.21) and (10.59),

$$r^2\frac{d^2R}{dr^2} + 2r\frac{dR}{dr} - aR = 0, \tag{11.51}$$

$$\frac{d^2B}{d\beta^2} - [ak^2(\operatorname{sn}\beta)^2 + b]B = 0, \tag{11.52}$$

$$\frac{d^2C}{d\gamma^2} - [ak^2(\operatorname{sn}\gamma)^2 + b]C = 0, \tag{11.53}$$

where a and b are arbitrary constants of separation. We see, from Chapter 9, that the solutions of (11.52) and (11.53) can be expressed in terms of Lamé functions. Put $a = \nu(\nu + 1)$. Then V can be expressed as the product of r^ν (or $r^{-\nu-1}$) and two Lamé functions $B(\beta)C(\gamma)$, with the appropriate parameters.

PARABOLIC CYLINDER COORDINATES (ξ, η, ζ)

$V = A(\xi)B(\eta)C(\zeta)$, where, from (11.22) and (10.59),

$$\frac{d^2A}{d\xi^2} - (a\xi^2 + b)A = 0, \tag{11.54}$$

$$\frac{d^2B}{d\eta^2} - (a\eta^2 - b)B = 0, \tag{11.55}$$

$$\frac{d^2C}{d\zeta^2} + aC = 0, \tag{11.56}$$

where a and b are arbitrary constants of separation. We see, from Chapter 5, that the solutions of (11.54) and (11.55) can be expressed in terms of parabolic cylinder functions. Then V can be expressed as the product of $\sin(a^{1/2}\zeta)$, or $\cos(a^{1/2}\zeta)$, and two parabolic cylinder functions $A(\xi)B(\eta)$, with the appropriate parameters.

COORDINATES OF THE PARABOLOID OF REVOLUTION (ξ, η, ϕ)

$V = A(\xi)B(\eta)\Phi(\phi)$, where, from (11.23) and (10.59),

$$\frac{d^2A}{d\xi^2} + \frac{1}{\xi}\frac{dA}{d\xi} - \left(\frac{a}{\xi^2} + b\right)A = 0, \tag{11.57}$$

$$\frac{d^2B}{d\eta^2} + \frac{1}{\eta}\frac{dB}{d\eta} - \left(\frac{a}{\eta^2} - b\right)B = 0, \tag{11.58}$$

$$\frac{d^2\Phi}{d\phi^2} + a\Phi = 0, \tag{11.59}$$

where a and b are arbitrary constants of separation. We see, from Chapter 3, that the solutions of (11.57) and (11.58) can be expressed in terms of Bessel functions. Thus V can be expressed as the product of $\sin(a^{1/2}\phi)$, or $\cos(a^{1/2}\phi)$, and two Bessel functions $A(\xi)B(\eta)$, with the appropriate parameters.

ELLIPTIC CYLINDER COORDINATES (u, v, w)

$V = A(u)B(v)C(w)$, where, from (11.24) and (10.59),

$$\frac{d^2A}{du^2} - (ac^2 \sinh^2 u + b)A = 0, \tag{11.60}$$

$$\frac{d^2B}{dv^2} - (ac^2 \sin^2 v - b)B = 0, \tag{11.61}$$

$$\frac{d^2C}{dw^2} + aC = 0, \tag{11.62}$$

where a and b are arbitrary constants of separation. We see, from Chapter 9, that the solutions of (11.60) and (11.61) can be expressed in terms of Mathieu functions (or modified Mathieu functions). Thus V can be expressed as the product of an exponential function $C(w)$ and two Mathieu functions $A(u)B(v)$, with the appropriate parameters.

ELLIPSOIDAL COORDINATES (α, β, γ)

$V = A(\alpha)B(\beta)C(\gamma)$, where, from (11.28) and (10.59),

$$\frac{d^2A}{d\alpha^2} - [l(\text{sn } \alpha)^2 + m]A = 0, \tag{11.63}$$

$$\frac{d^2B}{d\beta^2} - [l(\text{sn}\,\beta)^2 + m]B = 0, \tag{11.64}$$

$$\frac{d^2C}{d\gamma^2} - [l(\text{sn}\,\gamma)^2 + m]C = 0, \tag{11.65}$$

where l and m are arbitrary constants of separation. We see, from Chapter 9, that the solutions of (11.63) to (11.65) can be expressed in terms of Lamé functions. Thus V can be expressed as the product of three Lamé functions, with the appropriate parameters.

PROLATE SPHEROIDAL COORDINATES (u, v, ϕ)

$V = A(u)B(v)\Phi(\phi)$, where, from (11.29) and (10.59),

$$\frac{d^2A}{du^2} + \coth u\,\frac{dA}{du} - \left(\frac{a}{\sinh^2 u} + b\right)A = 0, \tag{11.66}$$

$$\frac{d^2B}{dv^2} + \cot v\,\frac{dB}{dv} - \left(\frac{a}{\sin^2 v} - b\right)B = 0, \tag{11.67}$$

$$\frac{d^2\Phi}{d\phi^2} + a\Phi = 0, \tag{11.68}$$

where a and b are arbitrary constants of separation. Put $\xi = \cosh u$ and $\eta = \cos v$. Then (11.66) and (11.67) become

$$(1 - \xi^2)\frac{d^2A}{d\xi^2} - 2\xi\frac{dA}{d\xi} + [b - a(1 - \xi^2)^{-1}]A = 0, \tag{11.69}$$

$$(1 - \eta^2)\frac{d^2B}{d\eta^2} - 2\eta\frac{dB}{d\eta} + [b - a(1 - \eta^2)^{-1}]B = 0. \tag{11.70}$$

We see, from Chapter 7, that the solutions of (11.69) and (11.70) can be expressed in terms of Legendre functions. Put $a = \mu^2$ and $b = \nu(\nu + 1)$. Then there are particular solutions of Laplace's equation of the form

$$V = \begin{pmatrix} P_\nu^\mu(\cosh u) \\ Q_\nu^\mu(\cosh u) \end{pmatrix} \begin{pmatrix} P_\nu^\mu(\cos v) \\ Q_\nu^\mu(\cos v) \end{pmatrix} \begin{pmatrix} \sin \\ \cos \end{pmatrix} \mu\phi\,.$$

OBLATE SPHEROIDAL COORDINATES (u, v, ϕ)

$V = A(u)B(v)\Phi(\phi)$, where, from (11.30) and (10.59),

$$\frac{d^2A}{du^2} + \tanh u\,\frac{dA}{du} + \left(\frac{a}{\cosh^2 u} - b\right)A = 0, \tag{11.71}$$

$$\frac{d^2B}{dv^2} + \cot v \frac{dB}{dv} - \left(\frac{a}{\sin^2 v} - b\right)B = 0, \tag{11.72}$$

$$\frac{d^2\Phi}{d\phi^2} + a\Phi = 0, \tag{11.73}$$

where a and b are arbitrary constants of separation. In (11.71), put $\xi = i \sinh u$. Then (11.71) becomes

$$(1 - \xi^2)\frac{d^2A}{d\xi^2} - 2\xi \frac{dA}{d\xi} + [b - a(1 - \xi^2)^{-1}]A = 0. \tag{11.74}$$

Here again, the solutions of (11.72) and (11.74) can be expressed in terms of Legendre functions. Put $a = \mu^2$ and $b = \nu(\nu + 1)$. Then there are particular solutions of Laplace's equation of the form

$$V = \begin{pmatrix} P_\nu^\mu(i \sinh u) \\ Q_\nu^\mu(i \sinh u) \end{pmatrix} \begin{pmatrix} P_\nu^\mu(\cos v) \\ Q_\nu^\mu(\cos v) \end{pmatrix} \begin{pmatrix} \sin \\ \cos \end{pmatrix} \mu\phi .$$

11.4 Green's Function for Laplace's Equation

Consider first the two-dimensional form of Laplace's equation, given by (11.31), or, in polar coordinates, from (11.18) with $z = 0$,

$$\frac{\partial^2 V}{\partial \rho^2} + \frac{1}{\rho}\frac{\partial V}{\partial \rho} + \frac{1}{\rho^2}\frac{\partial^2 V}{\partial \phi^2} = 0. \tag{11.75}$$

It is easily verified that, if $\rho \neq 0$, one solution of (11.75) is

$$V = C \log \rho ,$$

where C is an arbitrary constant. More generally, any function of the form

$$V = C \log \rho' \tag{11.76}$$

satisfies (11.31), where $\rho'^2 = (x - \xi)^2 + (y - \eta)^2$.

Consider now the Green's function $G(x, y; \xi, \eta)$ for (11.31). From the definition of the Green's function, given in §10.8, we see that

$$\Delta G = \left[\frac{\partial^2}{\partial x^2} + \frac{\partial^2}{\partial y^2}\right] G(x, y; \xi, \eta) = -\delta(x - \xi, y - \eta). \tag{11.77}$$

On using Green's theorem, (10.95), with $u = G$ and $v = 1$, we see that

$$\iint_R \Delta G \, dx \, dy = \int_C \frac{\partial G}{\partial n} \, ds, \tag{11.78}$$

where dn is the element of the outward normal to a closed curve C which surrounds the simply connected region R.

It is more convenient at this stage to change to polar coordinates. From the definition of the δ function given in §10.8,

$$\delta(x - \xi, y - \eta) = \frac{\delta(\rho')}{2\pi\rho'}. \tag{11.79}$$

In polar coordinates, with origin at the point $P(\xi, \eta)$, (11.77) becomes

$$\Delta G = \left[\frac{\partial^2}{\delta\rho'^2} + \frac{1}{\rho'}\frac{\partial}{\partial\rho'} + \frac{1}{\rho'^2}\frac{\partial^2}{\partial\phi^2}\right]G = -\frac{\delta(\rho')}{2\pi\rho'}. \tag{11.80}$$

Now the right side is independent of ϕ, and thus we look for a solution in which G is a function of ρ' only.

Now from the definition of the δ function, we see, from (11.78) and (11.80), that

$$\int_C \frac{\partial G}{\partial n}\, ds = -\iint_R \frac{(\rho\delta')}{2\pi\rho'}\, \rho'\, d\rho'\, d\theta = -1$$

for any finite contour C surrounding the point P. Let C be the circle center P radius ε. Then

$$\int_0^{2\pi} \frac{dG}{d\rho'}\, \varepsilon\, d\theta = -1$$

for any finite radius ε (however small). This equation will be satisfied if $dG/d\rho'$ has a singularity of the type $(-1/2\pi\rho')$ at the point P.

Thus the Green's function for the two-dimensional form of Laplace's equation (11.31) is

$$G(x, y; \xi, \eta) = -\frac{1}{2\pi}\log \rho' + \gamma(x, y; \xi, \eta), \tag{11.81}$$

where

$$\rho'^2 = (x - \xi)^2 + (y - \eta)^2$$

and $\gamma(x, y; \xi, \eta)$ is a solution of (11.31), γ and its first and second derivatives being continuous in the simply connected region R for which (ξ, η) is an internal point. The point (ξ, η) is sometimes said to be a *source point*. We see from (11.76) that G satisfies Laplace's equation at all points except the point (ξ, η).

By a similar analysis (using spherical polar coordinates), we find that in the three-dimensional case, $dG/d\rho'$ must have a singularity of the type

$(-1/4\pi\rho'^2)$ at the corresponding source point, where $\rho'^2 = (x-\xi)^2 + (y-\eta)^2 + (z-\zeta)^2$. Thus the Green's function for Laplace's equation (11.33) is

$$G(x, y, z; \xi, \eta, \zeta) = \frac{1}{4\pi\rho'} + \gamma(x, y, z; \xi, \eta, \zeta), \tag{11.82}$$

where $\gamma(x, y, z; \xi, \eta, \zeta)$ is a solution of (11.33), γ and its first and second derivatives being continuous throughout the region R. The Green's function may be physically interpreted as the potential at a given point (x, y, z) due to a source of strength $1/4\pi$ at the point (ξ, η, ζ). The Green's function for the two-dimensional case can be interpreted as the potential due to a two-dimensional source of strength $1/2\pi$ at the point (ξ, η).

11.5 Solutions of Poisson's Equation

The solution of Poisson's equation

$$\Delta V = \frac{\partial^2 V}{\partial x^2} + \frac{\partial^2 V}{\partial y^2} + \frac{\partial^2 V}{\partial z^2} = f(x, y, z) \tag{11.83}$$

can be found using the methods given in Chapter 10. Thus, if f is some simple function of the independent variables, the methods given in §10.3 will provide a particular integral. Alternatively, the particular integral can be found as a multiple integral, using the method of §10.4. Other solutions of Poisson's equation in terms of integrals are given in §11.6.

As stated in §10.2, the general integral of (11.83) will be obtained by adding any particular integral of (11.83) to the most general integral of the associated homogeneous equation (11.33). However, the choice of the most suitable particular integral (when more than one is known, often depends on the boundary conditions of a given problem (see Sagan [1961] and Binns and Lawrenson [1963]).

The method of separation of variables (§10.6) is capable of providing an immediate answer to the problem if $f(x, y, z)$ has certain forms. If $f(x, y, z) = g(x)Y(y)Z(z)$, there will be a particular solution of (11.83) of the form

$$V = \bar{X}(x)Y(y)Z(z),$$

where $\bar{X}$ satisfies the equation

$$\frac{d^2\bar{X}}{dx^2} + a\bar{X} = g(x), \tag{11.84}$$

where a is a constant and Y and Z satisfy (11.38) and (11.39). The solutions of (11.84) can be found by the methods of Chapter 2; the solution for Y

and Z can be found from §11.3. Thus, if

$$f = g(x)\begin{pmatrix}\sin\\ \cos\end{pmatrix}(\sqrt{b}\,y)e^{\pm\sqrt{a+b}\,z},$$

the particular integral of (11.83) will be of the form

$$V = \bar{X}(x)\begin{pmatrix}\sin\\ \cos\end{pmatrix}(\sqrt{b}\,y)e^{\pm\sqrt{a+b}\,z}.$$

As with Laplace's equation, the method of separation of variables can be applied to find particular solutions of Poisson's equation, referred to other sets of orthogonal curvilinear coordinates, using the results of §11.2. We give here examples of such particular solutions.

CYLINDRICAL POLAR COORDINATES (ρ, ϕ, z)

If $f = g(\rho)\Phi(\phi)Z(z)$, $V = \bar{R}(\rho)\Phi(\phi)Z(z)$, where, from (11.18),

$$\frac{d^2\bar{R}}{d\rho^2} + \frac{1}{\rho}\frac{d\bar{R}}{d\rho} + \left(\frac{a}{\rho^2} + b\right)\bar{R} = g(\rho), \tag{11.85}$$

where a and b are arbitrary constants of separation, and Φ and Z satisfy (11.41) and (11.42). If $g(\rho) = \rho^{\mu-1}$, where μ is any constant, we see, from §3.21, that the solutions of (11.85) can be expressed in terms of Lommel functions. Putting $a = -\nu^2$ and $b = \beta^2$, we see that, if $f = \rho^{\mu-1}\Phi(\phi)Z(z)$, a particular solution of Poisson's equation is

$$V = \beta^{-\mu-1}s_{\mu,\nu}(\beta\rho)\Phi(\phi)Z(z), \tag{11.86}$$

where s is the Lommel function defined in §3.16.

SPHERICAL POLAR COORDINATES (r, θ, ϕ)

If $f = R(r)g(\theta)\Phi(\phi)/r^2$, $V = R(r)\bar{\Theta}(\theta)\Phi(\phi)$, where, from (11.19),

$$\frac{d^2\bar{\Theta}}{d\theta^2} + \cot\theta\frac{d\bar{\Theta}}{d\theta} + \left(a + \frac{b}{\sin^2\theta}\right)\bar{\Theta} = g(\theta), \tag{11.87}$$

where a and b are arbitrary constants of separation, and R and Φ satisfy (11.44) and (11.46). In (11.87), put $\zeta = \cos\theta$. Then (11.87) becomes, with $g(\theta) = G(\zeta)$,

$$(1-\zeta^2)\frac{d^2\bar{\Theta}}{d\zeta^2} - 2\zeta\frac{d\bar{\Theta}}{d\zeta} + [a + b(1-\zeta^2)^{-1}]\bar{\Theta} = G(\zeta). \tag{11.88}$$

Putting $a = \nu(\nu+1)$ and $b = -\mu^2$, we see from §7.22 that, if

$$g(\theta) = (\cos\theta)^{2\sigma-2}(\sin\theta)^{\mu+2\tau-2},$$

where σ and τ are any constants, the solutions of (11.88) can be expressed in terms of the nonhomogeneous Legendre functions. Thus, if $f = (\cos\theta)^{2\sigma-2} \times (\sin\theta)^{\mu+2\tau-2}R(r)\Phi(\phi)/r^2$, a particular solution of Poisson's equation is

$$V = R(r)t_{\nu,\sigma}^{\mu;\tau}(\cos\theta)\Phi(\phi), \tag{11.89}$$

where t is the nonhomogeneous Legendre function defined in §7.22. We see, from §11.3, that $R(r)$ will be of the form r^ν or $r^{-\nu-1}$.

More generally, if $V = F(r, \theta, \phi)$ is a solution of Poisson's equation (11.83) then the equation

$$\Delta V = \frac{1}{r^5} f\left(\frac{1}{r}, \theta, \phi\right) \tag{11.90}$$

has a particular integral

$$V = \frac{1}{r} F\left(\frac{1}{r}, \theta, \phi\right). \tag{11.91}$$

This can be stated in an alternative form. If $F(x, y, z)$ is a solution of Poisson's equation (11.83), then the equation

$$\Delta V = \frac{\partial^2 V}{\partial x^2} + \frac{\partial^2 V}{\partial y^2} + \frac{\partial^2 V}{\partial z^2} = \frac{1}{r^5} f\left(\frac{x}{r^2}, \frac{y}{r^2}, \frac{z}{r^2}\right) \tag{11.92}$$

has a particular integral

$$V = \frac{1}{r} F\left(\frac{x}{r^2}, \frac{y}{r^2}, \frac{z}{r^2}\right). \tag{11.93}$$

COORDINATES OF CONFOCAL CONES (r, β, γ)

If $f = R(r)g(\beta)C(\gamma)/\{r^2[(\text{sn}\,\gamma)^2 - (\text{sn}\,\beta)^2]\}$, $V = R(r)\bar{B}(\beta)C(\gamma)$, where, from (11.21),

$$\frac{d^2\bar{B}}{d\beta^2} - [ak^2(\text{sn}\,\beta)^2 + b]\bar{B} = k^2 g(\beta), \tag{11.94}$$

where a, b, and k are constants (a and b are arbitrary constants of separation), and R and C satisfy (11.51) and (11.53). If $g(\beta) = (\text{sn}\,\beta)^{2\sigma-2}$, where σ is any constant, we see, from §9.6, that the solution of (11.94) can be expressed in terms of the nonhomogeneous Heun functions. Putting $a = \nu(\nu+1)$, $b = -h$, we see that, if $f = (\text{sn}\,\beta)^{2\sigma-2}R(r)C(\gamma)/\{r^2[(\text{sn}\,\gamma)^2 - (\text{sn}\,\beta)^2]\}$, a particular solution of Poisson's equation is

$$V = \tfrac{1}{4} f_\sigma[k^{-2}, \tfrac{1}{4}hk^{-2}; -\tfrac{1}{2}\nu, \tfrac{1}{2}(\nu+1), \tfrac{1}{2}, \tfrac{1}{2}; (\text{sn}\,\beta)^2]R(r)C(\gamma)$$

where f_σ is the nonhomogeneous Heun function defined in §9.3.

PARABOLIC CYLINDER COORDINATES (ξ, η, ζ)

If $f = g(\xi)B(\eta)C(\zeta)/(\xi^2 + \eta^2)$, $V = \bar{A}(\xi)B(\eta)C(\zeta)$, where, from (11.22),

$$\frac{d^2\bar{A}}{d\xi^2} - (a\xi^2 + b)\bar{A} = g(\xi), \tag{11.95}$$

where a and b are arbitrary constants of separation, and B and C satisfy (11.55) and (11.56). If $g(\xi) = \xi^\sigma$, where σ is any constant, we see, from §5.16, that the solution of (11.95) can be expressed in terms of the nonhomogeneous parabolic cylinder functions. Putting $a = \frac{1}{4}\beta^4$ and $b = -(\nu + \frac{1}{2})\beta^2$, we see that, if $f = \xi^\sigma B(\eta)C(\zeta)/(\xi^2 + \eta^2)$, a particular solution of Poisson's equation is

$$V = \beta^{-\sigma-2}G_\nu^{(\sigma)}(\beta\xi)B(\eta)C(\zeta)$$

where G is the nonhomogeneous parabolic cylinder function defined in §5.14.

COORDINATES OF THE PARABOLOID OF REVOLUTION (ξ, η, ϕ)

If $f = g(\xi)B(\eta)\Phi(\phi)/(\xi^2 + \eta^2)$, $V = \bar{A}(\xi)B(\eta)\Phi(\phi)$, where, from (11.23),

$$\frac{d^2\bar{A}}{d\xi^2} + \frac{1}{\xi}\frac{d\bar{A}}{d\xi} - \left(\frac{a}{\xi^2} + b\right)\bar{A} = g(\xi), \tag{11.96}$$

where a and b are arbitrary constants of separation and B and Φ satisfy (11.58) and (11.59). If $g(\xi) = \xi^{\mu-1}$, where μ is any constant, we see from §3.21 that the solution of (11.96) can be expressed in terms of Lommel functions. Putting $a = \nu^2$ and $b = -\beta^2$ we see that, if $f = \xi^{\mu-1}B(\eta)\Phi(\phi)/(\xi^2 + \eta^2)$, a particular solution of Poisson's equation is

$$V = \beta^{-\mu-1}s_{\mu,\nu}(\beta\xi)B(\eta)\Phi(\phi),$$

where s is the Lommel function defined in §3.16.

ELLIPTIC CYLINDER COORDINATES (u, v, w)

If $f = g(u)B(v)C(w)/(\sinh^2 u + \sin^2 v)$, $V = \bar{A}(u)B(v)C(w)$, where, from (11.24),

$$\frac{d^2\bar{A}}{du^2} - (ac^2 \sinh^2 u + b)\bar{A} = c^2 g(u), \tag{11.97}$$

where a, b, and c are constants (a and b are arbitrary constants of separation) and B and C satisfy (11.61) and (11.62). If $g(u) = (\sinh u)^{2\sigma-2}$, where σ is any constant, we see, from §9.13, that the solution of (11.97) can be expressed in terms of the nonhomogeneous Mathieu functions. Putting $ac^2 = 4\theta$ and $b = p^2$ we see that, if $f = (\sinh u)^{2\sigma-2}B(v)C(w)/(\sinh^2 u + \sin^2 v)$, a particular solution of Poisson's equation is

$$V = e^{-i\pi\sigma}c^2 M_{p,\sigma}(-\theta;\, e^{(1/2)i\pi} \sinh u)B(v)C(w),$$

where $M_{p,\sigma}$ is the nonhomogeneous Mathieu function defined in §9.10.

ELLIPSOIDAL COORDINATES (α, β, γ)

If

$$f = \frac{a^2 - c^2}{(a^2 - b^2)^2} \{[(\text{sn}\,\alpha)^2 - (\text{sn}\,\beta)^2][(\text{sn}\,\alpha)^2 - (\text{sn}\,\gamma)^2]\}^{-1} g(\alpha)B(\beta)C(\gamma),$$

$V = \bar{A}(\alpha)B(\beta)C(\gamma)$, where, from (11.28),

$$\frac{d^2\bar{A}}{d\alpha^2} - [l(\text{sn}\,\alpha)^2 + m]\bar{A} = g(\alpha), \qquad (11.98)$$

where a, b, c, l, and m are constants (a and b are given by (11.25) and (11.26), l and m are arbitrary constants of separation) and B and C satisfy (11.64) and (11.65). If $g(\alpha) = (\text{sn}\,\alpha)^{2\sigma-2}$, where σ is any constant, we see, from §9.6 that the solution of (11.98) can be expressed in terms of the nonhomogeneous Heun functions. Putting $l = \nu(\nu + 1)k^2$ and $m = -h$ we see that, if

$$f = \frac{a^2 - c^2}{(a^2 - b^2)^2} (\text{sn}\,\alpha)^{2\sigma-2}\{[(\text{sn}\,\alpha)^2 - (\text{sn}\,\beta)^2][(\text{sn}\,\alpha)^2 - (\text{sn}\,\gamma)^2]\}^{-1} B(\beta)C(\gamma),$$

a particular solution of Poisson's equation is

$$V = \tfrac{1}{4} f_\sigma[k^{-2}, \tfrac{1}{4}hk^{-2};\, -\tfrac{1}{2}\nu, \tfrac{1}{2}(\nu + 1), \tfrac{1}{2}, \tfrac{1}{2};\, (\text{sn}\,\alpha)^2]B(\beta)C(\gamma),$$

where f_σ is the nonhomogeneous Heun function defined in §9.3.

PROLATE SPHEROIDAL COORDINATES (u, v, ϕ)

If $f = g(u)B(v)\Phi(\phi)/(\sinh^2 u + \sin^2 v)$, $V = \bar{A}(u)B(v)\Phi(\phi)$, where, from (11.29),

$$\frac{d^2\bar{A}}{du^2} + \coth u \frac{d\bar{A}}{du} - \left(\frac{a}{\sinh^2 u} + b\right)\bar{A} = c^2 g(u), \qquad (11.99)$$

where a and b are arbitrary constants of separation and B and Φ satisfy (11.67) and (11.68). In (11.99), put $\xi = \cosh u$. Then (11.99) becomes, with $g(u) = G(\xi)$,

$$(1 - \xi^2)\frac{d^2\bar{A}}{d\xi^2} - 2\xi\frac{d\bar{A}}{d\xi} + [b - a(1 - \xi^2)^{-1}]\bar{A} = -c^2 G(\xi). \qquad (11.100)$$

Putting $a = \mu^2$ and $b = \nu(\nu + 1)$, we see, from §7.20, that if

$$g(u) = (\cosh u)^{2\sigma-2}(\sinh u)^{\mu+2\tau-2},$$

where σ and τ are any constants, the solutions of (11.100) can be expressed in terms of the nonhomogeneous Legendre functions. Thus, if

$$f = (\cosh u)^{2\sigma-2}(\sinh u)^{\mu+2\tau-2}\begin{pmatrix} P_\nu^\mu(\cos v) \\ Q_\nu^\mu(\cos v)\end{pmatrix}\begin{pmatrix}\sin \\ \cos\end{pmatrix}\mu\phi \Big/ (\sinh^2 u + \sin^2 v),$$

a particular solution of Poisson's equation is

$$V = -c^2 t_{\nu,\sigma}^{\mu,\tau}(\cosh u)\begin{pmatrix} P_\nu^\mu(\cos v) \\ Q_\nu^\mu(\cos v)\end{pmatrix}\begin{pmatrix}\sin \\ \cos\end{pmatrix}\mu\phi,$$

where t is the nonhomogeneous Legendre function defined in §7.20.

OBLATE SPHEROIDAL COORDINATES (u, v, ϕ)

If $f = g(u)B(v)\Phi(\phi)/(\cosh^2 u - \sin^2 v)$, $V = \bar{A}(u)B(v)\Phi(\phi)$, where, from (11.30),

$$\frac{d^2\bar{A}}{du^2} + \tanh u\,\frac{d\bar{A}}{du} + \left(\frac{a}{\cosh^2 u} - b\right)\bar{A} = c^2 g(u), \tag{11.101}$$

where a and b are arbitrary constants of separation and B and Φ satisfy (11.72) and (11.73). In (11.101), put $\xi = i\sinh u$. Then (11.101) becomes, with $g(u) = G(\xi)$,

$$(1-\xi^2)\frac{d^2\bar{A}}{d\xi^2} - 2\xi\frac{d\bar{A}}{d\xi} + [b - a(1-\xi^2)^{-1}]\bar{A} = -c^2 G(\xi). \tag{11.102}$$

Here again, with $a = \mu^2$ and $b = \nu(\nu+1)$, we see that, if $g(u) = (\sinh u)^{2\sigma-2} \times (\cosh u)^{\mu+2\tau-2}$, where μ and τ are any constants, the solutions of (11.102) can be expressed in terms of the nonhomogeneous Legendre functions. Thus, if

$$f = (\sinh u)^{2\sigma-2}(\cosh u)^{\mu+2\tau-2}\begin{pmatrix} P_\nu^\mu(\cos v) \\ Q_\nu^\mu(\cos v)\end{pmatrix}\begin{pmatrix}\sin \\ \cos\end{pmatrix}\mu\phi \Big/ (\cosh^2 u - \sin^2 v),$$

a particular solution of Poisson's equation is

$$V = -e^{-i\pi[\sigma+\tau+(1/2)\mu]}c^2 t_{\nu,\sigma}^{\mu,\tau}(i\sinh u)\begin{pmatrix} P_\nu^\mu(\cos v) \\ Q_\nu^\mu(\cos v)\end{pmatrix}\begin{pmatrix}\sin \\ \cos\end{pmatrix}\mu\phi.$$

Particular integrals for other types of f function can be found by the same method. Thus, for cylindrical polar coordinates, if $f = R(\rho)\Phi(\phi)g(z)$, where R and Φ satisfy (11.40) and (11.41), a particular solution of Poisson's equation is $V = R(\rho)\Phi(\phi)\bar{Z}(z)$, where

$$\frac{d^2\bar{Z}}{dz^2} - b\bar{Z} = g(z).$$

The usefulness of the method of separation of variables is enhanced by observing that if f is the sum of a number of terms each of the desired form (e.g., a power series in one of the coordinates), the particular integral is the sum of the particular integrals corresponding to each term of f (see §10.2). This method can also be used if f is a function of two of the coordinates. Thus, if, in parabolic cylinder coordinates,

$$f = \frac{[\xi^{\sigma_1} B(\eta) + \eta^{\sigma_2} A(\xi)]C(\zeta)}{(\xi^2 + \eta^2)},$$

the particular integral of Poisson's equation can be expressed as the sum of two terms involving nonhomogeneous parabolic cylinder functions. More generally, the solutions of equations (11.85), (11.87), (11.94) to (11.99) and (11.101) can be found for any given function g by the method of variation of parameters (§1.5).

If f only involves one (or two) of the coordinates, the particular integral can be found by suppressing those terms arising from the unwanted coordinates. Thus, if, in cylindrical polar coordinates, $f = g(\rho)\Phi(\phi)$, where Φ satisfies (11.41), $V = \bar{R}(\rho)\Phi(\phi)$, where

$$\frac{d^2\bar{R}}{d\rho^2} + \frac{1}{\rho}\frac{d\bar{R}}{d\rho} + \frac{a}{\rho^2}\bar{R} = g(\rho),$$

that is,

$$(\theta^2 + a)\bar{R} = \rho^2 g(\rho), \tag{11.103}$$

where $\theta \equiv \rho d/d\rho$ and a is the only arbitrary constant of separation. A particular integral of (11.103) can then be found by the method given in §2.7; the complementary function of (11.103) is $C_1\rho^\nu + C_2\rho^{-\nu}$, where $a = -\nu^2$ and C_1 and C_2 are arbitrary constants.

Again, if in cylindrical polar coordinates, $f = g(\rho)$, the equation for V is

$$\frac{d^2V}{d\rho^2} + \frac{1}{\rho}\frac{dV}{d\rho} = g(\rho),$$

that is,

$$\theta^2 V = \rho^2 g(\rho), \tag{11.104}$$

which can be solved by the method given in §2.7; the complementary function of (11.104) is $C_1 + C_2 \log \rho$, where C_1 and C_2 are arbitrary constants.

The nature of the region throughout which the solution is required may well restrict our choice of separation constants. Thus, with spherical polar coordinates, if the range of ϕ is unrestricted, V being single-valued, we see that $\Phi(\phi)$ must have a period 2π; i.e., in (11.48), μ must be an integer. If the range of θ is unrestricted, the Legendre function $Q_\nu^\mu(\cos\theta)$ cannot occur in the solution for V, since this function has a singularity when $\cos\theta = 1$. As shown in §7.16, the nonhomogeneous Legendre function $s^{\mu}_{\nu,\sigma}(\cos\theta)$ can be expressed as a terminating series if $\sigma + \frac{1}{2}\mu - \frac{1}{2}\nu$ or $\sigma + \frac{1}{2} + \frac{1}{2}\mu + \frac{1}{2}\nu$ is zero or a negative integer, and thus this function would be a suitable function for the particular integral of Poisson's equation if the range of θ is unrestricted (e.g., in axisymmetric flow), provided that the source distribution f could be expressed as a series of terms of the form $(\cos\theta)^{2\sigma-2}(\sin\theta)^{\mu}R(r)\Phi(\phi)/r^2$. Similarly, in cylindrical polar coordinates, if the range of ϕ is unrestricted, ν must be an integer in (11.43) and in the corresponding solution of Poisson's equation.

11.6 Solutions of Poisson's Equation Using Green's Functions

The Green's functions for both the two-dimensional and three-dimensional form of Laplace's equation were given in §11.4. Using the results of §10.8, we can now determine the solution of Poisson's equation in terms of multiple integrals. The advantage of this method is its generality; the disadvantage is the awkward integrals we may have to solve.

From (11.82), together with (10.110), we see immediately that, if $f(x, y, z)$ is any function which with its first derivatives is continuous in the region R and vanishes outside R, a particular solution of Poisson's equation (11.83) is

$$V = -\frac{1}{4\pi}\iiint \frac{1}{\rho'} f(\xi, \eta, \zeta)\, d\xi\, d\eta\, d\zeta, \tag{11.105}$$

where $\rho'^2 = (x-\xi)^2 + (y-\eta)^2 + (z-\zeta)^2$, the integral being taken over the region R for which the point $P(x, y, z)$ is an interior point. If $f(x, y, z)$ is zero [e.g., if the point (x, y, z) is outside the distribution of matter], (11.105) is a solution of Laplace's equation. The corresponding formula for the two-dimensional case (with both V and f independent of z) is

$$V = \frac{1}{4\pi}\iint \log[(x-\xi)^2 + (y-\eta)^2] f(\xi, \eta)\, d\xi\, d\eta, \tag{11.106}$$

the point (x, y) being an interior point of the region of integration. These integrals can, of course, be expressed in terms of any of the orthogonal curvilinear coordinates given in §11.2.

Equation (11.105) can be written in the alternative form

$$V = -\frac{1}{4\pi}\iint \rho' f(\xi, \eta, \zeta)\, d\rho'\, d\omega, \tag{11.107}$$

where $d\omega$ is the element of solid angle of a cone with vertex at the point P. This form is particularly useful if $f = c$ (a constant) throughout a given region (as in the case of a homogeneous solid body). Equation (11.107) can then be integrated to give

$$V = -\frac{c}{8\pi}\int \rho'^2\, d\omega. \tag{11.108}$$

Using this expression, Routh [*107*, 1902] obtained a formula for the potential at an internal point of a solid homogeneous ellipsoid in terms of four infinite integrals.

Another method of finding the integral in (11.105) is to put

$$\rho' = [r^2 - 2rr'p + r'^2]^{1/2}, \tag{11.109}$$

where (r, θ, ϕ) and (r', θ', ϕ') are the spherical polar coordinates of the points $P(x, y, z)$, $P'(\xi, \eta, \zeta)$, and $p = \cos P\hat{O}P'$. Now

$$(1 - 2ph + h^2)^{-1/2} = 1 + P_1 h + P_2 h^2 + \cdots + P_n h^n + \cdots, \tag{11.110}$$

where P_n is a Legendre function of the nth order. From (11.109) and (11.110),

$$\frac{1}{\rho'} = \frac{1}{r'} + \frac{P_1 r}{r'^2} + \frac{P_2 r^2}{r'^3} + \cdots \qquad (r < r')$$

and (11.111)

$$\frac{1}{\rho'} = \frac{1}{r} + \frac{P_1 r'}{r^2} + \frac{P_2 r'^2}{r^3} + \cdots \qquad (r > r').$$

Also, for any given value of r', $f(\xi, \eta, \zeta)$ may be written

$$f(\xi, \eta, \zeta) = \sum_{n=0}^{\infty} X_n(r', \theta', \phi'),$$

where

$$X_n(r', \theta', \phi') = A_0 P_n(\cos\theta') + \sum_{m=1}^{n} (A_m \cos m\phi' + B_m \sin m\phi') P_n^m(\cos\theta').$$

We consider separately the part of the integral (11.107) which arises from points within the sphere with center O passing through the given point (x, y, z) and that part which arises from points outside this sphere. Using the results of the theory of attractions, it can be shown (MacRobert [*166*, 1947]) that

$$V = -\sum_{n=0}^{\infty} \frac{1}{2n+1}\left[r^{-n-1}\int_0^r X_n(r', \theta, \phi) r'^{n+2}\, dr' + r^n \int_r^{\infty} X_n(r', \theta, \phi) r'^{-n+1}\, dr'\right]. \tag{11.112}$$

We see that, in this case also, V is expressed in terms of a number of integrals. Similar methods can be applied to the two-dimensional case given by (11.106), the Green's function and f being expressed in terms of polar coordinates (see Morse and Feshbach [*1188*, 1953b]).

11.7 Solutions of the Wave Equation

The properties of solutions of the wave equation (11.7) are fully set out in Whittaker and Watson [1935], Webster [1947], Bateman [1918], and Sneddon [1957]. We shall here briefly summarize various properties of these solutions.

Consider first the one-dimensional form of the wave equation

$$\frac{\partial^2 V}{\partial x^2} - \frac{1}{c^2}\frac{\partial^2 V}{\partial t^2} = 0, \tag{11.113}$$

where c is a constant. Equation (11.113) can be reduced to the two-dimensional form of Laplace's equation (11.31) on writing $y = ict$. The general solution of (11.113) is thus

$$V = \phi_1(x + ct) + \phi_2(x - ct), \tag{11.114}$$

where ϕ_1 and ϕ_2 are arbitrary functions (physically, each function represents a wave, one wave traveling to the right with velocity c, the other wave traveling to the left with the same velocity).

Similarly the two-dimensional form of the wave equation

$$\frac{\partial^2 V}{\partial x^2} + \frac{\partial^2 V}{\partial y^2} - \frac{1}{c^2}\frac{\partial^2 V}{\partial t^2} = 0 \tag{11.115}$$

can be reduced to the three-dimensional form of Laplace's equation (11.33) on writing $z = ict$, and the corresponding solutions can be found immediately from those given in §11.3. Thus a particular solution of (11.115) is, from (11.43),

$$V = J_{\pm\nu}(\beta\rho)\begin{pmatrix}\sin\\ \cos\end{pmatrix}\nu\phi\begin{pmatrix}\sin\\ \cos\end{pmatrix}\beta ct. \tag{11.116}$$

Consider now the three-dimensional wave equation

$$\frac{\partial^2 V}{\partial x^2} + \frac{\partial^2 V}{\partial y^2} + \frac{\partial^2 V}{\partial z^2} - \frac{1}{c^2}\frac{\partial^2 V}{\partial t^2} = 0. \tag{11.117}$$

As shown in §10.3, one solution is

$$V = Ce^{lx + my + nz + pct}, \tag{11.118}$$

where l, m, n, p, and C are constants such that

$$l^2 + m^2 + n^2 = p^2 . \tag{11.119}$$

As shown by Whittaker, the general solution of the wave equation (11.117) can be written

$$V = \int_{-\pi}^{\pi} \int_{-\pi}^{\pi} f(x \sin u \cos v + y \sin u \sin v + z \cos u + ct, u, v)\, du\, dv . \tag{11.120}$$

Consider next the solution of (11.117) by the method of separation of variables. If the solution of (11.117) is taken to be of the form

$$V = U(x, y, z)e^{\pm ikct} , \tag{11.121}$$

or the similar forms

$$V = U(x, y, z)\begin{pmatrix}\sin \\ \cos\end{pmatrix} kct , \tag{11.122}$$

where k is a constant, we see that (11.117) reduces to

$$(\Delta + k^2)U = 0 , \tag{11.123}$$

where

$$\Delta \equiv \frac{\partial^2}{\partial x^2} + \frac{\partial^2}{\partial y^2} + \frac{\partial^2}{\partial z^2} .$$

Equation (11.123) is Helmholtz's equation; it is the space form of the wave equation. We shall now discuss in detail the application of the method of separation of variables as applied to (11.123).

If the solution of (11.123) is assumed to be of the form

$$U = X(x)Y(y)Z(z) ,$$

we see from §10.6 that X, Y, and Z satisfy the equations

$$\frac{d^2X}{dx^2} + (k^2 + a)X = 0 , \tag{11.124}$$

$$\frac{d^2Y}{dy^2} + bY = 0 , \tag{11.125}$$

$$\frac{d^2Z}{dz^2} - (a + b)Z = 0 , \tag{11.126}$$

where a and b are arbitrary constants of separation (which may be imaginary). We see that the solutions of the wave equation can be put in the form (11.118) with $p = \pm ik$, or in alternative forms such as

$$V = \binom{\sin}{\cos}\left(\sqrt{k^2 + a}\, x\right)\binom{\sin}{\cos}\left(\sqrt{b}\, y\right) e^{\pm\sqrt{a+b}\, z \pm ikct}$$

or

$$V = \binom{\sin}{\cos} lx \binom{\sin}{\cos} my \binom{\sin}{\cos} nz \binom{\sin}{\cos} kct,$$

where $l^2 + m^2 + n^2 = k^2$.

As in §11.3, the method of separation of variables can be applied to find solutions of Helmholtz's equation referred to other sets of orthogonal curvilinear coordinates, using the results of §11.2. We give here examples of these results.

CYLINDRICAL POLAR COORDINATES (ρ, ϕ, z)

$V = R(\rho)\Phi(\phi)Z(z)e^{\pm ikct}$, where, from (11.18),

$$\frac{d^2R}{d\rho^2} + \frac{1}{\rho}\frac{dR}{d\rho} + \left(\frac{a}{\rho^2} + b + k^2\right)R = 0, \qquad (11.127)$$

where a and b are arbitrary constants of separation, and Φ and Z satisfy (11.41) and (11.42). Putting $a = -\nu^2$ and $b = \beta^2$, we see, from §11.3, that there are particular solutions of the wave equation of the form

$$V = J_{\pm\nu}([\beta^2 + k^2]^{1/2}\, \rho)\binom{\sin}{\cos}\nu\phi\; e^{\pm\beta z}\binom{\sin}{\cos}kct.$$

SPHERICAL POLAR COORDINATES (r, θ, ϕ)

$V = R(r)\Theta(\theta)\Phi(\phi)e^{\pm ikct}$, where, from (11.19),

$$r^2\frac{d^2R}{dr^2} + 2r\frac{dR}{dr} + (k^2r^2 - a)R = 0, \qquad (11.128)$$

where a is an arbitrary constant of separation and Θ and Φ satisfy (11.45) and (11.46). We see, from Chapter 3, that the solutions of (11.128) can be expressed in terms of Bessel functions. Thus there are particular solutions of the wave equation of the form

$$V = r^{-(1/2)}J_{\pm[\nu+(1/2)]}(kr)\begin{pmatrix}P_\nu^\mu(\cos\theta)\\ Q_\nu^\mu(\cos\theta)\end{pmatrix}\binom{\sin}{\cos}\mu\phi\binom{\sin}{\cos}kct. \qquad (11.129)$$

COORDINATES OF CONFOCAL CONES (r, β, γ)

$V = R(r)B(\beta)C(\gamma)e^{\pm ikct}$, where, from (11.21), R satisfies (11.128) and B and C satisfy (11.52) and (11.53). Thus V can be expressed as the product of a Bessel function $R(r)$ and two Lamé functions $B(\beta)C(\gamma)$, with the appropriate parameters, times $e^{\pm ikct}$.

PARABOLIC CYLINDER COORDINATES (ξ, η, ζ)

$V = A(\xi)B(\eta)C(\zeta)e^{\pm ikct}$, where, from (11.22),

$$\frac{d^2C}{d\zeta^2} + (k^2 + a)C = 0, \tag{11.130}$$

where a is an arbitrary constant of separation and A and B satisfy (11.54) and (11.55). We see, from §11.3, that V can be expressed as the product of $\exp[\pm i(k^2 + a^2)^{1/2}\zeta \pm ikct]$ and two parabolic cylinder functions $A(\xi)B(\eta)$, with the appropriate parameters.

COORDINATES OF THE PARABOLOID OF REVOLUTION (ξ, η, ϕ)

$V = A(\xi)B(\eta)\Phi(\phi)e^{\pm ikct}$, where, from (11.23),

$$\frac{d^2A}{d\xi^2} + \frac{1}{\xi}\frac{dA}{d\xi} + \left(k^2\xi^2 - \frac{a}{\xi^2} - b\right)A = 0, \tag{11.131}$$

$$\frac{d^2B}{d\eta^2} + \frac{1}{\eta}\frac{dB}{d\eta} + \left(k^2\eta^2 - \frac{a}{\eta^2} + b\right)B = 0, \tag{11.132}$$

where a and b are arbitrary constants of separation and Φ satisfies (11.59). We see from §5.6 that the solutions of (11.131) and (11.132) can be expressed in terms of functions of the paraboloid of revolution. Thus V can be expressed as the product of $\exp(\pm ia^{1/2}\phi \pm ikct)$ and two functions of the paraboloid of revolution $A(\xi)B(\eta)$, with the appropriate parameters.

ELLIPTIC CYLINDER COORDINATES (u, v, w)

$V = A(u)B(v)C(w)e^{\pm ikct}$, where, from (11.24),

$$\frac{d^2C}{dw^2} + (k^2 + a)C = 0, \tag{11.133}$$

where a is an arbitrary constant of separation and A and B satisfy (11.60) and (11.61). We see, from §11.3, that V can be expressed as the product of $\exp[\pm i(k^2 + a)^{1/2}w \pm ikct]$ and two Mathieu functions $A(u)B(v)$, with the appropriate parameters.

11.8 Green's Function for Helmholtz's Equation

We shall now derive the Green's function for Helmholtz's equation (11.123). Consider first the one-dimensional form,

$$\frac{d^2U}{dx^2} + k^2U = 0. \tag{11.134}$$

Two elementary solutions of this equation are $Ce^{\pm ik(x-\xi)}$, where C and ξ are arbitrary constants. Now, from §1.14, the Green's function $G(x, \xi)$ must satisfy (11.134) at all points except the point $x = \xi$. Also dG/dx must have a discontinuity equal to -1 at the point $x = \xi$. It is readily seen that a Green's function satisfying these conditions is

$$G(x, \xi) = \left(\frac{i}{2k}\right) e^{ik|x-\xi|}. \tag{11.135}$$

Consider next the two-dimensional form of (11.123), referred to polar coordinates,

$$\frac{\partial^2 U}{\partial \rho^2} + \frac{1}{\rho}\frac{\partial U}{\partial \rho} + \frac{1}{\rho^2}\frac{\partial^2 U}{\partial \phi^2} + k^2 U = 0. \tag{11.136}$$

We see from §3.21 that, if U is independent of ϕ, (11.136) can be reduced to Bessel's equation of order zero. Thus one solution of (11.136) is

$$U = CY_0(k\rho)$$

where C is an arbitrary constant. More generally, any function of the form

$$U = CY_0(k\rho') \tag{11.137}$$

satisfies (11.123), where $\rho'^2 = (x - \xi)^2 + (y - \eta)^2$. Now, as $\rho' \to 0$, $Y_0(k\rho') \sim (2/\pi) \log \rho'$. Thus

$$\rho' Y_0(k\rho') \to 0 \qquad \text{as } \rho' \to 0.$$

Consider now the Green's function for (11.136). By analogy with (11.80) we see that for the two-dimensional wave equation

$$(\Delta + k^2)G = -\frac{\delta(\rho')}{2\pi\rho'}.$$

Proceeding as in §11.4, we find that

$$\int_C \frac{\partial G}{\partial n}\, ds = -1 - k^2 \iint G\rho'\, d\rho'\, d\theta \tag{11.138}$$

for any finite curve C surrounding the point $P(\xi, \eta)$, the double integral on the right side of (11.138) being taken over the area enclosed by C.

This equation will be satisfied by a function which (a) varies as $-(1/2\pi)\log \rho'$ as $\rho' \to 0$, and (b) is such that $\lim_{\rho' \to 0} (G\rho') = 0$. We see that one such function is $-\frac{1}{4}Y_0(k\rho')$. Thus the Green's function for the two-dimensional form of Helmholtz's equation (11.123) is

$$G(x, y; \xi, \eta) = -\tfrac{1}{4}Y_0(k\rho') + \gamma(x, y; \xi, \eta), \tag{11.139}$$

where

$$\rho'^2 = (x - \xi)^2 + (y - \eta)^2$$

and $\gamma(x, y; \xi, \eta)$ is a solution of (11.123), γ and its first and second derivatives being continuous in the simply connected region R for which (ξ, η) is an internal point. We see from (11.139) that G satisfies Helmholtz's equation at all points except the point (ξ, η).

Consider finally the three-dimensional form of Helmholtz's equation, referred to spherical polar coordinates,

$$\frac{\partial^2 U}{\partial r^2} + \frac{2}{r}\frac{\partial U}{\partial r} + \frac{1}{r^2}\frac{\partial^2 U}{\partial \theta^2} + \frac{\cot\theta}{r^2}\frac{\partial U}{\partial \theta} + \frac{1}{r^2 \sin^2\theta}\frac{\partial^2 U}{\partial \phi^2} + k^2 U = 0. \qquad (11.140)$$

It is easily verified that, if $r \neq 0$, one solution of (11.140) is

$$U = \frac{Ce^{ikr}}{r}$$

where C is an arbitrary constant. More generally, any function of the form

$$U = \frac{Ce^{ik\rho'}}{\rho'} \qquad (11.141)$$

satisfies (11.123), where

$$\rho'^2 = (x - \xi)^2 + (y - \eta)^2 + (z - \zeta)^2 .$$

By a similar analysis to that given above, we find that in the three-dimensional case the Green's function must (a) have a singularity of the type $(1/4\pi\rho')$ at the point (ξ, η), and (b) be such that $\lim_{\rho' \to 0} (G\rho'^2) = 0$. We see that one such function is $e^{ik\rho'}/4\pi\rho'$. Thus the Green's function for the three-dimensional form of Helmholtz's equation (11.123) is

$$G(x, y, z; \xi, \eta, \zeta) = \frac{e^{ik\rho'}}{4\pi\rho'} + \gamma(x, y, z; \xi, \eta, \zeta), \qquad (11.142)$$

where $\gamma(x, y, z; \xi, \eta, \zeta)$ is a solution of (11.123), γ and its first and second derivatives being continuous throughout the region R.

11.9 Other Solutions of the Wave Equation

In almost all the solutions of the wave equation given so far, it has been assumed that V is proportional to $\exp(\pm ikct)$. Other, more general, solutions can be obtained by regarding the wave equation (11.117) as a four-dimensional form of Laplace's equation. The methods used here are those given by Bateman [*199*, 1918]. On putting $s = ict$, (11.117) becomes

$$\frac{\partial^2 V}{\partial x^2} + \frac{\partial^2 V}{\partial y^2} + \frac{\partial^2 V}{\partial z^2} + \frac{\partial^2 V}{\partial s^2} = 0. \tag{11.143}$$

If V is independent of z, we see that (11.143) is equivalent to Laplace's equation in x, y, and s, and can be solved by the methods given in §11.3.

As shown by Bateman [*199*, 1918], (11.143) can also be transformed by the substitution

$$x = \rho \cos \phi, \qquad y = \rho \sin \phi, \qquad z = \sigma \cos \psi, \qquad s = \sigma \sin \psi.$$

Then, using the results of §11.2 for cylindrical polar coordinates, we find that (11.143) becomes

$$\frac{\partial^2 V}{\partial \rho^2} + \frac{1}{\rho}\frac{\partial V}{\partial \rho} + \frac{1}{\rho^2}\frac{\partial^2 V}{\partial \phi^2} + \frac{\partial^2 V}{\partial \sigma^2} + \frac{1}{\sigma}\frac{\partial V}{\partial \sigma} + \frac{1}{\sigma^2}\frac{\partial^2 V}{\partial \psi^2} = 0. \tag{11.144}$$

Applying the method of separation of variables to (11.144), we put $V = R(\rho)S(\sigma)\Phi(\phi)\Psi(\psi)$. Then

$$\frac{d^2 R}{d\rho^2} + \frac{1}{\rho}\frac{dR}{d\rho} + \left(c - \frac{a}{\rho^2}\right)R = 0, \tag{11.145}$$

$$\frac{d^2 S}{d\sigma^2} + \frac{1}{\sigma}\frac{dS}{d\sigma} - \left(c + \frac{b}{\sigma^2}\right)S = 0, \tag{11.146}$$

$$\frac{d^2\Phi}{d\phi^2} + a\Phi = 0, \tag{11.147}$$

$$\frac{d^2\Psi}{d\psi^2} + b\Psi = 0, \tag{11.148}$$

where a, b, and c are the arbitrary constants of separation. Now the solutions of (11.145) and (11.146) can be expressed in terms of Bessel functions. Put $a = \mu^2$, $b = v^2$, and $c = \beta^2$. Then, from §3.21, we see that the solution of (11.144) can be expressed in the form

$$V = \begin{pmatrix} J_\mu \\ J_{-\mu} \end{pmatrix}(\beta\rho)\begin{pmatrix} I_v \\ I_{-v} \end{pmatrix}(\beta\sigma)\begin{pmatrix} \sin \\ \cos \end{pmatrix}(\mu\phi)\begin{pmatrix} \sin \\ \cos \end{pmatrix}(v\psi).$$

Again, if in (11.143) we put

$$x = \tau \sin\theta \cos\phi, \quad y = \tau \sin\theta \sin\phi, \quad z = \tau \cos\theta \cos\psi, \quad s = \tau \cos\theta \sin\psi,$$

we find (Bateman [*200*, 1918]) that (11.143) becomes

$$\frac{\partial^2 V}{\partial \tau^2} + \frac{3}{\tau}\frac{\partial V}{\partial \tau} + \frac{1}{\tau^2}\frac{\partial^2 V}{\partial \theta^2} + \frac{2\cot 2\theta}{\tau^2}\frac{\partial V}{\partial \theta} + \frac{1}{\tau^2 \sin^2\theta}\frac{\partial^2 V}{\partial \phi^2} + \frac{1}{\tau^2\cos^2\theta}\frac{\partial^2 V}{\partial \psi^2} = 0. \quad (11.149)$$

Applying the method of separation of variables to (11.149), we put $V = T(\tau)\Theta(\theta)\Phi(\phi)\Psi(\psi)$. Then

$$\frac{d^2T}{d\tau^2} + \frac{3}{\tau}\frac{dT}{d\tau} + \frac{aT}{\tau^2} = 0, \quad (11.150)$$

$$\frac{d^2\Theta}{d\theta^2} + 2\cot 2\theta \frac{d\Theta}{d\theta} - \left(a + \frac{b}{\sin^2\theta} + \frac{c}{\cos^2\theta}\right)\Theta = 0, \quad (11.151)$$

$$\frac{d^2\Phi}{d\phi^2} + b\Phi = 0, \quad (11.152)$$

$$\frac{d^2\Psi}{d\psi^2} + c\Psi = 0, \quad (11.153)$$

where a, b, and c are the arbitrary constants of separation. Put $a = -4\nu(\nu+1)$, $b = p^2$, and $c = q^2$. We see that the solutions of (11.150) are of the form $\tau^{2\nu}$ and $\tau^{-2\nu-2}$. In (11.151), put $\xi = \sin^2\theta$. Then (11.151) becomes

$$\frac{d^2\Theta}{d\xi^2} + \left(\frac{1}{\xi} + \frac{1}{\xi - 1}\right)\frac{d\Theta}{d\xi} + \frac{1}{4}\left(a + \frac{b}{\xi} - \frac{c}{\xi - 1}\right)\frac{\Theta}{\xi(\xi - 1)} = 0. \quad (11.154)$$

As shown by Bateman (see also §6.22), the solutions of (11.154) can be expressed in terms of hypergeometric functions. On comparing (11.154) with the equation

$$\frac{d^2\Theta}{d\xi^2} + \left\{\frac{1 - \alpha - \alpha'}{\xi} + \frac{1 - \gamma - \gamma'}{\xi - 1}\right\}\frac{d\Theta}{d\xi} + \left\{-\frac{\alpha\alpha'}{\xi} + \frac{\gamma\gamma'}{\xi - 1} + \beta\beta'\right\}\frac{\Theta}{\xi(\xi - 1)} = 0, \quad (11.155)$$

where $\alpha + \alpha' + \beta + \beta' + \gamma + \gamma' = 1$, we find

$$\alpha = -\alpha' = \tfrac{1}{2}p, \qquad \beta = -\nu, \qquad \beta' = \nu + 1, \qquad \gamma = -\gamma' = \tfrac{1}{2}q.$$

Now, as shown in §6.22, the general solution of (11.155) is

$$\Theta = C_1\xi^\alpha(1 - \xi)^\gamma F(A, B; C; \xi) + C_2\xi^{\alpha+1-C}(1 - \xi)^\gamma \times F(A - C + 1, B - C + 1; 2 - C; \xi), \quad (11.156)$$

where

$$\begin{aligned} A &= \alpha + \beta + \gamma = \tfrac{1}{2}(p+q) - \nu, \\ B &= \alpha + \beta' + \gamma = \tfrac{1}{2}(p+q) + \nu + 1, \\ C &= 1 + \alpha - \alpha' = p + 1, \end{aligned} \tag{11.157}$$

and C_1 and C_2 are arbitrary constants. Thus the solution of (11.149) can be expressed in the form

$$V = \begin{pmatrix} \tau^{2\nu} \\ \tau^{-2\nu-2} \end{pmatrix} \Theta(\theta) \begin{pmatrix} \sin \\ \cos \end{pmatrix} (p\phi) \begin{pmatrix} \sin \\ \cos \end{pmatrix} (q\psi), \tag{11.158}$$

where

$$\Theta = \sin^p\theta \cos^q\theta [C_1 F(A, B; C; \sin^2\theta) + C_2 \sin^{2-2C}\theta \times F(A - C + 1, B - C + 1; 2 - C; \sin^2\theta)], \tag{11.159}$$

A, B, and C being given by (11.157).

More generally, as shown by Bateman [*200*, 1918], if $V = F(\tau, \theta, \phi, \psi)$ is a solution of the wave equation (11.149), then another solution is

$$V = \frac{1}{\tau^2} F\left(\frac{1}{\tau}, \theta, \phi, \psi\right). \tag{11.160}$$

This can be stated in an alternative form (Bateman [*200*, 1918]). If $V = F(x, y, z, s)$ is a solution of the wave equation (11.143), then

$$V = \frac{1}{\tau^2} F\left(\frac{x}{\tau^2}, \frac{y}{\tau^2}, \frac{z}{\tau^2}, \frac{s}{\tau^2}\right) \tag{11.161}$$

is also a solution, where

$$\tau^2 = x^2 + y^2 + z^2 + s^2.$$

If $p = -q = -\mu$, we see that (11.159) reduces to (Erdélyi [*125*, 1953a])

$$\Theta = C_1' P_\nu^\mu(\cos 2\theta) + C_2' Q_\nu^\mu(\sin 2\theta), \tag{11.162}$$

where C_1' and C_2' are two arbitrary constants and P_ν^μ and Q_ν^μ are the Legendre functions of the first and second kinds. Thus the solution of (11.149) can be expressed in the form

$$V = \begin{pmatrix} \tau^{2\nu} \\ \tau^{-2\nu-2} \end{pmatrix} \begin{pmatrix} P_\nu^\mu \\ Q_\nu^\mu \end{pmatrix} (\cos 2\theta) \begin{pmatrix} \sin \\ \cos \end{pmatrix} (\mu\phi) \begin{pmatrix} \sin \\ \cos \end{pmatrix} (\mu\psi), \tag{11.163}$$

or in the alternative forms

$$V = \begin{pmatrix} \tau^{2\nu} \\ \tau^{-2\nu-2} \end{pmatrix} \begin{pmatrix} P_\nu^\mu \\ Q_\nu^\mu \end{pmatrix} (\cos 2\theta) \begin{pmatrix} \sin \\ \cos \end{pmatrix} (\mu[\phi \pm \psi]). \tag{11.164}$$

These solutions of the wave equation are similar to those given for Laplace's equation by (11.48).

More generally, as shown by Bateman [*201*, 1918], if $V = F(r, \theta, \phi)$ is a solution of Laplace's equation (in spherical polar coordinates), then $V = F(\tau^2, 2\theta, \phi \pm \psi)$ is a solution of the wave equation (11.143).

THE RETARDED POTENTIAL

If, in spherical polar coordinates, V depends on r and t only, we see, from §11.2, that

$$\frac{\partial^2 V}{\partial r^2} + \frac{2}{r}\frac{\partial V}{\partial r} = \frac{1}{c^2}\frac{\partial^2 V}{\partial t^2};$$

that is,

$$\frac{\partial^2}{\partial r^2}(rV) = \frac{1}{c^2}\frac{\partial^2}{\partial t^2}(rV). \tag{11.165}$$

Now, from §10.3, one solution of (11.165) is

$$V = \frac{1}{r}\phi\left(t - \frac{r}{c}\right), \tag{11.166}$$

where ϕ is an arbitrary function. The corresponding solution of Laplace's equation is $V = 1/r$. The solution of the wave equation given by (11.166) is sometimes called the *retarded potential.*

11.10 Solutions of Lorenz's Equation

The solutions of Lorenz's equation

$$\frac{\partial^2 V}{\partial x^2} + \frac{\partial^2 V}{\partial y^2} + \frac{\partial^2 V}{\partial z^2} - \frac{1}{c^2}\frac{\partial^2 V}{\partial t^2} = f(x, y, z, t) \tag{11.167}$$

can be found by using the methods given in Chapter 10. We shall here discuss in detail the application of the method of separation of variables (§10.6). As in the case of Poisson's equation, this method is capable of providing an immediate answer to the problem if $f(x, y, z, t)$ has certain forms. We shall here confine our attention to those cases in which

$$f(x, y, z, t) = F(x, y, z)e^{\pm ikct}, \tag{11.168}$$

where k is a constant. We see that a solution of (11.167) is

$$V = U(x, y, z)e^{\pm ikct}, \tag{11.169}$$

where

$$(\Delta + k^2)U = \frac{\partial^2 U}{\partial x^2} + \frac{\partial^2 U}{\partial y^2} + \frac{\partial^2 U}{\partial z^2} + k^2 U = F(x, y, z). \quad (11.170)$$

This is the space form of Lorenz's equation; it is also known as the non-homogeneous Helmholtz equation.

If $f(x, y, z, t) = g(x)Y(y)Z(z)e^{\pm ikct}$, there will be a particular integral of (11.170) of the form

$$U = \bar{X}(x)Y(y)Z(z),$$

where $\bar{X}$ satisfies the equation

$$\frac{d^2\bar{X}}{dx^2} + (k^2 + a)\bar{X} = g(x), \quad (11.171)$$

where a is a constant of separation and Y and Z satisfy (11.125) and (11.126). The solution of (11.171) can be found by the methods of Chapter 2; thus, if

$$f(x, y, z, t) = g(x)\binom{\sin}{\cos}(\sqrt{b}\, y)e^{\pm\sqrt{a+b}\, z \pm ikct},$$

a particular integral of (11.167) is

$$V = \bar{X}(x)\binom{\sin}{\cos}(\sqrt{b}\, y)e^{\pm\sqrt{a+b}\, z \pm ikct}.$$

We shall now give examples of the application of the method of separation of variables in other sets of orthogonal curvilinear coordinates, using the results of §11.2.

CYLINDRICAL POLAR COORDINATES (ρ, ϕ, z)

If $f = g(\rho)\Phi(\phi)Z(z)e^{\pm ikct}$, $V = \bar{R}(\rho)\Phi(\phi)Z(z)e^{\pm ikct}$, where, from (11.18),

$$\frac{d^2\bar{R}}{d\rho^2} + \frac{1}{\rho}\frac{d\bar{R}}{d\rho} + \left(\frac{a}{\rho^2} + b + k^2\right)\bar{R} = g(\rho), \quad (11.172)$$

where a and b are arbitrary constants of separation and Φ and Z satisfy (11.41) and (11.42). If $g(\rho) = \rho^{\mu-1}$, where μ is any constant, we see, from §3.21, that the solutions of (11.172) can be expressed in terms of Lommel functions. Putting $a = -\nu^2$ and $b = \beta^2$, we see that if $f = \rho^{\mu-1}\Phi(\phi)Z(z)e^{\pm ikct}$, a particular solution of Lorenz's equation is

$$V = (\beta^2 + k^2)^{-(1/2)\mu-(1/2)} s_{\mu,\nu}([\beta^2 + k^2]^{1/2}\rho)\Phi(\phi)Z(z)e^{\pm ikct}, \quad (11.173)$$

where s is the Lommel function defined in §3.16.

SPHERICAL POLAR COORDINATES (r, θ, ϕ)

If $f = R(r)g(\theta)\Phi(\phi)e^{\pm ikct}/r^2$, $V = R(r)\overline{\Theta}(\theta)\Phi(\phi)e^{\pm ikct}$, where, from (11.19), R, $\overline{\Theta}$, and Φ satisfy (11.128), (11.87), and (11.46), respectively. As in §11.5, we find that, if $g(\theta) = (\cos\theta)^{2\sigma-2}(\sin\theta)^{\mu+2\tau-2}$ where σ, μ, and τ are any constants, $\overline{\Theta}(\theta)$ can be expressed in terms of the nonhomogeneous Legendre functions. Thus, if $f = (\cos\theta)^{2\sigma-2}(\sin\theta)^{\mu+2\tau-2}R(r)\Phi(\phi)e^{\pm ikct}/r^2$, there are particular integrals of Lorenz's equation of the form

$$V = R(r)t_{\nu,\sigma}^{\mu,\tau}(\cos\theta)\Phi(\phi)e^{\pm ikct}, \tag{11.174}$$

where t is the nonhomogeneous Legendre function defined in §7.22. We see, from §11.7, that $R(r)$ will be of the form $r^{-1/2}J_{\pm(\nu+1/2)}(kr)$.

COORDINATES OF CONFOCAL CONES (r, β, γ)

If $f = R(r)g(\beta)C(\gamma)e^{\pm ikct}/\{r^2[(\text{sn}\,\gamma)^2 - (\text{sn}\,\beta)^2]\}$, $V = R(r)\overline{B}(\beta)C(\gamma)e^{\pm ikct}$, where, from (11.21), R, $\overline{B}$, and C satisfy (11.128), (11.94), and (11.53), respectively. We see that $R(r)$ can be expressed in terms of Bessel functions. If $g(\beta) = [\text{sn}\,\beta]^{2\sigma-2}$, where σ is a constant, then, as shown in §11.5, $\overline{B}(\beta)$ can be expressed in terms of nonhomogeneous Heun functions. Thus, if $f = R(r)[\text{sn}\,\beta]^{2\sigma-2}C(\gamma)e^{\pm ikct}/\{r^2[(\text{sn}\,\gamma)^2 - (\text{sn}\,\beta)^2]\}$, V can be expressed as the product of $R(r)\exp \pm ikct$, a nonhomogeneous Heun function $\overline{B}(\beta)$, and a Lamé function $C(\gamma)$, with the appropriate parameters.

PARABOLIC CYLINDER COORDINATES (ξ, η, ζ)

If $f = g(\xi)B(\eta)C(\zeta)e^{\pm ikct}/(\xi^2 + \eta^2)$, $V = \overline{A}(\xi)B(\eta)C(\zeta)e^{\pm ikct}$, where, from (11.22), $\overline{A}$, B, and C satisfy (11.95), (11.55), and (11.130), respectively. If $g(\xi) = \xi^\sigma$, where σ is any constant, we see from §11.5 that $\overline{A}(\xi)$ can be expressed in terms of nonhomogeneous parabolic cylinder functions. Thus, if $f = \xi^\sigma B(\eta)\{\exp[\pm i(k^2 + a)^{1/2}\zeta \pm ikct]\}/(\xi^2 + \eta^2)$, V can be expressed as the product of $\exp[\pm i(k^2 + a)^{1/2}\zeta \pm ikct]$, and two parabolic cylinder functions $\overline{A}(\xi)B(\eta)$ (one nonhomogeneous and one homogeneous), with the appropriate parameters.

COORDINATES OF THE PARABOLOID OF REVOLUTION (ξ, η, ϕ)

If $f = g(\xi)B(\eta)\Phi(\phi)e^{\pm ikct}/(\xi^2 + \eta^2)$, $V = \overline{A}(\xi)B(\eta)\Phi(\phi)e^{\pm ikct}$, where, from (11.23),

$$\frac{d^2\overline{A}}{d\xi^2} + \frac{1}{\xi}\frac{d\overline{A}}{d\xi} + \left(k^2\xi^2 - \frac{a}{\xi^2} - b\right)\overline{A} = g(\xi), \tag{11.175}$$

where k, a, and b are constants (a and b are arbitrary constants of separation), and B and Φ satisfy (11.132) and (11.59). If $g(\xi) = \xi^\sigma$, where σ is any constant, we see, from §5.6, that the solution of (11.175) can be expressed in terms of nonhomogeneous functions of the paraboloid of revolution. Thus, if $f = \xi^\sigma B(\eta)\exp[\pm ia^{1/2}\phi \pm ikct]$, V can be expressed as the product of

$\exp[\pm ia^{1/2}\phi \pm ikct]$ and two functions of the paraboloid of revolution $\bar{A}(\xi)B(\eta)$ (one nonhomogeneous, one homogeneous), with the appropriate parameters.

ELLIPTIC CYLINDER COORDINATES (u, v, w)

If $f = g(u)B(v)C(w)e^{\pm ikct}/(\sinh^2 u + \sin^2 v)$, $V = \bar{A}(u)B(v)C(w)e^{\pm ikct}$, where, from (11.24), $\bar{A}$, B, and C satisfy (11.97), (11.61), and (11.133), respectively. If $g(u) = (\sinh u)^{2\sigma-2}$, where σ is any constant, we see, from §11.5, that $\bar{A}(u)$ can be expressed in terms of nonhomogeneous Mathieu functions. Thus, if

$$f = \frac{(\sinh u)^{2\sigma-2}B(v)\{\exp[\pm i(k^2 + a)^{1/2}w \pm ikct]\}}{(\sinh^2 u + \sin^2 v)},$$

V can be expressed as the product of $\exp[\pm i(k^2 + a)^{1/2}w \pm ikct]$ and two Mathieu functions $\bar{A}(u)B(v)$ with the appropriate parameters.

The remarks made in §11.5 on further extensions of the use of the method of separation of variables apply here also.

11.11 Solutions of Lorenz's Equation Using Green's Functions

The Green's functions for Helmholtz's equation were given in §11.8. Using the results of §10.8, we can now determine the solution of Lorenz's equation in terms of multiple integrals. We shall consider first the space form of Lorenz's equation, given by

$$(\Delta + k^2)U = \frac{\partial^2 U}{\partial x^2} + \frac{\partial^2 U}{\partial y^2} + \frac{\partial^2 U}{\partial z^2} + k^2 U = F(x,y,z). \qquad (11.176)$$

From (11.142), together with (10.110), we see that, if $F(x, y, z)$ is any function which, together with its first derivatives, is continuous in the region R and vanishes outside R, a particular solution of (11.176) is

$$U = -\frac{1}{4\pi}\iiint \frac{e^{ik\rho'}}{\rho'} F(\xi, \eta, \zeta)\, d\xi\, d\eta\, d\zeta, \qquad (11.177)$$

where $\rho'^2 = (x-\xi)^2 + (y-\eta)^2 + (z-\zeta)^2$ and the integral is taken over the region R for which the point $P(\xi, \eta, \zeta)$ is an interior point.

Then if, in (11.167),

$$f(x, y, z, t) = e^{\pm ikct}F(x, y, z),$$

we see that

$$V(x, y, z, t) = e^{\pm ikct}U(x, y, z). \qquad (11.178)$$

Similarly, in the two-dimensional case in which U satisfies the equation

$$\frac{\partial^2 U}{\partial x^2} + \frac{\partial^2 U}{\partial y^2} + k^2 U = F(x, y), \tag{11.179}$$

a particular solution of (11.179), is, from (11.139),

$$U = \tfrac{1}{4} \iint Y_0(k\rho')F(\xi, \eta)\, d\xi\, d\eta, \tag{11.180}$$

where

$$\rho'^2 = (x - \xi)^2 + (y - \eta)^2.$$

More generally, consider Lorenz's equation

$$\frac{\partial^2 V}{\partial x^2} + \frac{\partial^2 V}{\partial y^2} + \frac{\partial^2 V}{\partial z^2} - \frac{1}{c^2}\frac{\partial^2 V}{\partial t^2} = f(x, y, z, t). \tag{11.181}$$

By Fourier's theorem (Webster [*219*, 1947]) we may write

$$V(x, y, z, t) = \frac{1}{2\pi} \int_{-\infty}^{\infty} \int_{-\infty}^{\infty} V(x, y, z, \alpha) e^{i\lambda(t-\alpha)}\, d\alpha\, d\lambda, \tag{11.182}$$

and similarly for f. Using (11.177), (11.178), and (11.182), with $k = \lambda/c$, we can obtain a particular solution of (11.181) in the form (Webster [*221*, 1947])

$$\begin{aligned} V &= -\frac{1}{8\pi^2} \int_{-\infty}^{\infty} \int_{-\infty}^{\infty} d\alpha\, d\lambda \iiint \frac{e^{i\lambda(t-\alpha+\rho'/c)}}{\rho'} f(\xi, \eta, \zeta, \alpha)\, d\xi\, d\eta\, d\zeta \\ &= -\frac{1}{4\pi} \iiint \frac{f(\xi, \eta, \zeta, t + \rho'/c)}{\rho'}\, d\xi\, d\eta\, d\zeta, \end{aligned} \tag{11.183}$$

where the triple integral is taken over the region R.

Another particular integral of (11.181) is

$$V = -\frac{1}{4\pi} \iiint \frac{f(\xi, \eta, \zeta, t - \rho'/c)}{\rho'}\, d\xi\, d\eta\, d\zeta. \tag{11.184}$$

We see, from §11.9, that this is the volume integral of the retarded potential.

11.12 Other Solutions of Lorenz's Equation

We shall now obtain other solutions of Lorenz's equation which are analogous to those given in §11.9 for the wave equation.

On putting $s = ict$, (11.167) becomes

$$\frac{\partial^2 V}{\partial x^2} + \frac{\partial^2 V}{\partial y^2} + \frac{\partial^2 V}{\partial z^2} + \frac{\partial^2 V}{\partial s^2} = f\left(x, y, z, \frac{s}{ic}\right). \tag{11.185}$$

This equation, which is a four-dimensional form of Poisson's equation, can be solved by the methods given in Chapter 10. In certain cases we can use the method of separation of variables. If V and f are independent of z, we see that (11.185) is equivalent to Poisson's equation in x, y, and s, and can be solved by the methods given in §11.5.

As in §11.9, we put $x = \rho \cos \phi$, $y = \rho \sin \phi$, $z = \sigma \cos \psi$, and $s = \sigma \sin \psi$. Then, using the results of §11.2, we find that (11.185) becomes

$$\frac{\partial^2 V}{\partial \rho^2} + \frac{1}{\rho}\frac{\partial V}{\partial \rho} + \frac{1}{\rho^2}\frac{\partial^2 V}{\partial \phi^2} + \frac{\partial^2 V}{\partial \sigma^2} + \frac{1}{\sigma}\frac{\partial V}{\partial \sigma} + \frac{1}{\sigma^2}\frac{\partial^2 V}{\partial \psi^2} = f. \tag{11.186}$$

If $f = g(\rho)S(\sigma)\Phi(\phi)\Psi(\psi)$, $V = \bar{R}(\rho)S(\sigma)\Phi(\phi)\Psi(\psi)$, where

$$\frac{d^2\bar{R}}{d\rho^2} + \frac{1}{\rho}\frac{d\bar{R}}{d\rho} + \left(c - \frac{a}{\rho^2}\right)\bar{R} = g(\rho), \tag{11.187}$$

where a and c are arbitrary constants of separation and S, Φ, and Ψ satisfy (11.146) to (11.148). If $g(\rho) = \rho^{\mu-1}$, where μ is any constant, we see, from §3.21, that the solutions of (11.187) can be expressed in terms of Lommel functions. We find that, if

$$f = \rho^{\mu-1}\begin{pmatrix} I_\nu \\ I_{-\nu} \end{pmatrix}(\beta\sigma)\begin{pmatrix} \sin \\ \cos \end{pmatrix}(\mu\phi)\begin{pmatrix} \sin \\ \cos \end{pmatrix}(\nu\psi),$$

a particular solution of (11.186) is

$$V = \beta^{-\mu-1}s_{\mu,\nu}(\beta\rho)\begin{pmatrix} I_\nu \\ I_{-\nu} \end{pmatrix}(\beta\sigma)\begin{pmatrix} \sin \\ \cos \end{pmatrix}(\mu\phi)\begin{pmatrix} \sin \\ \cos \end{pmatrix}(\nu\psi).$$

If in (11.185) we put $x = \tau \sin \theta \cos \phi$, $y = \tau \sin \theta \sin \phi$, $z = \tau \cos \theta \cos \psi$, and $s = \tau \cos \theta \sin \psi$, (11.185) becomes

$$\frac{\partial^2 V}{\partial \tau^2} + \frac{3}{\tau}\frac{\partial V}{\partial \tau} + \frac{1}{\tau^2}\frac{\partial^2 V}{\partial \theta^2} + \frac{2 \cot 2\theta}{\tau^2}\frac{\partial V}{\partial \theta} + \frac{1}{\tau^2 \sin^2 \theta}\frac{\partial^2 V}{\partial \phi^2} + \frac{1}{\tau^2 \cos^2 \theta}\frac{\partial^2 V}{\partial \psi^2} = f. \tag{11.188}$$

If $f = T(\tau)g(\theta)\Phi(\phi)\Psi(\psi)/\tau^2$, $V = T(\tau)\bar{\Theta}(\theta)\Phi(\phi)\Psi(\psi)$, where

$$\frac{d^2\bar{\Theta}}{d\theta^2} + 2 \cot 2\theta \frac{d\bar{\Theta}}{d\theta} - \left(a + \frac{b}{\sin^2 \theta} + \frac{c}{\cos^2 \theta}\right)\bar{\Theta} = g(\theta), \tag{11.189}$$

where a, b, and c are arbitrary constants of separation and T, Φ, and Ψ satisfy (11.150), (11.152), and (11.153). In (11.189), put $\xi = \sin^2 \theta$. Then (11.189) becomes

$$\frac{d^2\bar{\Theta}}{d\xi^2} + \left(\frac{1}{\xi} + \frac{1}{\xi - 1}\right)\frac{d\bar{\Theta}}{d\xi} + \frac{1}{4}\left(a + \frac{b}{\xi} - \frac{c}{\xi - 1}\right)\frac{\bar{\Theta}}{\xi(\xi - 1)} = \frac{g(\theta)}{4\xi(1 - \xi)}. \tag{11.190}$$

Now, from (6.263), the equation

$$\frac{d^2\overline{\Theta}}{d\xi^2} + \left\{\frac{1-\alpha-\alpha'}{\xi} + \frac{1-\gamma-\gamma'}{\xi-1}\right\}\frac{d\overline{\Theta}}{d\xi} + \left\{-\frac{\alpha\alpha'}{\xi} + \frac{\gamma\gamma'}{\xi-1} + \beta\beta'\right\}\frac{\overline{\Theta}}{\xi(\xi-1)}$$
$$= \xi^{\alpha+\sigma-2}(1-\xi)^{\gamma+\rho-2}, \quad (11.191)$$

where $\alpha + \alpha' + \beta + \beta' + \gamma + \gamma' = 1$ and σ and ρ are any constants, has a particular integral

$$\overline{\Theta} = \xi^{\alpha}(1-\xi)^{\gamma} C_{1,\sigma}^{(\rho)}(A, B; C; \xi),$$

where the C function is the nonhomogeneous hypergeometric function defined in §6.20, and A, B, and C are given by (11.157).

Thus, if

$$f = \begin{pmatrix}\tau^{2\nu-2} \\ \tau^{-2\nu-4}\end{pmatrix}(\sin\theta)^{p+2\sigma-2}(\cos\theta)^{q+2\rho-2}\begin{pmatrix}\sin \\ \cos\end{pmatrix}(p\phi)\begin{pmatrix}\sin \\ \cos\end{pmatrix}(q\psi),$$

a particular integral of (11.188) is

$$V = \frac{1}{4}\begin{pmatrix}\tau^{2\nu} \\ \tau^{-2\nu-2}\end{pmatrix}\overline{\Theta}(\theta)\begin{pmatrix}\sin \\ \cos\end{pmatrix}(p\phi)\begin{pmatrix}\sin \\ \cos\end{pmatrix}(q\psi), \quad (11.192)$$

where $\overline{\Theta} = \sin^p\theta\cos^q\theta\, C_{1,\sigma}^{(\rho)}(A, B; C; \sin^2\theta)$, where A, B, and C are given by (11.157).

More generally, if $V = F(\tau, \theta, \phi, \psi)$ is a solution of Lorenz's equation

$$\Box V = f(\tau, \theta, \phi, \psi), \quad (11.193)$$

then the equation

$$\Box V = \frac{1}{\tau^6} f\left(\frac{1}{\tau}, \theta, \phi, \psi\right) \quad (11.194)$$

has the particular integral

$$V = \frac{1}{\tau^2} F\left(\frac{1}{\tau}, \theta, \phi, \psi\right). \quad (11.195)$$

This can be stated in an alternative form. If $V = F(x, y, z, s)$ is a solution of Lorenz's equation

$$\Box V = \frac{\partial^2 V}{\partial x^2} + \frac{\partial^2 V}{\partial y^2} + \frac{\partial^2 V}{\partial z^2} + \frac{\partial^2 V}{\partial s^2} = f(x, y, z, s), \quad (11.196)$$

then the equation

$$\Box V = \frac{1}{\tau^6} f\left(\frac{x}{\tau^2}, \frac{y}{\tau^2}, \frac{z}{\tau^2}, \frac{s}{\tau^2}\right) \tag{11.197}$$

has a particular integral

$$V = \frac{1}{\tau^2} F\left(\frac{x}{\tau^2}, \frac{y}{\tau^2}, \frac{z}{\tau^2}, \frac{s}{\tau^2}\right), \tag{11.198}$$

where $\tau^2 = x^2 + y^2 + z^2 + s^2$.

If $b = c = \mu^2$, (11.189) becomes, with $a = -4\nu(\nu+1)$ and $u = \cos 2\theta$,

$$(1-u^2)\frac{d^2\overline{\Theta}}{du^2} - 2u\frac{d\overline{\Theta}}{du} + [\nu(\nu+1) - \mu^2(1-u^2)^{-1}]\overline{\Theta} = \frac{1}{4}g(\theta). \tag{11.199}$$

Now, if $g(\theta) = (\cos 2\theta)^{2\sigma-2}(\sin 2\theta)^{\mu+2\rho-2}$, where σ and ρ are any constants, we see from §7.22 that the solution of (11.199) can be expressed in terms of nonhomogeneous Legendre functions. Thus, if

$$f = \begin{pmatrix} \tau^{2\nu-2} \\ \tau^{-2\nu-4} \end{pmatrix} (\cos 2\theta)^{2\sigma-2}(\sin 2\theta)^{\mu+2\rho-2} \begin{pmatrix} \sin \\ \cos \end{pmatrix}(\mu\phi) \begin{pmatrix} \sin \\ \cos \end{pmatrix}(\mu\psi),$$

a particular integral of (11.188) is

$$V = \frac{1}{4}\begin{pmatrix} \tau^{2\nu} \\ \tau^{-2\nu-2} \end{pmatrix} t_{\nu,\sigma}^{\mu,\rho}(\cos 2\theta) \begin{pmatrix} \sin \\ \cos \end{pmatrix}(\mu\phi) \begin{pmatrix} \sin \\ \cos \end{pmatrix}(\mu\psi), \tag{11.200}$$

where t is the nonhomogeneous Legendre function defined in §7.22. These solutions of Lorenz's equation are similar to those given for Poisson's equation by (11.89). Alternatively, we see that, if

$$f = \begin{pmatrix} \tau^{2\nu-2} \\ \tau^{-2\nu-4} \end{pmatrix} (\cos 2\theta)^{2\sigma-2}(\sin 2\theta)^{\mu+2\rho-2} \begin{pmatrix} \sin \\ \cos \end{pmatrix}(\mu[\phi \pm \psi]),$$

a particular integral of (11.188) is

$$V = \frac{1}{4}\begin{pmatrix} \tau^{2\nu} \\ \tau^{-2\nu-2} \end{pmatrix} t_{\nu,\sigma}^{\mu,\rho}(\cos 2\theta) \begin{pmatrix} \sin \\ \cos \end{pmatrix}(\mu[\phi \pm \psi]). \tag{11.201}$$

More generally, if $V = F(r, \theta, \phi)$ is a solution of Poisson's equation (in spherical polar coordinates)

$$\Delta V = f(r, \theta, \phi),$$

then

$$V = F(\tau^2, 2\theta, \phi \pm \psi) \tag{11.202}$$

is a solution of Lorenz's equation

$$\square V = 4\tau^2 f(\tau^2, \theta, \phi \pm \psi). \tag{11.203}$$

11.13 Solutions of the Diffusion Equation

The properties of solutions of the diffusion equation

$$\frac{\partial^2 V}{\partial x^2} + \frac{\partial^2 V}{\partial y^2} + \frac{\partial^2 V}{\partial z^2} - \frac{1}{k}\frac{\partial V}{\partial t} = 0 \tag{11.204}$$

are fully set out in Carslaw and Jaeger [1959], Webster [1947], Bateman [1918], and Sneddon [1957]. We shall here briefly summarize various properties of these solutions.

We see at once that, if the solution of (11.204) is taken to be of the form

$$V = \Phi(x, y, z)e^{-k\lambda^2 t},$$

where λ is a constant, (11.204) reduces to

$$(\Delta + \lambda^2)\Phi = 0. \tag{11.205}$$

Equation (11.205) is identical with Helmholtz's equation (11.123), solutions of which were discussed in detail in §11.7. In this section we shall consider other methods of solving (11.204). We follow the method given by Bateman [*211*, 1918].

Consider first the one-dimensional form of (11.204),

$$\frac{\partial^2 V}{\partial x^2} - \frac{1}{k}\frac{\partial V}{\partial t} = 0. \tag{11.206}$$

We take new variables, $s = x^2/4kt$ and t. Equation (11.206) then becomes

$$s\frac{\partial^2 V}{\partial s^2} + (\tfrac{1}{2} + s)\frac{\partial V}{\partial s} - t\frac{\partial V}{\partial t} = 0. \tag{11.207}$$

If the solutions of (11.207) are taken to be of the form $V = S(s)T(t)$ we find that

$$s\frac{d^2 S}{ds^2} + (\tfrac{1}{2} + s)\frac{dS}{ds} - \nu S = 0 \tag{11.208}$$

and

$$t\frac{dT}{dt} - \nu T = 0, \tag{11.209}$$

where ν is the arbitrary constant of separation.

From §4.25, we see that the solution of (11.208) can be expressed in terms of confluent hypergeometric functions. Thus a solution of (11.206) is

$$V = t^{\nu}\Phi\left(-\nu, \tfrac{1}{2}; -\frac{x^2}{4kt}\right)$$

$$= t^{\nu} \exp\left(-\frac{x^2}{4kt}\right)\Phi\left(\nu + \tfrac{1}{2}, \tfrac{1}{2}; \frac{x^2}{4kt}\right), \tag{11.210}$$

where Φ is the confluent hypergeometric function (see §4.2). In particular, with $\nu = -\frac{1}{2}$, one solution of (11.206) is

$$V = t^{-1/2} \exp\left(\frac{-x^2}{4kt}\right). \tag{11.211}$$

More generally, as shown by Bateman [*212*, 1918], if $V = F(x, t)$ is one solution of (11.206), then another solution is

$$V = t^{-1/2} \exp\left(\frac{-x^2}{4kt}\right) F\left(\frac{x}{t}, -\frac{1}{t}\right). \tag{11.212}$$

Consider next the two-dimensional form of (11.204),

$$\frac{\partial^2 V}{\partial x^2} + \frac{\partial^2 V}{\partial y^2} - \frac{1}{k}\frac{\partial V}{\partial t} = 0. \tag{11.213}$$

As shown by Bateman [*213*, 1918], (11.213) can be transformed by the substitution

$$x = \rho \cos \phi, \qquad y = \rho \sin \phi, \qquad s = \frac{\rho^2}{4kt}.$$

We find that (11.213) becomes (with independent variables s, ϕ, t)

$$s\frac{\partial^2 V}{\partial s^2} + (1 + s)\frac{\partial V}{\partial s} + \frac{1}{4s}\frac{\partial^2 V}{\partial \phi^2} - t\frac{\partial V}{\partial t} = 0. \tag{11.214}$$

If the solutions of (11.214) are taken to be of the form $V = S(s)T(t)U(\phi)$, we find that

$$s\frac{d^2 S}{ds^2} + (1 + s)\frac{dS}{ds} - \left(\nu + \frac{\mu^2}{4s}\right)S = 0, \tag{11.215}$$

$$t\frac{dT}{dt} - \nu T = 0, \tag{11.216}$$

and

$$\frac{d^2 U}{d\phi^2} + \mu^2 U = 0, \tag{11.217}$$

where μ and ν are arbitrary constants of separation.

The solutions of (11.215) can be expressed in terms of confluent hypergeometric functions. Thus a solution of (11.214) is

$$V = t^{\nu}\left(\frac{\rho^2}{4kt}\right)^{(1/2)\mu} \Phi\left(\tfrac{1}{2}\mu - \nu, 1 + \mu; \frac{-\rho^2}{4kt}\right)\binom{\sin}{\cos}(\mu\phi)$$

$$= t^{\nu}\left(\frac{\rho^2}{4kt}\right)^{(1/2)\mu} \exp\left(\frac{-\rho^2}{4kt}\right)\Phi\left(1 + \tfrac{1}{2}\mu + \nu, 1 + \mu; \frac{\rho^2}{4kt}\right)\binom{\sin}{\cos}(\mu\phi). \tag{11.218}$$

In particular, with $\mu = 0$ and $\nu = -1$, one solution of (11.214) is

$$V = \frac{1}{t}\exp\left(\frac{-\rho^2}{4kt}\right). \tag{11.219}$$

More generally, as shown by Bateman [*214*, 1918], if $V = F(s, t, \phi)$ is a solution of (11.214), another solution is

$$V = \frac{1}{t}\exp\left(\frac{-\rho^2}{4kt}\right)F\left(-s, -\frac{1}{t}, \phi\right). \tag{11.220}$$

This can be put in an alternative form. If $V = F(x, y, t)$ is a solution of (11.213), another solution is

$$V = \frac{1}{t}\exp\left[\frac{-(x^2 + y^2)}{4kt}\right]F\left(\frac{x}{t}, \frac{y}{t}, -\frac{1}{t}\right). \tag{11.221}$$

Finally, consider the three-dimensional form of the diffusion equation (11.204). As shown by Bateman [*214*, 1918], (11.204) can be transformed by the substitution

$$x = r\sin\theta\cos\phi, \qquad y = r\sin\theta\sin\phi, \qquad z = r\cos\theta, \qquad s = \frac{r^2}{4kt}.$$

We find that (11.204) becomes (with independent variables s, θ, ϕ, t)

$$s\frac{\partial^2 V}{\partial s^2} + \left(\frac{3}{2} + s\right)\frac{\partial V}{\partial s} + \frac{1}{4s}\frac{\partial^2 V}{\partial \theta^2} + \frac{\cot\theta}{4s}\frac{\partial V}{\partial \theta} + \frac{1}{4s\sin^2\theta}\frac{\partial^2 V}{\partial \phi^2} - t\frac{\partial V}{\partial t} = 0. \tag{11.222}$$

If the solutions of (11.222) are taken to be of the form $V = S(s)T(t)\Theta(\theta)U(\phi)$, we find that

$$s\frac{d^2 S}{ds^2} + \left(\frac{3}{2} + s\right)\frac{dS}{ds} - \left[\alpha + \frac{\nu(\nu + 1)}{4s}\right]S = 0, \tag{11.223}$$

$$t\frac{dT}{dt} - \alpha T = 0, \tag{11.224}$$

$$\frac{d^2\Theta}{d\theta^2} + \cot\theta \frac{d\Theta}{d\theta} + \left[\nu(\nu+1) - \frac{\mu^2}{\sin^2\theta} \right] \Theta = 0 , \qquad (11.225)$$

$$\frac{d^2 U}{d\phi^2} + \mu^2 U = 0 , \qquad (11.226)$$

where α, μ, and ν are arbitrary constants of separation. The solutions of (11.223) can be expressed in terms of confluent hypergeometric functions. Thus a solution of (11.222) is

$$V = t^{\alpha} \left(\frac{r^2}{4kt} \right)^{(1/2)\nu} \Phi\left(\tfrac{1}{2}\nu - \alpha, \nu + \tfrac{3}{2} ; \frac{-r^2}{4kt} \right) \binom{P_\nu^\mu}{Q_\nu^\mu} (\cos\theta) \binom{\sin}{\cos} (\mu\phi)$$

$$= t^{\alpha} \left(\frac{r^2}{4kt} \right)^{(1/2)\nu} \exp\left(\frac{-r^2}{4kt} \right) \Phi\left(\alpha + \tfrac{1}{2}\nu + \tfrac{3}{2} ; \nu + \tfrac{3}{2} ; \frac{r^2}{4kt} \right)$$

$$\times \binom{P_\nu^\mu}{Q_\nu^\mu} (\cos\theta) \binom{\sin}{\cos} (\mu\phi) . \qquad (11.227)$$

In particular, with $\mu = \nu = 0$, $\alpha = -\frac{3}{2}$, one solution of (11.222) is

$$V = t^{-3/2} \exp\left(\frac{-r^2}{4kt} \right) . \qquad (11.228)$$

More generally, as shown by Bateman [*215*, 1918], if $V = F(s, t, \theta, \phi)$ is a solution of (11.222), another solution is

$$V = t^{-3/2} \exp\left(\frac{-r^2}{4kt} \right) F\left(-s, -\frac{1}{t}, \theta, \phi \right) . \qquad (11.229)$$

This can be put in an alternative form. If $V = F(x, y, z, t)$ is a solution of (11.204), another solution is

$$V = t^{-3/2} \exp\left(\frac{-(x^2 + y^2 + z^2)}{4kt} \right) F\left(\frac{x}{t}, \frac{y}{t}, \frac{z}{t}, -\frac{1}{t} \right) . \qquad (11.230)$$

11.14 Green's Function for the Diffusion Equation

The Green's function for the diffusion equation in the form (11.205) can be obtained immediately from §11.8. However, it is usually more convenient to use a different solution of the diffusion equation.

Consider first the one-dimensional form of the diffusion equation

$$\frac{\partial^2 V}{\partial x^2} - \frac{1}{k} \frac{\partial V}{\partial t} = 0 . \qquad (11.231)$$

As shown in §11.13, one solution of (11.231) is

$$V = t^{-1/2} \exp\left(\frac{-x^2}{4kt}\right).$$

More generally, any function of the form

$$V = C(t-\tau)^{-1/2} \exp\left[\frac{-(x-\xi)^2}{4k(t-\tau)}\right] \tag{11.232}$$

satisfies (11.231), where C is an arbitrary constant.

Consider now the Green's function $G(x, t; \xi, \tau)$ for (11.231). We shall determine that Green's function which is zero for all $t < \tau$ (this is said to be a causality condition). From the definition of the Green's function given in §10.8, we see that, in this case,

$$\frac{\partial^2 G}{\partial x^2} - \frac{1}{k}\frac{\partial G}{\partial t} = -\delta(x-\xi)\delta(t-\tau). \tag{11.233}$$

Let $\rho = x - \xi$, $u = t - \tau$, and let g be the Fourier transform of G; that is,

$$g(p, u) = (2\pi)^{-(1/2)} \int_{-\infty}^{\infty} e^{ip(x-\xi)} G(x, t; \xi, \tau)\, dx. \tag{11.234}$$

The inverse Fourier transform is (Sneddon [*19*, 1951])

$$G(x, t; \xi, \tau) = (2\pi)^{-(1/2)} \int_{-\infty}^{\infty} e^{-ip(x-\xi)} g(p, u)\, dp. \tag{11.235}$$

From the definition of the δ function, we find

$$\int_{-\infty}^{\infty} e^{ip(x-\xi)} \delta(x-\xi)\, dx = 1. \tag{11.236}$$

On multiplying both sides of (11.233) by $\exp[ip(x-\xi)]$ and integrating with respect to x from $-\infty$ to $+\infty$, we obtain, on using (11.234) and (11.236),

$$\frac{1}{k}\frac{dg}{du} + p^2 g = (2\pi)^{-(1/2)}\delta(u), \tag{11.237}$$

provided that both G and dG/dx vanish at $\pm\infty$. One solution of (11.237) is

$$\begin{aligned} g &= 0 && (u < 0), \\ g &= (2\pi)^{-(1/2)} k e^{-kp^2 u}, && (u > 0). \end{aligned} \tag{11.238}$$

Applying the inverse Fourier transform (11.235), we find

$$G(x, t; \xi, \tau) = \frac{k}{2\pi} \int_{-\infty}^{\infty} e^{-ip(x-\xi) - kp^2(t-\tau)}\, dp, \qquad (t > \tau). \tag{11.239}$$

Now, if b is real and positive,

$$\int_{-\infty}^{\infty} e^{-iap-bp^2}\,dp = 2\int_0^{\infty}\cos(ap)e^{-bp^2}\,dp = \left(\frac{\pi}{b}\right)^{1/2} e^{-a^2/4b}. \quad (11.240)$$

From (11.239) and (11.240),

$$G(x, t; \xi, \tau) = \frac{1}{2}\left[\frac{k}{\pi(t-\tau)}\right]^{1/2} \exp\left[-\frac{(x-\xi)^2}{4k(t-\tau)}\right] \quad (t > \tau)$$

$$= 0 \quad (t < \tau). \quad (11.241)$$

We note that the causality condition is satisfied.

The Green's functions for the two- and three-dimensional forms of the diffusion equation can be found in a precisely similar manner, by considering double and triple Fourier integrals. The corresponding Green's functions are

$$G(x, y, t; \xi, \eta, \tau) = \frac{1}{4\pi(t-\tau)} \exp\left[\frac{-\rho'^2}{4k(t-\tau)}\right] \quad (t > \tau)$$

$$= 0 \quad (t < \tau), \quad (11.242)$$

where $\rho'^2 = (x-\xi)^2 + (y-\eta)^2$, and

$$G(x, y, z, t; \xi, \eta, \zeta, \tau) = \frac{1}{8k^{1/2}[\pi(t-\tau)]^{3/2}} \exp\left[\frac{-\rho'^2}{4k(t-\tau)}\right] \quad (t > \tau)$$

$$= 0 \quad (t < \tau), \quad (11.243)$$

where $\rho'^2 = (x-\xi)^2 + (y-\eta)^2 + (z-\zeta)^2$.

All three Green's functions, given by (11.241) to (11.243), satisfy the diffusion equation at all points except the source point. The three-dimensional Green's function may be physically interpreted as the temperature at a given point (x, y, z) at time t due to an instantaneous point source of heat of strength k generated at the point (ξ, η, ζ) at time τ. The other Green's functions may be interpreted in a precisely similar manner.

More generally, if in an infinite solid there is an initial temperature distribution $f(x, y, z)$ due to liberation of heat at $t = 0$, there being no subsequent generation of heat, the temperature at the point (x, y, z) at time t is

$$\frac{1}{8(\pi k t)^{3/2}} \int_{-\infty}^{\infty}\int_{-\infty}^{\infty}\int_{-\infty}^{\infty} f(\xi, \eta, \zeta) \exp\left(\frac{-\rho'^2}{4kt}\right) d\xi\, d\eta\, d\xi. \quad (11.244)$$

Analogous results follow if the spread of heating is restricted to one or two dimensions.

11.15 Solutions of the Nonhomogeneous Diffusion Equation

The solution of the nonhomogeneous diffusion equation

$$\frac{\partial^2 V}{\partial x^2}+\frac{\partial^2 V}{\partial y^2}+\frac{\partial^2 V}{\partial z^2}-\frac{1}{k}\frac{\partial V}{\partial t}=f(x, y, z, t) \tag{11.245}$$

can be found by using the methods given in Chapter 10. As shown in §11.1, if

$$f(x, y, z, t)=g(x, y, z)e^{-k\lambda^2 t},$$

where λ is a constant, we may put $V=\Phi(x, y, z)e^{-k\lambda^2 t}$. Equation (11.245) then reduces to

$$(\Delta+\lambda^2)\Phi=g(x, y, z). \tag{11.246}$$

Equation (11.246) is identical with the space form of Lorenz's equation (11.170), solutions of which were discussed in detail in §11.10. In this section we shall consider other methods of solving (11.245). These methods are analogous to those given in §11.13.

Consider first the one-dimensional form of (11.245),

$$\frac{\partial^2 V}{\partial x^2}-\frac{1}{k}\frac{\partial V}{\partial t}=f(x, t). \tag{11.247}$$

As in §11.13, we take new variables $s=x^2/4kt$ and t. Equation (11.247) then becomes

$$s\frac{\partial^2 V}{\partial s^2}+(\tfrac{1}{2}+s)\frac{\partial V}{\partial s}-t\frac{\partial V}{\partial t}=ktf(x, t). \tag{11.248}$$

If $ktf(x, t)=g(s)T(t)$, $V=\bar{S}(s)T(t)$, where

$$s\frac{d^2\bar{S}}{ds^2}+(\tfrac{1}{2}+s)\frac{d\bar{S}}{ds}-\nu\bar{S}=g(s), \tag{11.249}$$

ν being an arbitrary constant of separation, and T satisfies (11.209).

If $g(s)=s^{\sigma-1}$, where σ is any constant, we see, from §4.25, that the solutions of (11.249) can be expressed in terms of nonhomogeneous confluent hypergeometric functions. Thus, if $f=s^{\sigma-1}t^{\nu-1}$, where $s=x^2/4kt$, a particular solution of (11.247) is

$$V=e^{-i\pi\sigma}kt^{\nu}\Lambda_{0,\sigma}\left(-\nu, \tfrac{1}{2}; \frac{-x^2}{4kt}\right)=e^{-i\pi\sigma}kt^{\nu}\theta_{\sigma}\left(-\nu, \tfrac{1}{2}; \frac{-x^2}{4kt}\right)$$

$$=kt^{\nu}\exp\left(\frac{-x^2}{4kt}\right)\Lambda_{1,\sigma}\left(\nu+\tfrac{1}{2}, \tfrac{1}{2}; \frac{x^2}{4kt}\right), \tag{11.250}$$

where θ and Λ are nonhomogeneous confluent hypergeometric functions defined in Chapter 4.

Another particular solution of (11.247) is

$$V = e^{-in\sigma} kt^{\nu} \Theta_{\sigma}\left(-\nu, \tfrac{1}{2}; \frac{-x^2}{4kt}\right). \tag{11.251}$$

If σ or $\sigma - \frac{1}{2}$ is a positive integer, as shown in §4.18, the Θ function can be expressed as a terminating series in $(x^2/4kt)$. In particular, if $f = 1$, $\sigma = \nu = 1$ and a particular solution of (11.247) is $V = -kt$.

More generally, if $V = F(x, t)$ is one solution of (11.247), then

$$V = t^{-1/2} \exp\left(\frac{-x^2}{4kt}\right) F\left(\frac{x}{t}, -\frac{1}{t}\right) \tag{11.252}$$

is a solution of

$$\frac{\partial^2 V}{\partial x^2} - \frac{1}{k}\frac{\partial V}{\partial t} = t^{-5/2} \exp\left(\frac{-x^2}{4kt}\right) f\left(\frac{x}{t}, -\frac{1}{t}\right).$$

Consider next the two-dimensional form of (11.245),

$$\frac{\partial^2 V}{\partial x^2} + \frac{\partial^2 V}{\partial y^2} - \frac{1}{k}\frac{\partial V}{\partial t} = f(x, y, t). \tag{11.253}$$

As in §11.13, we take new variables

$$x = \rho \cos\phi, \qquad y = \rho \sin\phi, \qquad s = \frac{\rho^2}{4kt}. \tag{11.254}$$

Equation (11.253) becomes

$$s\frac{\partial^2 V}{\partial s^2} + (1 + s)\frac{\partial V}{\partial s} + \frac{1}{4s}\frac{\partial^2 V}{\partial \phi^2} - t\frac{\partial V}{\partial t} = ktf(x, y, t). \tag{11.255}$$

If $ktf(x, y, t) = g(s)T(t)U(\phi)$, $V = \bar{S}(s)T(t)U(\phi)$, where

$$s\frac{d^2\bar{S}}{ds^2} + (1 + s)\frac{d\bar{S}}{ds} - \left(\nu + \frac{\mu^2}{4s}\right)\bar{S} = g(s), \tag{11.256}$$

μ and ν being arbitrary constants of separation, and T and U satisfy (11.216) and (11.217).

If $g(s) = s^{(1/2)\mu + \sigma - 1}$, where σ is any constant, the solution of (11.256) can be expressed in terms of nonhomogeneous confluent hypergeometric functions. Thus, if

$$f = s^{(1/2)\mu + \sigma - 1} t^{\nu - 1} \binom{\sin}{\cos}(\mu\phi),$$

where s is given by (11.254), a particular solution of (11.253) is

$$V = e^{-i\pi\sigma}kt^{\nu}\left(\frac{\rho^2}{4kt}\right)^{(1/2)\mu}\Lambda_{0,\sigma}\left(\tfrac{1}{2}\mu - \nu, 1 + \mu; \frac{-\rho^2}{4kt}\right)\binom{\sin}{\cos}(\mu\phi)$$

$$= e^{-i\pi\sigma}kt^{\nu}\left(\frac{\rho^2}{4kt}\right)^{(1/2)\mu}\theta_{\sigma}\left(\tfrac{1}{2}\mu - \nu, 1 + \mu; \frac{-\rho^2}{4kt}\right)\binom{\sin}{\cos}(\mu\phi)$$

$$= kt^{\nu}\left(\frac{\rho^2}{4kt}\right)^{(1/2)\mu}\exp\left(\frac{-\rho^2}{4kt}\right)\Lambda_{1,\sigma}\left(1 + \tfrac{1}{2}\mu + \nu, 1 + \mu; \frac{\rho^2}{4kt}\right)$$

$$\times\binom{\sin}{\cos}(\mu\phi), \quad (11.257)$$

where θ and Λ are nonhomogeneous confluent hypergeometric functions defined in Chapter 4.

Another particular solution of (11.253) is

$$V = e^{-i\pi\sigma}kt^{\nu}\left(\frac{\rho^2}{4kt}\right)^{(1/2)\mu}\Theta_{\sigma}\left(\tfrac{1}{2}\mu - \nu, 1 + \mu; -\frac{\rho^2}{4kt}\right)\binom{\sin}{\cos}(\mu\phi). \quad (11.258)$$

If σ or $\sigma + \mu$ is a positive integer, as shown in §4.18, the Θ function can be expressed as a terminating series in $(\rho^2/4kt)$. In particular, if $f = 1$, $\mu = 0$, and $\sigma = \nu = 1$ and a particular solution of (11.253) is $V = -kt$.

More generally, if $V = F(x, y, t)$ is a solution of (11.253), then

$$V = t^{-1}\exp\left[\frac{-\rho^2}{4kt}\right]F\left(\frac{x}{t}, \frac{y}{t}, -\frac{1}{t}\right) \quad (11.259)$$

is a solution of

$$\frac{\partial^2 V}{\partial x^2} + \frac{\partial^2 V}{\partial y^2} - \frac{1}{k}\frac{\partial V}{\partial t} = t^{-3}\exp\left(\frac{-\rho^2}{4kt}\right)f\left(\frac{x}{t}, \frac{y}{t}, -\frac{1}{t}\right),$$

where $\rho^2 = x^2 + y^2$.

Finally, consider the three-dimensional form of the nonhomogeneous diffusion equation (11.245). As in §11.13, we take new variables

$$x = r\sin\theta\cos\phi, \qquad y = r\sin\theta\sin\phi, \qquad z = r\cos\theta, \qquad s = r^2/4kt. \quad (11.260)$$

Equation (11.245) becomes

$$s\frac{\partial^2 V}{\partial s^2} + \left(\frac{3}{2} + s\right)\frac{\partial V}{\partial s} + \frac{1}{4s}\frac{\partial^2 V}{\partial \theta^2} + \frac{\cot\theta}{4s}\frac{\partial V}{\partial \theta} + \frac{1}{4s\sin^2\theta}\frac{\partial^2 V}{\partial \phi^2} - t\frac{\partial V}{\partial t}$$

$$= ktf(x, y, z, t). \quad (11.261)$$

If $ktf(x, y, z, t) = g(s)T(t)\Theta(\theta)U(\phi)$, $V = \bar{S}(s)T(t)\Theta(\theta)U(\phi)$, where

$$s\frac{d^2\bar{S}}{ds^2} + \left(\frac{3}{2} + s\right)\frac{d\bar{S}}{ds} - \left[\alpha + \frac{\nu(\nu+1)}{4s}\right]\bar{S} = g(s), \tag{11.262}$$

α and ν being arbitrary constants of separation, and T, Θ, and U satisfy (11.224), (11.225), and (11.226), respectively. If $g(s) = s^{(1/2)\nu+\sigma-1}$, where σ is any constant, the solutions of (11.262) can be expressed in terms of nonhomogeneous confluent hypergeometric functions. Thus, if

$$f = s^{(1/2)\nu+\sigma-1}t^{\alpha-1}\binom{P_\nu^\mu}{Q_\nu^\mu}(\cos\theta)\binom{\sin}{\cos}(\mu\phi),$$

where s is given by (11.260), a particular solution of (11.245) is

$$V = e^{-i\pi\sigma}kt^\alpha\left(\frac{r^2}{4kt}\right)^{(1/2)\nu}\Lambda_{0,\sigma}\left(\tfrac{1}{2}\nu - \alpha, \nu + \tfrac{3}{2}; \frac{-r^2}{4kt}\right)\binom{P_\nu^\mu}{Q_\nu^\mu}(\cos\theta)$$
$$\times \binom{\sin}{\cos}(\mu\phi)$$
$$= e^{-i\pi\sigma}kt^\alpha\left(\frac{r^2}{4kt}\right)^{(1/2)\nu}\theta_\sigma\left(\tfrac{1}{2}\nu - \alpha, \nu + \tfrac{3}{2}; \frac{-r^2}{4kt}\right)\binom{P_\nu^\mu}{Q_\nu^\mu}(\cos\theta)$$
$$\times \binom{\sin}{\cos}(\mu\phi)$$
$$= kt^\alpha\left(\frac{r^2}{4kt}\right)^{(1/2)\nu}\exp\left(\frac{-r^2}{4kt}\right)\Lambda_{1,\sigma}\left(\alpha + \tfrac{1}{2}\nu + \tfrac{3}{2}, \nu + \tfrac{3}{2}; \frac{r^2}{4kt}\right)\binom{P_\nu^\mu}{Q_\nu^\mu}(\cos\theta)$$
$$\times \binom{\sin}{\cos}(\mu\phi), \tag{11.263}$$

where θ and Λ are nonhomogeneous confluent hypergeometric functions defined in Chapter 4.

Another particular solution of (11.245) is

$$V = e^{-i\pi\sigma}kt^\alpha\left(\frac{r^2}{4kt}\right)^{(1/2)\mu}\Theta_\sigma\left(\tfrac{1}{2}\nu - \alpha, \nu + \tfrac{3}{2}; \frac{-r^2}{4kt}\right)\binom{P_\nu^\mu}{Q_\nu^\mu}(\cos\theta)$$
$$\times \binom{\sin}{\cos}(\mu\phi). \tag{11.264}$$

If σ or $\sigma + \nu + \frac{1}{2}$ is a positive integer, as shown in §4.18, the Θ function in (11.264) can be expressed as a terminating series in $(r^2/4kt)$. In particular, if $f = 1$, $\mu = \nu = 0$, and $\sigma = \alpha = 1$, and a particular solution of (11.245) is $V = -kt$.

More generally, if $V = F(x, y, z, t)$ is a solution of (11.245), then

$$V = t^{-3/2} \exp\left(\frac{-r^2}{4kt}\right) F\left(\frac{x}{t}, \frac{y}{t}, \frac{z}{t}, -\frac{1}{t}\right) \tag{11.265}$$

is a solution of

$$\frac{\partial^2 V}{\partial x^2} + \frac{\partial^2 V}{\partial y^2} + \frac{\partial^2 V}{\partial z^2} - \frac{1}{k}\frac{\partial V}{\partial t} = t^{-7/2} \exp\left(\frac{-r^2}{4kt}\right) f\left(\frac{x}{t}, \frac{y}{t}, \frac{z}{t}, -\frac{1}{t}\right),$$

where $r^2 = x^2 + y^2 + z^2$.

11.16 Solutions of the Nonhomogeneous Diffusion Equation Using Green's Functions

The Green's functions for the diffusion equation were given in §11.14. Using the results of §10.8, we can determine the solutions of the nonhomogeneous diffusion equation in terms of multiple integrals.

From (11.243), together with (10.110), we see that, if $f(x, y, z, t)$ is a function which, with its first derivatives, (a) vanishes for all $t < 0$, (b) is continuous in the region R, and (c) vanishes outside R, a particular solution of (11.245) is, with $u = t - \tau$,

$$V = -\frac{1}{8\pi^{3/2}k^{1/2}} \int_0^t \frac{d\tau}{u^{3/2}} \iiint \exp\left(\frac{-\rho'^2}{4ku}\right) f(\xi, \eta, \zeta, \tau) d\xi\, d\eta\, d\zeta, \tag{11.266}$$

where $\rho'^2 = (x - \xi)^2 + (y - \eta)^2 + (z - \zeta)^2$ and the integral is taken over the region R for which the point $P(\xi, \eta, \zeta)$ is an interior point. The complementary function is to be added to this particular integral.

Thus, if at $t = 0$, $V = V_0(x, y, z)$, from (11.244), the required solution of (11.245) is

$$V = \frac{1}{8(\pi kt)^{3/2}} \iiint \exp\left(\frac{-\rho'^2}{4kt}\right) V_0(\xi, \eta, \zeta) d\xi\, d\eta\, d\zeta$$
$$- \frac{1}{8\pi^{3/2}k^{1/2}} \int_0^t \frac{d\tau}{u^{3/2}} \iiint \exp\left(\frac{-\rho'^2}{4ku}\right) f(\xi, \eta, \zeta, \tau)\, d\xi\, d\eta\, d\zeta, \tag{11.267}$$

where the triple space integral is taken over the region R. At $t = 0$ we see that the second integral vanishes, and the limiting value of the first term on the right side of (11.267) is $V_0(x, y, z)$ (see Carslaw and Jaeger [*53*, 1959]).

This result can be applied directly to find the temperature distribution in a heated body. If, in an infinite solid, the initial temperature distribution V at $t = 0$ is $V_0(x, y, z)$, and the rate of generation of heat at a subsequent time is $Kf(x, y, z, t)$, we find (from §11.1) that the temperature at the point (x, y, z) at time t is

$$V = \frac{1}{8(\pi k t)^{3/2}} \int_{-\infty}^{\infty} \int_{-\infty}^{\infty} \int_{-\infty}^{\infty} V_0(\xi, \eta, \zeta) \exp\left(\frac{-\rho'^2}{4kt}\right) d\xi\, d\eta\, d\zeta$$
$$+ \frac{1}{8\pi^{3/2} k^{1/2}} \int_0^t \frac{d\tau}{u^{3/2}} \int_{-\infty}^{\infty} \int_{-\infty}^{\infty} \int_{-\infty}^{\infty} \exp\left(\frac{-\rho'^2}{4ku}\right) f(\xi, \eta, \zeta, \tau)\, d\xi\, d\eta\, d\zeta . \tag{11.268}$$

Analogous integrals for the one- and two-dimensional cases can be found in a precisely similar manner.

PROBLEMS

1. If two systems satisfy, respectively, the equations

$$\frac{\partial^2 U}{\partial x^2} + \frac{\partial^2 U}{\partial y^2} = a \quad \text{and} \quad \frac{\partial^2 V}{\partial \xi^2} + \frac{\partial^2 V}{\partial \eta^2} = b ,$$

where (x, y) and (ξ, η) are two sets of orthogonal Cartesian coordinates and a and b are two constants, show that, if $x = n\xi$, $y = n\eta$, and $a = mb$, then $U = mn^2 V$ is a solution of the first system.

[The two systems are said to be analogues of one another. A physical example is the analogy between the torsional stress function (for a member of constant cross section subjected to torsion) and the deflection of a membrane (or soap film) subjected to a small differential pressure. The boundary conditions must be similar in the two cases. At an unstressed outer boundary, the stress function is zero; the corresponding condition for the membrane is that the elevation must be zero at the boundary (i.e., the boundary must be a plane curve) (Griffith and Taylor [1917]).]

2. Toroidal coordinates (η, θ, ϕ) are related to rectangular Cartesian coordinates (x, y, z) by the equations

$$x = \frac{c \sinh \eta \cos \phi}{\cosh \eta - \cos \theta}, \quad y = \frac{c \sinh \eta \sin \phi}{\cosh \eta - \cos \theta}, \quad z = \frac{c \sin \theta}{\cosh \eta - \cos \theta}.$$

Show that

$$\Delta V = \frac{(\cosh \eta - \cos \theta)^3}{c^2 \sinh \eta} \left[\frac{\partial}{\partial \eta} \left(\frac{\sinh \eta}{\cosh \eta - \cos \theta} \frac{\partial V}{\partial \eta} \right) + \frac{\partial}{\partial \theta} \left(\frac{\sinh \eta}{\cosh \eta - \cos \theta} \frac{\partial V}{\partial \theta} \right) + \frac{1}{\sinh \eta (\cosh \eta - \cos \theta)} \frac{\partial^2 V}{\partial \phi^2} \right].$$

(The surfaces $\eta =$ constant are toroids, i.e., ring-shaped closed surfaces.)

3. Using the results of Problem 2, show that, in toroidal coordinates, the solution of Laplace's equation can be put in the form

$$V = (\cosh \eta - \cos \theta)^{1/2} H(\eta)\Theta(\theta)\Phi(\phi),$$

where

$$\frac{d^2H}{d\eta^2} + \coth \eta \frac{dH}{d\eta} - \left(\nu^2 - \frac{1}{4} + \frac{\mu^2}{\sinh^2 \eta}\right)H = 0,$$

and

$$\frac{d^2\Theta}{d\theta^2} + \nu^2\Theta = 0, \qquad \frac{d^2\Phi}{d\phi^2} + \mu^2\Phi = 0,$$

where μ and ν are arbitrary constants of separation. Hence show that

$$V = (\cosh \eta - \cos \theta)^{1/2} \begin{pmatrix} P^{\mu}_{\nu-(1/2)} \\ Q^{\mu}_{\nu-(1/2)} \end{pmatrix} (\cosh \eta) \begin{pmatrix} \sin \\ \cos \end{pmatrix} (\nu\theta) \begin{pmatrix} \sin \\ \cos \end{pmatrix} (\mu\phi).$$

(If the problem involves a complete toroid, the solution must have a period of 2π in both θ and ϕ. In that case, μ and ν must be integers.)

4. Show that, in elliptic cylinder coordinates, Laplace's equation has elementary solutions u, v, $e^u \cos v$, $e^u \sin v$, $\cosh(\nu u)\sin(\nu v)$, and $\sinh(\nu u) \times \sin(\nu v)$. Determine the solution which satisfies the boundary conditions $u = a$, $\partial V/\partial u = 0$, and $u \to \infty$, $V = V_0 + by$.

(This solution represents the velocity potential due to the two-dimensional flow of a perfect fluid past an ellipse. Alternatively, the solution can represent the potential due to the flow of electricity in a thin sheet of metal in which there is an elliptical hole, the field at infinity being uniform.)

5. Show that the Green's function for the two-dimensional form of Laplace's equation which has a singularity at the point $P(\xi, \eta)$ inside the circle $x^2 + y^2 = 1$ and vanishes on the circumference of the circle is

$$-\frac{1}{2\pi} \log \frac{r_1}{r_2} + \frac{1}{2\pi} \log \sqrt{\xi^2 + \eta^2},$$

where r_1 and r_2 are the distances from the point P and its inverse P' to the point (x, y) (Courant and Hilbert [*377*, 1953]).

6. Show that the solution of the equation

$$\frac{\partial^2 u}{dx^2} + k^2 u = -\delta(x - \xi)\delta(y - \eta),$$

where $u(0, y) = u(a, y) = 0$ is

$$u = (k \sin ka)^{-1} \sin kx \sin k(a - \xi)\delta(y - \eta) \qquad (0 \leqslant x < \xi),$$
$$u = (k \sin ka)^{-1} \sin k(a - x) \sin k\xi\, \delta(y - \eta) \qquad (a \geqslant x > \xi).$$

Using the formula

$$\delta(y-\eta) = \frac{2}{b}\sum_{1}^{\infty} \sin\frac{n\pi y}{b}\sin\frac{n\pi\eta}{b},$$

show that the solution of the equation

$$\frac{\partial^2 u}{\partial x^2} + \frac{\partial^2 u}{\partial y^2} = -\delta(x-\xi)\delta(y-\eta)$$

in the region $0 \leqslant x \leqslant a$, $0 \leqslant y \leqslant b$, which satisfies the conditions $u(0, y) = u(a, y) = u(x, 0) = u(x, b) = 0$, can be put in the form

$$u = \frac{2}{b}\sum_{1}^{\infty} \frac{\sinh(n\pi x/b)\sinh\{n\pi(a-\xi)/b\}\sin(n\pi y/b)\sin(n\pi\eta/b)}{(n\pi/b)\sinh(n\pi a/b)} \qquad (0 \leqslant x \leqslant \xi),$$

$$u = \frac{2}{b}\sum_{1}^{\infty} \frac{\sinh(n\pi\xi/b)\sinh\{n\pi(a-x)/b\}\sin(n\pi y/b)\sin(n\pi\eta/b)}{(n\pi/b)\sinh(n\pi a/b)} \qquad (\xi < x \leqslant a).$$

7. Using the result of Problem 2, show that, in toroidal coordinates, if $f = (\cosh\eta - \cos\theta)^{5/2}\, g(\eta)\Theta(\theta)\Phi(\phi)$, the solution of Poisson's equation can be put in the form $V = (\cosh\eta - \cos\theta)^{1/2}\overline{H}(\eta)\Theta(\theta)\Phi(\phi)$, where

$$\frac{d^2\overline{H}}{d\eta^2} + \coth\eta\frac{d\overline{H}}{d\eta} - \left(v^2 - \frac{1}{4} + \frac{\mu^2}{\sinh^2\eta}\right)\overline{H} = c^2 g(\eta)$$

and Θ and Φ satisfy the equations given in Problem 3, μ and v being arbitrary constants of separation. Hence show that, if

$$g(\eta) = (\cosh\eta)^{2\sigma-2}(\sinh\eta)^{\mu+2\tau-2},$$

where σ and τ are constants,

$$V = -c^2(\cosh\eta - \cos\theta)^{1/2} t^{\mu,\tau}_{v-(1/2),\sigma}(\cosh\eta)\binom{\sin}{\cos}(v\theta)\binom{\sin}{\cos}(\mu\phi),$$

where t is the nonhomogeneous Legendre function defined in §7.20.

8. A two-dimensional system satisfies the equation

$$\Delta V = \frac{A}{\rho^2}\sin 2\phi,$$

where (ρ, ϕ) are cylindrical coordinates. Find a solution, for which V is a function of ϕ only, which satisfies the boundary conditions $\partial V/\partial\phi = 0$ at $\phi = \pm\alpha$.

(If V is the stream function, this is the equation satisfied by slow flow of a viscous fluid in a sector with boundaries $\phi = \pm\alpha$. In this case, A is proportional to the rate of flow.)

9. Derive Poisson's equation referred to prolate spheroidal coordinates for an axisymmetric system.

In prolate spheroidal coordinates, a system satisfies the equation

$$\Delta V = \frac{\cos v}{\sinh^2 u + \sin^2 v}.$$

Show that a particular integral of this equation is $-c^2 S^0_{1,1}(\cosh u) \times P^0_1(\cos v)$, where S is the nonhomogeneous Legendre function defined in §7.16. Determine the solution for V which satisfies the boundary conditions $V = \text{constant}$, on the spheroid $u = u_0$, and $V = V_0 + bz$ as $z \to \infty$.

10. Using the Green's function, show that the potential at an internal point P of a solid homogeneous ellipsoid (semiaxes a, b, c) can be expressed in the form

$$V = \tfrac{1}{4}\rho \int (R_1^2 + R_2^2)\, d\omega,$$

where ρ is the density and R_1 and R_2 are the radial heights of the double cone through P with solid angle $d\omega$ which cuts the ellipsoid.

Hence show that V can be put in the form

$$V = \pi\rho abc \int_0^\infty \frac{1}{Q}\left\{1 - \frac{x^2}{a^2+u} - \frac{y^2}{b^2+u} - \frac{z^2}{c^2+u}\right\} du,$$

where $Q^2 = (a^2+u)(b^2+u)(c^2+u)$ (Routh [*107*, 1902]).

11. Show that, on making the substitution $x + iy = u$, $x - iy = v$, the equation

$$\frac{\partial^2 V}{\partial x^2} + \frac{\partial^2 V}{\partial y^2} + \frac{\partial^2 V}{\partial z^2} + \frac{\partial^2 V}{\partial s^2} = 0$$

becomes

$$4\frac{\partial^2 V}{\partial u\, \partial v} + \frac{\partial^2 V}{\partial z^2} + \frac{\partial^2 V}{\partial s^2} = 0.$$

Verify that, if the latter equation has one solution $\theta(u, v, z, s)$, another solution is

$$\frac{1}{u}\theta\left(\frac{uv + z^2 + s^2}{u}, -\frac{a^2}{u}, \frac{az}{u}, \frac{as}{u}\right),$$

where a is a constant. Hence show that, if one solution of the first equation is $F(x, y, z, s)$, another solution is

$$(x + iy)^{-1} F\left[\frac{r^2 - a^2}{2(x + iy)}, \frac{r^2 + a^2}{2i(x + iy)}, \frac{az}{x + iy}, \frac{as}{x + iy}\right],$$

where $r^2 = x^2 + y^2 + z^2 + s^2$ (Bateman [*161*, 1932]).

12. Solve the one-dimensional form of the wave equation

$$\frac{\partial^2 u}{\partial x^2} - \frac{1}{c^2}\frac{\partial^2 u}{\partial t^2} = f(x, t)$$

by expanding both u and $f(x, t)$ in the form

$$u(x, t) = \sum_{n=1}^{\infty} u_n(t) \sin\frac{nx}{c}, \qquad f(x, t) = \sum_{n=1}^{\infty} f_n(t) \sin\frac{nx}{c}.$$

[As in Problem 5, Chapter 2, we see that u_n is given by

$$-\frac{c^2}{n}\int_0^t f_n(\tau) \sin n(t - \tau)\, d\tau + A \sin nt + B \cos nt.]$$

13. Solve the equation

$$\frac{\partial^2 \xi}{\partial t^2} = c^2 \frac{\partial^2 \xi}{\partial x^2} + f \cos \sigma t$$

with the boundary conditions $\xi = 0$ for $x = 0$ and $x = l$.

[If ξ is the time-integral of the horizontal displacement, this is the equation for the one-dimensional forced motion of water in a canal closed at both ends. The frequency of the forced motion is σ, that of the free motion is $r\pi c/l$, where r is an integer. When the forcing frequency is equal to that of a free mode of odd order, ξ becomes infinite; in that case, the amplitude becomes so great that the equation is no longer valid (Lamb [*266*, 1953]).]

14. A two-dimensional wave motion satisfies the equation (in polar coordinates)

$$\frac{\partial^2 \xi}{\partial \rho^2} + \frac{1}{\rho}\frac{\partial \xi}{\partial \rho} - \frac{1}{c^2}\frac{\partial^2 \xi}{\partial t^2} = a \cos \omega t,$$

where a, c, and ω are constants. Show that the solution of this equation which gives a finite value of ξ at $\rho = 0$ can be put in the form

$$\xi = AJ_0(k\rho) \cos \omega t + \frac{ac^2}{\omega^2} \cos \omega t,$$

where A is a constant.

[This is the equation for the vibration of a circular membrane driven by a periodic force which is uniformly distributed over the membrane, ξ being the displacement. At the clamped edge $\rho = \rho_0$, $\xi = 0$; this determines the value of A (McLachlan [*86*, 1934]).]

15. Show that a particular solution of

$$(\Delta + k^2)w + \frac{dZ}{dy} = 0$$

is

$$w = \frac{1}{4\pi}\iiint \frac{dZ}{d\eta}\frac{e^{ik\rho'}}{\rho'}\, d\xi\, d\eta\, d\zeta\,.$$

Hence show that, if $\bar{Z}$ is the mean value of Z throughout the region R near the origin O (and if Z vanishes outside this region), w is given by

$$w = \frac{T\bar{Z}}{4\pi}\frac{d}{dr}\left(\frac{e^{ikr}}{r}\right)\frac{y}{r}$$

at points sufficiently far from O, where T is the volume of the region R.

[If w is the rotation, this is the equation satisfied by a solid body subjected to a periodic force Z (Rayleigh [2, *419*, 1945]).]

16. If $F(x, y, z, s)$ is a solution of

$$\frac{\partial^2 V}{\partial x^2} + \frac{\partial^2 V}{\partial y^2} + \frac{\partial^2 V}{\partial z^2} + \frac{\partial^2 V}{\partial s^2} = f(x, y, z, s),$$

show (by a method similar to that of Problem 11) that the equation

$$\frac{\partial^2 V}{\partial x^2} + \frac{\partial^2 V}{\partial y^2} + \frac{\partial^2 V}{\partial z^2} + \frac{\partial^2 V}{\partial s^2}$$

$$= \frac{a^2}{(x+iy)^3} f\left[\frac{r^2 - a^2}{2(x+iy)}, \frac{r^2 + a^2}{2i(x+iy)}, \frac{az}{x+iy}, \frac{as}{x+iy}\right]$$

has a particular integral

$$(x+iy)^{-1} F\left[\frac{r^2 - a^2}{2(x+iy)}, \frac{r^2 + a^2}{2i(x+iy)}, \frac{az}{x+iy}, \frac{as}{x+iy}\right],$$

where $r^2 = x^2 + y^2 + z^2 + s^2$ and a is a constant.

17. Show that, by making the substitution

$$\Theta = \frac{1}{K_0}\int_0^v K\, dv,$$

the equation

$$\rho c \frac{\partial v}{\partial t} = \frac{\partial}{\partial x}\left(K \frac{\partial v}{\partial x}\right) + \frac{\partial}{\partial y}\left(K \frac{\partial v}{\partial y}\right) + \frac{\partial}{\partial z}\left(K \frac{\partial v}{\partial z}\right) + A,$$

where ρ and c are constants and K is a function of v only, can be reduced to the form

$$\Delta\Theta - \frac{1}{k}\frac{\partial\Theta}{\partial t} = -\frac{A}{K_0}.$$

[If v is the temperature, the first equation is that for heat conduction with heat supplied at the rate A, allowing for variation of the thermal conductivity with temperature but not with position (Carslaw and Jaeger [*10*, 1959]).]

18. Show that the solution of the equation

$$\nu \frac{\partial^2 u}{\partial y^2} - \frac{\partial u}{\partial t} = f e^{i(\sigma t + \varepsilon)}$$

with the boundary conditions $u = 0$ at $y = 0$ and $\partial u/\partial y = 0$ at $y = h$ is

$$u = \frac{if}{\sigma}\left\{1 - \frac{\cosh[(1+i)\beta(h-y)]}{\cosh[(1+i)\beta h]}\right\} e^{i(\sigma t+\varepsilon)},$$

where $\beta = (\sigma/2\nu)^{1/2}$.

[If u is the horizontal velocity, this is the equation for the horizontal motion of an infinite mass of water of uniform depth h acted upon by a periodic force, ν being the kinematic viscosity. If βh is large, the velocity is independent of ν and the viscosity does not affect the motion (Lamb [*622*, 1953]).]

19. The solution of the equation

$$\frac{\partial^2 v}{\partial x^2} - \frac{1}{k}\frac{\partial v}{\partial t} = 0$$

in the semi-infinite region $0 < x < \infty$, with the conditions $v = f(x)$ when $t = 0$, and $v = 0$ at $x = 0$ for all t, is

$$v = \frac{1}{2\sqrt{\pi k t}} \int_0^\infty f(x')\{e^{-(x-x')^2/4kt} - e^{-(x+x')^2/4kt}\}\, dx'.$$

Hence show that the solution of the equation

$$\frac{\partial^2 v}{\partial x^2} - \frac{1}{k}\frac{\partial v}{\partial t} = -\frac{A_0}{K} \qquad (x > 0, t > 0),$$

which satisfies the conditions $v = a + bx$ when $t = 0$ and $v = 0$, $x = 0$ when $t > 0$ is

$$v = \left(a + \frac{ktA_0}{K} + \frac{A_0x^2}{2K}\right)\text{erf}\,\frac{x}{2\sqrt{kt}} + \frac{A_0x}{K}\left(\frac{kt}{\pi}\right)^{1/2} e^{-x^2/4kt} - \frac{A_0x^2}{2K}.$$

[If v is the temperature, this is the equation for the heat flow in a semi-infinite solid in which heat is produced at the rate A_0, the surface $x = 0$ being kept at zero temperature (Carslaw and Jaeger [*79*, 1959]).]

20. The solution of the equation

$$\frac{\partial^2 v}{\partial r^2} + \frac{1}{r}\frac{\partial v}{\partial r} - \frac{1}{k}\frac{\partial v}{\partial t} = 0 \qquad (0 \leqslant r < a, t > 0)$$

with $\partial v/\partial t = 1$, $t = 0$, and $v = 0$, $r = a$, $t > 0$, is

$$v = -\frac{2}{ak}\sum_{n=1}^{\infty} e^{-k\alpha_n^2 t}\frac{J_0(r\alpha_n)}{\alpha_n^3 J_1(a\alpha_n)},$$

where α_n are the positive roots of $J_0(a\alpha) = 0$.

Hence show that the solution of

$$\frac{\partial^2 v}{\partial r^2} + \frac{1}{r}\frac{\partial v}{\partial r} - \frac{1}{k}\frac{\partial v}{\partial t} = -\frac{A_0}{K} \qquad (0 \leqslant r < a, t > 0)$$

with $v = 0$ for $r = a$, $t > 0$, is

$$v = \frac{A_0(a^2 - r^2)}{4K} - \frac{2A_0}{ak}\sum_{n=1}^{\infty} e^{-k\alpha_n^2 t}\frac{J_0(r\alpha_n)}{\alpha_n^3 J_1(a\alpha_n)}.$$

[If v is the temperature, this is the equation for heat flow in an infinite cylinder with zero initial and surface temperature, heat being produced at the rate A_0 (Carslaw and Jaeger [*204*, 1959]).]

21. Show that the solution of

$$\frac{1}{k}\frac{\partial v}{\partial t} = \frac{1}{r^2}\frac{\partial}{\partial r}\left(r^2\frac{\partial v}{\partial r}\right) + \frac{A_0}{Kr}\sin\left(\frac{\pi r}{a}\right) \qquad (0 \leqslant r < a, t > 0)$$

with $v = 0$, $t = 0$ and $v = 0$, $r = a$, $t > 0$, is

$$v = \frac{A_0a^2}{\pi^2 rK}(1 - e^{-k\pi^2 t/a^2})\sin\frac{\pi r}{a}.$$

[If v is the temperature, this is the equation for heat flow in a sphere with zero initial and surface temperature, heat being produced at the rate $(A_0/r)\sin(\pi r/a)$ (Carslaw and Jaeger [*244*, 1959]).]

Bibliography and References

APPELL, P., and KAMPÉ DE FERIET, J., 1926. *Fonctions hypergéométriques et hypersphériques*. Paris: Gauthier-Villars.

BABISTER, A. W., 1959. Generalized modified Struve functions. *Quart. Jour. Maths*, **10**, 214.

BABISTER, A. W., 1961. An inhomogeneous hypergeometric function. *Math. Zeitschrift*, **76**, 164.

BAILEY, W. N., 1935. Generalized hypergeometric series. *Cambridge Tracts in Mathematics*, No. 32. New York: Cambridge U.P.

BARNES, E. W., 1908*a*. A new development of the theory of the hypergeometric function. *Proc. London Math. Soc.*, **6**, 141.

BARNES, E. W., 1908*b*. On generalized Legendre functions. *Quart. Jour. Maths*, **39**, 97.

BATEMAN, H., 1918. *Differential equations*, New York: Longmans.

BATEMAN, H., 1932. *Partial differential equations of mathematical physics*. New York: Cambridge U.P.

BINNS, K. J., and LAWRENSON, P. J., 1963. *Analysis and computation of electric and magnetic field problems*. New York: Pergamon.

BLAND, D. R., 1961. *Solutions of Laplace's equation*. Baltimore: Routledge.

BUCHHOLZ, H., 1953*a*. *Die konfluente hypergeometrische Funktion*. Berlin: Springer.

BUCHHOLZ, H., 1953*b*. Die Lösungen einer besonderen Whittakerschen inhomogen Differentialgleichung. *Math. Zeitschrift*, **57**, 167.

CARSLAW, H. S., and JAEGER, J. C., 1947. *Operational methods in applied mathematics*. New York: Oxford U.P.

CARSLAW, H. S., and JAEGER, J. C., 1959. *Conduction of heat in solids*. New York: Oxford. U.P.

CODDINGTON, A., and LEVINSON, N., 1955. *Theory of ordinary differential equations*. New York: McGraw.

COURANT, R., and HILBERT, D., 1953. *Methods of mathematical physics*. New York: Interscience.

DUFF, G. F. D., 1956. *Partial differential equations*. New York: Oxford U.P.

ERDÉLYI, A., 1937. Integraldarstellungen hypergeometrischer Funktionen. *Quart. Jour. Maths*, **8**, 267.

ERDÉLYI, A., 1953*a*. *Higher transcendental functions*, Vol. 1. New York: McGraw.

ERDÉLYI, A., 1953*b*. *Higher transcendental functions*, Vol. 2. New York: McGraw.

ERDÉLYI, A., 1954*a*. *Tables of integral transforms*, Vol. 1. New York; McGraw.

ERDÉLYI, A., 1954*b*. *Tables of integral transforms*, Vol. 2. New York; McGraw.

ERDÉLYI, A., 1955. *Higher transcendental functions*, Vol. 3. New York: McGraw.

ERDÉLYI, A., 1956. *Asymptotic expansions*. New York: Dover.

FORSYTH, A. R., 1929. *Differential equations*. New York: Macmillan.

FRIEDMAN, B., 1956. *Principles and techniques of applied mathematics*. New York: Wiley.

FUCHS, L., 1868. Zur Theorie der linearen Differentialgleichungen mit veränderlichen Coefficienten, *Journal für die reine und angewandte Mathematik*, **68**, 354.

GRIFFITH, A. A., and TAYLOR, G. I., 1917. The use of soap films in solving torsion problems. *British Advisory Comm. Aeronautics, Tech. Report*, Vol. 3, p. 920.

HEUN, K., 1889*a*. Zur Theorie der Riemann'schen Functionen zweiter Ordnung mit vier Verzweigungspunkten. *Math. Annal.*, **33**, 161.

HEUN, K., 1889*b*. Beitrage zur Theorie der Lamé'schen Functionen. *Math. Annal.*, **33**, 180.

HOBSON, E. W., 1931. *Spherical and ellipsoidal harmonics*. New York: Cambridge U.P.

INCE, E. L., 1939. The periodic Lamé functions. *Proc. Roy. Soc. Edinburgh*, **60**, 47.

INCE, E. L., 1926. *Ordinary differential equations*. New York: Dover.

KAMKE, E., 1930. *Differentialgleichungen reeller Funktionen*. Leipzig: Akademische Verlagsges.

KELLOGG, O. D., 1929. *Foundations of potential theory*. Berlin: Springer.

KLEIN, F., 1933. *Hypergeometrische Funktion*. Berlin: Springer.

LAMB, H., 1953. *Hydrodynamics*. New York: Cambridge U.P.

LINDEMANN, F., 1883. Uber die Differentialgleichung der Functionen des elliptischen Cylinders. *Math. Annal.*, **22**, 117.

MCLACHLAN, N. W., 1934. *Loud speakers*. New York: Oxford U.P.

MCLACHLAN, N. W., 1936. Integrals involving Bessel and Struve functions. *Phil. Mag.*, **21**, 437.

MCLACHLAN, N. W., 1947. *Theory and application of Mathieu functions*. New York: Oxford U.P.

MCLACHLAN, N. W., 1955. *Bessel functions for engineers*, 2nd ed. New York: Oxford U.P.

MACROBERT, T. M., 1947. *Spherical harmonics*. London: Methuen.

MOON, P., and SPENCER, D. E., 1961. *Field theory handbook*. Berlin: Springer.

MORSE, P., and FESHBACH, H., 1953*a*. *Methods of theoretical physics*, Vol. 1. New York: McGraw.

MORSE, P. and FESHBACH, H., 1953*b*. *Methods of theoretical physics*, Vol. 2. New York: McGraw.

MURPHY, G. M., 1960. *Ordinary differential equations and their solutions*. Princeton, N.J.: Van Nostrand.

PIAGGIO, H. T. H., 1937. *Differential equations*. London: G. Bell.

POOLE, E. G. C., 1921. On certain classes of Mathieu functions. *Proc. London Math. Soc.*, **20**, 374.

POOLE, E. G. C., 1934. Bessel functions as limits of Legendre functions. *Quart. Jour. Maths*, **5**, 186.

POOLE, E. G. C., 1936. *Theory of linear differential equations*. New York: Oxford. U.P.

RAINVILLE, E. D., 1945. The contiguous function relations for ${}_pF_q$ with applications to Bateman's $J_n^{u,v}$ and Rice's $H_n(\zeta, p, v)$. *Bull. Am. Math. Soc.*, **51**, 714.

RAYLEIGH, LORD, 1945. *Theory of sound*, 2nd rev. ed. New York: Dover.

ROUTH, E. J., 1902. *Analytical statics*, Vol. 2. New York: Cambridge U.P.

SAGAN, H., 1961. *Boundary and eigenvalue problems in mathematical physics*. New York: Wiley.

SMITH, F. C., 1938. Relations among the fundamental solutions of the generalized hypergeometric equation when $p = q + 1$. *Bull. Am. Math. Soc.*, **44**, 429.

SNEDDON, I. N., 1951. *Fourier transforms*. New York: McGraw.

SNEDDON, I. N., 1957. *Elements of partial differential equations*. New York: McGraw.

SNOW, C., 1952. Hypergeometric and Legendre functions with applications to integral equations of potential theory. *Natl. Bur. Std. Appl. Math. Series 19*.

THOMAE, J., 1879. Uber die Functionen welche durch Reihen von der Form

$$1 + \frac{p}{1}\frac{p'}{q'}\frac{p''}{q''} + \frac{p}{1}\frac{p+1}{2}\frac{p'}{q'}\frac{p'+1}{q'+1}\frac{p''}{q''}\frac{p''+1}{q''+1} + \cdots$$

dargestellt werden.
Journal für die reine und angewandte Mathematik, **87**, 26.

WATSON, G. N., 1944. *Theory of Bessel functions*. New York: Cambridge U.P.

WEBSTER, A. G., 1947. *Partial differential equations of mathematical physics*. New York: Hafner.

WHITTAKER, E. T., and WATSON, G. N., 1935. *Modern analysis*. New York: Cambridge U.P.

Index

Adjoint boundary conditions, 340
Adjoint equation, 12
Adjoint operators, 336, 339–340
Analogues, 398
Apparent singularity, 16
Associated homogeneous equation, 1, 318
Asymptotic expansion, 24

Bernoulli's equation, 4
Bessel functions, 54–57
  connection with Legendre functions, 238, 251
  contour integrals for, 55–57
  hypergeometric form, 54
  modified, 55
  of first kind, 54
  of second kind, 54
  solutions of Laplace's equation, 355, 357
  solutions of wave equation, 370, 372, 376
Bessel's equation, 53–54
  singular points of, 62
  solutions of, 54
Bibliography, 406–408
Bilinear concomitant, 13, 25, 336
Boundary conditions, 26–27, 332, 342, 361
  adjoint, 340
  Dirichlet, 342
  Neumann, 342

Calculus, symbolic, 33
Cauchy's method, 8
Causality condition, 391
Characteristic equation, 34, 48
Characteristic values, 285, 299, 300, 306, 307
Complementary function, 2, 318
Complete integral, 318
Complete primitive, 2
Conduction of heat, equation of, 344, 350, 404–405
  see also Diffusion equation
Confluent hypergeometric equation, 92
  singular points of, 103, 146
  solutions of, 93
  Whittaker's form, 139, 143–144
Confluent hypergeometric functions, 92–96, 167
  contour integrals for, 94–96
  solutions of diffusion equation, 388–390
  Whittaker's, 143–145, 150
Constants of separation, 331–332

Determinantal equation, 48
Determining factor, 23
Diffusion equation, 350, 387–392
  Green's function, 390–392
  separation of variables, 387–390
  solutions of, 387–390
    one-dimensional, 387
    three-dimensional, 389
    two-dimensional, 388
Dirac's delta function, 28, 338
Duhamel's theorem, 42, 48

Elliptic functions, 296, 297, 352
  Weierstrasse's 313
Elliptic integrals, 191–192, 248
Equation for functions of paraboloid of revolution, 139, 143, 149
Equation for parabolic cylinder functions, 139, 144, 149
Equations of mathematical physics, 348–398
  diffusion equation, 350, 387–392
    nonhomogeneous, 348–350, 393–398
  Helmholtz's equation, 349, 371–375
    nonhomogeneous, 349, 380
  Laplace's equation, 348, 353–361
  Lorenz's equation, 348, 349, 379–387
  Poisson's equation, 348, 361–370
  Wave equation, 349, 370–373, 375–379
    nonhomogeneous, 348

Equations with constant coefficients, 33–52, 319–327
particular initial conditions, 38
Equations with variable coefficients, 46
Error function, 114
Euler's equation, 43
Exact nonhomogeneous equation, 11

Forcing function, 1, 43
Fourier transform, 346
Fresnel integrals, 50, 140
Fuchsian equation, 267

General integral of partial differential equation, 318
Generalized hypergeometric equation, 266
singular points, 267
solutions of, 266–267
Generalized hypergeometric function, 141, 223, 266
Generalized modified Struve functions, 92, 96–121, 145–147
asymptotic expansion, 117, 147
connection with modified Struve function, 92, 97, 113, 145
contour integrals for, 96–100
degenerate cases, 110–113
differential equations for, 103–104, 146
integrals connected with, 118–121
Mellin-Barnes integral, 114
numerical values, 140
particular values, 104–108, 113
poles, 106, 108
power series for, 108–110, 146
relations between contiguous functions, 100–103
transformation formulas, 108
zeros, 116
Green's functions, 26–28, 337–342, 346–347
diffusion equation, 390–392
nonhomogeneous, 397–398
Helmholtz's equation, 373–375
Laplace's equation, 359–361
Lorenz's equation, 382–383
Poisson's equation, 368–370
reciprocity condition, 341

Heat conduction, equation of, 344, 350, 404–405
see also Diffusion equation
Helmholtz's equation, 349, 371–375
Green's function, 373–375
nonhomogeneous, 349, 380
separation of variables, 371–373
Heun functions, 284–286
Heun's equation, 283–286
connection with hypergeometric equation, 285
singular points, 287
solutions of, 284–286
Homogeneous equation, 1
solution in power series, 14
Hypergeometric equation, 163
confluent, 92
singular points, 172
solutions of, 164
Hypergeometric functions, 164–167
confluent, 92–96, 167
connection with Legendre functions, 191, 236
contour integrals for, 164–167
generalized, 141, 223, 266
power series for, 185
solutions of wave equation, 377

Incomplete beta function, 29, 52, 104–105, 152, 179, 182–184, 186, 192–193, 204
Incomplete gamma function, 29, 50, 113–114, 122
Indicial equation, 14, 16, 19, 20
descending, 23
Influence function, 28
Integral transforms, 335–337, 346
Integrating factor, 3, 12
Irregular singularity, 15, 20
at infinity, 23

Kernel of an integral, 336–337

Lagrange identity, 13, 24, 336
Laguerre polynomials, 110–111
Lamé's equation, 298
solutions of, 298, 300
Lamé's formula, 351
Laplace's equation, 348, 353–361
Green's function, 359–361
separation of variables, 354–359
solutions of, 353–359, 399
two-dimensional, 353, 359
Laplace transform, 38–42
Laplacian operator Δ, 350-353
Legendre functions, 235–238
connection with Bessel functions, 238, 251
connection with hypergeometric functions, 191, 236
contour integrals for, 237–238
solutions of Laplace's equation, 355, 358, 359, 399

Legendre functions, *continued*
solutions of wave equation, 372, 378
Legendre's equation, 235–236
solutions of, 235–238
Legendre's linear equation, 43
Linear equations, first order, 3–4
Logarithmic solutions, 18
Lommel functions, 76–85
asymptotic expansion, 78–80
differential equations for, 76, 86
integrals connected with, 83
Mellin-Barnes integral, 78
particular values, 81
power series for, 77–78
recurrence formulas, 80
solutions of Lorenz's equation, 380, 384
solutions of Poisson's equation, 362, 364
Lorenz's equation, 348, 349, 379–387
Green's functions, 382–383
separation of variables, 379–382, 384–386
solutions of, 379–387

Mathieu's equation, 284, 302–303
singular points, 302
solutions of, 302–303
Mejer's G function, 26
Mellin-Barnes integrals, 25
confluent hypergeometric functions, 125–127
hypergeometric functions, 194, 205
Lommel functions, 78
Struve functions, 63, 114
Modified Struve function, 72–76
differential equation for, 74
hypergeometric form, 75
integrals connected with, 75

Neumann's polynomial, 90
Nonhomogeneous confluent hypergeometric functions, 92–139
asymptotic expansion, 124
connection with Lommel functions, 135
connection with Whittaker's functions, 148
differential equations for, 121, 132, 136–139
integrals connected with, 130–132
Mellin-Barnes integrals, 125–127
particular values, 129
power series for, 121–124, 133
recurrence formulas, 127, 135
relations between contiguous functions, 127–128, 136
solutions of diffusion equation, 393–396
see also Generalized modified Struve functions
Nonhomogeneous diffusion equation, 348–350, 393–398
Green's function, 397–398
solutions of, 393–398
one-dimensional, 393
three-dimensional, 395
two-dimensional, 394
Nonhomogeneous equation, 1
solution in power series, 16
Nonhomogeneous generalized hypergeometric functions, 265–281
degenerate cases, 272
differential equations for, 265–266, 270–272, 277
integrals connected with, 273–277, 280–281
power series for, 267–268, 277–278
recurrence formulas, 279
relations between contiguous functions, 269–270, 279–280
zeros, 273
Nonhomogeneous Helmholtz's equation, 349, 380
Nonhomogeneous Heun equation, 283, 287, 295–296
related differential equations, 309–315
solutions of, 287–291
Nonhomogeneous Heun functions, 283, 287–295
connection with Legendre functions, 297
differential equations for, 287, 309–314
differential relations for, 292–294
integrals connected with, 294–295
power series for, 287–290
recurrence formulas, 291
solutions of Lorenz's equation, 381
solutions of Poisson's equation, 363, 365
transformation formulas, 288–291
Nonhomogeneous hypergeometric function $B(a, b; c; z)$, 163–200
asymptotic expansion, 196
connection with elliptic integrals, 192
connection with Legendre functions, 191
connection with modified Struve functions, 120, 168
contour integrals for, 167–171
degenerate cases, 187–190
differential equations for, 163, 172–175, 178–179
in terms of elementary functions, 193
integrals connected with, 198–200
Mellin-Barnes integral, 194

Nonhomogeneous hypergeometric function $B(a, b; c; z)$, *continued*
particular values, 179–184, 191–194
poles, 181
power series for, 184–187
relations between contiguous functions, 173, 176–178
transformation formulas, 172
zeros, 195
Nonhomogeneous hypergeometric functions, C, f, and F, 201–221
analytic continuation, 205–207
connection with $B(a, b; c; z)$, 243
connection with Legendre functions, 202, 205, 212
differential equations for, 163, 201, 210, 215–221
integrals connected with, 209–210
Mellin-Barnes integral, 205
particular values, 204–205, 212
power series for, 201–203, 210–211
recurrence formulas, 207, 213
relations between contiguous functions, 208, 213–215
solutions of Lorenz's equation, 385
Nonhomogeneous Lamé equation, 284, 295–297, 313–314
degenerate cases, 301
solutions of, 296–301
Nonhomogeneous Lamé functions, 297–301
characteristic values, 299, 300
differential equations for, 296
power series for, 297–299
Nonhomogeneous Legendre equation, 234–235
solutions of, 242, 244, 249, 252, 256
Nonhomogeneous Legendre function R, 226, 238–252
connection with hypergeometric functions, 239–240, 242, 247
connection with Legendre functions, 226, 239
connection with Struve functions, 241, 251
contour integrals for, 238–239
differential equations for, 242, 244, 249
for real values of argument, 248–250
integrals connected with, 250–252
particular values, 248–249
power series for, 247
relations between contiguous functions, 245–247
transformation formulas, 241
zeros, 250
Nonhomogeneous Legendre functions, s S, and t, 252–262
connection with Lommel functions, 254
differential equations for, 252, 257, 260–262
for real values of argument, 256, 260
integrals connected with, 256
particular values, 253
power series for, 252–253, 258
recurrence formulas, 254–255, 258–259
relations between contiguous functions, 255–256, 259
solutions of Lorenz's equation, 381, 386
solutions of Poisson's equation, 363, 366, 400
Nonhomogeneous Mathieu equation, 284, 301, 303–304
degenerate case, 308–309
modified, 315
solutions of, 304–305
Nonhomogeneous Matheiu functions, 303–309
characteristic values, 306, 307
connection with Heun functions, 304–305
connection with Lamé functions, 308
connection with Legendre functions, 309
differential equations for, 303–304, 314–315
power series for, 304–308
solutions of Lorenz's equation, 382
solutions of Poisson's equation, 364
Nonhomogeneous parabolic cylinder functions, 144, 151–160
asymptotic expansion, 155
connection with modified Struve functions, 152
degenerate cases, 154
differential equations for, 149, 156, 159–160
power series for, 152, 156
recurrence formulas, 152–154, 158–159
solutions of Lorenz's equation, 381
solutions of Poisson's equation, 364
zeros, 155
Nonhomogeneous Riemann equation, 226, 228–234
connection with hypergeometric equation, 230
connection with Legendre's equation, 232–234
Nonhomogeneous wave equation, 348
Nonhomogeneous Whittaker functions, 143–149
connection with Lommel functions, 148

Nonhomogeneous Whittaker functions, *continued*
  differential equation for, 147
  power series for, 147
  see also Generalized modified Struve functions
Nonlinear equations, 91, 142, 162, 223, 264
Nucleus of an integral, 25, 336

Operational methods, 33–37, 43–47, 322–326, 328–330
Operator D, 33, 322
Operator δ, 43, 328
Operator p, 225
Ordinary point, 14, 16
Orthogonal curvilinear coordinates, 351–353
  cylindrical polar, 351, 355, 362, 372, 380
  ellipsoidal, 352, 357, 365
  elliptic cylinder, 352, 357, 364, 373, 382
  oblate spheroidal, 353, 358, 366
  of confocal cones, 351, 356, 363, 372, 381
  of paraboloid of revolution, 352, 357, 364, 373, 381
  parabolic cylinder, 352, 356, 364, 373, 381
  prolate spheroidal, 353, 358, 365
  spherical polar, 351, 355, 362, 372, 381
  toroidal, 398–400

P function, Riemann's, 225–228
Parabolic cylinder functions, 150–151
  solutions of Laplace's equation, 357
  solutions of wave equation, 373
Partial differential equations, 317–398
  boundary conditions, 332
  general nonhomogeneous, 317–319
  Green's functions, 337–342, 346–347
  integral transforms, 335–337
  particular integral, 322–326
  separation of variables, 330–334
  with constant coefficients, 319–327
  with homogeneous derivatives, 326–327
  see also Equations of mathematical physics
Particular integral, 2
  for partial differential equation, 322–326
Periodic solutions, 49–50
Poisson's equation, 348, 361–370
  Green's function, 368–370
  separation of variables, 361–367
  solutions of, 361–370, 400
  two-dimensional, 367
Power series solution, 14, 16–24
  near an irregular singular point, 20
  near an ordinary point, 16
  near a regular singular point, 17

Real singularity, 16
Reducible equations, 43, 327–328
Reduction of order, 4
References, 406–408
Regular singularity, 15, 17
Resonance, 49
Retarded potential, 379, 383
Riemann's equation, 225–228
  connection with Legendre's equation, 231–232
Riemann's P function, 225–228
  connection with Legendre functions, 232

Self-adjoint, 12
Separation of variables, 330–334
  diffusion equation, 387–390
    nonhomogeneous, 393–396
  Helmholtz's equation, 371–373
  Laplace's equation, 354–359
  Lorenz's equation, 379–382, 384–386
  Poisson's equation, 361–367
  wave equation, 371–373, 376–379
Simultaneous equations, 47, 52
Singular point, 14
  at infinity, 21
Solution by differentiation, 9
Solution in terms of integrals, 24, 37
Source of sound, 349
Source point, 360
Struve function, 53, 58–72
  asymptotic expansion, 65
  contour integrals for, 58–59
  differential equation for, 61
  hypergeometric form, 62
  integrals connected with, 66–72
  Mellin-Barnes integrals, 63
  particular values, 64
  power series for, 62
  recurrence formulas, 59–61
  zeros, 64

Two-point boundary problem, 43

Variation of parameters, 5

Wave equation, 349, 370–373, 375–379
  separation of variables, 371–373, 376–379
  solutions of, 370–373, 375–379
  see also Helmholtz's equation
Weber's equation, 144, 150
  singular points, 150

Weber's equation, *continued*
solutions of, 150
Weierstrasse's elliptic function, 313
Whittaker functions, 139, 143–145, 150
Whittaker's equation, 139, 143–144
Wronskian determinant, 6, 30